NUCLEAR PHYSICS

An Introduction

W. E. BURCHAM, F.R.S.

Nuclear Physics

AN INTRODUCTION

McGRAW-HILL BOOK COMPANY INC.

NEW YORK-SAN FRANCISCO

Library of Congress Catalog Card Number
63–15005

08920

Printed in Great Britain

This book is intended primarily for the undergraduate who is approaching the end of a first-degree course in physics. It may also be found useful by graduates who are undertaking courses in which a knowledge of nuclear physics is required and by research students who wish to renew their acquaintance with the elementary parts of the subject. An experimental standpoint is adopted, since most nuclear physicists are concerned to some degree with experimental techniques. Mathematical symbols are freely used in a descriptive manner but only straightforward mathematical techniques, such as normally appear in a University Course in physics, are required. It is assumed that the reader has completed a general introductory course in modern physics, including the elements of the special theory of relativity and of atomic spectroscopy.

Nuclear physics is a diffuse and complex subject, which at elementary level is apt to tax the memory rather than the understanding of the student. It is possible to present the results of more than sixty years of experimental and theoretical work in a strictly logical form, but such an approach often conceals or obscures the interest and importance of the historical development. On the other hand a detailed historical treatment is not practicable in a book which is to be of a convenient size and which is to relate to a course which must be given in perhaps one or two University terms at the most. In the present book, therefore, a compromise has been adopted. Part A contains much historical material, particularly in the discussion of radioactivity (chap. 2), and attempts (chap. 3) to pick out the aspects of atomic physics of most significance in nuclear studies. The content of both these chapters may well have been covered by the student in other courses before he enters upon nuclear physics proper, but they have been included for completeness as essential background material. The remainder of the book then attempts to present the subject in something approaching a logical sequence. Chapter 4, completing Part A, gives what today appears to be justifiable prominence to the interaction between atomic and nuclear moments, since this field of work has contributed extensively to our knowledge of nuclear properties. Part B treats the experimental side of the subject in what is considered to be adequate, but not excessive detail, in view of the important advances that have stemmed directly from improvements in technique. In Part C the results of measurements of the static properties of nuclei are assembled and are set out as far as possible within the co-ordinating framework now provided by the single-particle shell model. Nuclear reactions are similarly discussed in Part D. The basic structure of nuclei has been left until Part E which is at present a single chapter on nuclear forces. In the original plan of the book it had been hoped to supplement this by a discussion of the Wigner supermultiplet theory and by a chapter on cosmic radiation and mesons, but this plan was abandoned in view of the necessity for keeping the book to a reasonable size. The scope of the work is, therefore, such as to exclude most of high energy physics and although much of what is presented is relevant to work in this subject, the contributions of the high energy physicist to our understanding of nuclear structure regrettably receive scant attention. It is also a matter of regret that room has not been found for an account of the many important applications of nuclear physics in modern technology; a brief account of the best-known of these applications, the nuclear reactor, has been included among the appendices.

In selecting illustrative material for the various sections of the book emphasis has been placed on relevance, significance and ease of assimilation, and published data have been freely used. No attempt is made to give an exhaustive treatment of all types of nuclear process and the number of references quoted has been kept to a minimum. The references given at the ends of the chapters are often to articles of the review type, which are suitable for further reading, and which themselves usually contain extensive reference lists.

I am indebted to a large number of friends and colleagues for assistance at all stages in the preparation of this book; many errors have been avoided by their vigilance, but those that remain are my own responsibility. Chapters have been read by H. Burkhardt, L. Castillejo, K. F. Chackett, G. V. Chester, N. Feather, M. A. Grace, G. W. Greenlees, J. V. Jelley, J. S. C. McKee, P. B. Moon, D. A. O'Connor, R. E. Peierls, W. B. Powell, L. Riddiford, K. F. Smith and J. Walker. I should like to thank G. Pyle for help with the proof-reading and Doreen Kellett for tracing some of the diagrams. I must acknowledge with gratitude the patience and skill of my typists, Susan Wiggin, Susan Tennant, Susan Dorté and my wife Mary, who have had to deal with a frequently amended manuscript. Finally, the kindness, courtesy and efficiency of the publishers, Messrs. Longmans, have helped materially throughout the preparation of the work.

Birmingham, March 1962   W. E. B.

CONTENTS

Part A   The Nuclear Atom

Part B   Experimental techniques of nuclear physics

Part E   The basic interactions of nuclear physics

PLATES

1 Expansion chamber tracks of α-rays from radium (C. T. R. Wilson, *Proc. roy. Soc.* A, **87**, 277, 1912).

2 Expansion chamber tracks of fast and slow β-rays (electrons) produced by hard X-rays (C. T. R. Wilson, *Proc. roy. Soc.* A, **104**, 192, 1923).

3 Expansion chamber tracks of recoil electrons due to beam of soft X-rays. Some of the short tracks are due to Auger electrons (C. T. R. Wilson, *Proc. roy. Soc.* A, **104**, 1, 1923).

4 Expansion chamber track of carbon ion, showing delta rays (J. C. Bower).

5 Nuclear resonance signal from protons in ferric nitrate solution (N. Bloembergen *et al.*, *Phys. Rev.*, **73**, 686, 1948).

6 A positron of energy 63 MeV passes through a lead plate and emerges with an energy of 23 MeV (C. D. Anderson, *Phys. Rev.*, **43**, 491, 1933).

7 Hydrogen bubble chamber tracks of 1 GeV protons, showing a proton–proton collision (J. B. Kinson).

8 Tracks of protons in different emulsions. A Ilford Half-Tone, B Ilford C2, C Kodak NT4 (C. F. Powell, taken from Ref. 6.18).

9 Track of 170 MeV proton, including a nuclear scattering, recorded in a spark chamber (J. G. Rutherglen).

10 Expansion chamber photograph showing ejection of a proton from a nitrogen nucleus by an α-particle (P. M. S. Blackett and D. S. Lees, *Proc. roy. Soc.* A, **136**, 325, 1932).

11 Expansion chamber photograph showing disintegration of lithium by protons with the emission of pairs of α-particles in opposite directions (P. I. Dee and E. T. S. Walton, *Proc. roy. Soc.* A, **141**, 733, 1933).

12 Expansion chamber photograph of disintegration of nitrogen by neutrons (N. Feather, *Proc. roy. Soc.* A, **136**, 709, 1932).

13 Expansion chamber tracks of fission fragments emerging from a uranium foil bombarded by slow neutrons (J. K. Boggild *et al*, *Phys. Rev.* **71**, 281, 1947).

14 Disintegration star produced by a high-energy proton in nuclear emulsion (C. F. Powell *et al.*, Ref. 6.19).

15 Expansion chamber photograph of the β-decay of ^{6}He, showing tracks of the decay electron and recoil nucleus (J. Csikai and A. Szalay, *Soviet Physics*, **8**, 749, 1959).

ACKNOWLEDGMENTS

For permission to reproduce photographs or to redraw diagrams we are indebted to the following: Academic Press Inc., New York: Ajzenberg-Selove, *Nuclear Spectroscopy* and Coles, *Advances in Electronics*; Akademische Verlagsgesellschaft, Frankfurt: Kopferman, *Kernmomente*; Akademische Verlagsgesellschaft, Leipzig: *Zeit. fur Physik. Chemie*; the authors concerned and the American Institute of Physics: *Rev. Sci. Inst.*; the Editor, *Ann. Rev. Nucl. Sci.*; Brookhaven National Laboratory: *Report B.N.L.*; Cambridge University Press: Wilson, *Principles of Cloud Chamber Technique* and Wilkinson, *Ionisation Chambers and Counters*; Clarendon Press, Oxford: Bacon, *Neutron Diffraction* and Heitler, *Quantum Theory of Radiation*; McGraw-Hill Book Co. Inc.: Evans, *The Atomic Nucleus* and White, *Introduction to Atomic Spectra*; The Macmillan Company, New York: Shankland, *Atomic & Nuclear Physics*; Laboratory for Nuclear Science, Massachusetts Institute of Technology: *Progress Report*; National Research Council, Ottawa: *Canadian Journal of Research*; North Holland Publishing Company: *Nucl. Instrum. and Methods*, Siegbahn, *Beta and Gamma Spectroscopy* and Wapstra *et al.*, *Nuclear Spectroscopy Tables*; Pergamon Press, Oxford: *Progress in Nuclear Physics*; Pergamon Press Inc., New York: Jelley, *Cherenkov Radiation* and Littler & Raffle, *An Introduction to Reactor Physics*; Sir Isaac Pitman & Sons Ltd.: Chadwick, *Radioactivity*; Philips Research Laboratories, Eindhoven: *Philips Technical Review*; Professor Powell; the Editors, *Rev. Mod. Phys.* and *Phys. Rev. Letters*; the authors concerned, the Institute of Physics and The Physical Society: *Proc. Phys. Soc.*; Stichting Physica: *Rep. Prog. Phys.*; Royal Danish Academy: *Kgl. Danske Videnskab Selskab*; Royal Swedish Academy of Science: *Arkiv. fur Fysik*; Royal Society: *Proc. Roy. Soc. A*; Editors, *Science Progress*; United Kingdom Atomic Energy Authority: *A.E.R.E. Harwell Reports*; Springer-Verlag, Heidelberg: *Zeits. fur Physik* and *Naturwissenschaften*; Taylor & Francis Ltd.: *Phil. Mag.*; United States Atomic Energy Commission: Rossi & Staub, *Ionization Chambers & Counters*; D. Van Nostrand Company Inc.: Korff, *Electron & Nuclear Counters*; John Wiley & Sons, Inc.: Livingston, *High Energy Accelerators*, Hughes, *Neutron Optics*, Blatt & Weisskopf, *Theoretical Nuclear Physics* and Segrè, *Experimental Nuclear Physics*.

We are indebted to the Universities of Birmingham, Cambridge, Glasgow, Hull, Keele and Liverpool for permission to reproduce questions from various past examination papers, and McGraw-Hill Book Company for material from *The Atomic Nucleus* by R. D. Evans, copyright © 1955.

Part A

THE NUCLEAR ATOM

1.

INTRODUCTION

1.1 General survey

Nuclear physics was born, in a rather obscure and unrecognized way, in 1896 with Becquerel's discovery of naturally occurring radioactivity. The significance of this phenomenon was perhaps rather overshadowed by Röntgen's discovery of X-rays in the year preceding and by Thomson's demonstration of the existence of the electron in the year following. It was not to be foreseen at that time that the curious radiations from uranium were the first observed manifestations of a specific atomic nucleus, whose existence was not only to coordinate within two decades such diverse phenomena as the X-radiation and the electronic structure of atoms, but also within half a century to place in the hands of man the richest source of energy that seems likely to come his way. The vast and complex subject of nuclear physics that has developed over these years is based on twin structures of experiment and theory which have risen together, sometimes the one seeming the more advanced, sometimes the other. The experimental structure includes the extensive empirical data of atomic spectroscopy and the considerable body of information on natural radioactivity and more lately on nuclear transformations. The theoretical structure is essentially the quantum theory of Planck which grew from its origin in 1900 to maturity in the quantum mechanics of Bohr, Schrödinger, Heisenberg, Dirac, Born and Jordan. This is in turn linked to the observable properties of material particles by the concept of the de Broglie wavelength and by Bohr's principle of complementarity, sometimes referred to as the principle of wave-particle duality.

There is a mathematical theorem which states that no system of electric charges at rest can be stable if the forces between the charges are of 'ordinary' type, such as those governed by the inverse square law or some simple power of distance. The possibility of an atomic structure in which extraordinary forces operated was of course ruled out by the detailed verification of Rutherford's hypothesis of the nucleus in 1911. The nuclear atom was conceived in order to explain the results of experiments on the scattering of the α-particles by thin metallic foils. The unexpectedly prolific scattering of these heavy particles through very large angles was inconsistent with a uniform diffuse atomic structure and led both qualitatively and quantitatively to the suggestion of a central nucleus in which should reside the whole of the positive charge and most of the mass of the atom. The exact fit of the experimental results to the scattering law first given by Rutherford and now associated with his name showed that the Coulomb law of force indeed held good down to distances of about 10^{-12} cm, many times smaller than known atomic dimensions. No extraordinary forces therefore seemed to operate over the greater part of the atomic volume and stability of the nuclear atom could only be achieved by allowing the electrons to move about the nucleus in mechanically stable orbits. This simple model and the quantum laws given by Planck were used by Bohr in 1913 to explain, with dramatic success, the numerical relationships between the frequencies of the lines in the Balmer series of atomic hydrogen. In the next few years, the Rutherford–Bohr atom, with its central nucleus of mass A units and charge $+Ze$, was used to marshal and interpret much of the evidence of optical spectroscopy. In X-ray spectroscopy the work of Moseley confirmed the role suggested for the charge number Z as the atomic number of the element concerned, and this number was seen to be more fundamental for prediction of chemical properties than the chemical atomic weight of elements which later often proved to be mixtures of isotopes. In radioactive phenomena, the successive transformations of uranium, thorium and actinium could be ascribed to the central nucleus and these elements and their decay products could be accommodated with certainty in the periodic system by application of the displacement law of Russell and Soddy. The suggestion of isotopic constitution arising from this work was directly confirmed by the positive ray parabolas found by Thomson and accurately established by the mass spectra obtained for the majority of elements by Aston.

Despite this formidable total of positive evidence for the

Rutherford–Bohr atom it was evident from the beginning that the model was unstable according to classical electrodynamics. An electron with charge e moving in a closed orbit is continuously accelerated towards the centre of force and must radiate, according to electromagnetic theory, at the rate

$$\frac{\mathrm{d}W}{\mathrm{d}t} = \frac{2}{3}\frac{e^2 f^2}{c^3} \text{ ergs sec}^{-1} \qquad (1.1)$$

where f is the instantaneous value of the acceleration and c is the velocity of light. The orbit should consequently contract indefinitely. The denial of this consequence was Bohr's first postulate, namely that the state of motion of an electron in an atom should be *stationary* (non-radiating). The second postulate, that the quantization of angular momentum should determine the actual orbits from the infinity of possibilities, and the third postulate, that the frequency of the light emitted in an atomic transition between stationary states of energies E_i and E_f should be given by the relation

$$h\nu = E_i - E_f \qquad (1.2)$$

where h is Planck's constant, provided the quantitative basis for the theory. Although Bohr always insisted on the necessity for a correspondence between classical and quantum theories in the limit of large quantum numbers the juxtaposition of classical and non-classical concepts in the Bohr theory of the atom became less attractive as the development of theory proceeded. There was in particular the difficulty that despite the many successes of the concept of photons with quantized energy, yet light appeared to be propagated in all respects as a wave motion. The way to a new approach to atomic phenomena was opened by de Broglie, who in 1924 suggested that electrons might behave as waves. The experimental verification of de Broglie's hypothesis of material waves with wavelength

$$\lambda = \frac{h}{p} \qquad (1.3)$$

for a particle of momentum p is well known; the theoretical techniques of analysis according to de Broglie's ideas were developed under the name of *wave mechanics* by Schrödinger in 1926. At about the same time an alternative and more fundamental approach to the same problem was made by Heisenberg who realized that the wave-like properties of matter implied a revision of traditional methods of thought, at least in so far as atomic phenomena were concerned. Heisenberg proposed that detailed pictures and models which did not correspond to experimentally observable quantities should not appear in the theory. Such ideas as orbits of definite radius for electrons in an atom or protons in a nucleus are then excluded and the theory treats only *observable* quantities such as energy and momentum. Orbital frequencies no longer have a meaning and are replaced by the experimentally observed radiative transition probabilities. It was soon realized that the techniques appropriate for describing observables of this kind were those of matrix algebra and these have been adopted by modern *quantum mechanics*; it has been shown that the wave mechanics of Schrödinger is a precisely equivalent method. It is crucial to both systems of calculation that electron distributions shall be interpreted statistically, so that it is no longer possible to say with precision that an electron is at a given point in space, but only that the probability of it being there is known. Both systems also lead to Heisenberg's famous *uncertainty principle* according to which the precision of measurement of connected mechanical quantities is limited by the value of Planck's constant, i.e.

$$\Delta E . \Delta t > \hbar$$
$$\Delta p_x . \Delta x > \hbar \qquad (1.4)$$

where ΔE and Δt are the uncertainty in energy and time of observation in a given state of a particle, Δp_x and Δx are the uncertainty in linear momentum and position and $\hbar = h/2\pi$. The uncertainty relations are intimately connected with the wave description of matter and rest in fact on the supposition of wave-particle duality; the 'complementarity' of the measurements implied in Eq. 1.4 has been emphasized by Bohr.

Much of nuclear physics is concerned with particles moving slowly relative to light, and for problems of this sort, among which are found many collision phenomena, the original non-relativistic methods are adequate. Einstein's celebrated energy-mass relation of special relativity

$$E = mc^2 \qquad (1.5)$$

was involved in de Broglie's proposition of material waves, but it remained for Dirac to set up the relativistic form of quantum mechanics and to show that it predicted the existence of an anti-electron or positron. This particle was discovered in the cosmic radiation in 1932. Pauli had shown by considering the statistical distribution of electrons among possible states of motion that a new degree of freedom, beyond those given by spatial coordinates, was necessary. When Goudsmit and Uhlenbeck suggested that this was in fact an electron spin, it was found that this new property could be satisfactorily fitted into the Dirac theory. The *Pauli exclusion principle* as now formulated, states that for particles with half-integral spin, only two (with spins opposed) are permitted in any one state of motion. This principle, on which is based the current interpretation of the periodic system of the elements, ranks with Heisenberg's uncertainty principle as one of the fundamental laws of nature; together they underlie the theoretical structure within which an understanding of the phenomena of nuclear physics is to be achieved.

The development of nuclear physics itself was not remarkable over the period of the great theoretical advances just discussed. In 1919 Rutherford achieved the disintegration of the nitrogen nucleus by α-particle bombardment in an apparatus of rugged simplicity, and although this great experiment showed how the structure, as distinct from the existence, of the nucleus might be studied, the subsequent decade saw only a gradual increase in experimental activity. Natural α-particles remained the main nuclear projectiles until well into the 1930s; they were used by Chadwick in 1932 in the experiments which led to the discovery of the neutron, by Curie and Joliot (1934) in the first demonstration of 'artificial' radioactivity and (for the production of neutrons) by Hahn and Strassmann in the experiments which first showed the phenomena of fission (1938–9). By this time, however, the development of nuclear accelerators had been rewarded and once the artificial disintegration of lithium by protons had been announced by Cockcroft and Walton (1932) progress became extremely rapid. The greater part of our present-day detailed knowledge of nuclear properties is derived from accelerator experiments. That this knowledge can be fitted with some success into a reasonable theory of nuclear structure is primarily due to the early emergence of the neutron–proton nuclear model, and to the existence of well-tried theoretical methods for its development. The assumption of this model had no serious consequence for the theory of β-decay for it was evident for many reasons that nuclei could not reasonably contain electrons. The suggestion by Pauli of a light particle, the neutrino, which would be created together with an electron in the transformation of a neutron into a proton in beta decay enabled Fermi (1934) to provide the basic framework of the necessary theory of this process. The neutrino has proved one of the most elusive of fundamental particles but positive evidence of its existence has now been obtained and its role in nuclear processes has assumed major significance.

The discovery of the fission of uranium and similar bodies by thermal neutrons has had much less influence on the development of an understanding of the nucleus than might have been expected from the overwhelming economic impact of the process. The importance for theory of Anderson's discovery of the positron (1932), of Neddermeyer and Anderson's discovery of the μ-meson (1936) and of Powell's discovery of the parent π-meson (1947), all in the cosmic radiation, is much greater. The π-meson is particularly interesting since it may play the part of an exchange particle in theories of nuclear forces of the type first suggested by Yukawa. Despite the low intensity of the cosmic radiation, it has proved the source of many new unstable particles in addition to the π- and μ-mesons and although many of these particles are now produced copiously by accelerators, the natural cosmic radiation is still the only means of studying nuclear phenomena at energies of about 100 GeV and above. The need for such studies, and for the great variety of high energy experiments now being conducted with accelerating machines, is founded on a desire to understand the relation between the new particles and the fields which describe them in as much detail as the relation between electrons and the electromagnetic field is understood. One result of such an understanding might be explicit knowledge of the force between nucleons, which is responsible for the stability of complex nuclei. This force is known at the moment only semi-empirically, but the consequences for nuclear structure of many of its general properties can be worked out and the behaviour of stable nuclei can thus be used as a check on the validity of deductions from high energy nucleon–nucleon or meson–nucleon experiments. It is unwise therefore to draw any sharp lines of distinction between low energy nuclear physics, high energy physics and cosmic ray physics, although experimentally they may appear rather sharply differentiated. In content of information these fields of study overlap and mutually fertilize one another and the future is likely to see them merge even more closely in the pursuit of a deeper understanding of the structure of matter. In the future, as in the past, it is to be hoped and expected that the apparent complexity of many nuclear phenomena will be resolved by simplifying developments in both theory and experiment.

The main events in the history of nuclear physics are summarized in Table **1.1**, which is taken mainly from the similar table given by Evans (Ref. 1.7).

The important discoveries of K-mesons and hyperons, which took place between 1947 and 1954 have been omitted from this list in view of the scope of this book.

1.2 The fundamental particles, their interactions and the conservation laws

1.2.1. THE PARTICLES AND THEIR PROPERTIES. The fundamental particles of physics may be described, rather naïvely, as those which have no obvious substructure. A complex nucleus is not a fundamental particle, because it can be thought of as an assembly of neutrons and protons of constant composition. A neutron or proton, however, is at present considered fundamental because its resolution into more elementary entities cannot be demonstrated and because it is subject to conservation laws. Such particles are not necessarily stable, but they decay into other particles of the same general type, also in accordance with conservation laws.

The elementary particles with which this book is concerned are the following:

a) the *electron* and *proton*, which are charged particles familiar from atomic physics,

b) the *neutron*, an uncharged particle produced copiously in nuclear reactions, and an important constituent of complex nuclei,

TABLE 1.1 Chronology of main advances in the growth of nuclear physics

ADVANCE	DATE	PHYSICIST
Periodic system of the elements	1868	Mendeléev
Discovery of X-rays	1895	Röntgen
Discovery of radioactivity	1896	Becquerel
Discovery of electron	1897	J. J. Thomson
The quantum hypothesis	1900	Planck
Mass–energy relation	1905	Einstein
The expansion chamber	1911	Wilson
Isotopes suggested	1911	Soddy
Nuclear hypothesis	1911	Rutherford
Nuclear atom model	1913	Bohr
Atomic numbers from X-ray spectra	1913	Moseley
Positive ray parabolas for neon isotopes	1913	J. J. Thomson
Transmutation of nitrogen by α-particles	1919	Rutherford
Mass spectograph	1919	Aston
Wavelength of material particles	1924	de Broglie
The wave equation	1926	Schrödinger
Diffraction of electrons	1927	Davisson and Germer; G. P. Thomson
Uncertainty principle	1927	Heisenberg
Wave mechanical barrier penetration	1928	Gamow, Condon, Gurney
The cyclotron	1930	Lawrence
The electrostatic generator	1931	Van de Graaff
Discovery of deuterium	1932	Urey
Discovery of the neutron	1932	Chadwick
Transmutation of lithium by artificially accelerated protons	1932	Cockcroft and Walton
Discovery of the positron	1932	Anderson
Hypothesis of the neutrino	1933	Pauli
Neutrino theory of beta decay	1934	Fermi
Discovery of artificial radioactivity	1934	Curie and Joliot
Neutron-induced activity	1934	Fermi
Hypothesis of heavy quanta (mesons)	1935	Yukawa
Discovery of the μ-meson	1936	Anderson and Neddermeyer
Magnetic resonance principle	1938	Rabi
Discovery of fission	1939	Hahn and Strassmann
The principle of phase-stable accelerators	1945	Macmillan, Veksler, Oliphant
Discovery of π-meson	1946	Powell
Discovery of antiproton	1956	Chamberlain, Segrè, Wiegand, Ypsilantis
Non-conservation of parity	1956	Lee and Yang
Observation of (anti) neutrino	1956	Reines and Cowan

1*

c) the *neutrino*, an uncharged particle of zero rest mass invoked in the theory of beta decay,

d) the *photon* or quantum of radiation, familiar in atomic physics and of similar importance in nuclear physics,

e) the π- and μ-*mesons*, particles of mass between that of the electron and that of the proton, which are of importance respectively for the theory of nuclear forces and for the understanding of cosmic ray phenomena.

Each of these particles, although conveniently known by that name, participates in the general wave-particle duality which is a characteristic of natural phenomena and is clearly apparent in atomic and sub-atomic events. For the purposes of classification it is most convenient generally to refer to the particle aspect.*

The main properties of the fundamental particles mentioned in this Section are listed in Table **1.2**. The properties of *mass, charge* and *angular momentum (spin)* are familiar classically and may be defined and measured for macroscopic objects. For such objects the properties assume a continuous range of values, but for the fundamental particles the masses have certain discrete values and charge and spin are multiples of fundamental units, namely the electronic charge and the Planck quantum $\hbar$. The *lifetimes* listed in the Table refer to the particles in a free state, in which case they decay exponentially and do not disappear by any type of interaction with other bodies. The decay law is that familiar from natural radioactivity (Sect. 2.3.4), namely

$$N_t = N_0 e^{-t/\tau} \tag{1.6}$$

where N_t is the number of particles existing at time t, N_0 is the number present at time $t = 0$ and τ is the mean lifetime.

Column 3 of Table **1.2** is headed 'antiparticle'. The presumption that each particle has a counterpart of opposite charge but equal rest mass derives from the theory of the positron given

---

* It is no accident that light enters our ordinary experience mainly as a wave motion while electrons are most readily understood as particles. The difference is fundamental and is connected with the fact that the statistical properties of light quanta make it possible to define a *phase*, whereas this quantity is unmeasurable for the de Broglie waves associated with electrons. A discussion of this general question may be found in Ref. **1.13**.

TABLE 1.2   Properties of some fundamental particles

NAME	PARTICLE	ANTI-PARTICLE	REST MASS in units of electron mass	CHARGE in units of electron charge	SPIN, in units of $\hbar$	MEAN LIFETIME (sec.)	DECAY MODE
Electron	e^-	e^+	1	± 1	$\frac{1}{2}$	Stable	—
Proton	p	$\bar{p}$	1836	± 1	$\frac{1}{2}$	Stable	—
Neutron	n	$\bar{n}$	1839	0	$\frac{1}{2}$	$1 \cdot 1 \times 10^3$	$n \rightarrow p + e^- + \bar{\nu}$
Neutrino	ν	$\bar{\nu}$	0	0	$\frac{1}{2}$	Stable	—
Photon	γ	Self	0	0	1	Stable	—
Charged π-meson	π^+	π^-	273	± 1	0	$2 \cdot 6 \times 10^{-8}$	$\pi^+ \rightarrow \mu^+ + \nu$
Neutral π-meson	π^0	Self	264	0	0	10^{-16}	$\pi^0 \rightarrow 2\gamma$
μ-meson	μ^-	μ^+	207	± 1	$\frac{1}{2}$	$2 \cdot 2 \times 10^{-6}$	$\mu^+ \rightarrow e^+ + \nu + \bar{\nu}$

by Dirac, and extended to other particles by Pauli and Weisskopf, and from the clear experimental evidence for all the listed antibodies. In the case of the neutron, the distinction from the antiparticle rests on the relative direction of the vectors representing spin and magnetic moment. For the neutrino, the evidence is more subtle and is discussed in chapter 16; for the photon and neutral meson there is no distinction and in a formal sense each of these particles is self-conjugate.

There are now known to be at least 32 fundamental particles (including 16 antiparticles). It may be useful to state here the general classification of all these particles according to mass:

a) *leptons* (light particles) are the electrons, the neutrinos and (because of their behaviour) the μ-mesons.

b) *mesons* (particles of intermediate mass) have masses between that of the electron (m) and that of the proton $(1836m)$.

c) *baryons* (heavy particles) which are subdivided into
   (i) *nucleons*, the neutron and proton
   (ii) *hyperons*, the particles of mass greater than that of the neutron $(1839m)$ but which behave as if they contain just one nucleon.

1.2.2. INTERACTIONS BETWEEN PARTICLES: THE CONSERVATION LAWS. The effect of one fundamental particle on another, or their mutual interaction, now appears to be one of three main types, each of which is more important than the gravitational effect. These are:

a) *Electromagnetic interactions*, which are familiar from atomic physics, and include the force between charges at rest and in motion, and the effects of the electric and magnetic fields of radiation on a charge distribution.

b) *Weak interactions*, which essentially describe the behaviour of leptons, and of which the best-known example is β-decay, e.g. of the μ-meson (Table **1.2**).

c) *Strong interactions*, among which appear the specifically nuclear forces between nucleons responsible for binding these particles together into a complex nucleus. The forces between π-mesons and protons are also strong interactions.

We assume that all such interactions are constrained by general principles. Chief among these are the *conservation laws* for the mechanical quantities *total energy, linear momentum* and *angular momentum*. These are classically familiar quantities which are known to assume a continuous range of values in macroscopic problems. When quantum mechanics must be applied, i.e. when the de Broglie wavelength of a particle is no longer negligible with respect to the dimensions of the system or enclosure in which it appears, the conservation of energy and of momentum are still assumed to apply, although the limits set by the uncertainty principle become important in particular situations. In many problems, too, such as those of the simple harmonic oscillator or of the hydrogen atom, the energy and angular momentum take *discrete* values and are said to be *quantized*, in a way which is not encountered in classical physics. These conservation laws may be related to certain specific properties of the space–time framework within which we conduct our experiments.

Among the most interesting conservation laws are those relating to numbers of particles and to charge, which cannot so far be deduced and are really based on experience. It seems likely that the total number of nucleons in the universe (with antiparticles counted negatively) is a constant, and that if a new proton is created, it is always accompanied by an anti-proton, e.g.

$$p + p \ (+\text{energy}) \rightarrow p + p + p + \bar{p} \qquad (1.7)$$

Decay of a neutron does not alter the number of nucleons:

$$n \rightarrow p + e^- + \bar{\nu} \qquad (1.8)$$

The *conservation of nucleons* with certain necessary extensions to include hyperons, is implicit in our present description of all nuclear processes. There is also excellent evidence (ch. 5) for the joint production (or annihilation) of positron–electron pairs from (or into) radiation under suitable circumstance according to the process

$$\gamma \rightleftarrows e^+ + e^- \qquad (1.9)$$

Conservation of electrons is not valid because of decay processes of type (1.8), but if neutrinos and μ-mesons are suitably included it is possible reasonably to postulate a *conservation of leptons*.

An even more compelling reason for asserting the conservation of nucleons is that if processes of the type

$$p \to e^+ + \gamma \qquad (1.10)$$

were possible with a lifetime short on the cosmological scale, then the universe as we know it would be evidently decaying away. The conservation of particles also follows directly from the conservation of charge since particles and antiparticles have equal and opposite charges to a high degree of accuracy. The conservation of charge will be assumed throughout in our analysis of nuclear processes.

1.3 Terminology

Although international recommendations on symbols, units and nomenclature exist (International Union of Pure and Applied Physics, S.U.N. Commission Document U.I.P.9, 1961; reprinted in *Physics Today*, **15**, 19, 1962), these are still not comprehensive and are unfortunately not yet adopted uniformly in the major journals. In the present book the main concern has been to avoid ambiguity in terminology and the resulting symbols are a compromise between the S.U.N. recommendations and the practice of the American Institute of Physics.

1.3.1. SPECIFIC DEFINITIONS

nucleus   a general term for the finite structure of neutrons and protons constituting the centre of force in an atom.

nuclide   a specific nucleus, with given proton number Z and neutron number N.

isotope   one of a group of nuclides each having the same proton number Z.

isotone   one of a group of nuclides each having the same neutron number N.

isobar   one of a group of nuclides each having the same mass number A.

isomer   a nuclide excited to a long lived state from which beta or gamma decay ensues (ch. 13).

1.3.2. NOMENCLATURE AND SYMBOLS

atomic number	Z
mass number	A
proton number	P or Z
neutron number	$N = A - Z$
charge of electron	$-e$
electron mass	m (gm)
electron rest mass	m_0 (gm)
mass of a particle x	$\begin{cases} m_x \text{ (gm)} \\ M_x \text{ (atomic mass units)} \end{cases}$
mass of a neutral atom	$M(A, Z)$ (atomic mass units)
mass of a heavy particle	M (gm)
rest mass of a heavy particle	M_0 (gm)
reduced mass of a heavy particle	M_0 (gm)
magnetic moment of a particle x	μ_x
Bohr magneton	μ_0
nuclear magneton	μ_N
principal quantum number	n, n_i
orbital quantum number	L, l_i
spin quantum number	S, s_i
total angular momentum quantum number	J, j_i
magnetic quantum number	M, m_i
nuclear spin quantum number	I
isobaric spin quantum number	T
hyperfine quantum number	F
rotational quantum number	J, K
quadrupole moment	Q
Rydberg constant	R

Mechanical quantities

velocity	v
momentum	p
kinetic energy	T
potential energy	V
total energy	E

Nuclear radii are conveniently measured in *femtometers* (1 fm $= 10^{-13}$cm) and nuclear areas in *barns* (1 barn $= 10^{-24}$cm^2).

Electrical quantities

The mixed CGS system of units is used throughout and magnetic fields are represented by the symbol H (gauss).

Symbols for *chemical elements* are written:

mass number   state of ionization
$$^{14}_{7}N^{6+}_{2}$$
atomic number   atoms per molecule

A two-body *nuclear reaction*, in which a particle a bombards a nucleus X with the result that a residual nucleus Y and a particle b are produced, i.e.

$$X + a \rightarrow Y + b$$

will be abbreviated $X(a,b)Y$.

References

The literature of nuclear physics is very extensive. The following books, among many others, provide a general background.

1.1 R. E. Peierls, *The Laws of Nature*, Allen and Unwin, 1955.

1.2 A. P. French, *Principles of Modern Physics*, Wiley, 1958.

1.3 M. R. Wehr and J. A. Richards, *Physics of the Atom*, Addison-Wesley Publishing Co. Inc., 1960.

A general coverage of nuclear physics, mainly from the experimental point of view, is given in:

1.4 D. Halliday, *Introductory Nuclear Physics*, Wiley, 1955.

1.5 I. Kaplan, *Nuclear Physics*, Addison-Wesley Publishing Co. Inc., 1955.

1.6 R. S. Shankland, *Atomic and Nuclear Physics*, The Macmillan Company, 1960.

1.7 R. D. Evans, *The Atomic Nucleus*, McGraw-Hill Book Co., 1955.

Facsimiles of important papers in nuclear physics are collected by:

1.8 Beyer, *Foundations of Nuclear Physics*, Dover Publications Inc., 1949.

Among theoretical and general works on the subject the following should be mentioned:

1.9 J. M. Blatt and V. F. Weisskopf, *Theoretical Nuclear Physics*, Wiley, 1952.

1.10 E. Fermi, *Nuclear Physics*, University of Chicago, 1950.

1.11 H. A. Bethe and P. Morrison, *Elementary Nuclear Theory*, Wiley 1956.

1.12 L. R. B. Elton, *Introductory Nuclear Theory*, Pitman, 1959.

1.13 R. E. Peierls and others, 'A Survey of Field Theory', *Rep. progr. Phys.*, **18**, 423, 1955.

1.14 M. A. Preston, *Physics of the Nucleus*, Addison-Wesley Publishing Co. Inc., 1962.

Historical reviews which may be consulted include:

1.15 N. Bohr, The Rutherford Memorial Lecture 1958, *Proc. phys. Soc.*, **78**, 1083, 1961.

1.16 C. D. Anderson, 'Early work on the positron and the muon', *Amer. J. Phys.*, **29**, 825, 1961.

Convenient tabulations of nuclear data are given by:

1.17 O. R. Frisch (ed.), *The Nuclear Handbook*, Newnes, 1958.

2. NATURAL RADIOACTIVITY AND THE DISCOVERY OF THE NUCLEUS

The radioactivity found in naturally occurring elements is not a basically different phenomenon from the radioactivity now known to be a property of several hundred artificially produced nuclei. It might therefore be discussed as part of the treatment of the spontaneous emission of radiations given later in this book. Natural radioactivity has, however, such a deep historical significance for nuclear physics, and has affected the whole development of the subject, including its terminology, to such a marked extent, that it seems proper to give at the outset a review of the steps that led to the nuclear hypothesis.

2.1 The discovery of radioactivity and the separation of radium

In 1896 Becquerel had been studying the luminescence of uranium salts excited by ordinary light. He had observed that the luminescent radiations were capable of casting shadows of opaque objects which could be recorded by a photographic plate wrapped in black paper. This phenomenon had also been demonstrated as one of the most dramatic and potentially valuable properties of the newly discovered X-rays and it seemed at first that the luminescent radiation from uranium might be similar to the X-rays themselves. The outstanding discovery* made by Becquerel was that the shadow-casting radiation from uranium persisted even when the exciting light was removed. He showed also that the radiation was found with all uranium compounds in proportion to their uranium content and that spontaneous emission of radiation, or *radioactivity*, was a property of the uranium atom itself in its normal state. It is now known that the radiations studied by Becquerel were the fast electrons emitted in the β-decay of daughter products of the nucleus ^{238}U; Becquerel himself showed that the radiations could be deviated by a magnetic

---

* H. Becquerel, *Comptes Rendus*, **122**, 501, 1896.

field. He also found that the new radiations could discharge an electrified body and this discovery led quickly to the use of ionization chambers for quantitative assessment of the strength of the radiation, or *activity*.

After the announcement of Becquerel's work, Pierre and Marie Curie surveyed many other elements for radioactive emission and discovered that thorium showed a similar degree of activity. They also found that the uranium ore known as pitchblende contained more activity than was expected from the chemical estimation of the uranium content and they rightly deduced the presence of other active elements. They then attacked the problem of separating these elements from the uranium, and from the other elements present in the pitchblende. Their chemical procedures first led them to concentrate a substance which seemed to behave chemically rather like bismuth, but which had a considerably greater activity than had uranium. This substance was separated from bismuth by volatilization, and, as the first new radioactive element to be isolated, was given the name *polonium*,* after Mme. Curie's native country. The activity of the separated polonium was later found to decrease slowly (see Table **2.1**,† $t_{1/2} = 138$ days) and by itself was insufficient to account for the excess activity of the pitchblende. The Curies therefore continued their work and next found another highly active substance which behaved chemically like barium, and was named by its discoverers *radium*.‡ Neither polonium nor radium was obtained in sufficient quantity in the first extractions to permit a determination of atomic weight, and the Curies therefore set themselves the task of extracting the radium element from as much ore as they could obtain. The tireless patience of their work, which began with chemical separations and ended with repeated fractional crystallizations of radium and barium chlorides, is well known (Ref. 2.6). As fractionation proceeded, the specific activity of the product was found to have increased, and in the end about 0·1 g of radium, as chloride, was obtained from 1 ton of ore. Radium was shown to be several million times as active as

---

* Pierre and Marie Curie, *Comptes Rendus*, **127**, 175, 1898.

† For ease of reference, Tables **2.1** and **2.2** are placed at the end of the chapter, pp. 53–55.

‡ Pierre and Marie Curie, *Comptes Rendus*, **127**, 1215, 1898.

uranium (mass for mass) and Mme. Curie was able to make the first chemical determination of the atomic weight of the new element as 225; it was shown also to have a characteristic optical spectrum. The activity of radium appeared to be constant, in contrast with the polonium activity, and was sufficiently strong to account for the original observations on pitchblende. It is now known that the mass number of radium is 226 and that its half-life is 1622 years.

In 1897 the radiations from uranium had excited the attention of Rutherford, who was then working under J. J. Thomson in the Cavendish Laboratory. After studying the conductivity of gases induced by the uranium radiations he turned his attention to thorium and continued work on this substance during his tenure of the Professorship of Physics at McGill University, Montreal (1898–1907). This was the heroic age of radioactivity, in which, mainly as a result of the work of Rutherford, Soddy and their collaborators, the subject was placed upon a quantitative basis and the stage was set for the appearance of the nuclear atom.

2.2   The radioactive radiations

The early experiments of Curie and of Rutherford showed that the radiations from radioactive substances contained components of different penetrating power, as assessed by their absorption in matter. The less penetrating rays, which were completely absorbed by a few cm of air or by a thin sheet (about 0·005 in.) of metal were called α-*rays*. The more penetrating components, which were absorbed by about 1 mm of lead were named β-*rays*. Both the α- and β-rays were shown to be corpuscular in character by magnetic deflection methods. In 1900 Villard identified a third and even more penetrating type of ionizing radiation, capable of traversing as much as 10 cm of lead. These rays could not be deviated by a magnet and were described as γ-*radiation*; they are now known to be electromagnetic in nature. Fig. 2.1 illustrates the difference between the radiations. The first decade of the study of radioactivity saw a great increase in knowledge of the nature and origin of these radiations and resulted in the development of several sensitive instruments (ch. 6) for their detection. Many experiments however were carried out with an ionization chamber connected to a Dolezalek electrometer; the active sample was placed on one of the electrodes inside the chamber (Fig. 2.6). This apparatus permitted the observation of decay rates and if absorbing foils were placed over the sample the radiations emitted could be distinguished according to their penetrating power. In this way specific radioactive bodies were classified according to their radiation properties. After 1908 the weaker sources of α-rays were often investigated by 'scintillation'

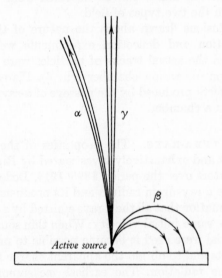

Fig. 2.1. Effect of a magnetic field (perpendicular to the plane of the diagram) on α-, β- and γ-rays (Ref. 2.1).

counting. In this method the flashes of light produced when the α-rays struck a screen of zinc sulphide or other suitable material were observed and counted using a low power microscope.

The techniques of electric and magnetic deflection, which had already been used for the study of electrons and ions, were also applied extensively in analysis of the radioactive radiations. In a uniform magnetic field H a particle of mass m, charge e and velocity v perpendicular to H describes a circle of radius ρ in a plane perpendicular to the lines of force, where

$$H\rho = \frac{mc}{e}v \qquad (2.1)$$

and c is the velocity of light. In a uniform electric field E the particle describes a parabola in a plane parallel to the lines of force and the deflection in a certain distance l in the field is given by

$$\frac{1}{2}\frac{Ee}{m}\left(\frac{l}{v}\right)^{2} \qquad (2.2)$$

assuming that v is initially at right-angles to E. From eqq. 2.1 and 2.2 both e/m and v can be obtained from the observed deflections in the two types of field.

The conclusions drawn about the nature of the radiations from ionization and deflection experiments were strikingly verified when the actual tracks of particles were made visible in the Wilson expansion chamber (ch. 6). Plates 1, 2 and 3 show the effects produced by the passage of α-rays and X-rays through such a chamber.

2.2.1 THE ALPHA-RAYS. The properties of the α-rays were continuously and exhaustively investigated by Rutherford and his collaborators over the period 1898–1914. Deflection experiments on the α-rays from radium and its products showed to a first approximation that all the α-rays emitted by a single parent body had the same initial velocity. When thin sources of radioactive material were used it became possible to make accurate measurements and to obtain the apparent charge to mass ratio e_α/m_α for the radiation. The earliest measurements ranged between 4300 and 6400 e.m.u. per g. Although these values were not refined to the value 4820 until 1914 (Rutherford and Robinson) they were adequate to suggest that the actual value was probably half that $(e_H/m_H = 9652)$ obtained for the hydrogen ion from electrolysis and gaseous conduction experiments. The results indicated that the α-rays were actually behaving as *particles* of mass comparable with that of a light atom.

The velocity of emission of the α-particles was also determined in absolute units from the deflection experiments. Velocities (and thence energies) were also determined, once an absolute measurement had been made, by observing the relative ranges of different α-particle groups in air under standard conditions (15°C and 760 mm). All measurements confirmed the homogeneity in energy of the particles emitted from a given parent.

Details of these techniques will be discussed in chapter 7; Table **2.1** gives the energies for a number of natural α-emitters.

To determine the mass of the α-particles from the deflection experiments, it was necessary to measure the charge in absolute units. This was obtained by Rutherford and Geiger (1908) following their development of methods for counting single particles. Using a type of proportional counter (ch. 6) they found that the number of α-particles emitted per second from the product now known as RaC′ in equilibrium with 1 g of radium was 3.4×10^{10}.* The total charge collected due to the α-particles from a source of RaC′ was then determined using the apparatus shown in Fig. 2.2, and the strength of the source was related to a standard source by comparison of γ-ray activities. The α-particle charge was thus found to be $+9.3 \times 10^{-10}$ e.s.u.; subsequent experiments have yielded a more accurate value which is just twice that of the electronic charge and of opposite sign. The α-particle therefore had a mass approximately 4 times that of the proton and appeared to be a helium atom with a double positive charge.

Several important quantitative conclusions were drawn from the experiment of Rutherford and Geiger, including a value for the half-life of radium (Table **2.2**) and figures for the rate of production of helium and for the evolution of heat by radioactive salts (Table **2.2** and Sect. **2.3**). The general agreement between those predictions which could be independently tested and actual observation confirmed the conclusion that the α-particle was a charged helium atom. This conclusion was further supported by the fact that radioactive ores were known to contain helium. The most elegant confirmation of the hypothesis was provided by an experiment of Rutherford and Royds in 1909 (Fig. 2.3). In this work α-particles from a large quantity of the active gas radon (Table **2.1**) which had been compressed into a tube A, entered an evacuated space through the walls of the tube. After a period of a few days, the accumulated gases in the space were compressed into the capillary V and by exciting the contents of the capillary electrically, the characteristic optical spectrum of helium was observed. No such spectrum was seen in test experiments in which ordinary helium was

---

* This figure is now known more accurately (Table **2.2**, p. 55).

allowed to stand for a few days in the tube A. It follows that on neutralization by collection of electrons (from residual gases in the apparatus) α-particles at rest give rise to helium gas.

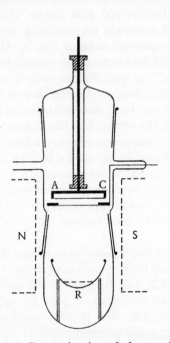

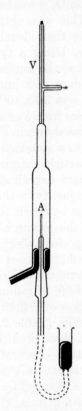

Fig. 2.2. Determination of charge of the α-particle (Rutherford and Geiger, *Proc. roy. Soc.* A, **81**, 162, 1908). A source of RaC was placed in the vessel R and the charge communicated to the screened plate AC by the α-particles from RaC′ was found from electrometer readings. The magnetic field was necessary in order to prevent the loss of secondary electrons from the plate AC.

Fig. 2.3. Identification of the neutralized α-particle with the helium atom (Rutherford and Royds, *Phil. Mag.*, **17**, 281, 1909).

This striking experiment helped to establish a remarkable conclusion that had begun to emerge, most clearly in the mind of Rutherford, from the study of radioactivity. This was that the atoms of matter were no longer to be regarded as immutable or indestructible, since some of them, notably uranium, radium, radon and thorium could spontaneously emit atoms of helium.

This idea now seems neither exciting nor improbable; in the early years of the century it constituted a scientific revolution. The development of the *transformation theory* is described in Sect. 2.4.1.

2.2.2. THE BETA RAYS. The electric and magnetic deflections obtained with β-rays corresponded both in direction and rough magnitude with those observed with the cathode rays in a discharge tube. The β-particles were thus negatively charged; their specific charge e_β/m_β, however, seemed to decrease with increasing velocity and the velocities themselves were distributed over a range of values up to a certain limit. For low velocities the value of e_β/m_β was $1\cdot76 \times 10^7$ e.m.u. per g which is almost exactly the value found for electrons. The decrease in the observed e/m for higher velocities is fully accounted for by the special theory of relativity, according to which the mass of a particle moving with velocity v is

$$m = \frac{m_0}{\sqrt{1 - v^2/c^2}} \qquad (2.3)$$

where m_0 is the rest mass, effective only for very slow particles.*

The β-rays could thus be identified with ordinary electrons, endowed, because of their small mass, with velocities approaching that of light. They were distinguished from the α-particles not only by their specific charge, but also by their inhomogeneity in energy. This identification of the β-particles did not clarify the problems of their origin and energy distribution, for which a satisfactory solution had to wait for some thirty years (ch. 16).

Magnetic deflection experiments, as will be shown in more detail in chapter 7, yield accurate momentum distributions of the β-particles from a given parent body. Detailed examination of this distribution shows that it contains a number of narrow, apparently homogeneous lines superimposed upon a general continuous distribution with an upper limit (Fig. 2.4). These lines (internal conversion lines) are associated with the emission of γ-radiation and not with the primary β-ray process; they do not appear in general when a source which does not emit γ-rays is studied. The substance RaE is of this latter type

---

* For $v = \frac{1}{2}c$, $m = 1\cdot15m_0$.

and its continuous spectrum of β-particles has been closely investigated. The decay process for this body is now known to be

$$\text{RaE} \xrightarrow{\beta} \text{RaF} \xrightarrow{\alpha} \text{Stable lead}$$

and by counting of individual α- and β-particles it was established that the continuous β-spectrum contained just one particle per transformation.

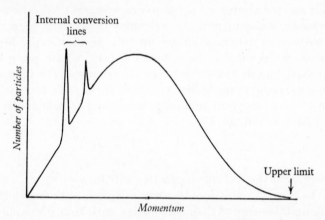

Fig. 2.4. Schematic representation of the momentum distribution of β-rays from a radioactive source.

The maximum energies of β-particles from the heavy radioactive elements are shown in Table **2.1**; present methods of measurement are discussed in chapters 6 and 7.

2.2.3. THE GAMMA RAYS. The most penetrating component of the natural radiations is not deflected by magnetic fields, and interacts with matter as do X-rays. The γ-rays were therefore identified as electromagnetic radiation, and this conclusion was supported by the success of Rutherford and Andrade and of Frilley in diffracting these rays by crystals. The diffraction experiments indicated that the γ-rays probably had a line spectrum, and for some time it was considered that they arose as a result of the passage of β-particles, with which they were often associated, through the atomic structure. The electromagnetic interactions (photoelectric effect; Compton effect, ch. 5) were applied to determine the energy of the γ-rays and these energies were found to be commensurate with those observed in α- and β-emission. Relations between the energies of the γ-radiations themselves were extensively investigated by Ellis and as the accuracy of these experiments increased little doubt was left that the γ-rays formed the electromagnetic spectrum of a radiating system (now known to be the product nucleus) excited in the primary radioactive process of α- or β-emission.

2.3 General properties of the radiations

2.3.1. CONSTANCY OF RADIOACTIVITY WITH TIME. Spontaneous emission of α-, β- and γ-rays was proved by Becquerel to be an atomic rather than a molecular phenomenon. The decay rate is not affected* by the chemical environment of the active atom and has not been influenced by variations of temperature and pressure.

2.3.2. PRODUCTION OF HELIUM BY RADIOACTIVE MATERIALS. The identification of the α-particle as a charged helium atom explained the occurrence of this gas in radioactive minerals. The counting experiments of Rutherford and Geiger permitted an accurate prediction of the rate of production of helium from radium (see Table **2.2**) but the first measurements (Ramsey and Soddy 1903, Dewar 1908) of the evolution of helium from radium salts gave results differing slightly from the calculated value. The discrepancy was removed in 1911 by the more accurate work of Boltwood and Rutherford.

2.3.3 GENERATION OF HEAT IN RADIOACTIVE MATERIALS. The amount of energy liberated in a single radioactive process is given by the kinetic energy of the emitted particle, together with that of the recoiling residual fragment and the figures in Table **2.1** show that these energies (≈ 5 MeV) are very large compared with the energies involved in the individual chemical reactions between molecules ($\approx$ eV) Even before the nuclear hypothesis, this aspect of radioactivity had convinced Rutherford that some completely new mechanism, not envisaged in

---

* This is not quite true. A special case will be discussed in chapter 13.

early theories of atomic structure, was necessary to explain
the radioactive process.

The heating effect due to the α-rays from 1 g of radium in
equilibrium with its products was calculated from the counting
experiment of Rutherford and Geiger, using the known mass
and velocity of the α-rays. The result obtained (Table 2.2) was
about 10% less than the value observed by Rutherford and
Robinson (1912), owing to heat developed by absorption of β-
and γ-rays.

The actual amount of heat developed by 1 g of radium and
its products per second (≈ 2 cal) may seem small in comparison
with the 8000 calories released in the oxidation of 1 g of carbon
to carbon dioxide, but it must be remembered that the emission
from radium continues with a half-life of 1600 years. Altogether,
before its activity has reached negligible proportions the 1 g of
radium will have emitted $3 \cdot 2 \times 10^9$ calories. Despite this large
value the energy released by radioactive materials has, as
emphasized by Rutherford, little practical application because
the amount of natural radioactive material which can be
concentrated safely, allowing for biological hazards, is really
very small. The release of nuclear energy on a large scale
involves stimulation of a particular process (fission) in a large
mass of material in a space of relatively small dimensions; it was
first achieved nearly fifty years after the discovery of radioactivity. The total mass of radioactive material in the earth is
nevertheless very large, and the total emission of heat from this
constituent of the geological crust must be taken into account
in estimates of the age of the earth based on thermal data.

2.3.4. THE DECAY LAW.   Soon after commencing his experiments in Montreal on the properties of thorium, Rutherford
found that an active gas, now known to be an emanation isotope, could be swept away from thorium oxide into an ionization
chamber by an air current. When the air current was stopped
the conductivity of the chamber diminished with time according to a geometrical law, falling to half value in about
1 min (a time now known to be 51·5 sec). This was the first
observation of the *radioactive decay law*; all the other radioactive materials investigated until then had been long lived or
in equilibrium with long-lived parents.

Further experiments of this type, on other radioactive bodies which in due course became available, showed that the decay law for a given mass of material was accurately exponential.

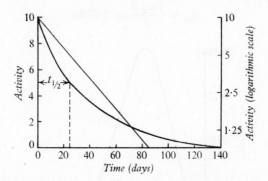

Fig. 2.5*a*. Exponential decay curve (UX₁), showing half-life. The straight line is a logarithmic plot of the activity (Ref. 2.1).

Fig. 2.5a illustrates the decay of activity observed in a typical case. If the activity is assumed to be due to an atom by atom process, it is of course proportional to the rate of decrease of the number of the atoms N_t present at time t, i.e.

$$\text{activity} = \frac{\mathrm{d}N_t}{\mathrm{d}t}$$

The observed exponential decay then requires further that

$$\text{activity} = \frac{\mathrm{d}N_t}{\mathrm{d}t} = -\lambda N_t \tag{2.4}$$

$$N_t = N_0 e^{-\lambda t} \tag{2.5}$$

where N_0 is the number of active atoms present at the beginning of the observations, $(t = 0)$ and λ is the *radioactive decay constant*. The *mean life* of the atoms is

$$\tau = \frac{\displaystyle\int_{N_0}^{0} t\,\mathrm{d}N_t}{\displaystyle\int_{N_0}^{0} \mathrm{d}N_t} = \frac{\displaystyle\int_{0}^{\infty} t\,\frac{\mathrm{d}N_t}{\mathrm{d}t}\,\mathrm{d}t}{\displaystyle\int_{0}^{\infty} \frac{\mathrm{d}N_t}{\mathrm{d}t}\,\mathrm{d}t} = \frac{1}{\lambda} \tag{2.6}$$

The interval $t_{1/2}$ during which half the atoms disappear by decay (*half-value period* or *half-life*) is given by

$$N_0/2 = N_0 e^{-\lambda t_{1/2}}$$

from which

$$t_{1/2} = \frac{\log_e 2}{\lambda} = 0 \cdot 693\tau \qquad (2.7)$$

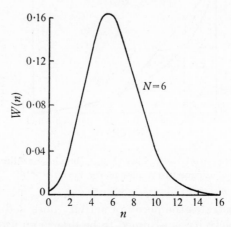

Fig. 2.5b. Poisson distribution for $N = 6$ (Segrè, *Experimental Nuclear Physics*, Vol. III).

The exponential law of decay is characteristic of all radioactive processes and has been checked in vast numbers of experiments over extensive periods. It describes the disappearance by decay of short-lived unstable particles and excited states as well as of long-lived radioactive elements. A law of such general application must have some general basis, and it is simple to show that it may be deduced from the assumption that for a given atom the probability p of decay in a time Δ is independent of the previous life of the atom. For if this is so then, for small enough Δ

$$p = c\Delta$$

where c is a constant and the probability that the atom shall not have disappeared in a time $t = k\Delta$ is

$$\begin{aligned} q &= (1 - c\Delta)^k \\ &= (1 - c\Delta)^{t/\Delta} \\ &= [(1 - c\Delta)^{-(1/c\Delta)}]^{-ct} \end{aligned}$$

and letting Δ become zero, while $k\Delta$ remains finite

$$q = e^{-ct}$$

and the decay law 2.5 follows, putting $c = \lambda$.

The random nature of radioactive emission was demonstrated by observation of fluctuations of the number of α-particles emitted by a given source in a given time interval. If N is the number of particles expected on the average in the interval, the probability of observing n particles in this interval is given by the Poisson distribution for random events:

$$W(n) = \frac{N^n e^{-N}}{n!} \tag{2.8}$$

This distribution is shown for $N = 6$ in Fig. 2.5b; it was checked by Rutherford and Geiger by recording on tape the time of appearance of individual α-particles. These and many similar experiments have abundantly verified the conclusion that α-particles are emitted at random in time.

2.4   Origin of alpha and beta rays

2.4.1 THE TRANSFORMATION THEORY.   Our understanding of the nature of radioactive transformations dates generally from the arrival of Rutherford in Montreal in 1898 and especially from his subsequent association with Soddy. The years 1898–1911 saw a great increase in empirical knowledge of radioactive bodies, and the nature of the individual radiations as well as the general properties of radioactivity were established as described in Sects. **2.2** and **2.3**. In order to account for these facts, foremost among which was the appearance of new chemical substances, Rutherford and Soddy (1903)* proposed the *transformation theory* according to which atoms of a radioactive substance disintegrate spontaneously, with the emission of either an α- or a β-particle, and with the formation of a new chemical atom. This new atom may itself disintegrate similarly in succession and in this way a *radioactive series* of atoms, all genetically linked, arises. The transformations at the beginning of the thorium series, for instance, are

Thorium $\xrightarrow{\alpha}$ Mesothorium I $\xrightarrow{\beta}$ Mesothorium II

$$\xrightarrow{\beta} \text{Radiothorium} \xrightarrow{\alpha} \text{Thorium X} \xrightarrow{\alpha} \tag{2.9}$$

* E. Rutherford and F. Soddy, *Phil. Mag.*, 5, 576, 1903.

Each of these products has a definite chemical behaviour, which can be used in extracting it from a mixture of active elements.

The combination of chemical and physical techniques used in characterizing a series of radioactive transformations is well illustrated by the early work of Rutherford and Soddy* on thorium. In work with this element they found that the body described as thorium X (ThX) could be extracted by precipitating the thorium as hydroxide with ammonia and evaporating the filtrate to dryness. When this operation was

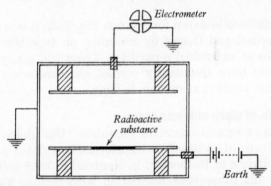

Fig. 2.6. Ionization chamber and electrometer used by Rutherford and Soddy (*Phil. Mag.*, **4**, 370, 1902) in early studies of radioactivity.

complete it was noted that (a) the thorium itself was reduced in activity temporarily, although it recovered its original strength in time, and (b) that the ThX activity in the filtrate decayed exponentially with a half-life of about 4 days. Fig. 2.6 shows the ionization chamber used, and Fig. 2.7 the growth and decay curves obtained in this experiment. Such curves are now familiar in many other cases, and are wholly accounted for by assuming that thorium produces a chemically *dissimilar* body ThX as a result of its own decay, and that ThX decays, when separated, with its own characteristic half-life. The recovery of the initial thorium activity is due to creation of further ThX by decay until an equilibrium value is reached at which the production and decay rates of ThX are equal. That this equilibrium value is apparently constant indicates only that the

* E. Rutherford and F. Soddy, *Phil. Mag.*, **4**, 370, 1902.

half-life of the original thorium is very long. The chemical and physical dissimilarity of Th and ThX (now known to be an

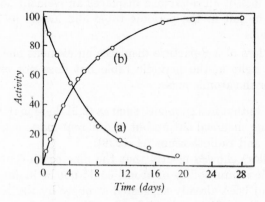

Fig. 2.7

a) Decay of ThX extracted from thorium.
b) Recovery of ThX activity in a thorium sample after a chemical separation of ThX (Rutherford and Soddy, *Phil. Mag.*, 4, 370, 1902).

isotope of radium) and their obvious genetic relationship proved that one type of atom must be decaying into another.

2.4.2 THE DISCOVERY OF ISOTOPES: THE DISPLACEMENT LAWS. An important discovery, closely linked with the transformation theory, was made by Soddy and others over the years 1906–11. It was that some bodies could be formed in radioactive decay which were physically distinct on the basis of their radioactive properties but were chemically *identical* since it was impossible to separate them by available chemical techniques. Table 2.1 includes many such examples, notably thorium and radiothorium, radium and mesothorium, uranium I and uranium II. These bodies were finally postulated by Soddy in 1911 to be *isotopes* of each other, that is to say they occupied the same place in the chemical system of the elements, but were nevertheless different physically. The property in which they differed became clear as soon as the nature of the radioactive radiations was established, and the *displacement laws* of Soddy, Russell and Fajans had been formulated (1913). These laws summarize a great deal of experience in the statements that

  i) the loss of an α-particle displaces an element two places to the left in the periodic table and lowers its mass by 4 units,

  ii) the loss of a β-particle displaces an element one place to the right in the periodic table but does not essentially alter the atomic mass.

It follows that in a sequence such as (2.9) there may be atoms of the same chemical nature but of different mass, e.g. thorium ($A = 232$) and radiothorium ($A = 228$).

These laws showed clearly that the nineteenth-century concept of the immutability of atoms could not be maintained, as indeed had been already suggested strongly by the generation of helium in radioactive materials. Within a few years the *artificial* transmutation of atoms was to be demonstrated in Rutherford's laboratory at Manchester (1917–19), while the objective demonstration of the existence of the isotopes of neon by J. J. Thomson (1913) and Aston (1919) in a sense only supplemented what was already convincing evidence.

2.4.3. THE RADIOACTIVE SERIES. It is not proposed to give in this book an account of the intricate procedures by which the physical and chemical nature of all the naturally occurring radioactive bodies were established. The unambiguous characterization of one of the natural series would be a not inconsiderable task even today with the highly developed resources of a radiochemical laboratory and the full support of nuclear theory. That a clear understanding of the basic phenomena could have been reached in only a few years after the discovery of radioactivity is a tribute to the genius of Rutherford and his fellow workers.

In general it was assumed that whenever a new half-life was discovered, a new radioelement might be involved and attempts were then made to separate it chemically and to identify it, if possible, by an atomic weight determination. Observation of genetic relationships between activities after chemical separations often indicated sequences of transmutations, and the application of the displacement laws permitted the atomic weights of new bodies to be deduced from those of known parents. The detection of a radioactive inert gas (emanation) and the identification of the stable end products of a decay chain provided important fixed points in the series.

In this way the radioactive bodies listed in Table **2.1** were identified, and their grouping into the three natural radioactive families was established. These families are the thorium series, the uranium–radium series and the uranium–actinium series. In addition another family, the neptunium series, has now been prepared artificially. In each series α- and β-emission are the main decay processes and the resulting sequences of elements and isotopes are generally similar between the families, but there are differences in detail. Since mass number changes are due only to the emission of α-particles the members of each series have masses which differ by multiples of 4 units. The naturally occurring series originate from nuclei with lives long compared with that of the earth. Neptunium has a relatively short life, but it is the longest lived member of its series. Each series terminates when the decay process results in the formation of a stable nucleus, which becomes the end product; the parents and end products of the 4 series are shown in Table **2.3**.

TABLE 2.3   Parents and end products of radioactive series

NAME OF SERIES	MASS NUMBER	PARENT	HALF-LIFE	END PRODUCT
Thorium	$4n$	^{232}Th	$1 \cdot 4 \times 10^{10}$ yr.	^{208}Pb
Neptunium	$4n+1$	^{237}Np	$2 \cdot 2 \times 10^{6}$ yr	^{209}Bi
Uranium–radium	$4n+2$	^{238}U	$4 \cdot 5 \times 10^{9}$ yr	^{206}Pb
Uranium–actinium	$4n+3$	^{235}U	$7 \cdot 2 \times 10^{8}$ yr	^{207}Pb

The naturally occurring series thus end in lead isotopes; this, of course, accounts for the presence of lead as well as helium in radioactive ores and for the difference between the isotopic constitution of this 'radiogenic' lead and the ordinary element.

The three naturally occurring families all include an emanation or inert gas (radon, thoron, actinon) as noticed by Rutherford (Sect. 2.3.4). This emanation engenders by recoil against α-decay an active deposit of products, which came to be known as the A, B, C members of each family, on surfaces to which it is exposed. The active deposit (formerly known as 'induced activity') is increased in the presence of an electric field, showing that the recoil 'A' particles are ionized.

In order to simplify the presentation of data on the radioactive series, the results of the nuclear theory will be assumed. The radioactive bodies can then be displayed on diagrams showing number of neutrons and number of protons in each nuclide as in Fig. 2.8. In this figure certain subsidiary decay chains have been omitted in the interests of clarity.

Most of the radioactive elements disintegrate in a definite manner with the ejection of an α- or β-particle. It will be seen, however, from Fig. 2.8 that a few undergo dual decay or *branching*. One of the best-known cases of this phenomenon is found in the thorium active deposit, in which ThB decays as follows

$$
\begin{array}{ccc}
 & \text{ThC}' & \\
 & \beta\nearrow \quad \nwarrow\alpha & \\
 & 64\% & \\
\text{ThB}\rightarrow\text{ThC} & & {}^{208}\text{Pb(ThD)} \\
 & \alpha\searrow 36\% \quad \nearrow\beta & \\
 & \text{ThC}'' &
\end{array} \qquad (2.10a)
$$

The final product reached by each branch is the same and the energy release is also the same.

In the case of the body UX_2 there is a competition between β- and γ-decay, as shown below

$$
\begin{array}{ccc}
 & \text{UX}_2 & \\
\beta\nearrow & \searrow & \beta\ 99\cdot88\% \quad 1\cdot18\ \text{min} \\
\text{UX}_1 & \gamma \Big| 0\cdot12\% & \\
 & \searrow & \searrow \text{U}_{\text{II}} \\
 & \text{UZ} & \\
 & \beta\ 6\cdot7\ \text{hr} \longrightarrow &
\end{array} \qquad (2.10b)
$$

The nuclei UX_2 and UZ both result from the decay of UX_1 and both decay by β-emission, but with different half-lives, into the same element UII. They are therefore essentially the same body and the difference between their decay properties is now explained by supposing that UX_2 is an *isomer* of UZ, that is to say it is the UZ nucleus excited to a metastable level of long

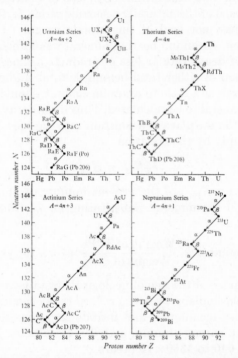

Fig. 2.8. The main decay chains of the four radioactive series. The $4n$ (thorium), $4n+2$ (uranium-radium), and $4n+3$ (uranium-actinium) series are found in nature but the $4n+1$ (neptunium) series must be prepared artificially. The historical names are shown on the diagram and the accepted chemical symbols on the axis (Segrè, *Experimental Nuclear Physics*, Vol. III).

life, from which β-decay to the ground state of the end product UII takes place. Such isomeric states are now well known in many lighter nuclei and are associated with nuclear levels between which there is a large spin difference (Sect. **13.5**). This first example of nuclear isomerism was established by Hahn (1921).

2.4.4 THE AGE OF MINERALS: NATURALLY OCCURRING ACTIVITIES NOT CONNECTED WITH URANIUM OR THORIUM. It will be seen from the decay chains shown in Fig. 2.8 that the decay of the parent body and its products is accompanied (a) by the evolution of helium from the emitted α-particles, and (b) by the formation of lead of a particular atomic weight for each of the naturally occurring series. If, for example, neither helium nor lead of this atomic weight ($A = 206$) was present when a uranium bearing mineral was formed, and if no alteration of decay rate or loss of products has occurred, then determination of either total helium or total 'radiogenic' lead in the mineral, as a ratio to uranium content, should permit the age of the mineral to be calculated. Thus if the decay of uranium is assumed to take place at a constant rate the age t of a mineral is given simply by the equation

$$\lambda_U N_U t = N_{Pb} \tag{2.11}$$

where N_U and N_{Pb} are the present number of atoms of ^{238}U and ^{206}Pb in the mineral. Substituting for λ_U from Table 2.1 we find

$$\text{Age of mineral} = \frac{\text{Weight of } ^{206}\text{Pb}}{\text{Weight of } ^{238}\text{U}} \times 7 \cdot 5 \times 10^9 \text{ yr} \tag{2.12}$$

Many estimates of the age of geological strata have been made in this or in a similar way, using refined radiochemical and mass spectrometric techniques, and introducing corrections for the decay of the parent uranium activity. Results for pitchblende range from 640 to 1380×10^6 years.

Radioactive data can also indicate the much longer time which has elapsed since the *formation of the atoms* as distinct from the consolidation of the minerals of the earth. A simple, but probably unreliable, estimate may be based on the assumption that the two isotopes ^{238}U and ^{235}U were created in comparable amounts; their present relative abundance (140/1) and their known half-lives then indicate a passage of 5×10^9 years since formation.

More recently methods of dating based on naturally occurring activities other than those of the main series have been developed. These will not be discussed here, since their interest is primarily geological, but a list of the active elements concerned is given below, Table **2.4**. These are all low-energy β-emitters or electron capture (E.C.) bodies* with the exception of samarium and neodymium and their half-lives have been determined by careful observation of the activity of a known mass of material. In many cases detecting instruments of exceptionally low background were necessary in order to record the extremely weak activities.

TABLE 2.4   Naturally occurring active materials other than main families

Data taken mainly from Ref. 2.4

RADIOACTIVE ISOTOPE	HALF-LIFE (years)	RADIATION	OBSERVED PARTICLE ENERGY (MeV)
^{40}K	$1 \cdot 3 \times 10^9$	β^-, (E.C.)	$1 \cdot 32$
^{50}V	5×10^{15}	β^-, E.C.	$1 \cdot 19$, $2 \cdot 39$
^{87}Rb	5×10^{10}	β^-	$0 \cdot 273$
^{115}In	6×10^{14}	β^-	$0 \cdot 6$
^{138}La	1×10^{11}	β^-, (E.C.)	$0 \cdot 21$
^{144}Nd	3×10^{15}	α	$1 \cdot 8$
^{147}Sm	$1 \cdot 3 \times 10^{11}$	α	$2 \cdot 2$
^{176}Lu	$4 \cdot 5 \times 10^{10}$	β^-, E.C.	$0 \cdot 43$
^{187}Re	4×10^{12}	β^-	$0 \cdot 043$

2.4.5 THE TRANSFORMATION LAWS FOR SUCCESSIVE CHANGES. The basic calculations of the rate of growth of radioactive bodies from radioactive parents and the conditions for radioactive equilibrium, were developed by Rutherford and his collaborators. They were crucial for the quantitative evaluation of the decay chains presented in Sect. 2.4.3. The general problem is that of a series of bodies transforming in sequence

$$A \rightarrow B \rightarrow C \rightarrow D \ldots \qquad (2.13)$$

with different decay constants λ, and it is required to find the amount of a given product at any time after stated initial conditions. We consider for simplicity only the case in which

---

* For electron capture see chapter 16.

the active element B grows from its parent A. The equations governing this process are:

$$\left.\begin{array}{ll} \text{for the decay of A} & \dfrac{\mathrm{d}N_a}{\mathrm{d}t} = -\lambda_a N_a \\[3mm] \text{for the growth and} & \dfrac{\mathrm{d}N_b}{\mathrm{d}t} = \lambda_a N_a - \lambda_b N_b \\ \text{decay of B} & \end{array}\right\} \quad (2.14)$$

where N_a and N_b are the number of atoms of A and B present at time t. Eq. 2.14 may be solved to give N_a and N_b if the quantities of these two atoms present at time $t=0$ ($N_a(0)$ and $N_b(0)$) are known. For most purposes however it is the activity, or disintegration rate, which is experimentally required, and for these quantities we find

$$\left.\begin{array}{l} \text{Activity of A} = \lambda_a N_a = \lambda_a N_a(0)e^{-\lambda_a t} \\[1mm] \text{Activity of B} = \lambda_b N_b = \lambda_b N_b(0)e^{-\lambda_b t} \\[2mm] \qquad\qquad + \dfrac{\lambda_a \lambda_b}{\lambda_b - \lambda_a} N_a(0)[e^{-\lambda_a t} - e^{-\lambda_b t}] \end{array}\right\} \quad (2.15)$$

If initially B is not present, $N_b(0) = 0$ and then at any time

$$\frac{\text{activity of B}}{\text{activity of A}} = \frac{\lambda_b}{\lambda_b - \lambda_a}[1 - e^{-(\lambda_b - \lambda_a)t}] \qquad (2.16)$$

Two cases now arise:

a) $\lambda_b > \lambda_a$ (daughter shorter lived than parent).

The activity ratio 2.16 tends to the constant value $\lambda_b/(\lambda_b - \lambda_a)$ and both activities decay ultimately with the half-life of the parent. When the ratio $\lambda_b/(\lambda_b - \lambda_a)$ has been established, a state of *transient equilibrium* exists. The variation with time of the activity of radiothorium ($\lambda_b = 1 \cdot 2 \times 10^{-8}$ sec^{-1}) growing via the short lived MsTh2 from MsTh1 ($\lambda_a = 3.35 \times 10^{-9}$ sec^{-1}) is shown in Fig. 2.9. The product activity reaches a maximum at a time given by $\mathrm{d}N_b/\mathrm{d}t = 0$ or, from 2.15, with $N_b(0) = 0$

$$\lambda_a e^{-\lambda_a t} = \lambda_b e^{-\lambda_b t} \qquad (2.17)$$

and at this time, and at this time only

$$\lambda_b N_b = \lambda_a N_a \qquad (2.18)$$

In the regime of transient equilibrium, at later times, the activity of B is always greater than that of A.

If however $\lambda_b \gg \lambda_a$ then the ratio of activities tends to unity and we have the case of *secular equilibrium* in which B grows at a rate determined by its own decay constant until it reaches an activity equal to that of its parent. This case has already been illustrated (Fig. 2.7) in the production of ThX from radiothorium. In this case $\lambda_b = 2.2 \times 10^{-6}\,\mathrm{sec}^{-1}$ and λ_a $1.2 \times 10^{-8}\,\mathrm{sec}^{-1}$. Many other examples, including the growth of radon from radium, could be cited.

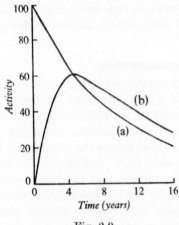

Fig. 2.9
a) Decay of MsTh1.
b) Growth of RdTh in equilibrium with MsTh1. A state of transient equilibrium with an activity ratio 1·39 is established after about 8 years. At 4·8 years the RdTh has a maximum activity equal to that of its parent. (Evans, *The Atomic Nucleus*).

In the case of a long-lived parent such as uranium or thorium it is clear that when secular equilibrium has been established the quantities of successive products present are given by the equations

$$\lambda_a N_a(0) = \lambda_b N_b = \lambda_c N_c = \ldots = \text{constant} \qquad (2.19)$$

The activities are constant throughout and the relative amounts of different products are inversely proportional to their decay constants. The stable end product of the series must be excluded from this statement since it continually accumulates. The same equation (2.19) governs the equilibrium quantity N_b

2*

of an active material produced in an accelerator or reactor at a constant rate p, i.e.

$$\lambda_b N_b = p \qquad (2.20)$$

b) $\lambda_b < \lambda_a$ (daughter longer lived than parent).

The activity ratio 2.16 increases continuously with time and there is no equilibrium in any significant sense. Transient equilibrium does indeed exist at the time given by 2.17 and the parent and daughter activities are then instantaneously equal.

The formulae used in this section have been elaborated by Bateman to deal with several successive decay products.

2.5   Radioactive measurements

2.5.1 DETERMINATION OF DECAY CONSTANTS. Direct application of Eq. 2.5 to determine the decay constant λ from observation of decay of activity is only convenient if the half-life lies between perhaps a minute and a few years. Table **2.1** shows that this interval covers the majority of the listed bodies but some important ones, including the long-lived parent materials uranium, radium and thorium, cannot be studied in this way. Several of the radio-elements which may now be produced artificially also require special methods. We may distinguish between methods useful when the half-life is very short and those applicable when the half-life is very long. For convenience of discussion the radioactive series shown in Fig. 2.8 will be assumed known.

a) *Half-life short* (< 1 min).

For a $t_{1/2}$ of about 1 min it may be possible to time the rate of discharge of an electroscope or ionization chamber receiving the radiations. For $t_{1/2}$ of about 0·1 sec a method applied to ThA by Moseley and Fajans may be used. This is illustrated in Fig. 2.10a; the ThA recoils continuously from the source to the surface of a moving disc, and is carried round to two detectors which receive the radiations from its decay. The difference in intensity in the two instruments is due to decay in the time interval corresponding to the passage of a point on the circumference of the disc from the first detector to the second.

Shorter lifetimes still may be determined by the *recoil-distance method* used by Jacobsen with RaC' ($t_{1/2} = 1·6 \times 10^{-4}$ sec).

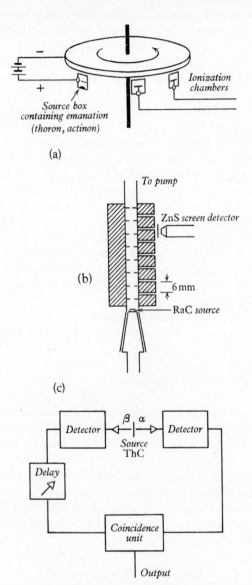

Fig. 2.10. Determination of half-lives
a) Rotating disc method of Moseley and Fajans for ThA ($t_{1/2} = 0 \cdot 158$ sec.).
b) Recoil-distance method of Jacobsen for RaC' ($t_{1/2} = 1 \cdot 6 \times 10^{-4}$ sec.).
c) Delayed coincidence method for ThC' ($t_{1/2} = 3 \times 10^{-7}$ sec.).

Ions of this product recoil from a parent body (RaC) with a velocity of about 5×10^5 cm sec^{-1} and move down an evacuated tube (Fig. 2.10b), at some point in which they decay. From the fall-off in intensity of α-emission down the length of the tube and from the known recoil velocity the decay constant can be found.

The lifetime of ThC' ($t_{1/2} = 3 \times 10^{-7}$ sec) has been found by the *delayed coincidence* method (Fig. 2.10c). In this method a signal is received in the particle detector from the β-particle emitted by the parent body ThC in the formation of ThC'. The α-particle from ThC' is received in a second detector at a certain time after the β signal and the intervals between the two signals will be distributed according to the decay law. They may be measured by delaying the β signal and observing the dependence of $\beta\alpha$ coincidences on the delay time.

Both the recoil-distance and delayed coincidence methods have been developed recently for the determination of short radiative lifetimes and are discussed further in chapter 13.

b) *Half-life long* (> 1 year).

From a mass of x g of radium, known in terms of a standard by its γ-ray activity, the number of α-particles emitted per second is

$$\lambda_{Ra} x \frac{N_0}{A} \qquad (2.21)$$

where N_0 is Avogadro's number and A the atomic weight of radium. This equation yields λ_{Ra} from the observed rate of α-emission; it was first used, as already described, by Rutherford and Geiger.

Radium itself is a daughter product of uranium I and intervening products have lives small compared with that of the earth. The radium content of minerals is therefore in equilibrium with the uranium parent and the activities of the two must be equal, i.e.

$$\lambda_U x_U \frac{N_0}{A_U} = \lambda_{Ra} x_{Ra} \frac{N_0}{A_{Ra}} \qquad (2.22)$$

The atomic weights are respectively $A_U = 238$ and $A_{Ra} = 226$ so that the decay constant for uranium can be obtained from that of radium with knowledge of the equilibrium ratio x_{Ra}/x_U. It is assumed that no chemical processes leading to alterations in the content of uranium, thorium and radium in the mineral have occurred.

Other methods for long half-lives are based on observation of growth of daughter products, e.g. radon, after chemical separations of parents from an equilibrium mixture. Modern developments of the direct determination of decay constants from activity measurements include the quantitative analysis of the active sample by the mass spectrometer.

2.5.2 STANDARDS OF ACTIVITY. Quantitative measurements on radioactive substances are practically always determinations of activity. The unit now used to express activity is the *curie**, which is defined (1950) as the 'quantity of any radioactive nuclide in which the number of disintegrations per second is $3 \cdot 700 \times 10^{10}$'. This is an extension of the original definition of the curie, which was based on the number of α-particles per second emitted by the radon in equilibrium with 1 g of radium (Table **2.2**). This number is now somewhat different from the value adopted in the definition, but the latter has received international recognition and provides a perfectly definite basis for quantitative work. The means by which an activity is measured in absolute units are discussed in chapter 7; in practice a detector of known efficiency is required, unless comparison with a standard can be made.

Radium standards of known mass and activity are maintained in Paris and Vienna. Sub-standards may be conveniently compared with these reference sources by utilizing the γ-ray activity.

2.5.3. HEALTH HAZARDS. The potentially dangerous nature of ionizing radiations was not realized by the first workers engaged on research with X-rays and radioactive materials. As a result, a number of injuries, particularly to the skin of the hands, occurred. The ingestion of radioactive dust by the uranium miners of Czechoslovakia also led to much damage to the tissues of the lung.

It is not proposed to enter here into either the detailed

---

* Abbreviated C, Cur or Ce.

biological effects of radiation or the procedure by which radio-active materials may be safely handled. Those whose work involves radiations should consult the many books on the subject (Ref. 2.8) and above all should adhere to the safety regulations which govern their particular occupation. It may, however, be useful to indicate the terminology of the subject, as at present recognized.

The biological effect of radiation is related, in quantitative measurements, to its power of producing ionization in air or in tissue. The *röntgen* is defined as 'that quantity of X or gamma radiation for which the associated corpuscular radiation in 0·001293 g of air produces ions carrying 1 e.s.u. of charge of either sign'. This corresponds to an energy release of 83·8 erg g^{-1} of air. For radium in equilibrium with its products, but screened by 0·5 mm of platinum, the ionization in air indicates a radiation intensity of 0·84 milliröntgens per hour at a distance of 1 m from a source of 1 millicurie. If X or gamma radiation is absorbed in biological tissue rather than in air, 1 röntgen deposits an energy of 93 ergs per g of tissue. A beam of *any* type of radiation which delivers this quantity of energy to 1 g of tissue is said to have an integrated intensity of one *röntgen equivalent physical* (r.e.p.); if the energy delivered is 100 erg g^{-1} the integrated intensity is defined to be 1 *rad*.*

The actual biological effect on a given organ of the body, for a given energy absorption, depends on the density of ionization. The effective integrated radiation intensity, sometimes known as the dose, is therefore obtained by multiplying the r.e.p. value by a *relative biological effectiveness* (R.B.E.); the result gives the integrated intensity (or dose) in *röntgens equivalent man* (r.e.m.) i.e.

$$\text{r.e.m.} = \text{r.e.p.} \times \text{R.B.E.}$$

The *maximum permissible weekly doses* for workers exposed to radiation are defined nationally and internationally in terms of the r.e.m.; the usual figure is that the weekly dose at depths in the body greater than 5 cm shall not exceed 300 millirem. In calculating this maximum exposure the values of R.B.E. given

* A rough working rule states that the radiation intensity at 1 foot from a source of c curies emitting γ-radiation of energy E (MeV) is 6 cE rads per hour.

in Table **2.5a** should be used. In calculations of the shielding required for nuclear reactors and accelerators it is often necessary to know the relation between dose and neutron flux as a function of energy; this is given in Table **2.5b**.

TABLE 2.5a Relative biological effectiveness of different radiations

RADIATION	R.B.E.
β-, X-, γ-rays	1
α-rays	10
Neutrons (MeV)	10
Heavy recoil nuclei	20

TABLE 2.5b Relation between dose rate and neutron flux density

NEUTRON ENERGY	R.B.E.	FLUX DENSITY equivalent to 2·5 millirem per h (n cm^{-2} sec^{-1})
Thermal	3·0	670
20 keV	5·0	280
100 keV	8·0	80
500 keV	10·0	30
1 MeV	10·5	18
5 MeV	7.0	18
10 MeV	6·5	17

2.6 The scattering of α-particles by matter and the hypothesis of the nucleus

2.6.1 LARGE-ANGLE SCATTERING. During his work on the deflection of α-rays in a magnetic field (1906) Rutherford found that the presence of a small amount of air in the vacuum apparatus affected the path of the particles. The magnitude of this effect, in comparison with the similar effect that could be produced by externally applied fields, indicated that the atom must be 'the seat of very intense electrical forces'. With his genius for wresting the maximum information from the smallest effect, Rutherford saw in these deflections a possible method of

studying the detailed structure of the atom. As soon as quantitative methods of counting α-rays had been established, as a
result of his work with Geiger, he started the investigation of
this structure, using α- and β-particles as probes, which was to
lead to the nuclear hypothesis.

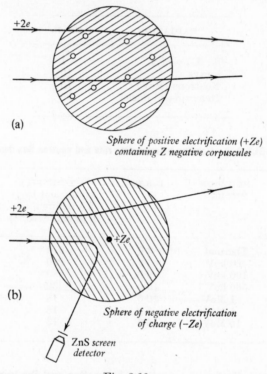

Fig. 2.11
a) The scattering of α-particles by a Thomson atom.
b) The scattering of α-particles by a nuclear atom.

At the time of the first experiment on the scattering of α-
particles during their passage through thin foils of metal, the
neutral atom was supposed, following the ideas of J. J. Thomson, to consist of a number of negatively charged electrons,
accompanied by an equal quantity of positive electricity
uniformly distributed throughout a sphere. The scattering of
charged particles by matter was supposed to be a multiple

effect, due to the statistical superposition of the results of a large number of atomic encounters, each with a small angle of deflection. Such a mechanism predicts that the angle of deflection of charged particles in passing through a thin foil should increase as $\sqrt{t}$ where t is the thickness of the foil (Fig. 2.11a). This conclusion was supported by the experiments of Crowther (1910) on β-particle scattering, which also revealed however that some β-particles were deviated through very large angles (diffuse reflection). This was not considered surprising in view of the small mass of the β-particle. When Geiger examined the deflection of α-particles by a gold foil, using the scintillation method of detection, which had been rendered quantitative by comparison with the electrical counting method, it was found that the α-particles were also deviated through small angles in large numbers. This was in qualitative agreement with prediction based on the Thomson theory of the atom. Rutherford then suggested that Marsden, a student working with Geiger, should look for large-angle scattering. The expectation was that such an effect would be very small, because of the large mass of the α-particle, if the main collisions were with the electrons of a diffuse charge distribution. The surprising result was found that a few α-particles were scattered through large angles, even greater than $90°$, from even the thinnest foils that could be used. In Rutherford's words, long after this observation, 'It was quite the most incredible event that has ever happened to me in my life. It was almost as incredible as if you had fired a 15-inch shell at a piece of tissue paper and it came back and hit you.'

This 'incredible event' dominated Rutherford's thinking in the winter of 1910–11. The sequel is related in a letter from Geiger to Chadwick: 'One day, obviously in the best of spirits, he came into my room and told me that he now knew what the atom looked like and how the large deflections were to be understood. On the very same day I began an experiment to test the relation expected between the number of particles and the angle of scattering.' Rutherford's picture of the atom was simply that the electrons would fill a sphere of atomic dimensions (radius $\approx 10^{-8}$ cm) but that their charge would be neutralized by a central positive charge on a *nucleus* of much smaller extent (radius $\approx 10^{-12}$ cm). If the atom contained Z

electrons, the nuclear charge would be $+Ze$ and since the electronic mass is small compared with that of an atom, most of the atomic mass, as well as the positive charge, would be concentrated in the nucleus. It was then shown by a straightforward and now celebrated calculation* that the Coulomb repulsion between the nucleus of a heavy atom and an incident α-particle would cause the α-particle to describe a hyperbolic orbit (Fig. 2.11b). Furthermore the sharp rise in the repulsive force, increasing as the inverse square of distance, as the α-particle approached the minute nucleus, would provide the strong fields necessary to cause the large-angle scattering.

Rutherford's calculations showed that the probability of deflection of an α-particle through an angle as a result of a single encounter with a nucleus was always greater than for multiple scattering in the electron distribution. He also deduced the statistical distribution of the singly scattered particles as a function of angle of scattering; the specific conclusions were that the number of α-particles detected at a certain point (Fig. 2.11b) after passage through a thin scatterer of a heavy element would be proportional to

a) $\mathrm{cosec}^4\theta/2$; where θ was the angle of scattering,
b) the thickness of the scatterer,
c) the square of the central nuclear charge,
d) the inverse square of the incident energy.

Each point was verified precisely in the careful experiments of Geiger and Marsden† over the years 1911–13. Darwin showed that any law of force other than that of the inverse square would be inconsistent with the data and the experiments indicated that for gold this law of force held down to less than 3×10^{-12} cm. The validity of the hypothesis of a nucleus of minute dimensions, endowed with all the positive charge and most of the mass of the atom, seemed beyond dispute.

2.6.2 THE NUCLEAR ATOM. The nuclear atom proposed by Rutherford in 1911 transformed the appearance of the whole

---

* A derivation of the Rutherford scattering law is given in Sect. 5.1.4. See E. Rutherford, *Phil. Mag.*, **21**, 669, 1911.

† H. Geiger and E. Marsden, *Phil. Mag.*, **25**, 604, 1913.

of atomic theory, and had profound implications throughout physics and chemistry. In the first place the concept effected an immediate separation between *nuclear* and *atomic* properties. The latter were clearly to be associated with the electrons, whose motions and mutual interactions were responsible for chemical binding, optical and X-ray spectra, and the macroscopic, observable properties of matter in bulk. The nucleus, on the other hand, was relatively remote and inaccessible to most influences except bombardment by fast particles; nuclear properties should be unaffected by the ordinary chemical and physical changes of their atoms and this was indeed a well-known characteristic of radioactivity. The energy changes in nuclear transformations were also clearly enormously larger (Sect. 2.3.3) than those involved in atomic rearrangements. The link between these two types of property was provided most convincingly by Moseley (1913), working in Rutherford's laboratory. He showed that the frequencies of the lines of the characteristic X-ray spectrum of the elements changed in a well-marked way from one element to another. The frequencies depended on the *atomic number* of the element concerned, defined as the ordinal number of the elements arranged in a sequence of increasing atomic weights. These results received an interpretation in the work of Bohr (1913) on the theory of spectra, for in this great achievement the nucleus played a fundamental role. The atomic number used by Moseley was in fact seen to be exactly the nuclear charge expressed in units of the electronic charge, or alternatively the number of electrons in the atom. The atomic number can thus in principle be determined from experiments of the type made by Geiger and Marsden and when these were sufficiently refined (Chadwick, 1920) it was found that the central nuclear charge number was indeed equal to Moseley's atomic number and to the number of electrons per atom, as determined by X-ray scattering experiments. It is thus obvious that the properties of the Rutherford–Bohr atom are of special significance for the nuclear physicist and chapter 3 of this book will outline some of the main features of this atomic model in its wave-mechanical aspect.

The hypothesis of the nucleus immediately clarified many phenomena of radioactivity. The α-particle was recognized to be the nucleus of the helium atom and the displacement laws could be re-stated in terms of the alteration of nuclear charge due to α- or β-emission. The nuclear charge of an atom determines its electronic configuration and hence its chemical properties. Isotopes must have the same nuclear charge but a different mass. The emission of α- and β-radiation results from the energetic instability of one nucleus with respect to another; and the γ-radiation is essentially the electromagnetic spectrum

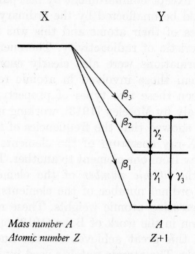

Fig. 2.12. Origin of radioactive γ-rays. A nucleus X is energetically unstable with respect to nucleus Y and decays with emission of an α- or β-particle. The nucleus Y is sometimes left in an excited state, from which γ-radiation arises. That the γ-radiation arises in Y rather than X is known from the energies of the 'internal conversion' electrons also observed (see Chapter 13).

of a nucleus (Fig. 2.12) having much the same relation to its structure as have optical radiations to that of the atom (cf. Sect. 2.2.3). The accumulation of helium in α-particle transmutations is an obvious consequence of the theory.

It will be surmised that Rutherford, having postulated the nucleus and defined its main properties of charge and mass, was eager to enquire into its structure. The small size and strong force field of the nucleus clearly made such an investigation difficult from the outset. Despite this, the same technique which revealed the existence of the nucleus seemed capable of yielding further information, and after the First World War, the bombardment of a variety of elements with α-particles continued intensively under Rutherford in the Cavendish Laboratory. The successful outcome of this work in the discovery of artificial transmutation and the enormous consequential expansion of nuclear physics forms the basic subject matter of Parts B, C, D and E of this book.

TABLE 2.1   Energies and half-lives of the naturally occurring radioactive substances

The data are taken from Ref. 2.4

Column 1 gives the names by which the naturally occurring radioactive substances are familiarly known. These names are based on the ordering of these bodies into individual families (Sect. 2.4.3). The present nuclear symbols given in column 2 show that the radioactive bodies are all isotopes of the elements numbered 81–92 inclusive in the periodic table.

The α-disintegration energies are corrected for the energy absorbed by nuclear recoil and are therefore greater than the observed α-particle energy.

Rare decay branches have been omitted in this table. Gamma-radiation following β-decay has also been ignored, and only the maximum β-energy (observed or calculated) is listed.

1. *Natural α-emitters (heavy elements)*

SUBSTANCE	NUCLEAR SYMBOL	α-DISINTEGRATION ENERGY (MeV)	HALF-LIFE $t_{1/2}\left(=\dfrac{0.693}{\lambda}\right)$
Uranium I	$^{238}_{92}$U	4·27	$4\cdot51 \times 10^9$ y
Uranium II	$^{234}_{92}$U	4·85	$2\cdot48 \times 10^5$ y
Ionium	$^{230}_{90}$Th	4·76	$8\cdot0 \times 10^4$ y
Radium	$^{226}_{88}$Ra	4·86	1622 y
Radon	$^{222}_{86}$Em	5·59	3·823 d
Radium A	$^{218}_{84}$Po	6·11	3·05 m
Radium C (0·04%)	$^{214}_{83}$Bi	5·61	19·7 m
Radium C′	$^{214}_{84}$Po	7·83	$1\cdot64 \times 10^{-4}$ s
Radium F (Polonium)	$^{210}_{84}$Po	5·40	138·401 d
Thorium	$^{232}_{90}$Th	4·08	$1\cdot39 \times 10^{10}$ y
Radiothorium	$^{228}_{90}$Th	5·52	1·91 y
Thorium X	$^{224}_{88}$Ra	5·78	3·64 d
Thoron	$^{220}_{86}$Em	6·40	51·5 s

Table 2.1 (cont.)

SUBSTANCE	NUCLEAR SYMBOL	α-DISINTEGRATION ENERGY (MeV)	HALF-LIFE $t_{1/2} \left(= \dfrac{0.693}{\lambda} \right)$
Thorium A	$^{216}_{84}\text{Po}$	6·90	0·158 s
Thorium C	$^{212}_{83}\text{Bi}$	6·21	60·5 m
Thorium C'	$^{212}_{84}\text{Po}$	8·95	$3·04 \times 10^{-7}$ s
Actino-uranium	$^{235}_{92}\text{U}$	4·64	$7·1 \times 10^8$ y
Protoactinium	$^{231}_{91}\text{Pa}$	5·14	$3·43 \times 10^4$ y
Radioactinium	$^{227}_{90}\text{Th}$	6·14	18·2 d
Actinium X	$^{223}_{88}\text{Ra}$	5·97	11·7 d
Actinon	$^{219}_{86}\text{Em}$	6·94	3·92 s
Actinium A	$^{215}_{84}\text{Po}$	7·50	$1·83 \times 10^{-3}$ s
Actinium C	$^{211}_{83}\text{Bi}$	6·75	2·16 m
Actinium C'	$^{211}_{84}\text{Po}$	7·59	0·52 s

2. *Natural β-emitters (heavy elements)*

SUBSTANCE	NUCLEAR SYMBOL	MAXIMUM β-PARTICLE ENERGY (MeV)	HALF-LIFE $t_{1/2} \left(= \dfrac{0.693}{\lambda} \right)$
Uranium X_1	$^{234}_{90}\text{Th}$	0·205	24·1 d
Uranium X_2	$^{234}_{91}\text{Pa}$	2·25	1·18 m
Radium B	$^{214}_{82}\text{Pb}$	1·02	26·8 m
Radium C	$^{214}_{83}\text{Bi}$	3·18	19·7 m
Radium C''	$^{210}_{81}\text{Tl}$	1·96	1·32 m
Radium D	$^{210}_{82}\text{Pb}$	0·064	19·4 y
Radium E	$^{210}_{83}\text{Bi}$	1·16	5·01 d
Mesothorium 1	$^{228}_{88}\text{Ra}$	0·053	6·7 y
Mesothorium 2	$^{228}_{89}\text{Ac}$	2·18	6·13 h
Thorium B	$^{212}_{82}\text{Pb}$	0·58	10·64 h
Thorium C	$^{212}_{83}\text{Bi}$	2·25	60·5 m
Thorium C''	$^{20}_{18}\text{Tl}$	1·79	3·1 m
Uranium Y	$^{231}_{90}\text{Th}$	0·38	25·6 h
Actinium	$^{227}_{89}\text{Ac}$	0·05	21·6 y
Actinium B	$^{211}_{82}\text{Pb}$	1·40	36·1 m
Actinium C (0·3%)	$^{211}_{83}\text{Bi}$	0·61	2·16 m
Actinium C''	$^{207}_{81}\text{Tl}$	1·45	4·79 m

TABLE 2.2   The 'classical' constants of radioactivity

Mainly taken from Ref. 2.1

Half-life of radium	1622 years
Number of α-particles emitted per second from 1 gm of radium	$3 \cdot 608 \times 10^{10}$
Number of α-particles emitted per second from 1 curie of radium	$3 \cdot 70 \times 10^{10}$
Volume of 1 curie of radon	$0 \cdot 64$ mm^3 at N.T.P.
Volume of helium produced per year by 1 gm of radium in equilibrium with its products	169 mm^3 at N.T.P.
Heat emitted per hour by 1 gm of radium in equilibrium with its products	148 calories

References

2.1   J. Chadwick, *Radioactivity and Radioactive Substances*, revised J. Rotblat, Pitman, 1953.

2.2   J. Chadwick, Rutherford Memorial Lecture, *Proc. roy. Soc.* A, **224**, 435, 1954.

2.3   E. Rutherford, J. Chadwick and C. D. Ellis, *Radiations from Radioactive Substances*, Cambridge University Press, 1930.

2.4   D. Strominger, J. M. Hollander and G. T. Seaborg, Table of Isotopes, *Rev. mod. Phys.*, **30**, 585, 1958.

2.5   *Experimental Nuclear Physics*, Vol. III, ed. Segrè, Wiley, 1959.

2.6   Eve Curie, *Madame Curie*, Heinemann, 1938.

2.7   A. S. Eve, *Rutherford*, Cambridge, 1939.

2.8   Medical Research Council, *The Hazards to Man of Nuclear and Allied Radiations* (Cmnd 1225), H.M.S.O., 1960.

2.9   Medical Research Council, *Introductory Manual on the Control of Health Hazards from Radioactive Materials*, H.M.S.O., 1961.

2.10   N. Feather, 'A History of Neutrons and Nuclei', *Contemp. Phys.*, **1**, 191, 1960.

2.11   N. Feather, 'Radioactivity', *Chambers's Encyclopaedia*, 1963.

3. THE SPECTROSCOPY OF ATOMS AND MOLECULES

Nuclear physics owes much to the development of atomic theory and to the extensive and precise measurements by spectroscopists of atomic transition frequencies. The nuclear model of the atom, as pointed out in Sect. 2.6.2, was quickly applied by Niels Bohr to elucidate the empirical regularities of the spectrum of atomic hydrogen and the existence round the nucleus of an electronic charge distribution exerts an important influence on many intrinsically nuclear phenomena. Apart from this, the interpretation of atomic structure offers a crucial test of the validity of the methods of wave mechanics. The interaction between the nucleus and the surrounding Z electrons is governed by the Coulomb law of force and to a very good approximation for many purposes the nucleus may be assumed to be a structureless point charge. The interactions between the individual electrons of the atom are also of the Coulomb type and all forces existing within the atom, as distinct from within the nucleus, are therefore known. The problem of predicting the energy levels of a simple atom is therefore in principle soluble. The methods of solution provided by the new mechanics for this problem are used continually in discussions of nuclear phenomena and will be briefly outlined in this chapter. No attempt is made to present even a brief treatment of all the phenomena of spectroscopy and attention is concentrated on those aspects of the subject which appear helpful in the interpretation of nuclear data; only non-relativistic motion is considered.

The original Bohr orbital theory of the hydrogen spectrum is of deep historical significance, and is easy to visualize, but it is not complete, particularly in respect of magnetic properties of atoms; an outline of this theory is given in Appendix 1.

3.1 The Schrödinger equation

The starting point of the wave-mechanical treatment of atomic properties is the experimental relation between the de Broglie wavelength λ of a material particle and its momentum p, i.e. $\lambda = h/p$, where h is Planck's constant. The connection between the de Broglie waves which determine the motion of the particle and the actual particle density at a point (x, y, z) in space was first given by Born, who supposed that if $\psi(x, y, z, t)$ were the amplitude of the de Broglie wave then

$$|\psi(x, y, z, t)|^2 \mathrm{d}x \, \mathrm{d}y \, \mathrm{d}z \qquad (3.1)$$

would be proportional to the probability of finding a particle within the volume of space $\mathrm{d}x \, \mathrm{d}y \, \mathrm{d}z$ at time t. This is similar to the well-known result in electromagnetic theory which associates an energy density with the square of the field amplitudes E and H. The modulus signs are written in 3.1 because it is part of the wave mechanical method that wave functions such as ψ can be complex, i.e. of the form $a + ib$, where a and b are real and $i = \sqrt{-1}$. In particular we may write, for the one-dimensional case,

$$\psi = \psi_0 \left\{ \cos 2\pi \left(\frac{x}{\lambda} - \nu t \right) + i \sin 2\pi \left(\frac{x}{\lambda} - \nu t \right) \right\}$$
$$= \psi_0 e^{2\pi i (x/\lambda - \nu t)} \qquad (3.2)$$

where λ is the wavelength and ν the frequency of the de Broglie waves. This particular form represents a plane monochromatic wave moving parallel to the axis of x and the corresponding probability density for particles of momentum p would be given by

$$|\psi|^2 = \psi_0^2 \qquad (3.3)$$

Such a plane wave is of course the solution of an equation, which may easily be derived. Thus by differentiating 3.2 twice we obtain

$$\frac{\mathrm{d}^2 \psi}{\mathrm{d}x^2} + \frac{4\pi^2}{\lambda^2} \, \psi = 0$$

or, substituting for λ in terms of the (non-relativistic) momentum $p = \sqrt{(2mT)}$ of the particle

$$\frac{\mathrm{d}^2 \psi}{\mathrm{d}x^2} + \frac{8\pi^2 m}{h^2} \, T\psi = 0 \qquad (3.4)$$

This is the well-known Schrödinger wave equation for a steady beam of particles of mass m and kinetic energy T moving in one direction in field-free space. In a more general form, which may also easily be derived, the Schrödinger equation may be taken to replace Newton's laws of motion for the particles considered.

3.2   Energy levels for a particle in a potential well

There are many problems in both atomic and nuclear physics in which a particle such as an electron or proton or neutron

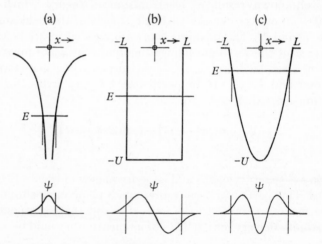

Fig. 3.1. One dimensional potentials and wave functions.

moves under the influence of forces which vary from point to point. Such a field of force may be expressed in terms of a potential which is a function of the coordinates, and we shall for convenience take V to give always the *potential energy* of the particle in the field of force. If the total energy of the particle is E the kinetic energy is

$$T = E - V \qquad (3.5)$$

and the one-dimensional Schrödinger equation 3.4 becomes

$$\frac{d^2\psi}{dx^2} + \frac{8\pi^2 m}{h^2}(E - V)\psi = 0 \qquad (3.6)$$

in which E is taken to be a constant and V and ψ are functions of coordinates but not of the time in problems of the steady state.

Fig. 3.1 shows a number of typical one-dimensional potentials. These are all drawn so that the potential energy has its minimum value at the origin O and is zero when the particle is at an infinite distance from O. Fig. 3.1a is the Coulomb potential energy $V = -e^2/|x|$ and extends out to infinity, since electrostatic attraction is a long-range force. Figs 3.1b and 3.1c are the potential graphs for short-range forces which differ from zero only over a distance L from the origin and have a finite depth U. In all three cases, if the particle concerned is taken to have zero energy at infinity, it will have a positive *kinetic* energy and an equal and opposite potential energy within the range of the forces, i.e. for all x in case (a) and for $|x| < L$ in cases (b) and (c).

Systems such as the hydrogen atom, or the deuteron, are bound, which means that work is necessary to remove the component particles to an infinite separation and the total energy of such a bound system must be taken to be negative. The lines marked E in Fig. 3.1 represent a total (negative) energy E; it will be seen that so long as the particle is closer to the centre of force than the intersection of the line E with the potential graph the kinetic energy T given by 3.5 is positive. At greater distances T is negative and this implies that the particle is, according to classical ideas, forbidden to enter this region.

Distributions of the type shown in Fig. 3.1, when extended to three dimensions, are said to provide a *potential well*. If the value of the potential depends only on the radial coordinate r from the centre and not on the individual coordinates x, y, z the potential is said to be *central* or *spherically symmetrical*. It is fundamental to the wave mechanical description of matter that a particle moving in a potential well can only have certain discrete values for its de Broglie wavelength and hence for its momentum and energy. Although this is quite different from the classical expectation it is nevertheless closely similar to the classical result of fitting standing waves into a given length of a stretched string. To find the permitted wavelengths, the Schrödinger equation for the steady state must be written in three-dimensional form and solved for the particular potential considered; we consider first for simplicity only the one-dimensional case. Writing 3.6 in the form

$$\frac{1}{\psi}\frac{d^2\psi}{dx^2} + \frac{2m}{\hbar^2}[E - V(x)] = 0 \tag{3.7}$$

it is seen that some general properties of the wave function can be deduced immediately without explicit solution. Since $d^2\psi/dx^2$ gives the sign of the curvature of a graph of ψ against x it follows that:

i) when $E - V(x)$ is negative, ψ and $d^2\psi/dx^2$ have the same sign and ψ is convex to the axis of x, and

ii) when $E - V(x)$ is positive, ψ and $d^2\psi/dx^2$ have opposite signs and ψ is concave to the axis of x.

Typical wave function graphs are shown in the bottom half of Fig. 3.1; it is clear that only certain discrete wavelengths can be fitted in to satisfy the boundary conditions imposed by the potential well. This means that the corresponding physical system can exist only with certain discrete energies and a set of energy levels thus arises naturally.

It is found that there is an important difference between long-range potentials of the type shown in Fig. 3.1a and the short-range potentials of Figs. 3.1b and c. In the former case the spacing of the energy levels tends to zero as the zero of energy (dissociation or ionization energy) is approached but for short-range potentials the level spacing is much more uniform and the distribution of levels may not vary much as the dissociation limit is passed. This is shown in Fig. 3.2; levels which can dissociate with the emission of a particle are said to be *virtual* and those which cannot are *bound*. The Coulomb potentials in an atom are long-ranged; the potentials between nucleons are short-ranged when Coulomb effects are subtracted.

The energies E_n obtained by solution of the Schrödinger equation for a particular problem are known as *eigenvalues* and the corresponding wave functions ψ_n as *eigenfunctions*; the state of motion characterized by E_n and ψ_n is an *eigenstate*.

3.3   The hydrogen atom

The wave-mechanical theory of the hydrogen atom, taken to be an electron moving in the central Coulomb field of a proton, is the best known example of the solution of the Schrödinger equation for a spherically symmetrical potential. Many of the results outlined in this section apply equally to central potential wells of any shape.

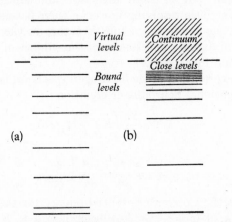

Virtual levels

Continuum

Close levels

Bound levels

(a)

(b)

Fig. 3.2. Energy levels (schematic) for (a) short-range and (b) long-range potentials.

The spectrum of atomic hydrogen is distinguished by the familiar red line H_α of the Balmer series. This line, and other members of the same series, have wave numbers given by the formula

$$\bar{\nu} = R_H\left(\frac{1}{2^2} - \frac{1}{n^2}\right) \text{cm}^{-1} \tag{3.8}$$

where n is an integer and R_H is the Rydberg constant for hydrogen. This expression may be deduced by application of Bohr's frequency condition

$$h\nu = E_i - E_f$$
or $$hc\bar{\nu} = E_i - E_f$$

to the energies of initial and final atomic states providing that these energies are determined by an integer n in accordance with the expression

$$E_n = -\frac{R_H hc}{n^2} \text{ ergs} = -\frac{R_H}{n^2} \text{cm}^{-1} \tag{3.9}$$

This set of levels exhibits the feature of progressively decreasing spacing as E_n tends to zero, when the excitation of the atom is sufficient to ionize it; the level structure is of the type shown in Fig. 3.2*b*.

The wave number of the red Balmer line H_α is about 15,000 cm^{-1}. When examined under moderate resolution it appears as a single line, but in 1887 Michelson and Morley, exploiting the large intrinsic resolving power of their parallel plate interferometer, demonstrated a fine structure in the line of about 0·3 cm^{-1} in extent. This has been the subject of much further investigation (Sect. **3.5**).

The interpretation of the hydrogen spectrum is based on the three-dimensional Schrödinger equation

$$\nabla^2\psi + \frac{2m}{\hbar^2}\left(E + \frac{e^2}{r}\right)\psi = 0 \qquad (3.10)$$

in which

$$\nabla^2 = \frac{\partial^2}{\partial x^2} + \frac{\partial^2}{\partial y^2} + \frac{\partial^2}{\partial z^2}$$

and where the Coulomb potential energy for the Rutherford-Bohr atom, $V(r) = -e^2/r$ has been inserted; E is the total energy of the electron. Since the potential is spherically symmetric, the operator ∇^2 is transformed into spherical polar coordinates and it is then found that a well-behaved solution can be obtained in the general form

$$\psi = R_{nl}(r)Y_l^m(\theta, \phi) \qquad (3.11)$$

Expressions for the spherical harmonics Y_l^m are given in Appendix 2. The integers l, m have a physical interpretation:

l is the *azimuthal, or orbital quantum number*. The angular momentum of the electron about the nucleus is $\sqrt{l(l+1)}\hbar$.*

m is the *magnetic quantum number*. The component of total

---

* In quantum mechanics the *absolute* value of angular momentum *vectors* is always of the form $\sqrt{l(l+1)}\hbar$, and we write this vector as **l**. The maximum observable *component* of **l** is $l\hbar$ and this is what is usually described as the angular momentum. More formally it is the average value of the z-component of the angular momentum vector taken in the state in which $m = l$. It is often convenient and unambiguous to drop the unit $\hbar$ and to speak of an angular momentum or spin l.

A similar relation exists between other vector quantities and their observable components, e.g. intrinsic spin (**s**, $s\hbar$), total angular momentum (**j**, $j\hbar$).

Quantum numbers for angular momentum may be integral or half-integral. Wave mechanics leads naturally to the former, but the matrix formulation of quantum mechanics also provides for the latter.

angular momentum about an axis of observation is $m\hbar$ and $|m| \leqslant l$ with successive values of m differing by unity, so that there are $(2l+1)$ m-values for each l.

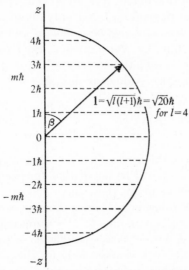

Fig. 3.3. Relation between a quantum mechanical vector $\mathbf{l}$ and its observable components. The angle β is given by $\cos\beta = m/\sqrt{l(l+1)}$ and has $2l+1$ values. The diagram is drawn for $l=4$, $m=3$, $\beta=48°$.

The relation between the vector $\mathbf{l}$ and the scalar $m\hbar$ is shown in Fig. 3.3; if an axis Oz is defined, perhaps by a very small magnetic field, the component along Oz may have one of the values $l\hbar, (l-1)\hbar, \ldots, -(l-1)\hbar, -l\hbar$ while the vector itself has an indeterminate direction and may be thought of as located on the surface of a cone surrounding Oz. It may be shown that in a spherically symmetrical potential field $\mathbf{l}$ is a constant of the motion, as in classical mechanics.

An electron with a prescribed angular momentum in a hydrogen atom can only be brought nearer to the nucleus if its energy is increased. For all states of motion in which $l > 0$, an extra effective potential arises and the equation for $R_{nl}(r)$ is

$$\frac{1}{r^2}\frac{\mathrm{d}}{\mathrm{d}r}\left(r^2\frac{\mathrm{d}R_{nl}}{\mathrm{d}r}\right) + \frac{2m}{\hbar^2}\left\{E + \frac{e^2}{r} - \frac{l(l+1)\hbar^2}{2mr^2}\right\}R_{nl} = 0 \quad (3.12)$$

The term with the factor $l(l+1)$ gives the effect of the 'centrifugal' potential energy and its presence modifies the shape of the potential well for the hydrogen atom. When, however, the wavelengths which are permitted for stationary states in this modified well are calculated, it is found that the corresponding energies E do not depend on l, but only on an integer n which is known as the *principal quantum number*, and the dependence is exactly as given in 3.9. For a given n, the l-values permitted are $0, 1, \ldots, (n-1)$ and the corresponding electron states are classified according to l-value as follows*:

$l = 0$:	s-states	$l = 3$:	f-states
$l = 1$:	p-states	$l = 4$:	g-states
$l = 2$:	d-states		etc.

The level system of the hydrogen atom, classified in this way, is shown in Fig. 3.4; it will be noted that for each n there are n levels of different l but all these have the same energy. This feature, known as l-degeneracy since there are n wave functions with different l corresponding to the same eigenvalue E_n of the Schrödinger equation, is a consequence of the shape of the Coulomb potential e^2/r and arises only for this potential. There is also a $(2l+1)$-fold degeneracy for each l associated with the magnetic quantum number m. In atoms more complicated than hydrogen, with a non-Coulomb field due to the screen of inner electrons round the nucleus, the l-degeneracy is removed and states of low l become relatively more stable. In all atoms the m-degeneracy may be removed by the action of a magnetic field on the electronic structure, since then the states of different m have different energies (Zeeman effect).

The electron density in the states of internal motion of the hydrogen atom is proportional to $|\psi|^2$ where ψ is a solution of the wave equation of the form 3.11. As far as the angular shape is concerned, the most important result is that in the ground state $(n=1, l=m=0)$ $Y_0^0(\theta, \phi)$ is independent of angle and the wave function is spherically symmetrical (s-state). No electric or magnetic moments due to the orbital motion of the

---

* The letters s, p, d, f derive from the historical description of spectral series as sharp, principal, diffuse, and fundamental. The small letters are used for single electron states; for the state of the atom as a whole, S, P, D, F are used.

electron therefore arise. This is contrary to the result of the simple Bohr theory in which the ground state has an orbital angular momentum $\hbar$ (Appendix 1). The states of the hydrogen atom with $l > 0$ have certain nodal planes for which $Y_l^m(\theta,\phi)$ vanishes; for $n > 1$ there are also radial nodes.

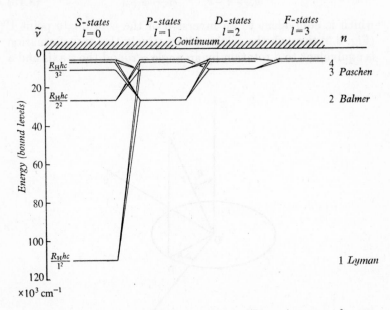

Fig. 3.4. Level system of the hydrogen atom. The main term values are given by $E_n = -Rhc/n^2$ and the binding energy of the ground state ($n = 1$) is 13·58 eV. Transitions permitted by the selection rule are shown. Lines ending on the levels with $n = 1, 2, 3$ respectively form the Lyman, Balmer and Paschen series.

The lines of the hydrogen spectrum result from transitions between levels of energies given by 3.9 in accordance with selection rules (Sect. 3.9.2). For the simplest case (electric dipole radiation), a change of parity (Sect. **3.4**) is required and the rules are:

$$\Delta n \quad \text{unrestricted}$$
$$\Delta l = \pm 1, \qquad \Delta m = 0, \pm 1$$

Representative transitions belonging to the well-known Balmer, Lyman and Paschen series are sketched in Fig. 3.4.

3+N.P.

3.4 Parity

The spherical harmonics (Appendix 2) may be regarded as 'even' (+) or 'odd' (−) functions of the coordinates according as l is even or odd. This follows by considering the transformation

$$\theta \to \pi - \theta, \qquad \phi \to \phi + \pi \tag{3.13}$$

which is equivalent to an inversion of the coordinate point P (Fig. 3.5) through the origin. Alternatively this transformation is equivalent to a rotation by an angle π round the z-axis and a

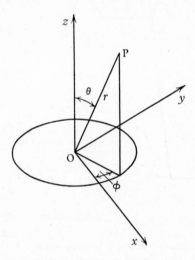

Fig. 3.5. Spherical polar coordinates.

reflection in the (xy) plane. The effect on the spherical harmonics and hence on the eigenfunctions for the states of the potential well is that

$$Y_l^m(\pi - \theta, \phi + \pi) = (-1)^l Y_l^m(\theta, \phi) = \pm\, Y_l^m(\theta, \phi)$$

while $|Y|^2$ of course remains unchanged.

The wave function ψ (3.11) thus contains more information than the squared modulus $|\psi|^2$ since it has the property of either changing sign or not on inversion of coordinates. This property is known as the *parity* of the state and provides a new two-valued quantum number (+ or −, i.e. even or odd).

A classical example of the idea of even or odd symmetry under inversion of coordinates is provided by the normal (transverse) modes of a stretched string. In Fig. 3.6 it is seen that there is (a) no change of sign and (b) a change of sign of amplitude when $x \to -x$. Moreover, if the string is acted on by a force which is symmetrical, e.g. by a blow at the origin, the type of symmetry of the motion remains unaltered but if an 'odd' force is applied the symmetry can be changed. The final parity is the product of the parities in the initial system (the vibration and the force).

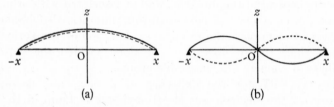

Fig. 3.6. Transverse vibrations of a string, (a) symmetrical, (b) anti-symmetrical with respect to the transformation $x \to -x$.

In atomic and nuclear physics, fundamental particles may be ascribed a parity*; electrons, protons and neutrons have even parity and their antiparticles odd parity. States of motion of a particle, as has just been seen, have a parity determined by orbital momentum or l-value and this applies not only to motion in a potential well but also to motion in a beam of particles. If therefore a nuclear state is constructed by assembling together in a potential well a number of neutrons and protons in different states of motion, the parity is determined by the product of the individual parities, including those of the motion. The importance of the concept of parity in atomic and nuclear problems is that in many (though not all) phenomena it appears to be conserved and therefore furnishes a useful quantum number and imposes limitations on transitions. The emission of radiation in particular is influenced by the symmetry of the initial and final atomic or nuclear states involved in the process.

---

* This is a result of quantum field theory.

3.5   Electron spin *

Although the gross features of simple spectra could be explained by wave mechanics, observations on the magnetic properties of atoms demanded an extra hypothesis. Thus the Stern-Gerlach experiment of 1922 and similar experiments showed that single electron atoms such as hydrogen could apparently align themselves in two ways in a magnetic field but no axis of alignment would be expected from wave mechanics because of the spherical symmetry of the electronic s-states. Also studies of the Zeeman effect, the splitting of spectral lines into several components in a magnetic field, seemed to demand half-integral quantum numbers instead of the integers l and m associated with orbital motion of electrons. A new quantum number also seemed necessary to complete the physical explanation of the periodic system since the numbers n, l, m alone yielded the wrong numbers of elements in successive groups.

The necessity for the existence of a new, non-classical property of the electron was clearly evident to Pauli in 1924, but it fell to Goudsmit and Uhlenbeck (1925) to suggest that this property was in fact an intrinsic angular momentum or spin, and that the corresponding quantum number should be half-integral. In accordance with general principles we then consider the total intrinsic angular momentum of an electron to be the vector s with absolute magnitude $\sqrt{s(s+1)}\hbar$. For electrons, the facts of spectroscopy and of magnetism indicate $s = \frac{1}{2}$ with $m_s\hbar$, the component of s along the axis, equal to $\pm \frac{1}{2}\hbar$. It is also necessary that the electron should possess an intrinsic magnetic moment μ_s and that this should stand in a certain ratio, known as the *gyromagnetic ratio*, to its mechanical moment, and should be parallel to it (but of opposite sign since the electron is negatively charged).†

The value of this ratio can be obtained simply, using the Bohr model, from the Stern-Gerlach experiment. This experiment was based on the idea that an electron with orbital angular momentum $l\hbar$ would have an orbital magnetic moment equal to the area of its orbit times the equivalent

---

* An account of the history of the concept of electron spin is given in Ref. 3.11.

† The tabulated value of the magnetic moment of the electron is the maximum observable component of μ_s and is written μ_e.

current due to the motion of the electron charge round the perimeter, i.e.

$$\mu_l = \pi r^2 \frac{ev}{2\pi rc} = \frac{evr}{2c} \tag{3.14}$$

The mechanical angular momentum along the axis Oz, perpendicular to the orbit, is

$$l\hbar = mvr \tag{3.15}$$

so that

$$\mu_l = l\hbar \frac{e}{2mc} = l\mu_0 \tag{3.16}$$

where $\mu_0 = e\hbar/2mc$ is the *Bohr magneton*, the fundamental unit of atomic magnetism. From 3.16 we obtain the gyromagnetic ratio for orbital motion of an electron as

$$\gamma_l = \frac{\text{magnetic moment}}{\text{mechanical moment}} = \frac{\mu_l}{l\hbar} = \frac{e}{2mc} \tag{3.17}$$

The magnetic moment of the hydrogen atom, found from the deflections observed in Stern-Gerlach experiments, is almost exactly one Bohr magneton, and if this is attributed wholly to intrinsic spin

$$\gamma_s = \frac{\text{magnetic moment}}{\text{mechanical moment}} = \frac{\mu_e}{s\hbar} = \frac{\mu_0}{\frac{1}{2}\hbar} = \frac{e}{mc} \tag{3.18}$$

This is twice the orbital value and cannot be deduced from any plausible electromagnetic model of the electron.

Equations 3.17 and 3.18 give the gyromagnetic ratios as dimensional quantities. It is also convenient to use the equivalent but dimensionless *g-factors* which are defined by the statement

$$g = \frac{\text{magnetic moment in Bohr magnetons}}{\text{mechanical moment in units of } \hbar} = \gamma . \frac{2mc}{e} \tag{3.19}$$

using the value of μ_0. From 3.17 and 3.18 we find that $g_s = 2$ and $g_l = 1$. If the sign of μ_l is taken to be positive for a rotating positive charge the electron g-factors are really negative.

Electron spin was introduced empirically, but, together with intrinsic magnetic moment, it is described by Dirac's relativistic theory of the electron. In relativistic problems the spin and orbital motion of an electron are intimately connected, but in many cases it is a good approximation to regard them as independent vectors, which may be combined according to the rules of quantum mechanics. The addition of the vectors l and s for an electron, to form a resultant vector **j** is shown in Fig. 3.7a. The vector **j** is the *total angular momentum* and has an absolute value $\sqrt{j(j+1)}\hbar$, a quantum number j and a resolved

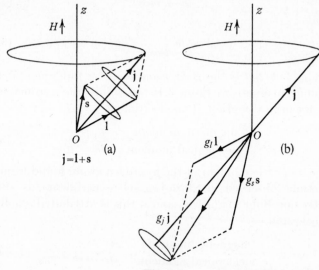

Fig. 3.7

a) Addition of the vectors l, s for a single electron to form a resultant j. The case of $j = l + s$ is shown.

b) Addition of the associated magnetic moments, with $g_s = -2$, $g_l = -1$, corresponding to negative charge. In a weak external field H, the vector **j** precesses round the direction of H.

part $m_j\hbar$.* Since $s = \frac{1}{2}$ for a single electron the only possible total quantum numbers are

$$j = l \pm \tfrac{1}{2} \tag{3.20}$$

---

* It is customary to use m or m_j for the resolved part of the total angular momentum and m_l, m_s for the resolved parts of the orbital and spin momenta for a single electron. In general the momenta of several electrons have to be considered and then the symbols **J**, **L**, **S** and m_J, m_L, m_S are used. When nuclear momenta are introduced as in chapter 4 and chapter 17, the latter symbols are generally used for the atomic momenta in all cases.

as may be seen by resolving the corresponding vectors along an axis defined by the *internal* magnetic field of the atom. The two states thus specified have slightly different energies because of magnetic interaction and the state of the lower j is the more stable. This *doublet structure* of the states of one-electron atoms due to *spin-orbit coupling* is fundamental to the spectroscopy of hydrogen and of the alkali metals and to X-ray spectra, in which a hole in one of the inner atomic shells behaves in a similar way to a single electron. In all these cases the Dirac theory has been used to calculate energy differences in the doublet structure, and the observed X-ray doublets are successfully predicted. In the case of hydrogen the energy of a doublet level may be written approximately (Ref. 3.10)

$$E_{nj} = -\frac{R_{\mathrm{H}} h c Z^2}{n^2} \left\{ 1 + \frac{\alpha^2 Z^2}{n^2} \left(\frac{n}{j + \frac{1}{2}} - \frac{3}{4} \right) \right\} \qquad (3.21)$$

with $Z = 1$, from which it appears that this energy depends only on j and not on the azimuthal quantum number. There is a slight but perfectly definite disagreement between this prediction and the experiments of Lamb and Retherford (1947), and this has had important consequences for quantum electrodynamics.* In (3.21) α is the *fine structure constant*.

The magnetic moments associated with the spin and orbital vectors of an electron may also be added, remembering the different g-factors for spin and orbital momentum, as shown in Fig. 3.7b. The resultant magnetic moment is not parallel to the resultant mechanical moment **j** and as a result of magnetic interaction the vectors **l** and **s** and their associated magnetic moments must be considered to precess rapidly about the direction of **j**. The component of resultant magnetic moment perpendicular to **j** averages out as a result of this precession

---

* Briefly, the Dirac theory does not include the possibility that the electron can emit and reabsorb virtual quanta. Such processes cause in effect a recoil of the electron and disturb its motion. The disturbance has a greater effect in s-states than in p-states because the s-electron wave function penetrates the nucleus. The s-state is therefore raised with respect to the p-state (Lamb shift). The same radiative effect leads to an 'anomalous' magnetic moment for the electron (Fundamental Constants, p. 728).

and the component parallel to $\mathbf{j}$ then becomes effectively the coupled magnetic moment. It may be written

$$\boldsymbol{\mu}_j = \frac{g_j \mu_0 \mathbf{j}}{\hbar} \qquad (3.22)$$

or, using maximum observable components

$$\mu_j = g_j \mu_0 j$$

where the *Landé factor* g_j is obtained by vector addition (Ref. 3.10, p. 201) in the form

$$g_j = \left\{ 1 + \frac{j(j+1) + s(s+1) - l(l+1)}{2j(j+1)} \right\} \qquad (3.23)$$

The Landé factor g_j (or g_J) may be positive or negative; with the convention adopted in this chapter it is negative for a single electron, as indicated in Fig. 3.7b.

The resultant magnetic moment determines the splitting of the energy levels of an atom in the Zeeman effect. The energy change ΔW may be computed either from the energy of the precessional motion of $\mathbf{j}$ and $\boldsymbol{\mu}_j$ round H (Fig. 3.7b) or directly from the formula

$$\Delta W = -(\boldsymbol{\mu}_j \cdot \mathbf{H})$$

$$= -\frac{g_j \mu_0 (\mathbf{j} \cdot \mathbf{H})}{\hbar}$$

$$= -m_j g_j \mu_0 H \qquad (3.24)$$

since $|\mathbf{j}| \cos \beta = m_j \hbar$ by the definition of m_j (cf. Fig. 3.3). If g_j is negative the state of higher m_j has the higher energy. The degeneracy with respect to the magnetic quantum number m_j is thus removed and the relative splitting of the energy levels is determined by the quantity $m_j g_j$. The number of energy levels or effective orientations in an applied field is determined by the quantum number j and is clearly $2j + 1$.

The introduction of electron spin provides the last main quantum number required by atomic spectroscopy. Each of the s, p, d, ... states, classified according to the orbital quantum number, is a double state, although for s-states ($l = 0$) this is trivial since the two sub-states do not differ in energy in the absence of an external field. The state of an atom as a whole, containing perhaps several unpaired electrons, is denoted by a symbol of the form

$$n\ ^{2S+1}L_J \tag{3.25}$$

where n is the principal quantum number,
$2S + 1$ is the spin multiplicity ($= 2$ for $S = \frac{1}{2}$),
L gives the orbital angular momentum,
J gives the total angular momentum, and
g_J is the corresponding g-factor.

In this nomenclature the doublet states of the sodium atom from which the familiar 'D' lines originate, are written $^2P_{3/2}$, $^2P_{1/2}$. The same quantum numbers complete the interpretation of the periodic system which may be based on a succession of states of the type predicted for a single electron atom. Thus we have the following sequence

$$n = 1 \quad l = 0 \quad m_l = 0 \qquad\qquad m_s = \pm\tfrac{1}{2} \quad \text{2 states} \quad K\text{-shell}$$

$$n = 2 \begin{cases} l = 0 & m_l = 0 \\ l = 1 & m_l = 1, 0, -1 \end{cases} m_s = \pm\tfrac{1}{2} \quad \text{8 states} \quad L\text{-shell}$$

For principal quantum number n, there are $2\sum\limits_{0}^{n-1}(2l+1) = 2n^2$ states and the closures of major shells (for given n) or sub-shells (for given n, l) correspond with the regularities of the succession of elements.

The fundamental fact that only two electrons may, in an atomic system, have the same quantum numbers, n, l, m and that these electrons have opposite spin, is the law of nature known as the *Pauli exclusion principle*. It is not confined to electrons and applies with equal rigour to all particles of spin $\frac{1}{2}$, such as nucleons. It may also be stated in the form that only one electron can have the 4 quantum numbers: n, l, m_l, m_s.

3.6 Statistics

The Pauli exclusion principle is an expression of one of the general consequences of the quantum mechanical treatment of a system of identical particles. In classical physics identical particles can still in principle be distinguished, and if there were two states of motion (such as levels in the hydrogen atom) a, b

3*

and two electrons 1, 2 it would be possible to assert that the system $a(1)b(2)$ differed from $a(2)b(1)$. In quantum mechanics it is a fundamental principle that identical particles cannot be so distinguished and the wave function used to describe such a system must prevent any discrimination. It may be thought for instance that electrons in two states of an atom are continually exchanging their positions so that a state is occupied by a particular electron for too short a time for observation.

For two different non-interacting or weakly interacting particles the probability of the occupation of the two states a, b is just the product of the probabilities of separate occupation and a suitable wave function would therefore be

$$\psi(1,\, 2) \,=\, \psi_a(1)\psi_b(2)$$

where a, b stand for the particular set of quantum numbers of the state and 1 is short for the coordinates x, y, z of electron 1. For identical particles, however, this gives too much information, since

$$\psi(2,\, 1) \,=\, \psi_a(2)\psi_b(1)$$

is a different function. Consider, however, the more elaborate functions

$$\psi(1,\, 2) \,=\, \psi_a(1)\psi_b(2) \pm \psi_a(2)\psi_b(1) \qquad (3.26)$$

For these

$$\psi(1,\, 2) \,=\, \pm \psi(2,\, 1)$$

and

$$|\psi(1,\, 2)|^2 \,=\, |\psi(2,\, 1)|^2$$

so that the observable density remains the same when the particles are interchanged. The wave functions 3.26 therefore meet the identity requirements of quantum mechanics; similar but more complex functions may be written down to describe an assembly of any number of indistinguishable particles.

The two wave functions 3.26 are respectively symmetric $(+1)$ and antisymmetric (-1) under interchange of particles. There is no simple *a priori* way of knowing which of the particles of nature are described by a particular type of function, but it may be settled by an appeal to experiment. Thus for electrons, the Pauli exclusion principle, as tested for instance in the periodic system, indicates that if a, b are the same state $\psi(1,\, 2)$ must vanish. It follows that assemblies of electrons are described by antisymmetrical wave functions. Protons, neutrons, μ-mesons and generally all nuclei of half-integral spin behave similarly. Such systems, for which the Pauli principle is valid, are said to obey the *Fermi-Dirac statistics*, whose best-known application is perhaps the electron theory of metals.

Symmetrical wave functions must be used to describe assemblies of photons, α-particles, π-mesons and nuclei with zero or integral spin in general. The Pauli principle does not limit the number of these particles in a given state and they are said to obey the *Einstein-Bose statistics*. A familiar example of the use of these statistics is the derivation of Planck's radiation law.

The statistics obeyed by a particle forming part of an assembly is a fundamental property, which has important applications in molecular phenomena (Sect. 3.8.3) and in nuclear models (ch. 9). It must be clearly distinguished from parity, which can be defined for single particles. The fundamental particles are classified as *fermions* or *bosons* according to their statistical behaviour.

3.7 Atoms with $Z > 1$

3.7.1 THE HELIUM ATOM. The simplest example of quantum mechanical effects due to the identity of electrons is furnished by the helium atom. The calculation of the energy levels of this system of two electrons in the field of a positive charge $2e$ follows the general method outlined in Sect. **3.3**. In the first place the electrostatic interaction between the electrons e^2/r_{12} is neglected in comparison with the interaction between either electron and the nucleus. The energy states available for each electron may be written

$$E_n = -\frac{(Z-\sigma)^2 R_{He}hc}{n^2} \text{ ergs} \qquad (3.27)$$

where $Z = 2$ for helium and $\sigma(\approx 1)$ represents the effect of the second electron in screening the nuclear charge. Since the electrons are fermions the wave functions must all be antisymmetrical, i.e. of the type (cf. 3.26)

$$\psi(1, 2) = \psi_a(1)\psi_b(2) - \psi_a(2)\psi_b(1) \qquad (3.28)$$

Now the wave functions ψ describe not only the spatial

motion (n, l, m) of the electrons, but also their spin direction (m_s) and since these are independent variables in the non-relativistic case it is also possible to express ψ (1, 2) as a product of a spatial function and a spin function. The overall requirement of antisymmetry is met if the space and spin functions have opposite symmetries. Since this type of separation of space and spin variables is important in many applications of quantum mechanics, we consider it in detail. Let

$$\psi_a(1) = u_a(1)\chi_{m_s}(1)$$

where u is the space function, and χ_{m_s} the spin function for electron 1; there will be two functions $\chi_{1/2}$ and $\chi_{-1/2}$, corresponding to the two possible spin orientations with respect to an axis of quantization. From products of this kind the following totally antisymmetric functions ψ (1, 2) can be formed

$$\left.\begin{array}{l} \text{i) } [u_a(1)u_b(2) - u_a(2)u_b(1)]\chi_{1/2}(1)\chi_{1/2}(2) \\[4pt] \text{ii) } [u_a(1)u_b(2) - u_a(2)u_b(1)][\chi_{1/2}(1)\chi_{-1/2}(2) + \chi_{1/2}(2)\chi_{-1/2}(1)] \\[4pt] \text{iii) } [u_a(1)u_b(2) - u_a(2)u_b(1)]\chi_{-1/2}(1)\chi_{-1/2}(2) \\[4pt] \text{iv) } [u_a(1)u_b(2) + u_a(2)u_b(1)][\chi_{1/2}(1)\chi_{-1/2}(2) - \chi_{1/2}(2)\chi_{-1/2}(1)] \end{array}\right\} \quad (3.29)$$

In (i), (ii) and (iii) the space wave function is antisymmetric and the spin function is symmetric; the two spins combine to a total spin number $S = s_1 + s_2 = 1$ with components $m_S = 1, 0, -1$ respectively. These wave functions describe the states of *ortho-helium* in which the two electrons may be thought of as having effectively parallel spins. For each spatial state there are three spin states, i.e. a *triplet system*. In (iv) the spin function is anti-symmetric and the electrons have effectively opposite spins. These are the states of *parahelium* with $S = s_1 - s_2 = 0$, $m_S = 0$ and form a *singlet system*.

The energy levels of the helium atom therefore group into two distinct series, the singlets and triplets. A transition between these states requires both a change of spatial symmetry and a spin inversion and such processes are improbable. The actual energies of the states are calculated by introducing the electrostatic interaction e^2/r_{12} between the electrons and averaging over the spatial distribution as given by the wave functions, according to the rules of quantum mechanics. If E_a,

E_b are the energies of the unperturbed single electron states, the perturbed energies are

$$E_a + E_b + L \pm K \tag{3.30}$$

where
$$L = \int \psi_a^*(1)\psi_b^*(2)\frac{e^2}{r_{12}}\psi_a(1)\psi_b(2) \, \mathrm{d}\tau_1 \, \mathrm{d}\tau_2 \tag{3.31}$$

and
$$K = \int \psi_a^*(1)\psi_b^*(2)\frac{e^2}{r_{12}}\psi_a(2)\psi_b(1) \, \mathrm{d}\tau_1 \, \mathrm{d}\tau_2 \tag{3.32}$$

and the integrals are taken over coordinate space; L is known as the *direct integral*, and K the *exchange integral*. The positive sign in 3.30 corresponds to the singlet system, parahelium, in which the electrons can approach very closely so that the averaged repulsive interaction is large. In the triplet system the space wave function is antisymmetric and vanishes when the electrons coincide; the averaged repulsion is therefore much smaller and the triplet state is more stable than the corresponding singlet. The energy levels and some transitions of the helium atom are shown in Fig. 3.8 with their spectroscopic designation. The spectroscopic symbol is based on the combination of the spins and orbital vectors of the single electron states, as illustrated in the following table (cf. also 3.25).

TABLE 3.1   States of the Helium Atom

SINGLE ELECTRON STATES	STATE OF ATOM	
	PARAHELIUM	ORTHOHELIUM
$1s + 1s$	↑↓ $^1S_0$	—
$1s + 2s$	↑↓ $^1S_0$	↑↑ $^3S_1$
$1s + 2p$	↑↓ $^1P_1$	↑↑ $^3P_{0,1,2}$

It will be noted that when the two electron states are the same, e.g. $1s + 1s$, or more generally $u_a = u_b$ in 3.29, the corresponding state of orthohelium does not occur. This is simply because it would imply two electrons in the same spin state and with the same orbital motion, and this is forbidden by the Pauli principle, which is of course embodied in the construction of the functions 3.29.

The difference in energy between the ortho- and para-helium states corresponding to given single electron states might appear to be associated with interaction between the spins. In fact, as may be seen from 3.31 and 3.32, it is of the order e^2/r_{12} and is better described as an electrostatic energy arising from the quantum mechanical exchange (or resonance) effect discussed in Sect. **3.6**. This electrostatic energy is much larger than magnetic interactions in light atoms, including spin-orbit coupling energies.

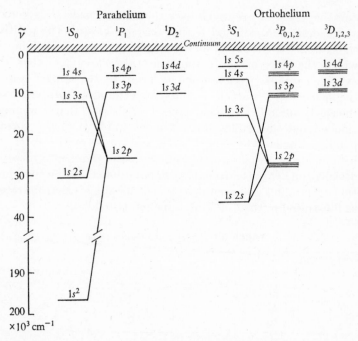

Fig. 3.8 Energy levels of parahelium and orthohelium showing that each P,D level of orthohelium is a triplet. The binding energy of the ground state is 24·77 eV. Typical radiative transitions are indicated; ortho-para transitions are forbidden.

It is instructive to compare the quantum mechanical resonance effect with the classical system of two coupled pendulums (Fig. 3.9). In the limit of zero coupling the normal modes have the same frequency, just as the 'unperturbed' states of the helium atom have the same energy. Each, however, corresponds to a different configuration, and when interaction is introduced the degeneracy is removed and different frequencies (or energies) appear.

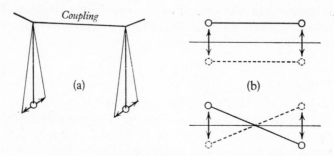

Fig. 3.9
a) Suspension of two identical pendulums from a string.
b) Position of bobs in the two normal modes, one symmetric and one antisymmetric.

3.7.2 COMPLEX ATOMS: COUPLING SCHEMES. The energy levels of complex atoms can in principle be obtained by solution of the Schrödinger equation once a suitable potential function $V(r)$ has been chosen. The method of the self-consistent field, introduced by Hartree, furnishes a convenient prescription for $V(r)$, which is obtained by successive approximations from trial solutions. This method has also been applied to nuclei. The atomic levels calculated in this and other similar ways are classified according to the combined values of the individual particle quantum numbers l, s, and j, but the method of combining the vectors is not unique. In light atoms the strongest couplings arise from the resonance energy and this effectively means that the intrinsic spin vectors s couple to give a resultant spin S where

$$S = s_1 + s_2 + s_3 + \ldots$$

The orbital momenta also couple to form a resultant **L** where

$$L = l_1 + l_2 + l_3 + \ldots$$

and finally the two resultants couple to give the total angular momentum **J** where

$$J = L + S \tag{3.33}$$

This coupling is known as the *Russell-Saunders or L–S scheme*. In heavier atoms the importance of the spin-orbit effect increases because it varies approximately as Z^4 whereas the resonance energy depends only on Z^3. This results in a coupling of individual spin and orbital motion to yield a resultant for each electron and a combination of these j values into the final angular momentum of the atom:

$$\mathbf{s}_1 + \mathbf{l}_1 = \mathbf{j}_1; \quad \mathbf{s}_2 + \mathbf{l}_2 = \mathbf{j}_2;$$
$$\mathbf{j}_1 + \mathbf{j}_2 + \ldots = \mathbf{J} \qquad (3.34)$$

This is known as the *j–j coupling scheme* and it is fundamental for the shell model of the nucleus (ch. 9). There are also coupling schemes intermediate between the $L–S$ and $j–j$ extremes.

General rules for the relative stability of the energy levels are known for Russell-Saunders coupling. They are that:

 i) Terms with the largest S lie lowest, e.g. triplets lie below singlets, as seen in the helium atom, Fig. 3.8.

 ii) For a given spin, terms with the largest L are lowest.

 iii) If a subshell is less than half filled with electrons the smallest J lies lowest (normal multiplet) but if the subshell is more than half filled the largest J lies lowest (inverted multiplet).

Thus for two p-electrons the order expected is $^3P_0$, $^3P_1$, $^3P_2$; $^1D_2$; $^1S_0$. The order for two p-nucleons would be reversed because nuclear forces are attractive in contrast with the forces between electrons.

The gradual transition from $L–S$ to $j–j$ coupling is illustrated in Fig. 3.10 which gives the energy levels for a series of atoms of increasing atomic weight, each with two electrons outside closed sub-shells. The number of states remains the same in the two extremes of coupling but the intervals change. For $L–S$ coupling the intervals between the levels of a multiplet such as $^3P_0$, $^3P_1$, $^3P_2$ are proportional to $(J+1)$ where J is the spin of the lower state, and this may be used for testing the validity of the $L–S$ scheme in particular cases.

3.8   Molecular binding and energy levels

Molecular binding, which is a phenomenon of fundamental importance for chemistry, is a good example of the quantum mechanical resonance effect already discussed in the theory of the helium atom. The main difference is that the exchange takes place not between two electronic states of one atom, but between the equivalent ground states of two atoms (in the case of a diatomic molecule). We consider here only the binding of the simplest systems, the hydrogen molecular ion (H_2^+) and the hydrogen molecule (H_2) since these sufficiently illustrate the theory of the homopolar (covalent) bond in chemistry and also provide many features of interest for nuclear physics.

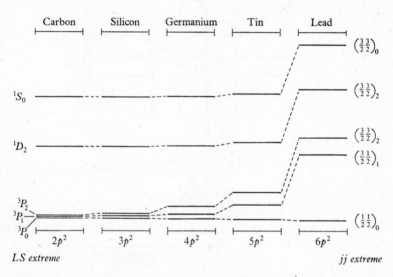

Fig. 3.10. Transition from L–S to j–j coupling in low states of atoms with two p-electrons (from Ref. 3.9). The symbols at the right-hand side give the j values of the two electrons in the j–j limit and the suffix gives the resultant spin.

3.8.1 THE HYDROGEN MOLECULAR ION. Consider the approach of a proton towards an unexcited hydrogen atom. For large separations the electron of the atom is undisturbed but as the second proton comes to within distances of $\approx 10^{-8}$ cm from the first the probability of electron transfer between the two protons increases. When this resonance transfer happens with a high enough frequency, the wave function of the electron between the two protons is sufficiently strong to produce binding. This may be seen from Fig. 3.11a which shows the way in which de Broglie waves may be fitted into the double potential well provided by the two protons. In the lowest state the symmetrical wave function ψ_S has a slightly longer wave-

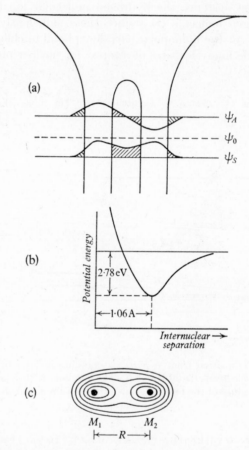

Fig. 3.11. Binding of the hydrogen molecular ion (Ref. 1.6)
a) Electron wave functions.
b) Potential energy as a function of internuclear distance.
c) Electron density contours.

length than the wave function ψ_0 of the single hydrogen atom ground state, while the antisymmetrical function ψ_A corresponds to a shorter wavelength. The electron density $\psi\psi^*$ between the nuclei is greater for ψ_S than for ψ_A and the energy E_S is less than the energy E_0 of an undisturbed hydrogen atom and a distant proton, i.e. binding results.

Detailed calculations involve the averaging of the electrostatic energy with wave functions which allow the possibility of quantum mechanical exchange of the electron between the two potential wells. The form of the potential energy curve for the ion, as a function of internuclear separation (Fig. 3.11b) is well predicted.

3.8.2 THE HYDROGEN MOLECULE. Experimentally the hydrogen molecule has an internuclear separation of 0·74 A and a binding energy of 4·72 eV. To produce this extra binding the second electron must also enter the space-symmetric state ψ_S (Fig. 3.11a) and this it can do, without infringing the Pauli principle, if its spin is opposite to that of the first electron. The ground state of the hydrogen molecule therefore has a wave function which is symmetrical in the spatial motion of the electrons, but antisymmetric in the spins, i.e. it is a singlet.

The detailed calculation of the binding energy first given by Heitler and London (1927) is more like that discussed for the helium atom than is the calculation for the molecular ion, since two electrons are present and their exchange interaction must be allowed for. The basic states are still the ground states of the two possible atoms that can be formed. The overall antisymmetry requirement predicts just one spatial state with singlet spin, and three antisymmetrical spatial states corresponding to parallel spins (triplet) of the electrons. The triplet states lead to repulsion; thus when two hydrogen atoms approach there is only one chance in four that they form a bound molecule.

The potential energy curve for the hydrogen molecule is of the form shown in Fig. 3.11b. The rise of the potential energy for small interaction distances occurs when the repulsion between the protons overcomes the attraction provided by the electrons. It is to be noted that it is not possible to increase the stability of the molecule further by adding a third electron to H_2, since this could not enter the state ψ_S without violating the Pauli principle. The exchange interaction thus shows a saturation effect.

3.8.3 GENERAL MOTION OF A DIATOMIC MOLECULE. In calculations of the binding energy of molecules it is assumed in a first approximation that the positions of the nuclei are fixed in space. This is not correct, since the nuclei can vibrate about their equilibrium positions and the molecule may also rotate about its centre of gravity. Because of the small mass of the electrons, their velocity is high and the electron distribution rapidly adjusts itself to the much slower nuclear motions; these motions do not appreciably affect the binding energy.

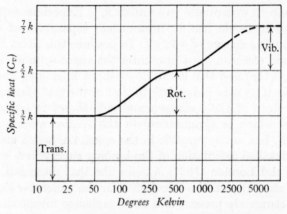

Fig. 3.12. Specific heat of molecular hydrogen (Ref. 1.6).

The electronic states of a molecule cannot be specified in the way that is appropriate for an atom because there is no single centre of force. There is, however, in general a symmetry axis, such as the line joining the nuclei in the case of a diatomic molecule, and quantum numbers for the electrons can be defined with respect to this axis. These quantum numbers and the corresponding energy states E_{elec}, can be studied by observation of molecular emission and absorption spectra in the optical wavelength range. The spectra under low resolution appear as bands but are in fact a series of lines; the energies involved are comparable with those found in atomic line spectra, i.e. $\approx 10,000$ cm^{-1}.

The effect of molecular vibrations and rotations can be seen clearly in the temperature variation of the specific heat of diatomic gases as well as in molecular spectra. Fig. 3.12 shows

the specific heat of hydrogen over the temperature range
10–5000 °K. The specific heat expected according to the kinetic
theory of gases is $\frac{5}{2}k$ per molecule if two degrees of freedom of
rotation are excited by the thermal motion and this is approximately the value found at room temperatures. At temperatures
of about 1500 °K and above, however, the specific heat rises and
this is explained by the incidence of vibration, which cannot be
excited strongly at lower temperatures because of the quantization of vibrational motion. The vibrational frequencies are
determined by the form of the potential energy curve (Fig.
3.11b) and may be written

$$\nu = \frac{1}{2\pi} \sqrt{\frac{K(M_1 + M_2)}{M_1 M_2}} \tag{3.35}$$

where K is an elastic factor and M_1, M_2 are the nuclear masses.
The quantized vibrational energies are

$$E_{\text{vib}} = (n + \tfrac{1}{2})h\nu \tag{3.36}$$

which shows that although some vibrational energy (zero point
energy) exists at very low temperatures, no energy can be absorbed by vibrational degrees of freedom from thermal motion
until

$$kT \approx h\nu \tag{3.37}$$

the spacing of the vibrational levels. For $T \approx 1500$ °K we have
$\bar{\nu} \approx 1000 \text{ cm}^{-1}$ which is considerably less than the spacing of
the electronic levels.

At temperatures below 300 °K the specific heat of hydrogen
drops below the kinetic theory value. This is also a quantum
effect, now in the rotational energy. The energies permitted for
a rotator must correspond to quantized angular momenta

$$\mathscr{I}\omega = \sqrt{J(J+1)}\hbar \tag{3.38}$$

where $\mathscr{I}$ is the moment of inertia of the molecule $(= (M_1 M_2/$
$M_1 + M_2)R^2$, Fig. 3.11c) and J is an integer. This gives

$$E_{\text{rot}} = \frac{1}{2}\mathscr{I}\omega^2 = \frac{J(J+1)}{2\mathscr{I}}\hbar^2 \tag{3.39}$$

and the lowest rotational state $(J = 1)$ will not be strongly excited when the temperature falls below the value given by

$$kT = \frac{\hbar^2}{\mathscr{I}} \tag{3.40}$$

For hydrogen $\mathscr{I} \approx 0.4 \times 10^{-40}$ gm cm^2 and the temperature at which rotation begins to disappear is from 3.40 about 180°K, corresponding to a frequency $\bar{\nu} = 128$ cm^{-1}. Equation 3.40 shows that the smaller $\mathscr{I}$, the more difficult it is to excite rotation and this is the reason that rotation about the internuclear axis does not take place. On the other hand, most diatomic molecules such as N_2 or Cl_2 have moments of inertia of the order of 10^{-38} gm cm^2 and the rotational energy differences correspond to a frequency $\bar{\nu} \approx 1$ cm^{-1}; i.e. the microwave region. These energy differences are much less than those corresponding to the vibrational motion. When rotational states are excited, the distribution of molecules among them, at temperature T, is given by the Boltzmann-type distribution

$$W(J) \propto (2J+1)\exp-[\hbar^2 J(J+1)/2\mathscr{I}kT] \tag{3.41}$$

in which the factor $2J+1$ is the *statistical weight* corresponding to the number of possible orientations in space of the vector **J**. This evidence now permits a qualitative picture of the energy levels of a molecule to be constructed (Fig. 3.13a). These levels are given formally by the expression

$$E = E_{\text{elec}} + E_{\text{vib}} + E_{\text{rot}} \tag{3.42}$$

but it must be noted that when a new electronic state is excited, the binding is altered, the internuclear separation changes and a new moment of inertia $\mathscr{I}'$ and a new force constant for the vibration are required.

Spectroscopic investigation of the vibrational and rotational motions may be made by observing the transitions directly or in the fine structure of electronic transitions. Fig. 3.13b shows the total absorption spectrum of CH_3Cl, in which the rotational, vibrational and electronic frequencies are well separated. They lie in the microwave, infra red, and optical regions of the wavelength range respectively. The frequencies of the lines of the molecular spectrum may be written formally, from 3.42 as

$$\nu = \nu_e + \nu_{vib} + \nu_{rot}$$

and the particular combinations of levels allowed to participate in transitions are given by *selection rules* (Sect. 3.9.2) for the appropriate quantum numbers. For electric dipole radiation,

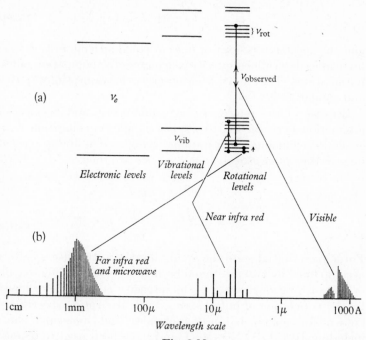

Fig. 3.13

a) Energy levels of a diatomic molecule (schematic) showing typical transitions in absorption (upwards) and emission (downwards). The diagram is not to scale.

b) Total absorption spectrum of methyl chloride showing bands similar to those expected for a diatomic molecule.

(D. K. Coles, in *Advances in Electronics*, Vol. II.)

these rules require that there shall be an electric dipole moment in the radiating system, and may be stated as follows:

For rotational transitions: $\Delta J = \pm 1$,

vibrational transitions: $\Delta J = \pm 1$, $\Delta n = \pm 1$,

electronic transitions: a change of electronic symmetry and $\Delta J = 0, \pm 1$.   (3.43)

Special considerations arise in the case of homonuclear diatomic molecules; these will be discussed in Sect. 3.8.4 in connection with the ortho and para forms of hydrogen and more generally in Sect. 4.2.4 in connection with the determination of nuclear spins.

From the selection rules we conclude that for *pure rotational spectra* the frequencies are

$$\nu_{\text{rot}} = \frac{\hbar}{2\pi \mathscr{I}} J \quad \text{with } J = 1, 2, \ldots \qquad (3.44)$$

and the spectrum is a set of lines of equal spacing $\hbar/2\pi\mathscr{I}$ with intensities determined by 3.41 which gives the population of the initial states. They have been observed in absorption for HCl and similar gases.

Because of the relative energy differences, and because of interaction between the two types of motion, vibration is in general accompanied by rotational changes. The frequencies of lines in the *vibrational-rotational spectra* are then

$$\nu = \nu_{\text{vib}} \pm \frac{\hbar}{2\pi\mathscr{I}} J$$

$$= \frac{E_{\text{vib}} - E_{\text{vib}}'}{h} \pm \frac{\hbar}{2\pi\mathscr{I}} J \qquad (3.45)$$

For a given initial state the main vibrational transition is thus accompanied by two rotational branches, corresponding to gain or loss of rotational energy. The intensity is again determined by the population of initial states. Such absorption spectra are known for many diatomic molecules and molecular ions, including HCl, LiH, NO, MgO, and have been used to deduce internuclear distances (from 3.44), vibration frequencies (from 3.45) and dissociation energies.

In the *electronic spectra* the main transition in the visible or ultra-violet region of the spectrum is accompanied by rotational-vibrational spectra which group into a number of bands centred on the particular vibrational energy change. The molecular moment of inertia changes in an electronic transition and the calculation of the rotational structure is more complicated. Since $\Delta J = 0, \pm 1$ are all permitted an electronic band contains three branches (except in the case of homonuclear molecules with zero electronic angular momentum in both states concerned in the transition).

The molecules so far considered have for simplicity been assumed linear but an important and more general case is that of the symmetric top molecule. The rotational energy of such a molecule is now determined by three principal moments of inertia $\mathscr{I}_A, \mathscr{I}_B, \mathscr{I}_C$ and is given by

$$E_{rot} = \frac{\hbar^2}{2\mathscr{I}_B} J(J+1) + \frac{\hbar^2}{2} \left(\frac{1}{\mathscr{I}_A} - \frac{1}{\mathscr{I}_C} \right) K^2 \qquad (3.46)$$

The new quantum number K ($|K| \leqslant J$) gives the component of the total angular momentum $\mathbf{J}$ along the molecular symmetry axis. The theory of this type of molecule is closely similar to the collective theory of deformed nuclei (ch. 12).

3.8.4 ORTHO AND PARA HYDROGEN.

The observed specific heat of hydrogen does not agree with calculations based on the series of rotational levels. This is because no account has been taken of the quantum mechanical symmetry properties of the nuclei. When this is correctly introduced it is found that there are two forms of each homonuclear diatomic molecule (ortho and para) and that the observed specific heats relate to a mixture of these two forms.

If the various mechanical motions of a diatomic molecule can be considered as independent, the total wave function can be written as a product

$$\psi = \psi_{\text{electronic} \atop \text{orbital}} \ \psi_{\text{electronic} \atop \text{spin}} \ \psi_{\text{vibration}} \ \psi_{\text{rotation}} \ \psi_{\text{nuclear} \atop \text{spin}} \qquad (3.47)$$

This wave function is chosen to be antisymmetric for the exchange of electrons in accordance with the requirements of Fermi-Dirac statistics, and we have seen (Sect. 3.8.2) that for molecular binding of hydrogen the two electrons have opposite spins. We now assume that a similar condition must be imposed on the nuclei, which, in the case of hydrogen, are also spin $\frac{1}{2}$ particles and should thus obey the same statistics as the electrons. The wave function ψ, for given electronic motion, should therefore be antisymmetric for exchange of the two protons.

The internuclear distance does not change when the nuclei are transposed and $\psi_{\text{vibration}}$ is therefore symmetric. The rotational wave functions however, to which correspond the eigenvalues 3.39, have the angular dependence $Y_l^m(\theta, \phi)$ with

$l = J$ and on transposition (Fig. 3.5)* are multiplied by a factor $(-1)^J$. The remaining nuclear factor relates to intrinsic spin, and for $I_1 = I_2 = \frac{1}{2}$ we know from the discussion already given for the helium atom (Sect. 3.7.1) that there are three symmetric spin functions with total spin number $I = 1$ and one anti-symmetric, with $I = 0$. These two possible nuclear spin combinations, parallel or antiparallel, are those of the two forms of hydrogen molecule, just as the same combination of electron spins correspond to the two sets of states of the helium atom. For overall antisymmetry in the nuclei, orthohydrogen must have only rotational states with J odd and parahydrogen only states with J even.

The two forms of hydrogen obviously possess different amounts of rotational energy at a given temperature and the specific heats are therefore expected to differ. The observed specific heat will depend on the equilibrium ratio of concentrations, and this may easily be predicted using 3.41. A factor of 3 must be introduced in favour of orthohydrogen because of the 3 symmetrical spin functions. The equilibrium concentration ratio at temperature T is then

$$\frac{C \text{ ortho}}{C \text{ para}} = 3 \frac{\sum\limits_{1,3,5...} (2J+1) \exp - E_J/kT}{\sum\limits_{0,2,4...} (2J+1) \exp - E_J/kT} \qquad (3.48)$$

where E_J is the value E_{rot} given by 3.39. As T increases this ratio approaches the limiting value 3, which is essentially reached at room temperature; for low temperatures the ratio tends to zero and the mixture resolves into pure parahydrogen. The room-temperature specific heat, calculated for a mixture $\frac{3}{4}$ ortho + $\frac{1}{4}$ parahydrogen, agrees with observation.

If the normal mixture is cooled from room temperature to a few degrees Kelvin, both forms will reach their lowest rotational state ($J = 1$ ortho, $J = 0$ para) but the ortho $\rightarrow$ para transition, although energetically possible, will be slow because of the necessity for spin inversion. It may be accelerated by cooling down over a catalyst such as carbon, and 100% parahydrogen can then be obtained.

---

* This transposition is of course just the parity operation (Sect. **3.4**); the parity of a rotational level is even or odd as its J-value.

The extension of these results to nuclei of arbitrary spin I in homonuclear diatomic molecules is discussed in Sect. 4.2.4.

3.9 Semi-classical theory of radiation

The production, propagation and absorption of radiation are fundamental processes in atomic and nuclear physics. So far as propagation is concerned, the classical electromagnetic theory of Maxwell appears entirely adequate, but in the interaction of radiation with matter, in the processes which lead to the creation or disappearance of the radiation, it is necessary to introduce the concept of photons. A satisfactory and comprehensive description of all radiative processes has only been achieved by the development of quantum field theory. For many purposes, however, a simple semi-classical theory, which describes the radiation field by Maxwell's equations and the sources of radiation by quantum mechanics, is useful. Such a theory can in particular predict rough orders of magnitude for the lifetimes of excited states and can give the polarization of emitted radiation. It includes as a limit the correspondence principle of Bohr, according to which the radiation from a quantized system must agree in frequency, intensity and polarization with that from a classical oscillator for sufficiently large quantum numbers. In this section we indicate certain results of this theory which are of general use in atomic and nuclear physics.

It may be noted that the success of the semi-classical theory is due to the fact that the non-classical phenomena of quantum electrodynamics are really only very small effects. Recoil due to the emission of virtual photons by electrons enters formulae in powers of α, the fine structure constant, and the corrections (as seen in the magnetic moment of the electron and μ-meson, in the Lamb shift, and in the theory of positronium) are negligible except when extremely accurate measurements are made.

3.9.1 SPONTANEOUS EMISSION; LINE WIDTH. According to Maxwell's theory an oscillating charge distribution emits radiation. In the case of a charge e, of mass m, oscillating simple harmonically with respect to a centre of force (Fig. 3.14a) we define a dipole moment

$$D = ea \cos \omega_0 t = ea \cos 2\pi\nu_0 t \qquad (3.49)$$

The instantaneous rate of radiation of energy into a solid angle $d\Omega$ at angle θ with the direction of a is given in Ref. 3.6 as

$$\frac{1}{4\pi} \frac{\ddot{D}^2}{c^3} \sin^2 \theta \, d\Omega \tag{3.50}$$

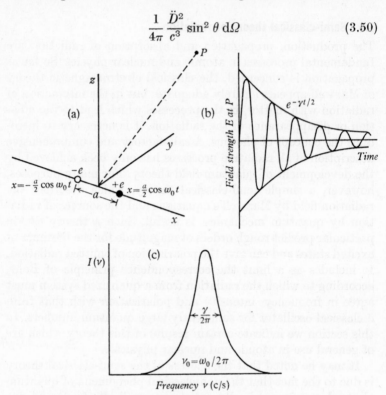

Fig. 3.14

a) Classical dipole oscillator of moment $ea \cos \omega_0 t$.
b) Damped wave train radiated by classical oscillator.
c) Fourier analysis of damped wave train.

The total rate of emission of energy is obtained by integrating 3.50 over a sphere as

$$\frac{dW}{dt} = \frac{2}{3} \frac{\ddot{D}^2}{c^3} = \frac{2}{3} \frac{e^2 a^2 \omega_0^4}{c^3} \cos^2 \omega_0 t \text{ erg sec}^{-1} \tag{3.51}$$

and the mean value of this over many cycles is

$$\overline{\frac{dW}{dt}} = \frac{1}{3} \frac{e^2 a^2 \omega_0^4}{c^3} \tag{3.52}$$

Classically this energy must be supplied by the oscillator, whose amplitude will therefore decrease (unless it is driven). At the time when the amplitude is a, the total energy is

$$W = \frac{1}{2} ma^2\omega_0^2 \tag{3.53}$$

and from 3.52 and 3.53, this can be expressed in the form

$$W = W_0 e^{-\gamma t} \tag{3.54}$$

where

$$\gamma = \frac{2}{3}\frac{e^2\omega_0^2}{mc^3} = \frac{8\pi^2 e^2 \nu_0^2}{3mc^3} \tag{3.55}$$

The corresponding electric field vector at P may be written

$$\mathbf{E} = \mathbf{E}_0 e^{-\gamma t/2} \cos \omega_0 \left(t - \frac{r}{c}\right) \tag{3.56}$$

and this damped harmonic wave may in turn be represented by a superposition of undamped waves covering a range of frequencies of the order γ. If the radiation is examined with a spectroscope of high resolution it appears as a line of *finite spectral width*. A Fourier analysis of the expression 3.56 shows that the spectral line has an *intensity* distribution near the oscillator frequency ν_0 given by

$$I(\nu) = \frac{\text{constant}}{(\nu - \nu_0)^2 + \frac{1}{4}\left(\dfrac{\gamma}{2\pi}\right)^2} \tag{3.57}$$

The damped wave train is shown in Fig. 3.14b and its frequency analysis in Fig. 3.14c, from which it is seen that the full width of the distribution at half maximum intensity is just $\gamma/2\pi$. The formula 3.57 represents the *Lorentz shape* of a spectral line.

In taking over these results into quantum theory, we assume that radiation arises as a result of a transition of a system such as an atom or a nucleus between two energy levels E_i and E_f as shown in Fig. 3.15 and that the frequency is given by the Bohr condition

$$h\nu_0 = E_i - E_f = E_0 \tag{3.58}$$

It is found that the line shape still has the Lorentz form, but the half-width is now interpreted as proportional to the transition probability per unit time for the system excited to the level E_i, i.e. to the reciprocal of the mean life τ of this level. By Heisenberg's uncertainty principle the mean life may also be expressed in terms of an energy width Γ of the level E_i given by

$$\Gamma\tau = \hbar = 6 \cdot 6 \times 10^{-16} \text{ eV sec} \qquad (3.59)$$

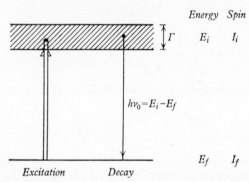

Fig. 3.15. Quantum picture of radiative process between levels of energy E_i and E_f.

In this representation the width of the spectral line is due to the level width Γ, or strictly to the sum of the widths of the two levels concerned in the transition, and the Lorentz shape of the line, in terms of energies, may be written

$$I(E) = \frac{\text{constant}}{(E - E_0)^2 + \frac{1}{4}\Gamma^2} \qquad (3.60)$$

where E_0 is given by 3.58. For the D-lines of sodium the *classical* line width $\gamma/2\pi$ corresponds to an energy width of 4×10^{-8} eV and a lifetime, by 3.59, of $1 \cdot 7 \times 10^{-8}$ sec. The remarkable precision of measurement offered by the Mössbauer effect (Sect. 13.6.3) has permitted the Lorentz shape for the 14·4 keV nuclear transition in ^{57}Fe ($\Gamma = 4 \cdot 6 \times 10^{-9}$ eV) to be examined and confirmed in detail.

It is not possible to calculate the quantum mechanical width or probability of spontaneous emission, from wave mechanics. This probability may indeed be deduced from the probability of the inverse process ($E_f + h\nu \rightarrow E_i$, Fig. 3.15) which is the excitation of a system by a light quantum, by application of a statistical argument. We prefer here, however, to use the classical approach starting with 3.51. If a suitable quantum mechanical form for the dipole moment D can be found and if the energy radiated from the excited system is to be carried away by photons of energy $h\nu_0$, the number emitted per unit time must be

$$\frac{2}{3}\frac{\ddot{D}^2}{h\nu_0 c^3} = \frac{2}{3}\frac{\ddot{D}^2}{\hbar\omega_0 c^3} \qquad (3.61)$$

and the mean time τ_1 required for the emission of a photon is the reciprocal of the time-averaged value of this quantity. The dipole moment is a function of the two states of the radiating system and of the time and it is customary to express it as

$$D(r, t) = 2D(r)\cos\omega_0 t = D(r)\{e^{i\omega_0 t} + e^{-i\omega_0 t}\} \qquad (3.62)$$

where $D(r)$ is a function of the states of motion only. If we consider the simple case in which the levels E_i, E_f are defined by the motion of a particle of charge e in a potential well, and if the corresponding wave functions are ψ_i, ψ_f then a suitable expression for $D(r)$ is

$$D(r) = e\int \psi_f^* \mathbf{r}\psi_i \, d\tau = e\bar{\mathbf{r}}_{if} \qquad (3.63$$

This effectively averages a vector quantity er of the dimensions of the classical dipole moment, with respect to the charge distribution in the initial and final states.

From 3.61, 3.62 and 3.63 we obtain for the dipole mean lifetime τ_1

$$\frac{1}{\tau_1} = \frac{4}{3}\frac{e^2\omega_0^3}{\hbar c^3}|\bar{\mathbf{r}}_{if}|^2 = \frac{\Gamma_1}{\hbar} \quad \text{from 3.59} \qquad (3.64)$$

This may also be written, remembering that $\omega_0 = 2\pi\nu_0 = E_0/\hbar$ as

$$\Gamma_1 = \frac{4}{3}e^2\left(\frac{E_0}{\hbar c}\right)^3|\bar{\mathbf{r}}_{if}|^2 \qquad (3.65)$$

so that the dipole width Γ_1 is proportional to the cube of the transition energy.

A classical charge distribution which may be completely described by a dipole moment is of course a very special case.

More generally several electric moments are required, as explained in more detail in Appendix 3, and when current loops develop as a result of the motion of the charges, magnetic moments also arise. An electric quadrupole moment would have dimensions $\approx \Sigma er^2$ and the electric 2^L-pole moment is $\approx \Sigma er^L$. When the charge distribution oscillates, radiation may be associated with each of these moments, but because of their more symmetrical nature they do not radiate so strongly as the dipole moment. It can be shown that in the *long wavelength approximation*, when the wavelength of the emitted radiation is very much greater than the dimension a of the radiating system, the intensity of radiation from each successively higher moment decreases by a factor $(a/\lambda)^2$. In most cases of interest the yield of high multipole radiation is very small. Thus for a sodium atom emitting $\lambda = 6000$ A we have $(a/\lambda)^2 \approx 10^{-5}$ while for a nucleus emitting radiation of energy 0.5 MeV, and with $a = 10^{-12}$ cm, $(a/\lambda)^2 = 10^{-3}$. Nuclei tend to show more higher order radiation than atoms because there are reasons for suppression of dipole radiation between many nuclear states.

These results may be carried over into the quantum mechanical treatment and formulae similar to 3.65 for the 2^L-pole width may be derived. For both electric and magnetic radiation for example

$$\Gamma_L \propto E_0^{2L+1} \qquad (3.66)$$

Such formulae are always expressible as a product of an energy dependent factor and a factor characteristic of the source for the particular type of radiation. The former factor is quite general, since it arises unambiguously as a result of the long wavelength approximation, but the latter is specific to the radiating system and must be calculated on the basis of a model of that system.

The expression 3.50 contains the angular distribution factor for classical dipole radiation; the intensity along the axis of the dipole is zero. The classical analogy shows that the angular distribution of radiation from the 2^L-pole moment contains powers of $\cos \theta$ up to $\cos^{2L} \theta$ only. The polarization of the radiation is also predictable from the classical moments.

3.9.2 MULTIPOLARITY; SELECTION RULES. A radiative transition is in principle possible between any two levels of an atom or nucleus, providing that one of them at least has a finite spin I. Whether such a process will in practice be observable in competition with other types of de-excitation, or with transitions from the excited state to other lower states, depends on the radiative width Γ. Whether radiation of a particular *type*, e.g. dipole or quadrupole, occurs at all between the two levels depends on certain absolute *selection rules*. If for instance the dipole moment 3.63 vanishes, then radiation of a higher order may become important. Selection rules for radiative processes are based ultimately on the properties of the electromagnetic field, particularly with respect to angular momentum and parity. If these quantities are conserved in the electromagnetic field, and all evidence so far available suggests that they are, then the emission of a photon of known properties must alter the state of the emitting system correspondingly, not only in energy, but in symmetry character.

It may be shown directly from Maxwell's equations that the electromagnetic radiation from an oscillating charge distribution of small dimensions transports angular momentum as well as energy. The two are connected by the result (Ref. 3.7, p. 802) that: z-component of angular momentum $= (M/\omega) \times$ energy in field where M is an integer. If one quantum of energy $\hbar\omega$ is emitted the z-component of angular momentum is $M\hbar$. The total angular momentum of the quantum is the vector $\mathbf{L}$ (of absolute value $\sqrt{L(L+1)}\hbar$ just as in the case of a particle), and $|M| \leqslant L$. The L-value defines the *multipolarity* of the photon, or of the corresponding process, as the number of units of angular momentum removed by the quantum emission. For radiation of multipolarity L to be observed, the corresponding moment must be finite. The angular distribution and polarization are then those corresponding to the radiation from a classical 2^L-pole moment (Sect. 3.9.1). We shall write the angular distribution function for radiation of multipolarity L with z-component M as

$$F_L^M(\theta) \tag{3.67}$$

This gives the intensity observed at an angle θ with respect to the z-axis. For dipole radiation we have

$$F_1^0(\theta) = 3 \sin^2 \theta$$
$$F_1^{\pm 1}(\theta) = \tfrac{3}{2}(1 + \cos^2 \theta) \tag{3.68}$$

corresponding to dipoles lying in the z-axis and rotating in the x–y plane respectively. The numerical factors are introduced so that the angular factor in the mean rate of radiation over a sphere is unity (cf. 3.50, 3.51, 3.52).

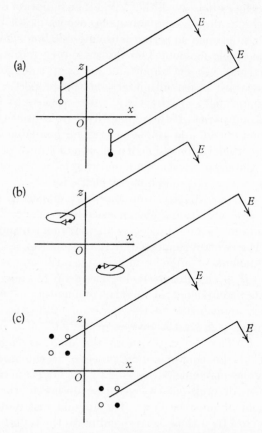

Fig. 3.16. Effect of parity operation on simple charge and current distributions. On inversion in the origin it is seen that (a) for an electric dipole the radiation field changes sign and is therefore of odd parity, (b) for a magnetic dipole and (c) for an electric quadrupole the radiation field is unaltered and is therefore of even parity.

In the case of motion of a single particle the angular momentum also determines the parity (Sect. **3.4**). This is not so for the electromagnetic interaction, which has fields of both even and odd parity. Fig. 3.16 illustrates this for the inversion through the origin of simple radiating systems. We note that radiation of given multipolarity may be either even or odd and that in particular the field of an electric dipole has odd parity while electric quadrupole and magnetic dipole fields are even. In general radiative processes are classed as of electric or magnetic type (E or M) to indicate the parity change, as shown in the following table; the multipolarity is given as a number following the letter denoting the radiation type.

TABLE 3.2 Classification of electromagnetic radiation

Type of radiation	$E1$	$E2$, $M1$	$E3$, $M2$
Name	Electric dipole	Electric quadrupole Magnetic dipole	Electric octupole Magnetic quadrupole
Multipolarity	1	2, 1	3, 2
Parity change	Yes	No	Yes

These observations on the radiation field now permit the *selection rules* for the sources of the radiation to be formulated (Refs. 3.3; 3.10). For angular momentum, we see that the multipolarity of the quantum emitted in the process shown in Fig. 3.15 is determined by the vector equation

$$\mathbf{I}_i - \mathbf{I}_f = \mathbf{L} \tag{3.69}$$

which implies for the quantum numbers

$$I_i + I_f \geqslant L \geqslant |I_i - I_f| \tag{3.70}$$

and for a specified axis Oz (Fig. 3.17a)

$$m_i - m_f = M \tag{3.71}$$

The inequality 3.70 may permit several multipolarities, e.g. states of spin 3 and 2 could give $L = 1, 2, 3, 4, 5$. Some of these, however, are forbidden by the *parity selection rule* which may be obtained from Table **3.2**. In the case 3^+ (even)$\rightarrow 2^-$ (odd) for instance $E1$, $M2$, $E3$, $M4$ and $E5$ radiation only would be allowed; in practice only the lowest multipoles, $E1$ and perhaps $M2$ would be effective, because of the factor $(a/\lambda)^2$ in the intensity formula (Sect. 3.9.1). The electromagnetic field does not provide any type of radiation with $L = 0$ (which would be a longitudinal wave) and for $I_i = I_f = 0$ radiation is *strictly forbidden*. Alternative processes for the nuclear $0 \to 0$ transition are discussed in chapter 13.

In 3.69 and 3.70 I is the total angular momentum quantum number. If spin-orbit coupling is weak, the quantum numbers L_i and S_i are also useful and spin and orbital vectors provide separate selection rules. Thus for electric dipole radiation, there is no interaction with intrinsic spins and we have (Ref. 3.3, p. 198): $\Delta I = 0, \pm 1$; $\Delta L_i = 0, \pm 1$; $\Delta S_i = 0$ and parity change,

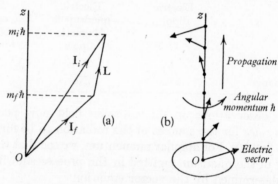

Fig. 3.17

a) Vector diagram (schematic) for emission of radiation of multipolarity L. The component of **L** along the axis Oz is $(m_i - m_f)\hbar$.

b) If Oz is taken to be the direction of propagation, then $m_i - m_f = \pm 1$ and the radiation observed in the direction Oz is circularly polarized.

e.g. the transitions $^1D \to {}^1P$, or $^2P \to {}^2S$ (sodium D-lines). Magnetic dipole radiation can arise either from orbital motion, or because an intrinsic spin changes its direction in an internal field. The corresponding rules (Ref. 3.3, p. 257) are

$$\Delta I = 0, \pm 1 \text{ and no parity change}$$
$$\Delta L_i = 0, \pm 1; \ \Delta S_i = 0 \text{ for orbital motion}$$
$$\Delta L_i = 0; \ \Delta S_i = 0, \pm 1 \text{ for spin-flip}$$

e.g. the transitions $^3S \to {}^1S$, $^3D \to {}^1D$.

For some purposes it is useful to describe the angular momentum of the photon itself as composed of an orbital part and an intrinsic spin of unity. If the axis of quantization is taken along the direction of emission, the orbital part of the angular momentum has no component in this direction. The intrinsic spin can have components $\pm\hbar$ only, the $M = 0$ component being excluded by the requirement that the electromagnetic wave shall be transverse. We consequently arrive at the picture of a photon propagating along Oz as a circularly polarized plane wave, with two possible directions of rotation of the electric vector (3.17b).

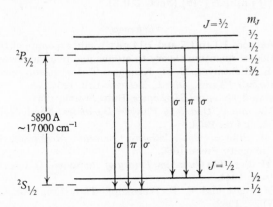

Fig. 3.18. Zeeman components of the D_2 line ($\lambda = 5890$ A) of the sodium atom, neglecting hyperfine structure. The separations of the substates are not shown to scale; in absolute units they are of the order of 10^{-4} cm^{-1} per gauss.

3.9.3. THE ZEEMAN EFFECT.

The line-splitting observed when a radiating atom or nucleus is situated in a magnetic field is a good example of the application of selection rules. For the sodium D-lines $^2P_{3/2,1/2} \rightarrow {}^2S_{1/2}$ the spin $\frac{3}{2}$ has four substates, $m_J = \pm\frac{3}{2}, \pm\frac{1}{2}$ and the spin $\frac{1}{2}$ has two substates, $m_J = \pm\frac{1}{2}$ and there is a parity change in the transitions. Application of the selection rule

$$\Delta J = \pm 1, 0; \qquad \Delta m_J = \pm 1, 0$$

predicts four components of electric dipole radiation for the D_1 line and six for D_2 (Fig. 3.18). If the magnetic field is taken to define the axis Oz, then components with $\Delta m_J = 0$ arise, in the classical analogy, from an electric dipole aligned with the axis of z. The corresponding radiation vanishes in the direction $\pm Oz$ itself and is plane polarized (π) when viewed in any other direction. The components with $\Delta m_J = \pm 1$, on the other hand, are circularly polarized when viewed along the lines of force and plane polarized when seen in planes perpendicular to the lines of force; they are known as σ components.* Classically these correspond to radiation from a dipole rotating in the x–y plane.

The angular distribution of the Zeeman components is given by the classical analogy as proportional to $\sin^2 \theta$ for $\Delta m_J = 0$ and to $(1 + \cos^2 \theta)$ for $\Delta m_J = \pm 1$, i.e. by the distribution functions $F_1^0(\theta)$ and $F_1^{\pm 1}(\theta)$ (Sect. 3.9.2).

References

3.1 References 1.1 to 1.7 and 1.14 give useful accounts of the application of quantum theory to atomic and nuclear phenomena.

3.2 F. K. Richtmyer, E. H. Kennard, T. Lauritsen, *Introduction to Modern Physics*, 5th ed., McGraw-Hill, 1955.

3.3 F. Mandl, *Quantum Mechanics*, Butterworth, 1957.

3.4 J. McConnell, *Quantum Particle Dynamics*, North Holland Publishing Co., 1958.

3.5 R. M. Sillitto, *Non-relativistic Quantum Mechanics*, Edinburgh University Press, 1960.

3.6 W. Heitler, *The Quantum Theory of Radiation*, Oxford University Press, 1944.

3.7 J. M. Blatt and V. F. Weisskopf, *Theoretical Nuclear Physics*, Wiley, 1952.

3.8 W. Heitler, *Elementary Wave Mechanics*, Oxford University Press, 1945.

3.9 H. E. White, *Introduction to Atomic Spectra*, McGraw-Hill, New York, 1934.

3.10 H. G. Kuhn, *Atomic Spectra*, Longmans, Green and Co., 1961.

3.11 B. L. Van der Waerden, 'Exclusion Principle and Spin' in *Theoretical Physics in the Twentieth Century* (Pauli Memorial volume), ed. M. Fierz and V. F. Weisskopf, Interscience, 1960.

---

* In magnetic dipole transitions, which are frequently encountered in nuclear processes, the electric and magnetic vectors are 90° displaced with respect to the vectors for an electric transition if the moments have the same axis. The π, σ nomenclature is then reversed.

4. NUCLEAR EFFECTS IN SPECTROSCOPY

The availability of a large body of information on the static properties of nuclei, properties such as angular momentum, magnetic moment and spatial extent, has greatly advanced the development of nuclear theory. Such properties are not invoked in the simple theory of the atom discussed in chapter 3, but much of the relevant information has been obtained by spectroscopy in the widest sense, in several regions of the electromagnetic spectrum. In ordinary optical spectroscopy, nuclear moment effects appear as small perturbations or splittings of spectral terms of much greater magnitude, and refined methods are necessary for their detection. Transitions between the hyperfine structure components of a spectral term are, however, also possible and the corresponding frequencies often lie in the microwave or radiofrequency region where accurate measurement is feasible. Microwave and radiofrequency methods, combined with the elegant techniques of the atomic and the molecular beam, have been responsible for a great increase in our knowledge of the electric and magnetic moments of the nuclear ground state; these and other methods will be briefly outlined in the present chapter.

4.1 Nuclear size and nuclear moments

The broad features of atomic spectra, as outlined in chapter 3, can be interpreted with the sole assumption of a nucleus of vanishingly small size and of infinite mass. The fine structure of spectral lines can be explained by the further addition of the concepts of electron spin and spin–orbit interaction, without the necessity for invoking additional nuclear properties. The hyperfine structure of line spectra, on a much smaller scale, cannot, however, be so explained, and in 1927 Goudsmit and Back, following earlier ideas of Pauli (1924), suggested that this effect in the bismuth spectrum might be due to the existence of a nuclear angular momentum, with which would be associated a magnetic moment. If nuclear magnetic moments are considered to arise partly as a result of circulating charges in the nucleus, it is clear that the nucleus must have a finite size, and small effects in optical spectroscopy should then result from the penetration of electronic wave functions of *s*-states into the nuclear volume. Both the spin and magnetic moment enter into the quantitative treatment of the hyperfine structure. In analogy with the electronic case (Sect. **3.5**) we define the following quantities:

a) *the nuclear angular momentum vector* **I**, with absolute magnitude

$$|\mathbf{I}| = \sqrt{I(I+1)}\hbar \qquad (4.1)$$

where I, the nuclear spin quantum number, is integral or half-integral. In accordance with the uncertainty principle the direction in space of the vector **I** cannot be determined, but if an axis Oz of quantization is defined, e.g. by an external magnetic field, the component of I along Oz will be observable and will have the value $m_I\hbar$ where m_I has one of the $2I+1$ values $I, (I-1), \ldots, -(I-1), -I$. This is exactly as shown for the vector **l** in Fig. 3.3, and the vector **I** is similarly considered to lie on a cone described round the axis Oz with semi-angle β given by

$$\cos\beta = \frac{m_I\hbar}{|\mathbf{I}|} = \frac{m_I}{\sqrt{I(I+1)}} \qquad (4.2)$$

The maximum value of the component of **I** is $I\hbar$ and this is usually known as the nuclear spin.

b) *the nuclear magnetic moment vector* $\boldsymbol{\mu}_I$, which is taken to be a vector parallel or anti-parallel to **I**. It may be expressed in absolute units or in nuclear magnetons, defined as $\mu_N = \dfrac{eh}{4\pi m_p c}$ in analogy with the Bohr magneton, but smaller by a factor of $m/m_p = 1/1836$. The observable value of $\boldsymbol{\mu}_I$, usually known as magnetic moment μ_I, is the z-component of $\boldsymbol{\mu}_I$ taken when m_I has its maximum value of I.

c) *the nuclear gyromagnetic ratio* γ_I, equal to the nuclear moment in absolute units divided by the nuclear spin also expressed in these units, i.e. in analogy with 3.18

$$\gamma_I = \frac{\boldsymbol{\mu}_I}{\mathbf{I}} = \frac{|\boldsymbol{\mu}_I|}{|\mathbf{I}|} = \left(\frac{\boldsymbol{\mu}_I}{\mathbf{I}}\right)_z \quad \text{or simply} \quad \frac{\mu}{I\hbar} \qquad (4.3)$$

The ratio of the nuclear moment expressed in nuclear magnetons, to the nuclear spin expressed in units of $\hbar$, is defined to be the dimensionless *nuclear g-factor*, g_I and is related to γ_I by the equation, analogous to 3.19

$$g_I = \gamma_I \frac{2m_p c}{e} \tag{4.4}$$

If the nuclear moment and spin are oppositely directed, as in the case of the neutron, μ_I, γ_I and g_I are negative. The g-factor defined in 4.4 has a value of the order of unity. For some purposes it has become customary to use nuclear g-factors defined in terms of the Bohr magneton and these g-factors are then of the order of $1/2000$. From 4.3

$$\mu_I = \gamma_I I \hbar = g_I I \mu_N \quad \text{(or } g_I I \mu_0) \tag{4.5}$$

d) *the nuclear electric quadrupole moment* Q_I, which measures the deviation of the nuclear charge distribution from a spherical shape; a discussion of this moment, which provides clear evidence for a finite nuclear size, is included in Appendix 3.

4.2   Nuclear effects in optical spectroscopy

4.2.1. NUCLEAR MASS. The energy levels of the hydrogen atom are given in 3.9 in terms of the Rydberg constant R_H for hydrogen. This differs from the Rydberg constant R_∞ for an infinitely heavy nucleus by a factor which corrects for the relative motion of the electron and nucleus. We may write in general

$$R_M = R_\infty \frac{M}{m + M} \tag{4.6}$$

where m is the electron mass and M the nuclear mass for a hydrogen-like atom. It is clear that the term energies and hence the frequencies of the associated spectral lines will depend on the nuclear mass. This will also be true for atoms not of hydrogen type and each separate isotope will lead to its own set of spectral lines. This isotope effect, purely dependent on nuclear mass, is most easily observable for the isotopes of light elements, and permitted the discovery of deuterium by Urey, Brickwedde and Murphy (1932). For the hydrogen isotopes the change in frequency expected for the H_α line ($\tilde{\nu} \approx 15{,}240 \text{ cm}^{-1}$)

observed by Urey and his co-workers, is $\Delta\tilde{\nu}\approx 4$ cm^{-1} or $\Delta\lambda=$ 1·8 A. For heavy atoms this isotope effect becomes small as may be seen by differentiating 4.6:

$$\frac{\Delta\tilde{\nu}}{\tilde{\nu}} = \frac{\Delta R_M}{R_M} \approx \frac{m}{M^2}\Delta M \qquad (4.7)$$

The nuclear mass also affects the rotational and vibrational energies of diatomic molecules (Sect. 3.8.3). The isotopes ^{13}C, ^{15}N, ^{17}O and ^{18}O were discovered by analysis of the electronic bands of carbon, nitrogen and oxygen. Pure rotational spectra, with which much lower frequencies are associated, have been studied by microwave methods (Sect. **4.3**).

4.2.2 NUCLEAR SIZE. A further type of isotope effect depending on nuclear volume arises because the nuclear charge is spread over a finite volume in space. The potential energy of an electron in interaction with the nucleus decreases less rapidly than for a point charge when the wave function begins to penetrate the nucleus; and the energies of the spectral terms are therefore shifted. The shift is seen as a difference between the term values of the several isotopes of a given element. This effect increases with increasing nuclear mass (in contrast with the isotope effect discussed in Sect. 4.2.1) and has been observed in many heavy elements. The results of such observations, like those on the similar phenomenon observed in μ-mesonic atoms (Sect. 11.2.3) provide important evidence on nuclear shapes.

4.2.3 NUCLEAR SPIN AND MAGNETIC MOMENT FROM HYPERFINE STRUCTURE. The total energy of an atom with unpaired electrons, containing a nucleus with spin, includes a term dependent on the interaction of the nuclear magnetic moment with the magnetic moment of the electrons, and with the magnetic field due to the electronic motion in the atom. The effect of externally applied fields is neglected for the present. It is now easy to see, following the method outlined in Sect. **3.5** in discussion of fine structure due to electronic spin–orbit interaction, that the energy levels of the atom are split into a group of states whose number may be determined by the nuclear spin and whose separation is dependent on the nuclear magnetic moment. Spectral lines originating between terms split in this way are seen under high resolution to form a multiplet, usually known as the *hyperfine structure*.

In addition to magnetic interaction, both internal and external electric fields contribute to the energy of the atom by coupling with the nuclear electric quadrupole moment Q_I. If the electric field gradient at the nucleus is q, the corresponding energy is written $b = eqQ_I$. Although quadrupole interactions contribute to many hyperfine structure patterns, they are not observable (Appendix 3) in the important cases in which $I = \frac{1}{2}$ or $J = \frac{1}{2}$. In the present chapter we shall consider for simplicity mainly atomic states of the single electron type, with $J = \frac{1}{2}$, for which $b = 0$.

If the total angular momentum due to electronic motion is **J** ($\neq 0$) and the nuclear spin is **I** ($\neq 0$) then the total mechanical angular momentum is **F** where

$$\mathbf{F} = \mathbf{I} + \mathbf{J} \qquad (4.8)$$

Quantum mechanically this vector sum can be performed in $2I + 1$ ways* if $\mathbf{I} < \mathbf{J}$ and $2J + 1$ ways if $\mathbf{J} < \mathbf{I}$ and each of these arrangements will correspond to a different relative orientation of the comparable vectors **I** and **J**. Each such arrangement also corresponds to a different energy. The internal magnetic field $\mathbf{H}_i$ at the nucleus, of 10^5–10^6 gauss, is proportional to **J** but opposite to this vector in a single electron atom because of the negative sign of the electronic charge. The nuclear magnetic moment $\mathbf{\mu}_I$ is parallel to **I**, but may be positive or negative. The interaction energy

$$W = -(\mathbf{\mu}_I \cdot \mathbf{H}_i) = -|\mathbf{\mu}_I||\mathbf{H}_i| \cos(\mathbf{\mu}_I \mathbf{H}_i)$$

may therefore be written

$$W = +a|\mathbf{I}||\mathbf{J}| \cos(\mathbf{IJ})$$

and introducing the quantum mechanical value for $\cos(\mathbf{IJ})$

$$W = \frac{a}{2}\{F(F+1) - I(I+1) - J(J+1)\} = \frac{aC}{2} \qquad (4.9)$$

The coupling constant a is proportional to the nuclear moment and if this is positive the hyperfine state with the lowest F has

---

* This may be seen by taking the direction Oz (Fig. 3.3) to refer to one of the vectors **I**, **J**.

the lowest W. The coupling constant a also contains the internal atomic field, which must be calculated from the electronic wave function. If this is known, μ_I can be deduced from the observed hyperfine structure intervals. The nuclear spin can in principle be obtained by counting components of the optical line when $I < J$,* but if the components cannot be resolved then the ratio of total intensity associated with transitions to two states of different F may be observed. This ratio is equal to the ratio of the *statistical weights* $2F + 1$ of the two states under normal circumstances when there is no reason for transitions to any particular substate m_F to be favoured.

The energy difference between the two states F and $F - 1$ is, according to 4.9, equal to aF; this interval is known as the hyperfine structure separation or *hfs splitting* ΔW and the corresponding $\Delta \nu$ is typically a few thousand Mc/s. The optical hyperfine structure of one of the sodium D-lines is shown in Fig. 4.1a. In this case $I = \frac{3}{2}$, $J = \frac{3}{2}$ for the initial state and $I = \frac{3}{2}$, $J = \frac{1}{2}$ for the final state. The components of the line are determined by the selection rules

$$\Delta F = \pm 1, 0 \qquad \Delta J = \pm 1, 0 \qquad \Delta l = \pm 1$$

and the magnitudes of the hfs splittings are shown. For the state with $I = J = \frac{3}{2}$ the intervals should be in the ratio $1:2:3$; deviations from such a regular sequence in the spectrum of europium gave the first indication of the existence of the electric quadrupole moments and now provide one method for the determination of these quantities. The hfs splitting of the $^2S_{\frac{1}{2}}$ ground state of hydrogen ($I = J = \frac{1}{2}$; $F = 0, 1$) is the source of the 21 cm 'galactic' $F = 1 \rightarrow F = 0$ radiation observed astronomically. The hyperfine separation in this case is simply the difference in energy between the states in which the nuclear moment and internal atomic field are parallel and antiparallel.

If an external magnetic field H_0 is applied to an atom with nuclear spin Zeeman effects occur in the hyperfine structure and may be discussed as in the electronic case (Sect. **3.5**). In weak fields the coupling between **I** and **J** persists and the resultant vector **F** orients in the field H_0. Each of the $2F + 1$

---

* See for example, K. L. van der Sluis and J. R. McNally, *J. opt. Soc. Amer.*, **45**, 65, 1955.

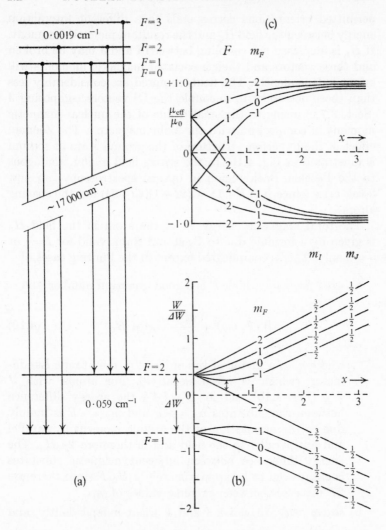

Fig. 4.1

a) Hyperfine structure of one of the sodium D-lines ($^2P_{3/2} \to {}^2S_{1/2}$).

b) Energy levels of the sodium atom in weak and intermediate magnetic fields. The Zeeman splitting of the hyperfine levels of the ground state is shown in units of $\varDelta W$ as a function of the quantity $x \approx 2\mu_0 H_0/\varDelta W$. A radiofrequency transition used in the 'flop-in' technique of magnetic resonance (Sect. 4.4.4) is also shown.

c) Effective magnetic moments of the sodium atom in the states shown in 4.1b.

permitted orientations corresponds to a different interaction
energy between the field H_0 and the resultant magnetic moment.
If H_0 is increased the coupling between **I** and **J** may be broken
and these vectors and their associated magnetic moments will
orient independently. The fields required are considerably less
than those necessary to uncouple the **LS** vectors composing **J**
(Sect. 3.7.2) owing to the small value of the nuclear magnetic
moment in comparison with the Bohr magneton. The Zeeman
effect of the hyperfine structure of the ground state of sodium
is illustrated in Fig. 4.1b. In the strong field region, analogous
to the Paschen-Back region in optical spectroscopy, no new
levels arise (since $\sum (2F+1) = (2I+1)(2J+1)$) but the spacing
alters.

The total magnetic energy W of the atom in the field H_0
is given by a formula due to Breit and Rabi, valid for $I = \frac{1}{2}$ or
$J = \frac{1}{2}$ only. This is complicated except in the limiting cases of

a) *weak fields* for which F is a good quantum number and

$$W(F, m_F) = \frac{aC}{2} - m_F g_F \mu_0 H_0 \qquad (4.10)$$

where g_F is a factor of the order of g_J the atomic Landé-
factor (which is often negative). For atoms with J
$= \frac{1}{2}$ (Fig. 4.1b) and for $F = I + \frac{1}{2}$ the energy difference
between the substates $m_F = +F$ and $m_F = -F$ is mainly
due to the orientation of the atomic moment μ_J parallel
and antiparallel to the field and is therefore $2\mu_J H_0$. The
energy difference between adjacent magnetic substates
is easily seen to be approximately $\mu_J H_0 / F$ since there are
$2F$ intervals between extreme values of m_F.

b) *strong fields*, in which **I** and **J** orient independently, and

$$W(m_I, m_J) = am_I m_J - m_I g_I \mu_0 H_0 - m_J g_J \mu_0 H_0 \qquad (4.11)$$

in which the first term measures the interaction between
nuclear and atomic moments and the other two give the
energy of these moments individually in the external
field. The nuclear term is usually negligible since g_I
$\approx 1/2000\, g_J$.

The Breit-Rabi formula may be used to calculate the effective magnetic moment

$$\mu_{\text{eff}} = -\frac{\partial W}{\partial H} \qquad (4.12)$$

of an atom in a magnetic field. The result for $I = \frac{3}{2}$, $J = \frac{1}{2}$ is shown in Fig. 4.1c; at high fields all moments tend to μ_0 since the nuclear and atomic moments are uncoupled and the former is negligible in comparison with the latter.

Experiments in which use is made of atomic moments

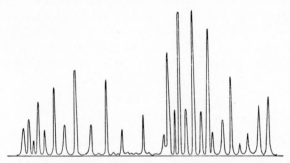

Fig. 4.2. Intensity of lines observed in $\lambda = 4650$ A band of $^3\text{He}_2$ (Dieke and Robinson, *Phys. Rev.*, **80**, 4, 1950).

usually give the interaction constants a and b in the first place. Evaluation of the moments μ_I and Q_I then necessitates adequate knowledge of electronic wave functions.

A very clear demonstration of the energy differences which arise when a nuclear moment orients in an internal field is provided by the Mössbauer effect (Sect. 13.6.3). By use of this effect the hyperfine structure of a *nuclear transition* can be observed by a resonant scattering technique of high precision. Values for the internal field H_i and for nuclear magnetic and electric moments can be obtained in favourable cases.

4.2.4 NUCLEAR SPIN AND STATISTICS FROM MOLECULAR SPECTRA. Successive lines of the electronic (emission) band spectra of homonuclear diatomic molecules (Sect. 3.8.4) are found to show an alternation in intensity. Fig. 4.2 shows the intensities observed in the spectrum of the light helium isotope ^3He.

This effect can be explained by an extension of the symmetry considerations already used in the discussion of ortho and para hydrogen (Sect. 3.8.4). If the nuclear spin is I, there are $2I + 1$ substates, with respect to an axis of quantization, for each nucleus. Combining these, there are $(2I + 1)^2$ spin functions of the type

$$\psi_s = \psi_{m'}(A)\psi_m(B) \tag{4.13}$$

with individual magnetic quantum numbers m, m' for the pair of nuclei. Since the nuclei are identical the probability function $|\psi_s|^2$ must not change on interchange of particles and the form 4.13 is therefore unsatisfactory. Instead we must construct a linear combination of pairs of functions of this type, as already used in the case of the helium atom for electrons, and in the case of ortho and para hydrogen. The suitable combinations are

$$\psi_{ss} = \psi_m(A)\psi_{m'}(B) + \psi_m(B)\psi_{m'}(A)$$

and $$\psi_{sa} = \psi_m(A)\psi_{m'}(B) - \psi_m(B)\psi_{m'}(A) \tag{4.14}$$

Since two functions of the type 4.13 combine to give two of type 4.14, there are still $(2I + 1)^2$ spin functions altogether. Of these $2I + 1$ have $m = m'$ and are obviously symmetrical in spin. Of the remaining $2I(2I + 1)$ functions with $m \neq m'$, half are of type ψ_{ss} and half of type ψ_{sa}. These are respectively symmetrical and antisymmetrical. In all, therefore there are

$$(I + 1)(2I + 1) \text{ symmetrical nuclear spin states}$$
$$I(2I + 1) \text{ antisymmetrical nuclear spin states} \tag{4.15}$$

The symmetrical spin states belong to the ortho form of the molecule and the antisymmetrical states to the para form; for hydrogen ($I = \frac{1}{2}$) the ratio of ortho to para states is 3 to 1.

In a molecule, rotational motion is in general present, and this causes the nuclei to change positions. The wave function for rotational motion, as discussed in Sect. 3.8.4, is symmetric or antisymmetric according as J is even or odd. If the nuclei have half-integral spin (Fermi-Dirac statistics) the total *nuclear* wave function $\psi_r\psi_s$ must be antisymmetrical and therefore the ortho molecules have only antisymmetrical *rotational* states and the para molecules symmetrical rotations. For particles obeying the Einstein-Bose statistics the situation is reversed.

From 4.15 we then obtain the following relative probabilities of even and odd rotational states

$$\text{Fermi–Dirac statistics}\quad \frac{\text{even } J}{\text{odd } J} = \frac{I}{I+1} \qquad (4.16)$$

$$\text{Einstein–Bose statistics}\quad \frac{\text{even } J}{\text{odd } J} = \frac{I+1}{I} \qquad (4.17)$$

These statistical weights modify the normal Boltzmann distribution of molecules between the rotational states in thermal equilibrium.

The selection rules for electric dipole radiative transitions, as given in Sect. 3.8.3, now imply that *homonuclear diatomic molecules exhibit no pure rotational, or rotational-vibrational spectrum.* This is because the change of rotational quantum number $\Delta J = \pm 1$ required in this case to provide the angular momentum removed by the radiation would result in a transition between symmetrical and antisymmetrical spin states. Such a transition is very improbable and the ortho and para forms should be regarded as non-combining. In an electronic emission band however, transitions take place between the rotational fine-structure levels of electronic energy states and the angular momentum and symmetry changes can in many cases be provided by the electronic change. Molecular symmetries will not be discussed here*; we note only that a spectrum of the type shown in Fig. 4.2 requires transitions with $\Delta J = 0$, and ± 1. The lines originating from a state of given J have an intensity proportional to the population, or statistical weight, of the state and from 4.16 and 4.17 it is apparent that the intensities of successive lines will stand in the ratio $I + 1/I$. In the case of the ^{3}He spectrum shown in Fig. 4.2 the ratio is $3/1$, indicating a spin $I = \frac{1}{2}$. It is also found, from knowledge of the molecular wave functions, that it is the odd J states in this case which are enhanced; the ^{3}He nuclei therefore obey Fermi–Dirac statistics.

Band-spectrum analysis therefore determines both spin and statistics and it has been applied for several of the lighter nuclei, particularly when atomic hyperfine effects are difficult to observe. Strikingly clear evidence is obtained for nuclei such as

---

* See Refs. 4.4 and 4.8.

^{4}He, ^{12}C or ^{14}C and even A, even Z nuclei in general. In these cases the states of odd J and the corresponding lines are absent, which indicates that $I = 0$ and that the nuclei obey Einstein-Bose statistics.

4.3 Nuclear effects in microwave spectroscopy

4.3.1. GASEOUS ABSORPTION SPECTROSCOPY. The microwave region of the electromagnetic spectrum ($0\cdot1$–$10\cdot0$ cm^{-1} approximately) is particularly suitable for studying rotational transitions in fairly heavy molecules. This is because of the availability of accurate frequency measuring apparatus and easily controllable klystron oscillators. The most useful technique is that of gaseous absorption spectroscopy, although similar effects may be found with solids and liquids; observations are made of the variation of the absorption coefficient of gas in a cell as the frequency of the incident radiation is varied. The structure visible in the absorption near the frequency of a rotational transition is a hyperfine effect but is not directly due to the nuclear magnetic moment. Molecular magnetic fields are small and the magnetic hyperfine structure is not observable because of collision broadening; the nuclear spins do however orient in the normal way in the internal field. Energy differences then arise because of the interaction of the nuclear electric quadrupole moment with the molecular electric field gradient. Since the axis of the quadrupole moment is fixed with respect to the nuclear spin axis, the *number* of hyperfine states is directly determined by the *nuclear spin* but their spacing is *not* determined by the nuclear magnetic moment. The electric quadrupole moment may be found if the molecular electric field can be calculated.

Nuclear spins have been determined by this method for ^{10}B, ^{33}S, ^{35}Cl and several other nuclei using suitable molecules consisting mainly of atoms with spin zero nuclei. The lighter, simpler molecules have rotational frequencies lying in the infra-red and cannot be studied by microwave methods since these techniques do not extend much above a frequency of 10 cm^{-1} (300,000 Mc/s).

It is also possible to observe the Zeeman splitting of the hyperfine lines in a given rotational transition. The energy differences arising in an applied external field H_0 are due to the nuclear magnetic moment and the resulting shape of a given hyperfine component of the absorption spectrum (e.g. $J=2$, $F=\frac{9}{2} \leftarrow J=1$, $F=\frac{9}{2}$ in a particular case) leads to a value for μ_I.

There are distinct rotational absorption lines for each isotopic species and microwave spectroscopy can be used for nuclear mass determination as a method of high precision. The method can be developed experimentally into one of high sensitivity and observable hyperfine patterns are obtainable with quantities of material as small as 1 μg. This makes possible a study of many radioactive isotopes produced by cyclotron and pile bombardments as well as ordinary stable nuclei.

4.3.2 ELECTRON PARAMAGNETIC RESONANCE. Fig. 4.1b shows the energy levels of an atom with $J=\frac{1}{2}$ and $I=\frac{3}{2}$ in a magnetic field H_0. If this diagram is continued to a magnetic field value of 5000 gauss ($x \approx 8$) the spacing between the group of levels with $m_J = \frac{1}{2}$ and $m_J = -\frac{1}{2}$ becomes $W_{\frac{1}{2}} - W_{-\frac{1}{2}} \approx 7 \Delta W \approx$ 0.4 cm^{-1}. This corresponds to a microwave quantum and absorption of energy in the microwave band, with reversal of the atomic moment, should be possible.

This possibility is realized most conveniently in the solid state. Many paramagnetic ions in crystalline solids behave as if their magnetic effect is due to a single electron spin and are characterized by a quantum number $S = \frac{1}{2}$. If their nuclei have a spin I, a hyperfine splitting arises, as in Fig. 4.1b, due to the internal interaction between nuclear and electronic moments. In an external field H_0 each of the two electronic levels, $m_S = \pm \frac{1}{2}$, is split into $2I+1$ hyperfine levels. Microwave absorption at a frequency $\nu_e \approx 2\mu_0 H_0/h$ reverses the electron spin direction with respect to the applied field H_0, and takes place between substates with the same value of m_I, because of the small interaction of the nuclear moment with the microwave field. For a given microwave frequency, $2I+1$ absorption peaks are then found as the field H_0 is increased. This is shown in Fig. 4.3b; a typical paramagnetic resonance absorption apparatus is shown in Fig. 4.3a.

The nuclear spin I may be found by counting the absorption peaks and the nuclear moment μ_I may be obtained from the spacing between them if the internal field can be calculated. The method is extremely sensitive and has been widely used,

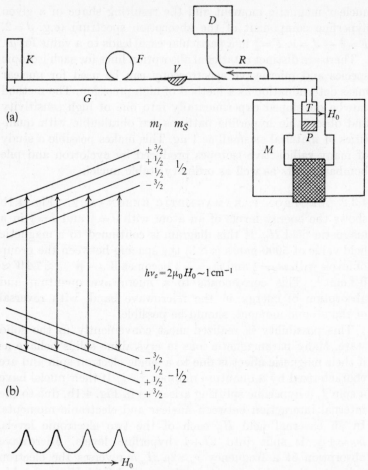

Fig. 4.3

a) Paramagnetic resonance absorption apparatus. K is a klystron which generates a microwave of constant frequency in the waveguide G. The specimen P is placed in a resonant cavity T mounted in the field H_0 of a magnet M. R is a directional coupler which conducts the signal reflected from T to the crystal detector D. The signal level is controlled by the wavemeter F and attenuator V. The detector output is recorded at a fixed frequency as the magnetic field is varied. Frequencies of 3×10^4 Mc/s and fields H_0 of 5000 gauss are typical (Van Wieringen, *Philips Tech. Review*, **19**, 301, 1958).

b) Energy levels of a paramagnetic ion with spin $S = \frac{1}{2}$ and nuclear spin $I = \frac{3}{2}$ in a field H_0. Absorption lines, corresponding to $\Delta m_I = 0$, are indicated (Bleaney and Stevens, *Rep. progr. Phys.*, **16**, 108, 1953).

not only for determinations of nuclear quantities but for investigations of the solid state. The mechanism by which spin reversal is achieved in electron paramagnetic resonance is the same as in the case of nuclear paramagnetic resonance and is discussed in Sect. 4.4.2.

4.4 Nuclear effects in radiofrequency spectroscopy

4.4.1 ORIENTATION AND PRECESSION OF NUCLEAR MAG-NETIC MOMENTS. In Sect. 3.5 it was shown that an atom with a permanent magnetic moment in a free state would orient in a uniform magnetic field and that the permitted orientations were specified by the quantum mechanical values of the magnetic quantum number m_J giving the component of total angular momentum along the magnetic field axis. This orientation was the basis of the Stern–Gerlach experiment on a collision free beam of atoms for the determination of magnetic moments of the order of μ_0, the Bohr magneton. Exactly similar orientation effects are observed with nuclei possessing a magnetic moment, and experiments of the Stern–Gerlach type can be adapted to measure nuclear moments and to indicate nuclear spins, although the deflections are scaled down by a factor of $\mu_N/\mu_0 = m/m_p = 1/1836$ compared with those obtained in the electronic case.

In an assembly of atoms in which the magnetic effects of the electronic shells may be disregarded (e.g. for completed shells or sub-shells with $S = L = 0$) the nuclei, with spin I, will have $2I + 1$ orientations β with respect to the lines of force of an external magnetic field H_0. (Sect. 4.1.) Classically the magnetic field H_0 exerts a couple on the nucleus due to interaction with the dipole moment μ_I, but owing to the collinear angular momentum, the classically expected motion is a precession of the spin vector about the field direction (axis Oz) with an angular velocity

$$\omega_0 = \frac{\text{Couple}}{\text{Angular momentum}} = \frac{|\mu_I| \sin \beta H_0}{|\mathbf{I}| \sin \beta} = \gamma_I H_0$$

$$= \frac{g_I \mu_0 H_0}{\hbar} \tag{4.18}$$

as may be seen from Fig. 4.4 and eqq. (4.3) and (4.5). This is the angular velocity of *Larmor precession*; it is independent of the orientation of the magnetic moment with respect to the z-axis, i.e. it is the same for any of the $2I+1$ orientations of **I** permitted quantum-mechanically. For a free proton the value of γ_p (see

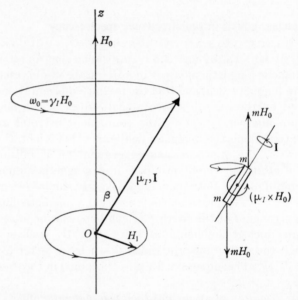

Fig. 4.4. Precession of nuclear moments. The inset diagram represents the classical case of a spinning magnet in a steady field. If a field H_1 is applied in the plane yOx and caused to rotate with angular velocity ω_0, a torque on μ_I is maintained and the angle β alters.

Fundamental Constants, p. 728) leads to an angular velocity of precession

$$\omega_0 = 2\cdot6753 \times 10^4 H_0 \text{ radians sec}^{-1}$$

or a frequency of precession.

$$\nu_0 = \frac{\omega_0}{2\pi} = 4\cdot258 \times 10^3 H_0 \text{ c/s} \qquad (4.19)$$

For magnetic fields H_0 of a few thousand gauss, ν_0 lies in the radiofrequency range of about 20 Mc/s.

An interesting example of the use of nuclear precession is

found in the work of Hillman, Stafford and Whitehead* on the polarization of high energy neutron beams. In these experiments it was at first thought necessary to move a rather complex counting apparatus round a target to investigate asymmetries of scattering. Later it was found much simpler to leave the counting apparatus in position and to rotate the direction of the neutron spin by passing the beam through a solenoid of length l producing a field H_0. For neutrons of 100 MeV energy the spin vector is rotated through an angle of 90° for $lH_0 = 1\cdot33 \times 10^6$ gauss cm. The same method was used by Pidd and Crane† in a direct determination of the gyromagnetic ratio of the free electron.

4.4.2 NUCLEAR PARAMAGNETISM AND NUCLEAR RESONANCE. The energy associated with the nuclear precessional motion is essentially the potential energy of the nuclear dipole in the field H_0, i.e.

$$
\begin{aligned}
W &= -(\boldsymbol{\mu}_I \cdot \mathbf{H}_0) = -|\mathbf{I}|\,\omega_0 \cos \beta \\
&= -m_I \hbar \omega_0 \\
&= -m_I h \nu_0 \quad \text{from (4.2) and (4.18)} \quad (4.20)
\end{aligned}
$$

The $(2I + 1)$ allowed orientations of $\boldsymbol{\mu}_I$ and $\mathbf{I}$ thus define a set of energy levels of spacing

$$
h\nu_0 = g_I \mu_0 H_0 = \frac{\mu_I H_0}{I} \text{ from (4.5) and (4.18)}
$$

If all these levels were equally populated in an assembly of nuclei, no resultant magnetization would be observed when the field H_0 was applied. In fact the populations are not equal because of the Boltzmann factor $e^{-W/kT}$ which, if there is some thermal contact between the nuclear spin system and its environment, increases the relative number of nuclei in the lower energy states. The observed magnetization can now be

---

* P. Hillman, G. H. Stafford and C. Whitehead, *Nuovo Cimento*, 4, 67, 1956.

† W. H. Louisell, R. W. Pidd and H. R. Crane, *Phys. Rev.*, 94, 7, 1954; A. A. Schupp, R. W. Pidd and H. R. Crane, *Phys. Rev.*, 121, 1, 1961.

evaluated exactly as in the case of a paramagnetic gas and the susceptibility is given by the Langevin–Curie formula

$$\chi_I = \frac{N|\mu_I|^2}{3kT} = \frac{N\gamma_I^2\hbar^2 I(I+1)}{3kT} \quad \text{from (4.3) and (4.1)} \quad (4.21)$$

where N is the number of nuclei per unit volume, k is Boltzmann's constant, and T is the absolute temperature. Since $\mu_I \approx 10^{-3}\mu_0$ this susceptibility is only about 10^{-6} of the usual static susceptibilities observed for atoms and is much too small to be determined directly with accuracy although the nuclear paramagnetic effect has been demonstrated for solid hydrogen. The gyromagnetic ratio γ_I however can be determined extremely accurately by use of a resonance principle introduced by Rabi, Zacharias, Millman and Kusch,* and the success of this method depends on the existence of the finite nuclear magnetization shown by 4.21.

To see how the resonance principle works, suppose that a small magnetic field H_1 is applied in the (xy) plane (Fig. 4.4) and allowed to rotate with angular velocity ω, i.e.

$$H_x = H_1 \cos \omega t \qquad H_y = H_1 \sin \omega t \qquad (4.22)$$

The effect produced by this field can be described in two ways. Classically we can consider the interaction of H_1 with the resultant magnetization of a macroscopic sample of material. This interaction is a torque tending to alter β. If the rotation of the field is in the sense opposite to the precession of the resultant magnetic vector about H_0 or of a different frequency there is no recurrent effect, but if the sense is the same and $\omega = \omega_0$ (resonance), energy is exchanged between the field H_1 and the motion and the angle β alters. Quantum mechanically we consider a single nucleus and envisage the absorption from the field of a quantum of resonance radiation which causes a transition (upward or downward) between the levels defined by 4.20. From 4.20 the transition between two adjacent levels corresponds to a unit change of magnetic quantum number, i.e.

$$\Delta m = \pm 1$$

---

* I. I. Rabi, J. R. Zacharias, S. Millman and P. Kusch, *Phys. Rev.*, **53**, 318, 1938; **55**, 526, 1939.

Since the transition only alters the magnetic moment of the system, it may be classified as a magnetic dipole ($M1$) interaction.

On either picture of the process there is a reorientation of the nuclear moments which can be detected as a reaction in the external radiofrequency circuit supplying the field H_1 or by direct induction effects in a pickup coil. The result of the energy exchange is to reduce the magnetization given by 4.21, i.e. to equalize the populations of adjacent levels; alternatively we may regard the energy supplied by H_1 as raising the 'spin temperature' of the system. The observable effect therefore saturates and after removal of the resonance field H_1 a finite time (relaxation time) must elapse before the original magnetization is re-established by thermal contact with the normal temperature lattice in which the nuclei are immersed. A study of these relaxation times gives important information on the structure of solids and liquids.

Historically nuclear magnetic resonance was first observed by Rabi and his collaborators using an atomic beam. It was suggested earlier however by Gorter* that nuclear reorientation effects should be detectable in ordinary material. This was demonstrated in 1946 by two groups of workers whose methods well illustrate the two ways of regarding the phenomenon, and will now be described. These macroscopic methods both depend upon the fact that although the nuclear magnetization is very small, a sufficiently large sample will provide a measurable effect at resonance. The first experiments were made with protons, which have the largest known g-factor and the known spin $I = \frac{1}{2}$. In this case magnetic resonance in a field H_0 corresponds to reversal of the spin direction and the frequency ν for resonance is given directly by the energy equation

$$h\nu = 2\mu_p H_0 \qquad (4.23)$$

which also follows from 4.18.

4.4.3 OBSERVATION OF NUCLEAR MAGNETIC RESONANCE ABSORPTION.

a) In the *nuclear induction experiment* of Bloch, Hansen and

---

* C. J. Gorter, *Physica*, **3**, 995, 1936.

Packard* represented in Fig. 4.5 a sample of a suitable dia-
magnetic material such as water is placed in a steady field
$H_z = H_0$. An inducing coil surrounds the sample and provides an
oscillatory field

$$H_x = 2H_1 \cos \omega t$$

This field is equivalent to two oppositely rotating fields of the
form 4.22, and the field rotating in the direction opposite to

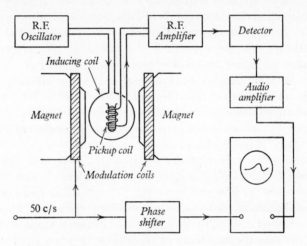

Fig. 4.5. Nuclear induction apparatus (Ref. 4.5).

that of the precession about H_0 may be disregarded. A pickup
coil with its axis at right angles to both H_0 and H_1 (and therefore relatively insensitive to direct pickup from the field H_1)
is used to detect the reorientation of the magnetization vector.
The output voltage of the pickup coil is amplified and displayed
as the y-deflection on an oscilloscope. It is convenient in
practice to modulate the field H_0 by a small 50-cycle field so
that the resultant magnetic field sweeps through the resonance
value $H_0 = \omega/\gamma_I$; the 50-cycle modulation can then provide the
time base for the oscilloscope.

The observation of a signal in a nuclear induction experiment
shows that the applied frequency ω is in resonance with

---

* F. Bloch, W. W. Hansen and M. Packard, *Phys. Rev.*, **69**, 127,
1946; **70**, 474, 1946.

the Larmor frequency of the protons in the solution in the applied field H_0 and that reorientation of the macroscopic nuclear magnetic moment is taking place. The shape of the signal depends on the relaxation time for the protons in the particular solution used and on the internal fields in the specimen. In the original experiment a sample of volume about 1·5 c.c. was used and with a frequency of 7·765 Mc/s the resonance field was $H = 1826$ gauss and signals of about a milliwatt were obtained on a 10-turn receiver coil.

b) In the *nuclear resonance absorption experiment* of Purcell, Torrey and Pound,* the sample forms part of a resonant circuit and the transmission of radiofrequency power through the circuit is measured as a function of a steady magnetic field H_0 applied to the sample. The radiofrequency oscillatory field H_1 developed by the circuit is at right angles to H_0. At the nuclear resonance field $H_0 = \omega/\gamma_I$ the extra absorption of power by the precessing nuclei lowers the Q-value of the resonant circuit, and a sharp change in the output power may be detected.

In the original experiment a cavity resonator filled with solid paraffin was used, and the resonant frequency was 29·8 Mc/s. The output from the cavity was balanced against a signal derived from the input in a bridge circuit, so that the resonant absorption could be clearly displayed. As the field H_0 was varied through the nuclear resonance value of 7100 gauss (conveniently by 50-cycle modulation), a 50% change in output power occurred. A typical signal is shown in Plate 5.

The elegant methods outlined in this section essentially measure nuclear gyromagnetic ratios, usually in terms of the accurately known value for the proton. If the spin number I is known, then the nuclear magnetic moment μ_I may be obtained in absolute units. If I is not known then the gyromagnetic ratio yields alternatively the nuclear g-factor by Eq. 4.4. The spin I may in fact be found from the resonance experiment itself if there are internal electric fields which disturb the even spacing of the magnetic substates. There is then a fine structure of $2I$ lines instead of a single resonance frequency. The induction method is able to give the sign of the

---

* E. M. Purcell, H. Torrey and R. V. Pound, *Phys. Rev.*, **69**, 37, 1946; **73**, 679, 1948.

nuclear magnetic moment if a rotating field, with a known sense of rotation, is applied from two coils with their axes set at 90°.

The relative simplicity of the apparatus required makes nuclear resonance very suitable for precision measurements of magnetic fields and many magnetometers have been based on the principle. The methods require fairly large quantities of material and many interesting relaxation effects due to the interaction of the nuclear spin system and the solid lattice have been studied. This forms a large subject in itself; for the purposes of nuclear physics, rather more information has been obtained from nuclear magnetic resonance in matter in such a state that relaxation effects may be entirely disregarded, i.e. in molecular and atomic beams.

4.4.4 NUCLEAR MOMENTS FROM MOLECULAR AND ATOMIC BEAM EXPERIMENTS. Fig. 4.6a shows a typical molecular beam apparatus of the type used by Stern and Gerlach to determine atomic magnetic moments. The essential parts are a source of atoms or molecules, a magnet providing an inhomogeneous deflecting field, a detector and a vacuum envelope maintained at such a low pressure that the beam is essentially collision free. If molecules such as H_2 or D_2, with no resultant magnetic moment due to the electronic motion are used, the deflection observed on the detector when the magnetic field is switched on is due either to the nuclear moments or to moments associated with the rotation of the molecule. Both effects are small and slow molecules and long magnetic fields are essential, but Stern* and his collaborators were able in 1933 to make the first measurements of the proton moment by this method.

Deflection patterns dependent on nuclear spin may also be observed in some cases with atomic beams, when electronic moments mainly determine the displacement (since $\mu_0 \approx 10^3 \mu_N$). The most successful method of experiment, known as the *zero moment technique* depends on the fact that the effective magnetic moment μ_{eff} vanishes at certain values of the applied field H_0 for nuclear spins greater than $I = \frac{1}{2}$, as may be seen in Fig. 4.1c.

---

* R. Frisch and O. Stern, *Zeits. fur Physik*, **85**, 4, 1933.

In an apparatus of the sort shown in Fig. 4.6a, equipped with a detector of extent comparable with the beam width, the observed beam will have maximum intensity for the zero-moment values of the magnetic field H_0. From these values of H_0 the nuclear moment can be found; typical results are shown in Fig. 4.6b.

(a)

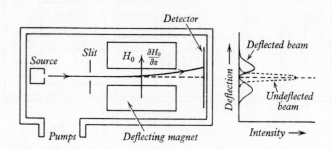

(b)

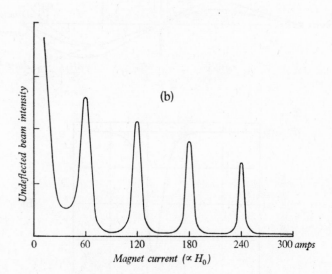

Fig. 4.6

a) Direct determination of atomic moments by the Stern-Gerlach method.

b) Zero-moment method for a nucleus with spin $9/2$. The undeflected beam is observed with a narrow detector as a function of deflecting field H_0 (Ref. 4.5).

The most important development of the technique of molecular beams is the application of the nuclear magnetic resonance principle of Rabi, Zacharias, Millman and Kusch, as illustrated in Fig. 4.7a. In this apparatus neutral atoms or molecules with

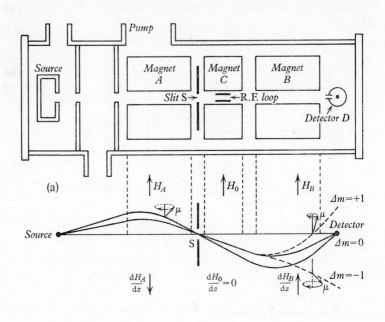

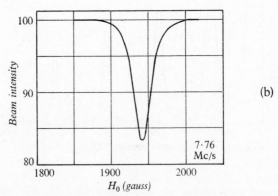

Fig. 4.7

a) Molecular beam magnetic resonance apparatus (Ref. 4.5).
b) Resonance curve for the ^{19}F nucleus observed in NaF (Rabi *et al.*, *Phys. Rev.*, **55**, 526, 1939).

zero electronic angular momentum (atomic state $J = 0$ or molecular Σ state), but with a magnetic moment μ_I associated with nuclear spin, leave a source as shown and enter an inhomogeneous magnetic field A. The magnetic moment vector orients with respect to the lines of force of the field A, and because the field is inhomogeneous the particles are deflected to an extent depending on the resolved part of μ_I. Those with certain suitable initial angles of travel will be able to pass through the collimating slit S and be brought to a focus on a detector D by a second field B in which H_B is parallel to H_A, but the gradient is reversed. If a steady *homogeneous* field H_0 is applied at C, parallel to the fields A and B, there is no resulting change in the magnetic state of the beam but a set of energy levels spaced by $h\nu_0$, where ν_0 is the Larmor frequency, is defined, as discussed in Sect. 4.4.2. A C-field of a few thousand gauss is sufficient to decouple the nuclei of a molecule so that they may be regarded as free. If now a radio-frequency magnetic field H_1 is produced by a coil parallel or perpendicular to the magnetic field H_0 there will be transitions between the energy levels when the resonance condition $\nu = \nu_0$ is fulfilled. If H_1 is perpendicular to H_0 transitions with $\Delta m_I = \pm 1$ may take place and the magnetic state of the beam is altered, i.e. the effective moment changes. The molecules which have suffered transitions enter the field B with an effective moment different from its value at field A and are not refocused at the detector (see Fig. 4.7a) so that the intensity drops. At resonance a large fraction of the molecules may undergo transitions with a suitably designed apparatus. The transmitted beam intensity is measured as a function of H_0 or the radiofrequency ν and resonance dips of the form shown in Fig. 4.7b are obtained. The detector D may be a surface ionization instrument in which incident molecules (or atoms) with low ionization potentials are ionized by impact on a heated tungsten wire and are then detected electrically. In the important case of hydrogen, a less sensitive detector depending on the change of temperature of a fine wire due to accumulation of gas molecules in a surrounding chamber was used.

Molecular beam experiments have yielded many nuclear g-values. The sign of the magnetic moment may be obtained if a magnetic field H_1 rotating in one direction is used instead of an oscillatory field. Deviations of the observed pattern of resonances from expectation may be due to electric quadrupole interactions and the first evidence for the existence of an electric quadrupole moment of the deuteron was obtained in this way.

The magnetic resonance method has also been extensively used with atomic beams, for which much larger deflections are obtained since the magnetic moments are of the order of μ_0. In certain forms of the apparatus the magnet B and the detector may be set to respond only to atoms which have undergone a particular type of transition, which reverses the electron spin, in the radio-frequency field ('*flop-in*' method). The nuclear spin may easily be deduced from weak field observations with such an apparatus for atoms in a $^2S_{1/2}$ state. In this case the Zeeman splitting, from 4.10, is $\mu_0 H_0/hF = 1{\cdot}40 H_0/F$ Mc/s. For a given field the frequency is set to a sequence of values indicated by this method until 'flop-in' transitions with $\Delta F = 0, \Delta m_F = \pm 1$ are observed; F is then determined and thence $I\ (= F - \frac{1}{2})$. A suitable transition is shown in Fig. 4.1b. When the nuclear spin has been determined the hyperfine structure splitting ΔW may be found by observations at higher fields. The nuclear magnetic moment (and electric quadrupole moment) may be deduced from the observed splitting if electronic wave functions are well enough known. This general method has been widely applied to the measurements of spins and moments of radioactive isotopes, for which detection methods are especially sensitive. A mixture of several active isotopes can be studied by setting the apparatus for a particular spin I and observing the decay curve of the activity collected at this setting. Fig. 4.8 shows the results of an investigation of the light caesium isotopes by this method. The observed nuclear spins can also be associated with a particular mass number by including an ionizer and a mass spectrometer in the detection equipment.

4.4.5 NEUTRON MOMENT MEASUREMENT. The molecular beam technique was adapted by Alvarez and Bloch[*] to measure the magnetic moment of the neutron. Use was made of the magnetic scattering of slow neutrons, as a result of which a slow neutron beam in passage through a strongly magnetized iron plate becomes partially polarized. The resulting spin

---

[*] L. Alvarez and F. Bloch, *Phys. Rev.*, **57**, 111, 1940.

distribution is then favourable for easy passage through a
second similarly magnetized plate. If however a radiofrequency
field is applied in a steady field H_0 between the two magnetized
plates the beam will tend to become depolarized at the resonance field, since the number of 'upward' and 'downward'

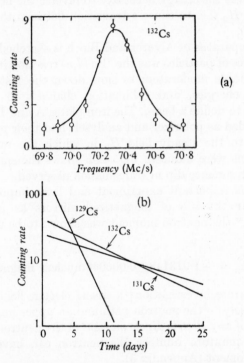

Fig. 4.8. Determination of spins and moments of radioactive caesium
isotopes by the 'flop-in' method.
a) Activity of ^{132}Cs collected as a function of frequency for a fixed
magnetic field.
b) Decay of activity of Cs isotopes collected at frequencies set for the
appropriate spins.
(From W. A. Nierenberg *et al.*, *Phys. Rev.*, **112**, 186, 1958; see also E. H.
Bellamy and K. F. Smith, *Phil. Mag.*, **44**, 33, 1953.)

transitions will be proportional to the number of neutrons
with spins in the corresponding states. Any reduction in
polarization will result in a drop of transmission of the beam
through the *two* magnetized plates, and observation of such a

drop may be used to determine the resonance field H_0 for a given radiofrequency. The neutron moment then follows from an equation similar to that already given for proton resonance,

$$h\nu = 2\mu_n H_0 \qquad (4.24)$$

which gives the energy necessary to reverse the neutron spin in the field H_0 (i.e. to cause a transition between the states with $m_I = \pm \frac{1}{2}$).

The apparatus of Alvarez and Bloch is sketched in Fig. 4.9a. The source of particles was the ^{9}Be (d,n) reaction in a cyclotron, with suitable moderators to slow down the fast neutrons to thermal energies, and collimating channels in hydrogenous material to define a beam. The iron plates A and B, which may be regarded as polarizer and analyser, had their magnetization parallel to the steady field H_0 in which the radiofrequency transitions were induced. Fig. 4.9b shows the small but quite definite resonance dip in transmission observed.

By this important experiment and later improvements, in particular the use of magnetized mirrors as polarizer and analyser,* the neutron moment was shown to be negative, and of value

$$\mu_n = -1\cdot913148 \pm 0\cdot000066 \text{ nuclear magnetons}$$

In a separate investigation† a strong electric field was applied transversely to the neutron path and an upper limit was set to the size of any *electric dipole moment* of the neutron. If parity is a good quantum number the neutron can have no electric dipole moment (Appendix 3).

4.4.6 THE DOUBLE RESONANCE TECHNIQUE. An interesting method of investigating excited atomic states, which can provide nuclear information, was introduced by Kastler and Brossel.‡ The method is essentially a paramagnetic resonance

---

* V. W. Cohen, N. R. Corngold and N. F. Ramsey, *Phys. Rev.*, **104**, 283, 1956.

† E. M. Purcell and N. F. Ramsey, *Phys. Rev.*, **78**, 807, 1950.

‡ Reviews are given by A. Kastler, *Proc. phys. Soc.*, **67**, 853, 1954, and by G. W. Series, *Rep. progr. Phys.*, **22**, 280, 1959.

experiment on electrons in excited states, and as in ordinary paramagnetic resonance, hyperfine effects may be observed. The technique may be illustrated for the sodium atom, in

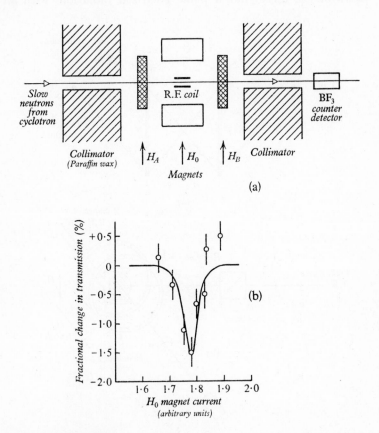

Fig. 4.9. Determination of magnetic moment of neutron by magnetic resonance method.

a) Schematic of apparatus.

b) Transmission dip at resonance obtained by Alvarez and Bloch (*Phys. Rev.*, **57**, 111, 1940) at a frequency of 1·84 Mc/s with $H_0 = 622$ gauss.

which the optical line of wavelength 5890A arises as a result of transitions between the $^2P_{3/2}$ and $^2S_{1/2}$ levels. If the atom is placed in a weak magnetic field H_0, the Zeeman states of these levels are as shown in Fig. 3.18, in which hyperfine structure is neglected. Absorption of unpolarized resonance radiation by the atom creates equal populations of the substates of the level* but if plane polarized radiation, with an

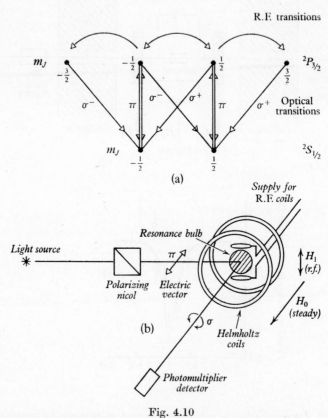

Fig. 4.10

a) Optical and radiofrequency transitions between Zeeman states of the $^2P_{1/2} \rightarrow {}^2S_{1/2}$ (5890 A) line of the sodium atom. The diagram shows excitation in plane polarized light.

b) Apparatus for optical double resonance experiment, showing excitation by π light and observation of σ light (Series, *Rep. prog. Phys.*, **22**, 280, 1959).

---

* In a weak field the Zeeman splitting of both the P and S states is small compared with usual (Doppler) line widths.

electric vector parallel to the magnetic field, is used the selection rule (Sect. 3.9.3)

$$\Delta m_J = 0$$

permits only the formation of the states with $m_J = \pm \frac{1}{2}$. This is shown in Fig. 4.10a, which displays the Zeeman states in a convenient way. This figure also shows that these states decay by emission of a mixture of plane polarized (π) radiation and circularly polarized (σ) radiation corresponding to downward transitions with $\Delta m_J = 0$ and ± 1 respectively. If the scattered radiation is observed along the lines of force of the field H_0, only circularly polarized components will be seen. Fig. 4.10b shows the experimental arrangement for detection of this radiation.

Suppose now that a radio-frequency field H_1 is applied in the xy plane. Then, at a frequency ν given approximately, from 4.11, by

$$h\nu = g_J \mu_0 H_0$$

where g_J is the electronic g factor for the $^2P_{3/2}$ state, transitions with $\Delta m_J = \pm 1$ can take place, transferring excited atoms with $m_J = \pm \frac{1}{2}$ to the $m_J = \pm \frac{3}{2}$ substates (Fig. 4.10a). These latter states can decay only by emission of σ radiation, and the proportion of this radiation in the scattered light therefore increases. The intensity of radiation observed along the field axis can therefore be used to determine when electron paramagnetic resonance absorption is taking place in the excited state. In a typical experiment a fixed radio-frequency of about 40 Mc/s is used and the field H_0 is varied in the neighbourhood of 20 gauss until an increase in σ radiation is detected. The resonance line shows structure as already discussed for paramagnetic resonance (Sect. 4.3.2) from which the hyperfine constants a and b may be deduced. From these, in turn, the nuclear moments μ_I and Q_I may be calculated. The method is particularly valuable in cases where the atomic ground state has $J = \frac{1}{2}$, since the quadrupole moment cannot be found by observation on such states alone.

A similar double resonance technique, using microwave and radiofrequency excitation, may be applied directly to the strong-field Zeeman levels of the hyperfine structure of the ground state.* It is possible using this method to determine the nuclear magnetic moment directly without that knowledge of the internal atomic field which is necessary when μ is derived from the hyperfine constant a.

4.5 Summary

The orders of magnitude of the effects of nuclear magnetic moments in spectroscopy are indicated in Sects. **4.2** and **4.4**. In zero magnetic field, the hyperfine splitting of atomic ground states (Fig. 4.1a) is about 0.06 cm^{-1} (1800 Mc/s). For paramagnetic ions in crystals the hyperfine splitting is rather less, ≈ 0.005 cm^{-1} (150 Mc/s).

Hyperfine structure cannot usually be fully resolved in optical lines which arise as $E1$ transitions between multiplets, but optical spectroscopy is important historically and also for studies of the isotope shift.

An external magnetic field of about 1000 gauss may decouple **I** and **J** almost completely, but internal fields of 10^5–10^6 gauss still exist and hyperfine structure is still observable. Magnetic resonance transitions ($M1$) within multiplets are observable in zero field but their main application is in externally applied fields in which case the resonance frequencies are

$$\left. \begin{array}{ll} \nu_e \text{ (paramagnetic resonance)} = 2.80 H_0 \text{ Mc/s} \\ \nu_0 \text{ (proton resonance)} \quad\quad = 0.00426 H_0 \text{ Mc/s} \end{array} \right\} H_0 \text{ in gauss}$$

Both optical and magnetic resonance measurements of the hyperfine structure give the coupling constants a, b from which nuclear moments may be obtained if internal atomic fields are known. Optical spectroscopy may give I directly. Magnetic resonance in systems in which strong internal fields do not arise, such as molecular beams and many solids and liquids, give g_I, from which μ_I may be calculated if I is known.

The following table lists the main quantities determined by the various techniques and indicates their general sensitivity (Ref. 4.5).

---

* This electron-nuclear double resonance technique (ENDOR) is described by J. Eisinger and G. Feher, *Phys. Rev.*, **109**, 1172, 1958.

TABLE 4.1   Determination of nuclear constants by spectroscopic methods

METHOD	QUANTITY DETERMINED	SENSITIVITY
1. Optical isotope shift	Nuclear size	10^{-6} g
2. Optical hfs	$I, a, b.$	—
3. Molecular spectra	I, statistics	—
4. Microwave absorption	I, b, mass	10^{-9} g
5. Microwave paramagnetic resonance	I, g_I (ratio)	10^{-12} g
6. Deflection of atomic and molecular beams	$I, a, b.$	—
7. Nuclear magnetic resonance	g_I, I	10^{-9} g (beams) 10^{-3} g (liquids and solids)
8. Double resonance	a, b	—
9. Mössbauer effect (special cases)	$H_t, \mu_I, b.$	—

References

4.1 E. R. Andrew, *Nuclear Magnetic Resonance*, Cambridge University Press, 1955.

4.2 R. J. Blin-Stoyle, *Theories of Nuclear Moments*, Oxford University Press, 1957.

4.3 O. R. Frisch, 'Molecular Beams', *Contemp. Phys.*, **1**, 3, 1959.

4.4 R. C. Johnson, *Molecular Spectra*, Methuen, 1949, p. 164.

4.5 K. F. Smith, 'Nuclear Moments and Spins', *Progr. nucl. Phys.*, **6**, 52, 1957.

4.6 D. J. E. Ingram, *Spectroscopy at Radio and Microwave Frequencies*, Butterworth, 1955.

4.7 M. H. L. Pryce, 'Magnetic Resonance', *Sci. Progr.*, **46**, 248, 1958.

4.8 H. Kopferman, *Nuclear Moments*, Academic Press, 1958.

4.9 N. F. Ramsey, *Molecular Beams*, Oxford University Press, 1956.

4.10 S. A. Goudsmit, 'Pauli and Nuclear Spin', *Physics Today*, **14**, 18, 1961.

4.11 H. Frauenfelder and R. M. Steffen, 'The Measurement of Electromagnetic Moments of Nuclear States', in *Nuclear Spectroscopy, Part A*, ed. F. Ajzenberg-Selove, Academic Press, 1960.

Part B

EXPERIMENTAL TECHNIQUES OF NUCLEAR PHYSICS

5. GENERAL PROPERTIES OF IONIZING RADIATIONS

The liberation of charge, or ionization, in ordinary neutral matter due to the passage of radiation has proved a property of the utmost importance for the development of nuclear physics. Ionizing radiations have long been familiar, and as a result of the many beautiful early experiments on the gaseous discharge the following types of ionizing radiation were distinguished:

a) *the positive rays* (or canal rays) which are now known as positive ions and which emerge through a hole in the cathode of a discharge tube,

b) *the cathode rays*, which are electrons and which were used for many striking demonstrations because of the ease with which they could be deflected by a magnet,

c) *X-rays*, which could not be deflected by electromagnetic fields at all.

These radiations were all produced by the application of an electric field to a gas at low pressure. The discovery of naturally occuring radioactivity provided a spontaneous source of similar radiations which were classified, as has been seen in chapter 2, into corresponding groups, namely the α-particles, β-particles and γ-rays.

In low energy nuclear physics a general division of radiations into heavy particles, light particles and electromagnetic radiation is familiar and clear. In high energy physics, where energies of many times the rest mass of the proton are encountered, the distinction is rather between radiations which interact strongly with nuclei and those which do not but the ionization produced by such particles is still an important experimental property.

The general types of ionization to be discussed are illustrated in Plates 1, 2 and 3 which show the tracks of α-particles and of fast and slow electrons in a cloud chamber. There are other forms of energy loss which contribute to the absorption or

retardation of radiations in matter and these will also
outlined. Many of the phenomena to be discussed are aton
in the sense that the interaction is between an incident parti
or photon and a free or bound electron; but some, including
the celebrated α-particle scattering process which led to the
discovery of the nucleus, yield specifically nuclear information,
e.g. the charge and size of the scattering centre. Most of the
interactions described have been applied in the design of nuclear
detectors (ch. 6).

5.1   Collisions between particles

5.1.1   GENERAL LAWS OF COLLISION (NON-RELATI-
VISTIC). Collisions between particles of all types, charged
or uncharged, heavy or light, are governed by the laws of
conservation of energy and of momentum. These laws determine the relations between angles of scattering and recoil and
give results which are independent of detailed mechanisms of the
collision, such as particular laws of force between the particles
or finite sizes of particles. Such considerations do influence
the distribution of angles observed in the scattering of a beam
of particles but for the individual scattering events the overall
deflection may be calculated from the laws of mechanics alone.

Consider a particle of mass M_1 incident with velocity v_1 on
a particle M_2 at rest (Fig. 5.1a). The collision may be either:

elastic in which there is no change of kinetic energy, or *non-
elastic* in which either or both particles absorb or emit energy
in some way, e.g. by excitation of an internal vibration or
oscillation. All nuclear transformations in which the system
$M_1 + M_2$ transforms into different particles $M_3 + M_4$ in the
final state will also be classed as non-elastic. (The term
inelastic is frequently used.)

It is useful to define a quantity

$$Q = \text{kinetic energy of final system}$$
$$- \text{kinetic energy of initial system}$$

and for elastic collisions $Q = 0$ while for non-elastic collisions
Q may be either positive or negative.

In *elastic collisions* M_1 will be deflected through an angle
θ_L with respect to its initial direction. To calculate the velocity
v_2 or angle ϕ_L of recoil of M_2 we write, in the non-relativistic

case when all particle velocities are negligible compared with the velocity of light,

$$\left.\begin{array}{l} M_1 v_1 = M_1 v_1' \cos \theta_L + M_2 v_2 \cos \phi_L \\ 0 = M_1 v_1' \sin \theta_L - M_2 v_2 \sin \phi_L \\ 0 = \frac{1}{2} M_1 v_1'^2 + \frac{1}{2} M_2 v_2^2 - \frac{1}{2} M_1 v_1^2 \end{array}\right\} \quad (5.1)$$

from which we obtain the useful relations

$$v_2 = 2 v_1 \frac{M_1}{M_1 + M_2} \cos \phi_L \quad \text{and} \quad \frac{M_2}{M_1} = \frac{\sin \theta_L}{\sin (2\phi_L + \theta_L)} \quad (5.2)$$

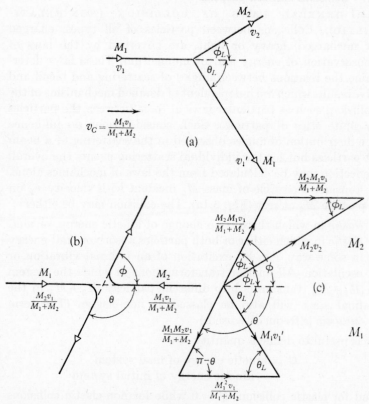

Fig. 5.1

a) Elastic collision (laboratory system).
b) Elastic collision (centre-of-mass system).
c) Momentum diagram which relates laboratory to centre-of-mass angles.

In *non-elastic collisions* equations 5.1 also hold with the introduction into the third equation of Q, the energy absorption or release in the reaction.

In both types of collision, when the final system contains only two particles, the paths of all the particles concerned are coplanar since there is no component of momentum perpendicular to that of the incident particle.

5.1.2 CENTRE-OF-MASS SYSTEM. The angles θ_L, ϕ_L shown in Fig. 5.1a are those which will be observed in an actual experiment in the laboratory which is performed by bombarding particles at rest (M_2) with particles moving with velocity v_1 (M_1). In the theoretical interpretation of details of a collision, this purely experimental asymmetry has to be removed by referring all motions and angles to the centre-of-mass of the system. If all measurements are made with respect to this point we replace the laboratory system of coordinates by an equivalent system in which the *total (vector) momentum is zero* and remains so in the absence of external forces.

This system is shown in Fig. 5.1b in which a velocity

$$v_C = \frac{M_1 v_1}{M_1 + M_2}$$

has been superimposed to bring the centre-of-mass to rest. The particles in this system approach the centre-of-mass from opposite directions with equal and opposite momenta

$$\frac{M_1 M_2}{M_1 + M_2} v_1 \quad \text{or} \quad M_0 v_1$$

where
$$M_0 = \frac{M_1 M_2}{M_1 + M_2}$$

is the reduced mass of the pair. In elastic scattering the particles are each turned through the same angle θ in the centre-of-mass system, since the total momentum must remain zero, and the relation between θ, which is required for analysis, and θ_L, which is actually observed, may be obtained as shown in the vector diagram 5.1c, i.e.

$$\tan \theta_L = \frac{\sin \theta}{\cos \theta + \dfrac{M_1}{M_2}} \tag{5.3}$$

From the diagram it is also seen that

$$\phi_L = \tfrac{1}{2}\phi = \frac{\pi}{2} - \frac{\theta}{2} \tag{5.4}$$

In *all* collision processes an energy of $\tfrac{1}{2}(M_1 + M_2)v_C{}^2$ is associated with the centre-of-mass motion and is not available for producing internal effects such as nuclear excitation. The energy remaining from the initial kinetic energy is thus

$$\tfrac{1}{2}M_1 v_1{}^2 - \tfrac{1}{2}(M_1 + M_2)\frac{M_1{}^2 v_1{}^2}{(M_1 + M_2)^2}$$

$$= \tfrac{1}{2}\frac{M_1 M_2 v_1{}^2}{M_1 + M_2} = \tfrac{1}{2}M_0 v_1{}^2 \tag{5.5}$$

which shows that the behaviour of the initial system in centre-of-mass coordinates may be described in terms of that of a particle of the reduced mass M_0 moving with the laboratory system incident velocity v_1. It is this energy* which can be used to initiate a nuclear reaction (Section 14.2.1).

5.1.3 CROSS-SECTIONS; BEAM ATTENUATION. The probability of occurrence of a particular collision process, such as the elastic scattering of a particle through a certain angle, is conveniently expressed as a *cross-section*. The origin of this concept may be understood from Fig. 5.2.

Consider a parallel beam of n_0 particles per sec incident on a thin slice of material of thickness t containing N scattering or absorbing centres per unit volume. If the probability of collision of any sort is determined by an area σ ascribed to each centre, then for a single incident particle the chance of collision in passing through the thin lamina dx of area A is

$$\frac{NA\,dx\,\sigma}{A} = N\sigma\,dx = \frac{dx}{\lambda}$$

---

* The energy associated with the centre-of-mass motion may also be written $\tfrac{1}{2}p^2/M$, where p is the incident momentum and M is the mass of the compound system. This expression may be used in calculation of the available energy for an incident photon (Sect. 13.6.3).

where $\lambda = 1/N\sigma$ is the 'mean free path' for collision. The attenuation of the beam is then described by the equation

$$\mathrm{d}n = -nN\sigma\,\mathrm{d}x$$

which gives

$$n_x = n_0 e^{-N\sigma x} = n_0 e^{-\mu x} \tag{5.6}$$

where $\mu = N\sigma = \dfrac{1}{\lambda}$, measured in cm^{-1}, is known as the *linear attenuation coefficient* of the material for the incident beam.

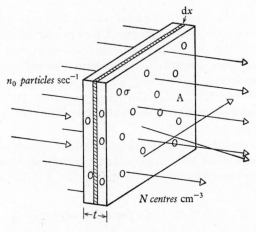

Fig. 5.2. The concept of cross-section, or collision area.

The quantity $\mu_m = \dfrac{\mu}{\rho}$, where ρ is the density, is the *mass attenuation coefficient* and is measured in $\mathrm{cm}^2\ \mathrm{gm}^{-1}$. It is useful to note that

$$\mu_m = \frac{\mu}{\rho} = \frac{N\sigma}{\rho} = \frac{\sigma}{m_A}$$

where m_A is the mass of a scattering centre.

In the thickness t of material

$$n_t = n_0 e^{-N\sigma t} \tag{5.7}$$

and if now attention is directed to the number of collisions which have actually taken place, namely the yield Y of the process, we find

$$Y = n_0 - n_t = n_0(1 - e^{-N\sigma t}) \qquad (5.8)$$
$$\approx n_0 N t \sigma$$

if the attenuation is small. Now Nt is the number of scattering centres per unit area of the material perpendicular to the incident beam and since from 5.8

$$\sigma = \frac{Y}{n_0 N t} \qquad (5.9)$$

we have the definition of the *total cross-section* σ as numerically equal to the probability of an event for one particle incident on a sample of material containing one scattering centre per cm^2 of projected area. From 5.9 σ is measured in cm^2 per atom or nucleus; for atoms, units of πa_0^2, where a_0 is the Bohr radius, are often used and for nuclei the *barn*, equal to 10^{-24} cm^2, is appropriate. The ratio n_t/n_o is usually known as the *transmission* of the sample.

If we consider only scatterings or other events which are observed in a small solid angle $d\Omega$ at a certain specified angle θ with the incident beam then we may define a *differential cross-section*

$$d\sigma = \sigma(\theta)\, d\Omega \text{ (cm}^2 \text{ per atom or nucleus)} \qquad (5.10)$$

which is the collision area associated with this type of event for each centre. If the phenomenon is independent of azimuth about the incident beam direction then

$$d\Omega = 2\pi \sin \theta\, d\theta \qquad (5.11)$$

and

$$d\sigma = 2\pi \sin \theta\, \sigma(\theta)\, d\theta \qquad (5.12)$$

from which the total cross-section is obtained by integration

$$\sigma = 2\pi \int_0^\pi \sigma(\theta) \sin \theta\, d\theta \qquad (5.13)$$

The quantity $\sigma(\theta) = \dfrac{d\sigma}{d\Omega}$ gives the *angular distribution* of the particular events; it is sometimes itself described as the differential cross-section, but strictly it is the differential cross-section per unit solid angle and is measured in cm^2 (atom or nucleus)$^{-1}$ steradian^{-1}.

The angular distribution $\sigma_L(\theta_L)$ observed in the laboratory system is related to the centre-of-mass angular distribution by the equation

$$\sigma(\theta) \sin \theta \, d\theta = \sigma_L(\theta_L) \sin \theta_L \, d\theta_L$$

which states that the same number of events is observed in each coordinate system for corresponding angles and solid angles. For *elastic scattering*, this gives, using 5.3,

$$\sigma_L(\theta_L) = \frac{(1 + 2\gamma \cos \theta + \gamma^2)^{3/2}}{1 + \gamma \cos \theta} \, \sigma(\theta) \qquad (5.14)$$

where $\gamma = M_1/M_2$. For *inelastic processes*, in which the particles M_1 and M_2 transform into particles M_3 and M_4 with an energy release Q, formulae 5.3, 5.4 and 5.14 also hold but with

$$\gamma = \sqrt{\frac{M_1 M_3}{M_2 M_4} \frac{E}{E + Q}}$$

where $E = \frac{1}{2} M_0 v_1^2$.

In this book we shall assume, unless specifically stated to the contrary, that all experimental quantities are converted to the centre-of-mass system (θ, ϕ) for comparison with theory.

5.1.4 COLLISION BETWEEN CHARGED PARTICLES—THE RUTHERFORD SCATTERING LAW. If the force of interaction between two particles is known, a detailed description of the collision process, subject still, however, to the general laws of section 5.1.1, may be given.

We consider a particle of mass M_1, charge ze, and velocity v_1 approaching a stationary particle of mass M_2 and charge Ze as shown in Fig. 5.3a and we again assume that the incident velocity is small compared with that of light. If the force between the particles at distance r is accurately given by the law of the inverse square, i.e.

$$F = \frac{zZe^2}{r^2} \qquad (5.15)$$

then it is known from the general theory of central orbits in dynamics that the particles describe hyperbolic orbits with respect to their centre-of-mass and with respect to one another. This solution was applied to the scattering of α-particles by matter by Rutherford (Sect. 2.6.1) and led to the theory of the nuclear atom.

Following Rutherford, we treat for simplicity the case of an infinitely heavy centre of force M_2 and a repulsive interaction. The orbit of M_1 is then a hyperbola with M_2 in the outer focus S (Fig. 5.3a) and the angle of deflection θ is $\pi - 2\psi$ where 2ψ is the angle between the asymptotes.

The orbit is determined essentially by the laws of conservation of angular momentum and of energy. If the perpendicular distance from S to the direction of incidence, known as the *impact parameter*, is p, then the velocity v at the apex A is given by the two equations

$$pv_1 = SA \cdot v \tag{5.16}$$

and

$$\tfrac{1}{2}M_1 v_1^2 = \tfrac{1}{2}M_1 v^2 + \frac{zZe^2}{SA}$$

The latter may be written

$$v_1^2 = v^2 + \frac{bv_1^2}{SA} \tag{5.17}$$

where

$$b = \frac{2zZe^2}{M_1 v_1^2} \tag{5.18}$$

is the *collision diameter* for the impact. Physically this quantity is the distance of closest approach in a head-on collision, at which the incident particle just comes to rest.

From 5.16 and 5.17 we obtain

$$p^2 = SA(SA - b) \tag{5.19}$$

and the distance SA is obtained from the geometry of the hyperbola using the fact that the eccentricity is sec ψ. This gives

$$SA = SO + OA = SO(1 + \cos\psi) = p \operatorname{cosec}\psi(1 + \cos\psi)$$

$$= p \cot\frac{\psi}{2} \tag{5.20}$$

and substituting in 5.19

$$p^2 = p \cot \frac{\psi}{2} \left(p \cot \frac{\psi}{2} - b \right)$$

$$= p^2 \cot^2 \frac{\psi}{2} - bp \cot \frac{\psi}{2}$$

or $\qquad\qquad b = 2p \cot \psi \qquad\qquad\qquad (5.21)$

and the relation* between the impact parameter and the angle of deflection θ is thus

$$b = 2p \tan \frac{\theta}{2}$$

or $\qquad\qquad p = \frac{b}{2} \cot \frac{\theta}{2} \qquad\qquad\qquad (5.22)$

The assumption of infinite mass for M_2 may be removed by replacing M_1 in formula 5.18 by the reduced mass M_0. The angle of deflection in formula 5.22 then becomes the angle of deflection in the centre-of-mass system and

$$b = \frac{2zZe^2}{M_0 v_1^2} \qquad\qquad\qquad (5.23)$$

These formulae may now be used to calculate the probability of scattering of the incident particle through an angle between θ and $\theta + d\theta$. Since this scattering corresponds to an impact parameter p given by 5.22 the differential cross-section, or collision area for this process is simply (Fig. 5.3)

$$d\sigma = 2\pi p \, dp$$

Substituting for p we obtain (cf. Sect. 5.1.3)

$$- d\sigma = \sigma(\theta) \, d\Omega = 2\pi \frac{b^2}{8} \cot \frac{\theta}{2} \operatorname{cosec}^2 \frac{\theta}{2} \, d\theta$$

whence

$$\sigma(\theta) = \frac{b^2}{16} \operatorname{cosec}^4 \frac{\theta}{2} \qquad\qquad (5.24)$$

$$= \left(\frac{zZe^2}{2M_0 v_1^2} \right)^2 \operatorname{cosec}^4 \frac{\theta}{2}$$

which is the well known scattering law of Rutherford, written

---

* A simplified derivation of this relation is given in Appendix 4.

here in centre-of-mass coordinates. From 5.8, 5.10, and 5.11, the actual number $\mathrm{d}Y$ of particles observed in a solid angle $\mathrm{d}\Omega$ is

$$\mathrm{d}Y = n_0 N t \left(\frac{zZe^2}{2M_0 v_1^2} \right)^2 \operatorname{cosec}^4 \frac{\theta}{2} \, \mathrm{d}\Omega \qquad (5.25)$$

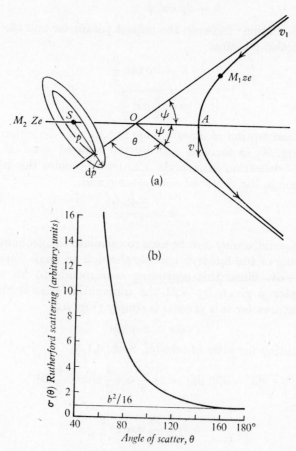

Fig. 5.3
a) Trajectory of a particle M_1 scattered elastically by a particle M_2 fixed at S.
b) Angular distribution of Rutherford scattering.

For 40 MeV α-particles incident on uranium the squared term has the value 0·02 barns; the $\mathrm{cosec}^4 \dfrac{\theta}{2}$ factor exhibits a rapid rise towards small angles, characteristic of the Coulomb interaction assumed (Fig. 5.3b).

The derivation of the Rutherford formula given here assumes that the law of force is accurately of the Coulomb type to a distance of approach less than the collision diameter b. If this is not so, there will be deviations from the angular distribution and energy dependence predicted by 5.16. Quite independently of the law of force, the classical method of discussing collisions in terms of definite trajectories will fail if these trajectories cannot be defined wave mechanically. It may be shown that the criterion for validity of the orbital picture is that the least distance of approach b shall be very much greater than the reduced de Broglie wavelength of the incident particle λ. This leads to the condition

$$\frac{2zZe^2}{\hbar v} \gg 1 \qquad (5.26)$$

for classical motion. For 40 MeV α-particles incident on uranium the quantity on the left-hand side of this equation is approximately equal to 20 and the classical condition is well satisfied. It will usually be so for slow particles and for high nuclear charges since the Coulomb barrier keeps the incident particle from approaching within the de Broglie wave length. For fast particles incident on electrons or light nuclei, the condition is not fulfilled and the full wave-mechanical treatment of scattering (ch. 14) must be used. The wave mechanical solution agrees exactly with the classical theory in the case of scattering by a pure inverse square law field and thus leads to Rutherford's scattering law. An essential modification, peculiar to wave mechanics, enters when the incident and target particles are identical, since there is then coherence between the waves representing the scattered and recoil particles and interference effects are observed (Sects. 5.3.1 and 14.2.2).

5.2 Passage of charged particles through matter

5.2.1 GENERAL. The main process by which a charged particle loses energy in passing through matter is interaction with atomic electrons, through the Coulomb force. When the work necessary to excite these electrons to new levels or to remove them from the atom is small compared with the incident particle energy, this process may be regarded as elastic. There is also a similar loss of energy to the nuclei of the stopping medium but this is small in comparison with the energy loss to electrons except in the special case of ions such as fission fragments carrying several electrons with them. Nuclear encounters are, however, of prime importance in determining the scattering of charged particles. The direct removal of electrons from neutral atoms by the incident particle is the *primary ionization*; the electrons so produced may have an energy up to $4m/M$ times the kinetic energy of the incident particle (mass M)* and their tracks may be seen in expansion chamber photographs (Plate 4) or in nuclear emulsions. The ionization produced by these *delta-rays* is known as the *secondary ionization* and is difficult to calculate theoretically. If the δ-rays have such a short range that they do not move an observable distance from the primary track, the only measurable quantity is the *total ionization*. When the incident particle is no longer able to ionize it has reached the end of its *range* in the stopping medium and will revert to a neutral atom.

Nuclear excitation and transformation processes may remove particles from a beam and therefore contribute to the effective absorption. If such mechanisms become important in comparison with ionization losses it is no longer possible to define a range for a particle in matter and the intensity of an incident beam as a function of thickness of matter traversed is given by the exponential law (Sect. 5.1.3) where the attenuation coefficient μ is determined by nuclear cross-sections. Such a law was originally proposed to account for the behaviour of both α-particles and β-particles in matter. When observations with thin sources were made it became clear that α-rays were characterized by a definite maximum range and that β-rays had a similar property when account was taken of their considerable scattering.

The close encounters between a fast charged particle and nuclei may lead to sudden accelerations. These in turn result

---

* The maximum electron velocity is obtained from 5.2, setting $M_1 = M$, $M_2 = m$ ($\ll M$) and $\cos \phi_L = 1$. See also 5.29.

in radiation according to the laws of electrodynamics and the '*bremsstrahlung*'* thus excited is an important mechanism of energy loss for electrons. Another form of radiative loss, essentially different from bremsstrahlung, is the *Cherenkov radiation* which arises from longitudinal polarization of a transparent medium when a charged particle traverses it at a velocity exceeding the phase velocity of light in the medium.

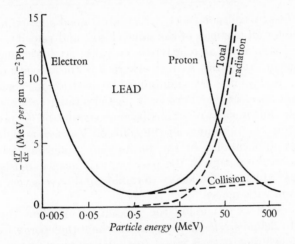

Fig. 5.4. Energy loss of electrons and protons in lead as a function of kinetic energy of particle (Ref. 5.11).

If T is the kinetic energy of a particle moving through an absorbing medium we write, neglecting nuclear transformations

$$-\frac{dT}{dx} = \textit{specific energy loss} \text{ (erg cm}^{-1}\text{) or}$$

$$\textit{absolute stopping power}$$

$$= \left(-\frac{dT}{dx}\right)_{\text{collision}} + \left(-\frac{dT}{dx}\right)_{\text{radiation}} \tag{5.27}$$

Table **5.1** gives approximate values of the energy loss of electrons and protons in water and Fig. 5.4 shows the variation of $\frac{dT}{dx}$ with energy for these particles in their passage through lead.

---

* Literally 'braking' or 'deceleration' radiation.

TABLE 5.1   Energy loss of a charged particle in 1 cm of water

PARTICLE	ENERGY	$\beta = \dfrac{v}{c}$	COLLISION LOSS	BREMS-STRAH-LUNG LOSS	CHEREN-KOV LOSS
Electron	100 MeV	1	2 MeV	2 MeV	2·7 keV
Proton	1000 MeV	0·87	2 MeV	0·01 keV	1·65 keV

Energy loss by collision (Sect. 5.2.2) is to a good approximation the same for all particles of the same charge and velocity and it reaches a minimum at relativistic energies. At lower energies the collision loss varies as $1/v^2$, where v is the velocity of the particle, and above the minimum bremsstrahlung becomes important for electrons. For heavy particles radiative losses are negligible, but nuclear reactions become significant for protons even before the minimum in the collision loss is reached. The region of applicability of the formula for collision loss thus depends on the nature of the particle; it is most extensive for μ-mesons, which are too heavy to radiate and have a very weak interaction with nuclei.

It is useful in discussing the passage of electrons through matter to define a *critical energy* ε, at which the energy loss by collision per unit path is equal to that lost by radiation. The path length of absorber from which an electron of energy much greater than ε (i.e. when radiation loss is the dominant process) emerges with a fraction $1/e$ of its initial energy is known as the *radiation length* X_0. Table **5.2** gives values of these quantities for certain materials.

TABLE 5.2   Radiation lengths and critical energies (Ref. 5.2)

MATERIAL	RADIATION LENGTH X_0 g cm^{-2}	CRITICAL ENERGY MeV
H	58	400
C	44·6	102
Fe	14·1	24·3
Pb	6·5	7·8
Air	37·7	84·2
Water	37·1	83·8
Glass	10·0–11·0	13·0–16·0

For energies well above the critical energy, radiation losses are proportional to T and to Z^2 (Sect. 5.2.3) while collision losses are mainly proportional to Z (Sect. 5.2.2) and nearly independent of T.

5.2.2. CLASSICAL THEORY OF ENERGY LOSS BY COLLISION. The basic theory has already been given in Section 5.1.3 and a direct calculation of the energy Q transferred by a massive particle to an electron gives (Eqq. 5.2 and 5.4)

$$Q = Q_0 \sin^2 \frac{\theta}{2} = Q_0 \frac{b^2/4}{p^2 + (b^2/4)} \qquad (5.28)$$

in the notation of Sects. 5.1.1 and 5.1.4. The quantity Q_0 is the maximum energy transferred and is easily seen to be

$$Q_0 = \tfrac{1}{2}mv_2^2 \approx \tfrac{1}{2}m(2v_1)^2 = \frac{4mT}{M} \qquad (5.29)$$

where T is the initial kinetic energy of the heavy particle of mass M.

From 5.28 the cross section (Sect. 5.1.3) for a transfer of energy between Q and $Q+dQ$ is

$$d\sigma = 2\pi p \, dp = -2\pi \frac{z^2 e^4}{mv^2} \frac{dQ}{Q^2} \qquad (5.30)$$

As the particle M passes through a thickness Δx of an absorber in which there are N atoms of atomic number Z per cm^3, the number of collisions in which energy between Q and $Q+dQ$ is transferred is $NZ \, \Delta x \, d\sigma$ and the total loss by collision is thus

$$-dT = -\int_{Q_{min}}^{Q_{max}} QNZ \, \Delta x \, d\sigma = 2\pi NZ \, \Delta x \frac{z^2 e^4}{mv^2} \int \frac{dQ}{Q} \qquad (5.31)$$

$$= -4\pi NZ \, \Delta x \frac{z^2 e^4}{mv^2}$$

$$\times \int_{p_{max}}^{p_{min}} \frac{p \, dp}{p^2 + (b^2/4)} \qquad (5.32)$$

from 5.28

$$= 2\pi NZ \, \Delta x \frac{z^2 e^4}{mv^2}$$

$$\times \log \left(\frac{p_{max}^2 + (b^2/4)}{p_{min}^2 + (b^2/4)} \right)$$

In this formula the lower limit p_{min} may be set equal to zero, corresponding to a head-on collision (energy transfer $2mv^2$) but

p_{max} is more difficult to define. It cannot be made infinite since this leads to an infinite energy loss owing to the large number of distant collisions with small energy transfers. For collisions with these large impact parameters, however, the electron can no longer be considered as free and interaction with such distant electrons is therefore approximately adiabatic, i.e. without net energy transfer. Bohr pointed out that this would be so if the collision time ($\approx p/v$) were about equal to the period of vibration of the electron concerned in its parent atom. We thus put

$$p_{max} = \frac{v}{\omega} \tag{5.33}$$

where ω is a characteristic frequency which must be calculated from an atomic model. Assuming that $p_{max} \gg \frac{b}{2}$, the stopping power formula becomes

$$-\frac{dT}{dx} = 2\pi NZ \frac{z^2 e^4}{mv^2} \log \frac{4p_{max}^2}{b^2} \tag{5.34}$$

$$= \frac{4\pi z^2 e^4}{mv^2} NZ \log \frac{mv^3}{\omega z e^2} \text{ erg. cm}^{-1} \tag{5.35}$$

using 5.23 and 5.33.

An expression of this form was first given by Bohr. Later Bethe and Bloch gave a quantum mechanical treatment of stopping power based on the Born approximation method of wave mechanics and valid subject to the condition (cf. 5.26)

$$\frac{2zZe^2}{\hbar v} \ll 1 \tag{5.36}$$

which means physically that the perturbation due to the incident particle does not seriously disturb the electronic motion for large impact parameters. The Bethe-Bloch formula is, to a good approximation,

$$-\frac{dT}{dx} = \frac{4\pi z^2 e^4}{mv^2} NZ \log \frac{2mv^2}{I} \tag{5.37}$$

where I is a parameter interpreted as a mean atomic excitation potential. This formula is extended to relativistic incident particles as follows:

$$-\frac{dT}{dx} = \frac{4\pi z^2 e^4}{mv^2} NZ\left\{\log \frac{2mv^2}{I} - \log (1-\beta^2) - \beta^2\right\} \quad (5.38)$$

where $\beta = v/c$. The quantity I is not the first ionization potential of the atom but can be calculated from the Thomas-Fermi electron distribution function for an atom in the form

$$I = kZ \quad (5.39)$$

where $k \approx 11.5$ eV; in practice I is deduced from experimental results.

It will be noted that formulae 5.37 and 5.38 (and similar formulae for ionization and δ-ray production) show that to a good approximation nonrelativistic collision loss of energy is proportional to the square of the charge of the particle, inversely proportional to the square of its velocity, and *independent of the mass of the particle*, i.e.

$$-\frac{dT}{dx} \propto \frac{z^2}{v^2} \quad (5.40)$$

The variation of collision loss with particle energy is shown in Figs. 5.4 and 5.8.

The *primary ionization* may be estimated by evaluating the number of collisions for which the energy transfer to an electron lies between Q_0, the maximum possible $(= 2mv^2)$, and I_0, the first ionization potential. From Sect. 5.1.3 this may be written

$$NZ\, \Delta x \int_{I_0}^{Q_0} d\sigma \quad (5.41)$$

and using 5.30 this becomes

$$2\pi NZ\, \Delta x\, \frac{z^2 e^4}{mv^2} \int_{I_0}^{Q_0} \frac{dQ}{Q^2} \quad (5.42)$$

which gives, for unit path, an ionization

$$2\pi NZ\, \frac{z^2 e^4}{mv^2}\left(\frac{1}{I_0} - \frac{1}{2mv^2}\right) \quad (5.43)$$

Since $I_0 \ll 2mv^2$ this is approximately

$$\frac{2\pi z^2 e^4 NZ}{mv^2 I_0} \text{ ion pairs cm}^{-1}. \quad (5.44)$$

For protons of 5 MeV energy passing through nitrogen at atmospheric pressure this formula indicates a primary ionization of the order of 600 ion pairs cm^{-1}. The observed ionization however is 2400 ion pairs cm^{-1} and the difference is to be accounted for by secondary ion production by the δ-rays ejected in the primary process. No simple formula analogous to Eq. 5.44 can be given for the total specific ionization but empirically at least it appears to follow roughly the same law of variation with velocity as the total energy loss.

The distribution of delta rays (Plate 4) along the track of a fast particle is obtained directly from 5.42 as

$$dn = \frac{2\pi N Z z^2 e^4}{mv^2} \frac{dT}{T^2} \qquad (5.45)$$

where dn is the number of delta rays with kinetic energy between T and $T + dT$ per unit length of track. The total number of such rays of energy greater than T is then given by

$$n = \frac{2\pi N Z z^2 e^4}{mv^2} \left[\frac{1}{T} - \frac{1}{2mv^2} \right] \qquad (5.46)$$

5.2.3 RADIATIVE LOSS OF ENERGY. If a particle of mass M and charge ze enters the field of a nucleus of charge Ze in an absorber the acceleration produced is proportional to zZ/M. According to classical electrodynamics the resulting radiation would have an intensity proportional to z^2Z^2/M^2. This radiation, which is the bremsstrahlung referred to in Sect. 5.2.1, is therefore much smaller for protons and mesons than for electrons (Table **5.1** and Fig. 5.4). For the latter particles it is an important mechanism of energy loss for energies above a few MeV, particularly in absorbers of high Z. At lower energies the bremsstrahlung produced by the impact of an intense beam of electrons on a massive target furnishes the continuous X-ray spectrum discovered by Röntgen and at extreme relativistic energies bremsstrahlung participates in the development of cosmic-ray showers.

Electrons of kinetic energy T may in passing through a thin absorber give rise in each radiative collision to a bremsstrahlung photon of any energy between 0 and T. Since small deflections are more probable than large, low energy quanta are emitted preferentially, but when the *energy loss* per unit frequency interval is calculated it is found that this is to a first approximation independent of the quantum energy. Bremsstrahlung therefore has an *equi-energy spectrum*, as shown in Fig. 5.5a.

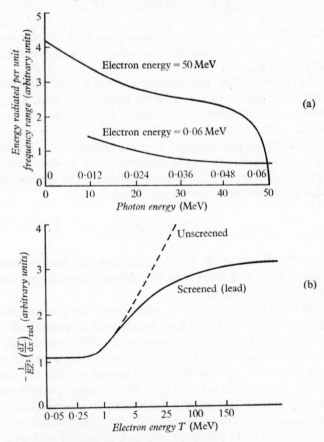

Fig. 5.5. Bremsstrahlung.

a) Radiation from 50 MeV electrons passing through lead and from 0.06 MeV electrons passing through aluminium. If the ordinate is divided at each point by the energy $h\nu$, the result gives the intensity distribution of the bremsstrahlung photons ($\propto 1/h\nu$).

b) Energy variation of radiative loss for electrons of kinetic energy T in lead, showing the effect of screening of nuclear charge by atomic electrons. Note that the ordinates must be multiplied by $E \ (= T + mc^2)$ to give the form of the energy loss, which rises very steeply with T (Ref. 5.11).

The total radiative loss of energy per cm path is obtained by integrating over the bremsstrahlung spectrum and may be written

$$-\left(\frac{\mathrm{d}T}{\mathrm{d}x}\right)_{\mathrm{rad}} = NEZ^2 f(Z, T) \tag{5.47}$$

where N is the number of atoms per cm^3 of the stopping material, $E(=T+mc^2)$ is the total energy of the incident electron and $f(Z,T)$ is a slowly-varying function of Z and T.

The variation of the radiative energy loss with inciden energy T is shown in Fig. 5.5b for electrons in lead. For a bare nucleus the radiative loss increases indefinitely·with energy, corresponding to production of photons at greater and greater distances from the nucleus. For an actual atom, however, a limit to the radiative loss is imposed owing to the screening of the nuclear charge by the atomic electrons. The bremsstrahlung radiation is emitted into a cone of semi-angle

$$\theta \approx \frac{mc^2}{mc^2 + T} \tag{5.48}$$

about the direction of the incident electrons and is thus constrained more and more into the forward direction as the electron energy increases.

Although bremsstrahlung can occur in electron-electron collisions the Z^2 factor in 5.47 means that as a practical source of energy loss it is a nuclear process. It differs essentially from the radiation discovered by *Cherenkov* which depends on the gross structure of the medium through which an incident particle passes. The electric field of a charged particle passing through matter produces a macroscopic polarization due to displacement of bound electrons. The time variation of this polarization can in principle lead to a radiation field at a point P (Fig. 5.6a). For slowly moving particles the field vectors at P, originating from the polarization produced at different points along the path of the particle, have no definite phase relationship, and the total radiation arising from this mechanism is very small because of cancellation. If the particle velocity exceeds the velocity of light in the medium, c/n, where n is the refractive index, coherence is possible between the contributions at P from the polarizations at different points along the path of the particle. This is because the radiation from point B (Fig. 5.6b) under these conditions is in phase with the radiation from point A, and a coherent wavefront can be propagated through the medium, if it is transparent, in the direction AC for which

$$\cos \theta = \frac{c}{n}\Big/ \beta c = \frac{1}{\beta n} \qquad (5.49)$$

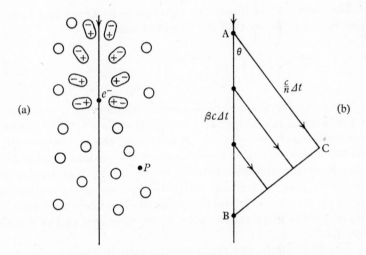

Fig. 5.6. Cherenkov radiation (Ref. 5.2).
a) Polarization of atoms of a transparent medium by passage of a charged particle.
b) Formation of coherent wavefront.

The Cherenkov radiation is thus due essentially to longitudinal polarization of the medium, it is emitted from all points along the path of the incident particle in directions lying on the surface of a cone with semi-angle given by 5.49, and unlike bremsstrahlung, it is independent of the mass of the moving particle. The electric vector of the Cherenkov radiation is perpendicular to the surface of the cone. The angle of emission increases with the particle velocity in contrast with the angular distribution of bremsstrahlung. Although the basic mechanism for Cherenkov energy loss resides in small energy transfers to atomic electrons, and is therefore present for all incident electron energies, coherence does not appear until the electron velocity reaches the critical value given by

$$\beta = \frac{1}{n} \tag{5.50}$$

and below this threshold there is effectively no radiation of this type.

The theory of the Cherenkov effect given by Frank and Tamm (see Ref. 5.2) shows that the radiative loss is

$$-\left(\frac{\mathrm{d}T}{\mathrm{d}x}\right)_C = \frac{4\pi^2 z^2 e^2}{c^2} \int \left(1 - \frac{1}{\beta^2 n^2}\right)\nu\, \mathrm{d}\nu \tag{5.51}$$

where the integration extends over all frequencies of emission ν for which the refractive index is such that $\beta n > 1$. This confines the radiation to wavelengths greater than those corresponding to the ultraviolet absorption bands of the medium, and above this limit the spectral distribution of energy loss is proportional to $\nu\, \mathrm{d}\nu$, in contrast with the equi-energy distribution, proportional to $\mathrm{d}\nu$, for bremsstrahlung. The Cherenkov light is therefore found predominantly at the blue end of the visible spectrum.

The Cherenkov effect is usually small in comparison with both ionization and other radiative losses (cf. Sect. 5.2.1) but it is thought to play an important part at energies greater than the energy of minimum ionization for a relativistic particle. Technically the phenomenon has become of considerable importance because of the production threshold and the highly directional angular distribution. These properties, together with the sharpness of the light pulse ($\ll 10^{-10}$ sec) and the concentration of energy into the visible region, have led to the development of energy selective, directional counters for use in high energy physics (see Sect. 6.1.7) particularly with protons and mesons, for which the Cherenkov energy loss is as large as with electrons.

The orders of magnitude of radiative losses are shown in Table **5.1**. The Cherenkov radiation loss is of the order of $0 \cdot 1\%$ of the energy loss by ionization for a relativistic particle in a typical transparent medium.

From 5.51 the number of quanta N emitted within a narrow spectral range λ_1 to λ_2 by a particle passing through a length l of medium can be obtained as

$$N = \frac{4\pi^2 z^2 e^2}{hc} l\left(1 - \frac{1}{\beta^2 n^2}\right)\left(\frac{1}{\lambda_1} - \frac{1}{\lambda_2}\right) \qquad (5.51a)$$

This gives typically about 10 photons per mm between 4000 and 6000 A for a relativistic electron passing through water.

5.3   Experimental results

From the formulae developed in Sections **5.1** and **5.2** it is clear that the slowing down of a charged passing through matter is mainly due to collisions with electrons, while the large angle scattering is mainly due to collisions with nuclei.

5.3.1. SCATTERING OF CHARGED PARTICLES.

The scattering of α-*particles* passing through matter due to collisions with electrons and to distant collisions with nuclei does not exceed a few degrees even for absorbers of thickness comparable with the particle range. Large angle scattering, due to close nuclear collisions, is described by the Rutherford scattering law, Eq. 5.24, and the first detailed verification of this law by Geiger and Marsden has already been described (Sect. 2.6.1). These early experiments were made with α-particles from radon and radium B + C, of about 7 MeV energy, and with fairly heavy scattering nuclei such as Ag and Au. In such cases the criterion of the validity of the classical theory (Eq. 5.26) is well satisfied and no deviations from the Rutherford scattering law were found. In particular it seemed that the Coulomb law of force between an α-particle and a nucleus was valid down to a distance of less than 10^{-12} cm. When the α-particle experiments were extended to lighter atoms two new effects were found which may be seen in Fig. 5.7, showing the results of Chadwick* for the scattering of α-particles in helium:

a) the intensity at about 45° in the laboratory system (90° centre-of-mass) for slow α-particles is just twice that predicted by 5.24, even allowing for the fact that scattered

---

* J. Chadwick, *Proc. roy. Soc.*, **A128**, 114, 1930.

and recoil particles cannot be distinguished. This is a quantum mechanical effect arising from the identity of the particles and consequent interference between the waves representing the scattered and recoil particles (Sect. 14.2.2).

b) The intensity at 45° as a function of increasing velocity of the α-particle at first falls off and then increases largely above the value expected from 5.24. This 'anomalous' scattering was also found with other light elements and was interpreted as evidence for a finite nuclear size or for non-Coulomb forces. Since the scattering at first decreases, the non-Coulomb nuclear force must be first attractive as the α-particle approaches the nucleus, but for close distances of approach all that could be concluded from the early experiments was that the force was stronger than the Coulomb repulsion.

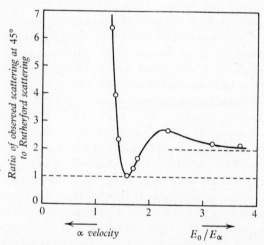

Fig. 5.7. Scattering of α-particles in helium at 45° laboratory angle (Chadwick, *Proc. roy. Soc.* A, **128**, 114, 1930).

Scattering of protons and α-particles by nuclei under conditions such that $b < \lambda$, so that the classical theory is inadequate, is now an important source of information on nuclear sizes. Interpretation must be based on a nuclear model and on the full wave mechanical theory of scattering, which is outlined in chapter 14. For the case $b > \lambda$, in which Rutherford scattering is expected both classically and quantum mechanically, many accurate verifications of the angular distribution (Fig. 5.3b) are now available for artificially accelerated particles and a wide variety of nuclei.

The scattering of *electrons* by nuclei and by other electrons was also studied in the early days of radioactivity with naturally occurring β-particle emitters as sources. Such electrons, and indeed all electrons of more than 100 keV in energy must be considered to be relativistic particles. This means that the Rutherford scattering law must be used, when applicable, in relativistic form but most cases of the scattering of electrons will not in fact be suitable for classical treatment because of the low value of the quantity $2zZe^2/\hbar v$. Suitable formulae based on the Born approximation of wave mechanics, which in fact requires $2zZe^2/\hbar v \ll 1$, have been given by Mott and others. Beta particles suffer large deflections in both nuclear and electronic collisions and the verification of the laws of deflection is experimentally difficult because of multiple scattering. Early experiments by Chadwick, using annular geometry, and by Schonland, together with a rough analysis of deflections observed in cloud chamber photographs showed that it was possible to obtain conditions of effectively single scattering, which merged into multiple scattering as the thickness of the scattering foil increased. The main effect is due to nuclear scattering (Mott scattering) because of the factor Z^2 in 5.24 but for the lightest elements such as hydrogen and helium, electronic scattering proportional to Z may be observed. The theoretical formula for electron-electron collisions (Möller scattering) includes an interference term due to identity of the two particles. Formulae have also been developed for positron-electron scattering and positron-nuclear scattering which differ from the electron case because of the different sign of charge (which reduces nuclear scattering of positrons in comparison with that of electrons) and because of the possibility of annihilation in $e^+ - e^-$ collisions. Experimental results on electron-nuclear scattering at about 2 MeV obtained by Van de Graaff and others[*] verify the Mott formula for distances of approach

---

* R. J. Van de Graaff, W. W. Buechner and H. Feshbach, *Phys. Rev.*, **69**, 452, 1946.

between electron and nucleus down to 7×10^{-13} cm. As the electron energy is increased the point-charge scattering formula becomes a worse approximation and the scattering of electrons of several hundred MeV has become the most important method of studying the size of the nuclear charge distribution. This is partly due to the fact that electrons do not cause nuclear transmutation directly and can therefore pass through the nucleus in a way that is improbable for neutrons or other strongly interacting particles.

The multiple scattering angle of charged particles in passing through absorbers is large for electrons and small for heavy particles. This dependence on particle mass has proved particularly useful in the identification of mesons and other new particles by observation of the deviations from linearity of their tracks in nuclear emulsions, in which elastic collisions with silver and bromine nuclei give rise to the effect. The mean square angle of multiple scattering of a particle of charge ze in a path length x of material is given by

$$\overline{\theta^2} = \frac{z^2 E_s^2}{p^2 \beta^2 c^2} \frac{x}{X_0} \tag{5.52}$$

where E_s is a constant ($= 21$ MeV), independent of the mass of the particle and of the nature of the medium, p is the momentum, $\beta = v/c$ and X_0 is the radiation length (Sect. 5.2.1) for the medium. For the example given in Table **5.1** the root mean square deflection of the proton is about 8′ of arc.

5.3.2 STOPPING POWER OF MATTER FOR CHARGED PARTICLES. The *absolute stopping power* of a material for a heavy charged particle is the quantity $- \mathrm{d}T/\mathrm{d}x$ given in 5.38 and expressed in ergs cm^{-1} or in an equivalent unit such as keV mgm^{-1} cm^2. It is usual to write

$$-\frac{\mathrm{d}T}{\mathrm{d}x} = \frac{4\pi z^2 e^4}{mv^2} N B \tag{5.53}$$

where N is the number of stopping atoms per cm^3 and B the *atomic stopping number* is given, for a non-relativistic particle, by the expression

$$B = Z \log \frac{2mv^2}{I} \tag{5.54}$$

The *stopping power per atom* ε is given by

$$\varepsilon = -\frac{1}{N}\frac{dT}{dx} \qquad (5.54)$$

and is often quoted in keV $\times$ cm^2 per atom.

The *relative stopping power S* of a material is the inverse ratio of the length of this material to the length of a standard substance required to produce a given energy loss, i.e.

$$S = \frac{(dT/dx)_1}{(dT/dx)_0} = \frac{N_1 B_1}{N_0 B_0} = \frac{\rho_1 B_1 A_0}{\rho_0 B_0 A_1} \qquad (5.55)$$

where ρ is the density and A the atomic weight of the material. For the standard substance, which was usually air at 15° C and 76 cm pressure in older work, and is now frequently aluminium, $S = 1$.

The *relative stopping power per atom* is simply the ratio of the atomic stopping numbers B, i.e.

$$S_{\text{at}} = \frac{B_1}{B_0} \qquad (5.56)$$

and the *relative stopping power per electron* is

$$S_{\text{el}} = \frac{B_1/Z_1}{B_0/Z_0} \qquad (5.57)$$

The stopping numbers B are now known fairly well as a result of many measurements but it is still useful for some purposes to employ the empirical rule first given by Bragg and Kleeman that

$$\text{atomic stopping power} \propto \sqrt{\text{atomic weight}}, \qquad (5.58)$$

together with the result that atomic stopping power is additive, so that for a complex molecule

$$\text{stopping power} \propto \sum n_r \sqrt{A_r}$$

where n_r is the number of atoms of weight A_r per molecule.

The variation of the stopping power, or energy loss by collision, for air is shown in Fig. 5.8. The curve may be placed on an absolute scale of energy loss once a value for I in 5.38 is calculated or observed. For all but the lightest elements it is a good approximation to assume that

$$I = kZ \quad \text{eV} \tag{5.59}$$

as predicted by Bloch, and extensive calculations of energy loss based on the value of $k = 11 \cdot 5$ eV have been made (Ref. 5.8).

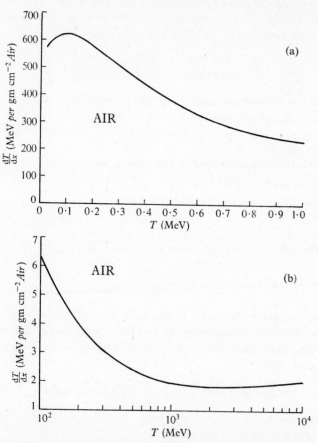

Fig. 5.8. Absolute stopping power of air for protons (collision loss), based on experimental observations (Ref. 5.6).

a) Low energy region ($\beta \ll 1$). The main part of the curve is described by 5.38. Below $T = 0 \cdot 1$ MeV the collision loss falls off because capture and loss of electrons reduces the effective charge of the proton.

b) High energy region ($\beta > 0 \cdot 4$). The curve is given by 5.38 using an experimental value for I. 'Minimum ionization' occurs for $T = 1500$ MeV.

Formula 5.38 is valid in its simple form only so long as the velocity of the incident particle remains large compared with the velocities of the atomic electrons and for slow particles corrections must be made for the binding of the K-electrons which can no longer be considered as free. These corrections, for the so-called non-participating electrons, are discussed by Evans (Ref. 5.1, p. 638). At relativistic energies the stopping power, as shown in Figs. 5.4 and 5.8 reaches a minimum value, known usually as 'minimum ionization' and then begins slowly to increase. The relativistic increase is in practice diminished for condensed media by a polarization of the medium which tends to screen distant atoms from the field of the incident particle (density effect), but the average ionization still increases with increasing energy owing to increase of the maximum possible energy transfer. If attention is confined to energy transfers of less than a certain specified amount, as may be necessary when useful quantitative measurements are to be made on the tracks of charged particles in nuclear emulsions or expansion chambers, the ionization is found to reach a constant value at high energies (Fermi plateau).

Experimental determinations of absolute stopping power, leading to values of I, have been made by measuring the energy of a beam of particles before and after the interposition of an absorber of known thickness in the path of the beam. The energy measurement may be made with a photographic emulsion (Sect. 6.2.4) or with an electrostatic or magnetic analyser. Such techniques have been used with both solids and gases and a large amount of data is available in review articles (Ref. 5.4) for protons, deuterons and helium ions. The special behavior of heavy ions including fission fragments is discussed later (Sect. 5.3.7). Relative stopping powers have also been determined for many elements for 340 MeV protons by observing the change of range of the particles when an absorber is placed in the beam. From these observations the stopping power per electron relative to aluminium was deduced and the I values for the elements were calculated with the assumption of a standard value of I for aluminium. Typical results are shown in Table 5.3, together with some older values of atomic stopping power relative to air based on magnetic deflection experiments with 6 MeV α-particles.

TABLE 5.3   Relative stopping powers

ELEMENT	Stopping power per *electron* relative to Al (340 MeV protons*)	Stopping power per *atom* relative to air (6 MeV α-particles)†
H	1·280	0·21
C	1·084	0·93
Al	1·000	1·45
Cu	0·924	2·43
Pb	0·804	4·35

* C. J. Bakker and E. Segrè, *Phys. Rev.*, **81**, 489, 1951.
† Ref. 5.7, Table XLVIII.

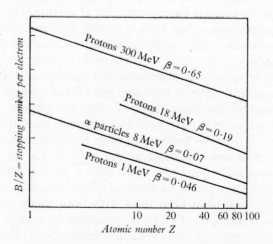

Fig. 5.9. Stopping number per electron (Ref. 5.1).

It will be noted that the effectiveness of an electron in retarding a charged particle is greater for the lighter elements; this is because I increases with Z in the expression 5.54 for B/Z and arises because of the increased nuclear binding of inner electronic shells of heavy atoms. Available information on the electronic stopping number B/Z is shown in Fig. 5.9 taken from Evans (Ref. 5.1, p. 664); this shows the expected dependence on both Z and v.

We may conclude that present experimental results support

the theory of energy loss of heavy charged particles by collision, according to which we may write, in the non-relativistic case (Eqq. 5.37, 5.39)

$$-\frac{dT}{dx} = \frac{z^2}{v^2} f(v) \tag{5.60}$$

The fall-off in dT/dx approximately as $1/v^2$, the dependence on z^2 and independence of mass are all verified by observation over the range of energy from about 50 keV to 300 MeV. The difficulties still remaining are chiefly concerned with calculations of I values for which a suitable atomic model is necessary. The additional complication of capture and loss effects at energies below about 1 MeV per nucleon is beyond the simple theory of stopping power and is discussed in Sect. 5.3.6.

It is less easy to make precise comparison between theory and experiment for the stopping power of matter for electrons. Although for light absorbers and electrons of a few MeV energy radiative losses may be neglected, difficulties still arise because of increased nuclear scattering and because of large straggling effects. These result from the large possible energy loss in a single collision, and will be discussed in Sect. 5.3.5.

5.3.3 RANGE–ENERGY CURVES. The theoretical range of a heavy charged particle is equal to its path length in matter because scattering is negligible. The range may formally be obtained by integration of the expression for energy loss, giving

$$R = \int_0^T \frac{dT}{dT/dx} \tag{5.61}$$

but in practice this cannot be carried out for the full range of the particle because of the corrections necessary to the explicit formula for dT/dx at low energies. Range–energy curves are therefore constructed semi-empirically by combining observations of the range of particles of known energy with integrations of the energy-loss formula over some particular region; for high energies the formula should be valid.

The first range–energy curve to be established was for α-particles in air. Energies of radioactive α-particles were obtained from the classical magnetic deflection experiments of Briggs, Rosenblum and Rutherford with a precision of 1 part in 10^5 in favourable cases. Ranges were measured by observing tracks in an expansion chamber or by allowing the α-particles to pass through a shallow ionization chamber which was then moved along until the particle terminated its range in the chamber. The ranges displayed in range–energy curves are by convention mean ranges, i.e. the average range of a group of

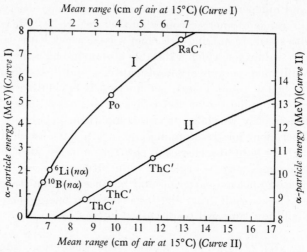

Fig. 5.10. Range–energy relation for α-particles (Ref. 5.1).

particles initially of homogeneous velocity and observed ranges must be reduced to mean values by correction for fluctuations, or straggling, as described in Sect. 5.3.5. It has recently become possible to obtain fixed points on the α-particle range–energy relation by using observations on the ranges, in an expansion chamber, of the particles from nuclear reactions with accurately known energy release, e.g. $^{10}B(n,\alpha)^7Li$ and $^6Li(n,\alpha)^3H$. The present α-particle range–energy curve, based on a conventional value of 8·57 cm of air at 15° C and 76 cm of mercury pressure for α-particles of energy 8·776 MeV (ThC$'$), is shown in Fig. 5.10.

If the energy loss equation is written in the form 5.60 then by substitution of $\frac{1}{2}Mv^2$ for the kinetic energy T we obtain

$$Mv\frac{dv}{dx} = \frac{z^2}{v^2}f(v) \qquad (5.62)$$

from which a range–velocity relation may in principle be obtained by integration. If the energy dependence of the function $f(v)$ could be neglected this would immediately give

$$R \propto \frac{M}{z^2} v^4 = \text{const.} \times v^4 \qquad (5.62\text{a})$$

for a given particle; empirically it was early found by Geiger that the range–velocity relation for α-particles is more nearly

$$R = \text{const.} \times v^3 \quad \text{(Geiger's rule)} \qquad (5.62\text{b})$$

Eq. 5.62 also shows that for a given velocity, for which $f(v)$ has the same value for all particles independently of mass and charge in a given stopping medium, the ranges of different particles are proportional to M/z^2. This is a particularly useful result since it enables a great many range–energy curves to be derived from one standard curve such as that for α-particles, providing that the necessary small corrections for different charge exchange effects can be applied. For particles of the same charge and velocity, the ranges are directly proportional to their mass, e.g. the ranges of protons, deuterons and tritons of energies 10, 20 and 30 MeV stand accurately in the ratio $1:2:3$.

The range–energy curve for protons in air (Ref. 5.1, p. 651) has been derived from the α-particle curve by using the relation

$$R_p = \frac{(M/z^2)_p}{(M/z^2)_\alpha} (R_\alpha - 0 \cdot 2 \text{ cm}) \qquad (5.63)$$

in which the correction $0 \cdot 2$ cm for the difference in charge exchange effects at the end of the range is derived from expansion chamber observations of the tracks of both particles by Blackett. For energies above 10 MeV, integration of the theoretical expression 5.38 with $I_{\text{air}} = 80 \cdot 5$ eV may be used in regions where direct measurements of $\mathrm{d}T/\mathrm{d}x$ are not available. Direct determinations of range for 340 MeV protons in several materials have been made.*

Ranges of protons and α-particles in other materials, such as aluminium or nuclear emulsion, and ranges of other particles, such as mesons, can be inferred by applying formulae already given. The tables now existing (Ref. 5.8) for a large number of materials have been drawn up semi-empirically using

---

* R. Mather and E. Segrè, *Phys. Rev.*, **84**, 191, 1951.

observed values of dT/dx and the functional form of the energy loss. Rough comparisons of ranges of a given particle in different substances may be based on the Bragg–Kleeman rule for stopping power (Sect. 5.3.2).

The range of a slow electron in matter, as may be seen in expansion chamber photographs (Plates 2, 3) may be much less

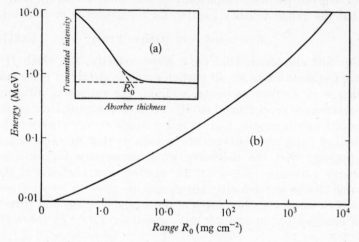

Fig. 5.11. Range–energy curve for electrons (Katz and Penfold, *Rev. mod. Phys.* **24**, 28, 1952).

than its path length because of large angle scattering. For the same reason the range is not sharply defined as it is for a heavy particle and depends on the method of measurement used. If a beam of electrons of homogeneous initial velocity is passed through an absorber the transmitted intensity as a function of absorber thickness is as shown in Fig. 5.11a. By extrapolation of the sloping part of the curve to the axis, or to the level of background, an extrapolated range R_0 may be defined and this procedure is sufficiently reproducible to permit such ranges to be used in establishing a range energy curve. To a good approximation, ranges expressed in mg cm^{-2} are independent of the material of the absorber. The relation $R_{\mathrm{mg\,cm^{-2}\,Al}} = 543E_0$ (MeV) $- 160$, first given by Feather, has been much used for finding the maximum energy in a β-ray spectrum. Fig. 5.11b shows an empirical curve based partly on measurements with homogeneous electrons and partly on β-ray spectra; in all cases the energies are determined by magnetic analysis. The slowing down of electrons in matter inevitably introduces a large straggling which is not only considerably greater in proportion than that for heavy particles but is also asymmetric, because of the high probability of loss of a large amount of energy in a single collision.

5.3.4 IONIZATION AND ASSOCIATED EFFECTS. Knowledge of the ionization produced by charged particles is of importance not only because it forms the basis of many methods of charged particle detection but also because it is the process by which radiation causes biological damage. All modern methods of radiation dosimetry are ultimately based on ionization measurements (Sect. 6.2.1). We consider here, however, only effects in gases.

The intense and continuous ionization along the path through a gas of a heavy charged particle (perhaps 30,000 ion pairs cm^{-1}) is well shown in expansion chamber photographs (Plate 1). The expansion chamber was in fact the first instrument used, by Feather and Nimmo, to study the variation of ionization along the path of a single α-particle, and it was possible to show that the density fell off rapidly in the last few mm of the range. This conclusion was consistent with earlier measurements on *beams* of α-particles passing through shallow ionization chambers, but such observations must be corrected for straggling before they yield the true single particle curve. The shallow ionization chamber has been used by Holloway and Livingston as a pulse instrument to give not only the relative ionization near the end of the range of a single α-particle, but also the absolute *specific ionization*, i.e. the total number of ion pairs per cm of path. The results are shown in Fig. 5.12, which also gives the specific ionization for protons obtained by Jentschke by differentiating a curve relating total ionization of single protons to their residual range (i.e. the range remaining to a particle of given velocity).

The proton and α-particle curves in Fig. 5.12 are displaced by the distance of 0·2 cm (eq. 5.63) which takes account of the different effective charge of the two particles, as a fraction of their full charge, in the last few mm of range. At greater residual ranges the ionizations tend to stand in the ratio 4 : 1 expected theoretically for equal velocities on the basis of a z^2 dependence of energy loss. Experimental observations practically always give total ionization, which includes in addition to the primary ions (Sect. 5.2.1) all additional secondary ions due to the absorption of δ-rays and radiation resulting from the primary

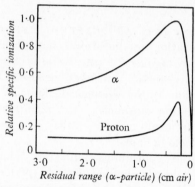

Fig. 5.12. Specific ionization of a single α-particle and a single proton in air at 15°C and 760 mm Hg. The maximum ionization is 6600 ion pairs mm⁻¹ for the α-particle and 2750 ion pairs mm⁻¹ for the proton (Ref. 5.1).

events. From the specific ionization and the specific energy loss dT/dx, the average expenditure of energy to form one ion pair (ω) is obtained. The general result of a great many measurements of ω is that it varies little with type of particle, incident velocity or type of gas in which the ionization is produced. Table 5.4 shows typical results:

TABLE 5.4   Energy in eV required to form one ion pair*

GAS	SLOW ELECTRONS (5 keV)	POLONIUM α-PARTICLES (5·3 MeV)	PROTONS (340 MeV)
Argon	27·0	25·9	25·5
Helium	32·5	31·7	29·9
Hydrogen	38·0	37·0	35·3
Nitrogen	35·8	36·0	33·6
Air	35·0	35·2	33·3
Oxygen	32·2	32·2	31·5
Methane	30·2	29·0	—

* Taken in part from Ref. 5.5, p. 57.

The measurements with α-particles are made by collection of ions, under conditions when recombination is small, either from the whole of the track of an α-particle or from a short section of it. The figures given in Table **5.4** for 340 MeV protons are due to Bakker and Segrè, who combined measurements of relative ionization in a particular gas and in argon with a separate observation that one 340 MeV proton produces 166 ion pairs per cm in argon at atmospheric pressure and 0° C. In this last experiment the ionization produced by a measured beam current of particles was recorded.

The ionization produced by beams of electrons and X-rays of known energy has been studied both in the expansion chamber and in ionization chambers. For X-rays passing through an ionization chamber the intensity of the beam is measured calorimetrically and the percentage of the beam absorbed by the ionization process must be estimated. For incident electrons the total charge collected is observed, together with the ionization produced by absorption in a gas. The availability of β-emitting radioactive isotopes has led to the development by Curran, Cockroft and Insch of an elegant method for finding ω, in which a weak source is placed inside a proportional counter. The counting rate gives the number n of particles and if the counter is then operated as an ionization chamber the total ion current i corresponding to absorption of the mean energy $\bar{E}$ of the radiations is obtained. We then have

$$\omega = \frac{ne\bar{E}}{i} \qquad (5.64)$$

These experiments have checked that for argon ω_A is constant within 2% up to an energy of about 1 MeV.

The existence of an ionization minimum and the subsequent rise in ionization predicted by 5.38 has been tested mainly for cosmic ray μ-mesons, for which radiative losses may be neglected. The momentum of the incident particle is found by magnetic deflection, and the ionization is recorded by making coincident observations in a proportional counter, or pressure ionization chamber, or expansion chamber. The incident particles may be selected for momentum by adjusting the magnetic field. The results of Ghosh, Jones and Wilson,[*] shown in

---

[*] S. K. Ghosh, G. M. D. B. Jones and J. G. Wilson, *Proc. phys. Soc. Lond.*, **67**, 331, 1954.

Fig. 5.13 illustrates the rise from the ionization minimum of about 40 ion pairs cm^{-1} of air and the 'Fermi plateau' (Sect. 5.3.2) for μ-mesons passing through argon.

Ionization in condensed media has been studied mainly in connection with the grain density resulting along the track of a charged particle passing through a photographic emulsion.

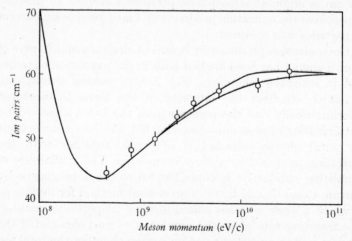

Fig. 5.13. Ionization by relativistic μ-mesons in oxygen excluding energy transfers of more than 1 keV. The curves are calculated theoretically.

The existence of a minimum density and the rise to a 'plateau' are well established, and the correlation of grain density with multiple-scattering angle forms an important method for identification of charged particles. In organic scintillating material (Sect. 6.1.6), for which light output might be expected to depend on ionization, no relativistic increase has yet been established.

5.3.5 STRAGGLING AND FLUCTUATION PHENOMENA. An average α-particle from a radioactive substance makes about 10^6 collisions resulting in small discrete energy transfers to electrons before coming to rest in an absorber. A group of such particles of initially uniform velocity, after passage through a certain thickness of matter, will show a distribution of velocities about a mean value owing to the statistical nature of the energy loss. The ranges of the particles will therefore be grouped about a mean value and since the number of collisions is large, and since also they are independent processes, the range (or energy) distribution may be expected to be approximately Gaussian. The *mean range* of the group has a definite value and it is this range which is always given in range energy tables.

The range straggling is estimated quantitatively in Ref. 5.1, p. 661. It is there shown that the standard deviation σ_R of the range distribution of heavy particles of energy T slowed down in an absorber is given by

$$\sigma_R^2 = 4\pi z^2 e^4 N Z \int_0^T \left(\frac{dT}{dx}\right)^{-3} dT \qquad (5.65)$$

where the symbols are those used in Sect. 5.2.2. By substitution from 5.37 for dT/dx and integration, neglecting the energy variation of the logarithmic term, we find approximately

$$\frac{\sigma_R^2}{R^2} = \frac{2m}{M} \frac{1}{\log \dfrac{2mv^2}{I}} \qquad (5.66)$$

For the α-particles of polonium ($E = 5\cdot3$ MeV, $R = 3\cdot84$ cm of air) we find $\sigma_R/R = 0\cdot9\%$. For protons of the same initial velocity as these α-particles, 5.66 shows that the straggling σ_R/R is just double that for the α-particles. This is because although the two particles make about the same number of energy transfer collisions in their range, the energy of the protons is only $\frac{1}{4}$ that of the α-particles and the straggling effect is therefore relatively greater.

In general the straggling for particles of mass number M, charge z and range R can be expressed in terms of the straggling of protons of range $z^2 R/M$ (Eq. 5.63, Sect. 5.3.3 shows that this is the range of protons of velocity equal to that of the particle z, M) by the formula

$$\left(\frac{\sigma_R}{R}\right)_{M, z, R} = \frac{1}{\sqrt{M}} \left(\frac{\sigma_R}{R}\right)_{1, 1, z^2 R/M} \qquad (5.66a)$$

The number of particles in a group of n_0 with ranges between

x and $x + dx$ can now be written, assuming a normal distribution

$$dn = \frac{n_0}{\sigma_R \sqrt{2\pi}} \exp -\frac{(x-R)^2}{2\sigma_R^2}\, dx \qquad (5.67)$$

$$= \frac{n_0}{\alpha \sqrt{\pi}} \exp -\left(\frac{x-R}{\alpha}\right)^2 dx \qquad (5.67a)$$

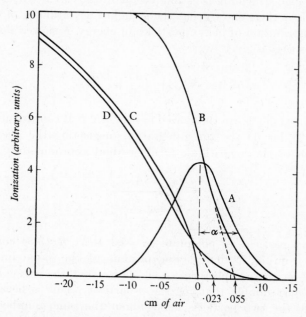

Fig. 5.14. Characteristics of range curves for polonium α-particles in air. A, range straggling distribution about the mean range; B, number-distance curve showing extrapolated range; C, differential specific ionization of a single α-particle of mean range; D, average ionization (Bragg) curve for a group of α-particles with the range distribution of curve A, showing the extrapolated ionization range. The straggling parameter α is shown (Holloway and Livingston, *Phys. Rev.*, **54**, 18, 1938).

in which R is the mean range and $\alpha = \sqrt{2}\sigma_R$ is the *range straggling parameter*. The *number-distance curve* follows immediately by integration; in this curve* (Fig. 5.14) the mean range

---

* M. G. Holloway and M. S. Livingston, *Phys. Rev.*, **54**, 18, 1938.

is at the point of inflection of the curve, and is the range reached by half of the particles. The intercept on the range axis of the linear part of the number-distance curve gives the *extrapolated number range* (ENR) which is readily determined in counting experiments. It is easily shown that this range exceeds the mean range by $\sqrt{\frac{\pi}{2}}\,\sigma_R$. Fig. 5.14 also shows the specific ionization curve of a single α-particle, which is drawn to terminate at the mean range of the straggled group, and by multiplying this by the straggling distribution for an initially homogeneous group, a curve known as the *Bragg* or average *ionization curve* is obtained. This is essentially the ionization measured in a very shallow chamber drawn along the path of a beam of α-particles passing through a gas. If the linear part of the Bragg curve is extrapolated to the range axis we obtain the *extrapolated ionization range* (EIR).

Straggling is normally shown and measured by the experiments which determine energy loss. It may be seen in the energy distribution of protons after passage through an absorbing foil and in any observation of a Bragg curve by an ionization chamber or a number–range curve by counters or an expansion chamber.

The assumption of a Gaussian distribution for the energy loss, although in approximate agreement with experiment for non-relativistic particles, neglects the effect of the small number of collisions with high energy loss, which contribute a 'tail' to the distribution. This effect is particularly marked for electrons because of the large energy loss which is possible in a single collision and a detailed theory has been given by Williams, by Landau and by Symon. The type of distribution found is shown in Fig. 5.15 which gives results of Goldwasser, Mills and Hanson* on the energy loss of 15·7 MeV electrons in a thin metal foil, determined by magnetic analysis, following the original studies of White and Millington. The characteristic asymmetrical shape of the 'Landau' distribution is clear; it is also necessary to take account of the density effect in condensed media to obtain agreement with experiment. The width of the

---

* E. L. Goldwasser, F. E. Mills and A. O. Hanson, *Phys. Rev.*, 88 1137, 1952.

Landau distribution has been measured and compared with theory for protons, electrons and μ-mesons (Ref. 5.5); it must always be taken into account in computing the most probable energy loss of a relativistic particle. As the velocity of the

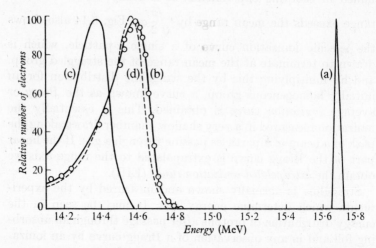

Fig. 5.15. Energy distribution of electron beam before and after passing through $0 \cdot 86$ g cm^{-2} of aluminium; (a) incident beam, (b) transmitted beam, (c) Landau theory, (d) Landau theory with density correction (Goldwasser *et al.*, *Phys. Rev.*, **88**, 1137, 1952).

particle decreases the relative importance of small energy transfers increases and the straggling tends to the symmetrical, Gaussian form.

5.3.6 CAPTURE AND LOSS (CHARGE EXCHANGE). It was found by Henderson in 1922 that a beam of α-particles passing through matter always consisted of a mixture of singly and doubly charged particles. The proportion of singly charged particles increases markedly towards the end of the range of the particles and a small component of neutral helium atoms also develops. These phenomena are due to rapid changes in the charge state of the helium ion resulting from pick-up of atomic electrons and to subsequent re-ionization by collision. The existence of the three beams may easily be demonstrated by a magnetic deflection experiment as shown in Fig. 5.16a; in

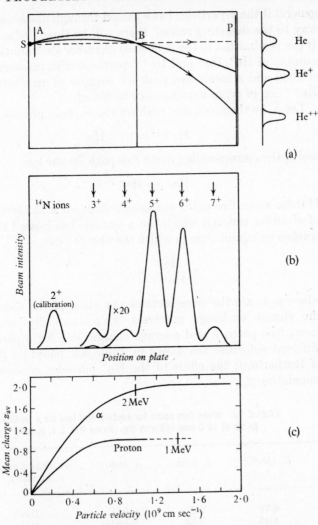

Fig. 5.16. Capture and loss of electrons by heavy charged particles.
a) Principle of apparatus; α-particles from a source pass through an absorber A and a collimating slit B in a vacuum box. They are deflected in a transverse magnetic field and the detector shows traces due to neutral, singly charged and doubly charged particles.
b) Results for nitrogen ions accelerated in a cyclotron (Stephens and Walker, *Proc. roy. Soc.* **A,229**, 376, 1955).
c) Average charge for protons and α-particles as a function of particle velocity (Ref. 5.1).

general if the α-particles have passed through absorber on their way to the detecting screen, there will be three distinct traces. If gas is admitted to the deflection chamber the variation in the number of He°, He$^+$ and He^{++} particles with pressure may be studied and a mean free path for capture of an electron by a He^{++} ion of given velocity may be found.

Let λ_c be the mean free path for the capture process

$$He^{++} + e^- \rightarrow He^+ \qquad (5.68)$$

and λ_l the corresponding mean free path for the loss

$$He^+ \rightarrow He^{++} + e^- \qquad (5.69)$$

If these mean free paths are small compared with the thickness of absorber through which the α-particle has passed the beam reaches an equilibrium in which the charge ratio, is

$$\frac{He^+}{He^{++}} = \frac{\lambda_l}{\lambda_c} = \frac{\sigma_c}{\sigma_l} \qquad (5.70)$$

where σ_l, σ_c are the cross-sections per atom of the absorber for the charge exchange processes. Experimentally determined mean free paths λ and average charges ez_{av} for α-particles of different velocities are shown in Table 5.5, based on the work of Rutherford; the effect of the He° particles is neglected in calculating z_{av}.

TABLE 5.5   Mean free paths for capture and loss for α particles in air at 15°C and 160 mm Hg. (From Ref. 5.1, p. 634)

E_α (MeV)	λ_c (mm)	λ_l (mm)	AVERAGE CHARGE NUMBER z_{av}
6·78	2·2	0·011	1·995
4·43	0·52	0·0078	1·985
1·70	0·037	0·0050	1·883
0·65	0·003	0·003	1·500

The Table shows that the interchange of charge near the end of the range of the α-particle is very rapid and may take place 1000 times in the last cm of air before the particle is brought to rest. The mean free paths seem to be independent of the nature of the absorber and are so short for low velocity particles that charge equilibrium is reached for extremely thin layers of matter. Thus α-particles of about 1 MeV emerging from a target of thickness of only a few μg cm^{-1} will already be partly in the He$^+$ state.

Theoretically the loss of an electron from a partially ionized atom is a further ionization, and in accordance with the formulae developed in Sect. 5.2.2 the corresponding cross-section should be proportional to $1/v^2$. The actual dependence is more nearly on $1/v$. The inverse capture process is much more velocity dependent and the cross-section law seems to vary between v^{-4} and v^{-12} under different conditions. Bohr has emphasized the importance for the process of capture and loss of the ratio between the velocity v of the incident ion and the orbital velocity u which an electron bound to this ion possesses. If $v > u$, for all electrons which can be bound to the ion, electron loss predominates and the ion becomes fully ionized; capture of electrons back into states for which $u < v$ is improbable. When $u = v$ this simple argument predicts that the capture and loss cross-sections should be nearly equal and this has been verified in experiments on artificially accelerated helium ions. The argument also permits a rough estimate to be made of the charge state of an ion of a given velocity.

The phenomenon of charge exchange has been extensively studied for protons and α-particles and also for fission fragments (Section 5.3.7) which carry a large number of electrons because of their high nuclear charge. Many of the phenomena are more clearly exhibited by the behaviour of accelerated heavy ions such as carbon or nitrogen passing through gases or through foils thick enough to produce charge equilibrium but thin enough to give little reduction of velocity. In the work of Stephens and Walker* 15·0 MeV nitrogen ions emerging from a cyclotron were passed through an organic film of thickness 10^{-5} cm and analysed magnetically (Fig. 5.16b), using a photographic emulsion as detector. The population of the possible ionic states of the beam is clearly shown. From experiments such as this the average charge of the ion for a given velocity can be found as

$$z_{\mathrm{av}} = zq_0 + (z-1)q_1 + \ldots + q_z \qquad (5.71)$$

---

* K. G. Stephens and D. Walker, *Proc. roy. Soc.*, **A229**, 376, 1955.

where q_z is the fraction of ions which have retained z electrons.

The variation of average charge with velocity for α-particles and protons is shown in Fig. 5.16c.

5.3.7 PASSAGE OF FISSION FRAGMENTS THROUGH MATTER. This requires special treatment because of the extreme importance of charge exchange in determining the energy loss of these particles and because of the significance of nuclear collisions at the end of their range.

Fission fragments (Sect. **14.**1) are groups of nuclei of mass number approximately $100(Z \approx 40)$ and $140(Z \approx 55)$ which are emitted in the disintegration of uranium with energies of about 100 MeV and 65 MeV respectively. They therefore have velocities of about 10^9 cm $\sec^{-1}$, comparable with that of a slow α-particle (2 MeV) and their range in air is found to be just over 2 cm. The initial velocities of fission fragments are not sufficient to detach more than about half their electrons and the corresponding ionization in matter is extremely dense, some 50 times that of an α-particle of energy 5 MeV. The initial fragment charge has been measured directly by Lassen, using a magnetic deflection method, and is as shown in Fig. 5.17a for the light and heavy fragments in solids and gases.

Lassen also measured the energy loss along the path of fission fragments in argon and his results are shown in Fig. 5.17b, which may be contrasted with the variation of specific ionization along the track of an α-particle near the end of its range (Fig. 5.12). The difference arises because the effective (or average) charge z_{ave} of the fission fragment decreases continually from its initial value as the fragment slows down owing to pickup of electrons whereas this process only becomes significant for the α-particle within a few mm of the end of its range. Fig. 5.17b shows also that towards the end of the range of the fission fragment the energy loss curve resembles that for a particle of constant charge. This is because in this region the fragment or *ionic* charge z_{ave} has become so small that the main mechanism of energy loss is a direct interaction between the *nuclear* charge ze of the fragment and the nuclear charge Ze of the absorbing atoms. This mechanism of energy loss exists also at higher velocities (and for light particles) but is then generally insignificant in comparison with the electronic loss.

The total specific energy loss of a fission fragment may be written in the form

$$-\frac{dT}{dx} = \frac{4\pi z_{av}^2 e^4 NZ}{mv^2} L_{electronic} + \frac{4\pi z^2 Z^2 e^4}{Mv^2} N L_{nuclear} \quad (5.72)$$

where M is the mass of the absorbing atoms and the quantities $L_{electronic}$ and $L_{nuclear}$ depend in detail on assumptions about the

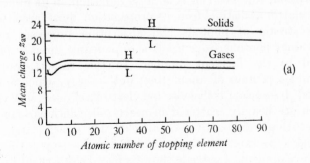

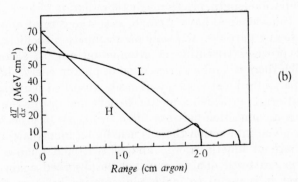

Fig. 5.17

a) Average charge of fission fragments in solid and gaseous stopping materials; H = heavy fragment, L = light fragment.
b) Energy loss along the path of fission fragments in argon at 15°C and 760 mm Hg. (From Bohr and Lindhard, *Kgl. Danske Videnskab. Selskab.*, **28**, No. 7, 1954.)

range of impact parameters for the two types of energy transfer. As the fragment velocity decreases the second term becomes predominant because of the fall of z_{av}. The nuclear energy transfers sometimes result in the ejection of recoil nuclei from the absorber atoms and these nuclear 'delta rays' may be seen along the tracks of fission fragments and other heavy ions in expansion chamber photographs.

5.4 Interaction of electromagnetic radiation with matter

5.4.1 GENERAL. The passage of electromagnetic radiation through matter is characterized by the exponential law of absorption, Eq. 5.6. This is because radiation, in its interaction with matter as distinct from its propagation, must be considered as a stream of photons and absorption processes remove individual photons from a beam to a degree directly proportional to the incident number. In this respect, radiation resembles protons of about 1000 MeV energy, which are 'absorbed' by nuclear collisions, and electrons of a few MeV energy which are heavily scattered in nearly all collisions in matter, rather than radioactive α-particles, for which large angle collisions are rare. Although at high energies (say > 100 MeV) the development of cascade showers may be described in terms of a radiation length, electromagnetic radiation of lower energy is not considered to have a range, as in the case of non-relativistic heavy particles, but only an attenuation coefficient μ.

The processes resulting in attenuation are (a) absorption, in which there is a direct conversion of photon energy in whole or in part into kinetic energy of easily absorbed particles, and (b) scattering, in which a photon is deflected out of the beam. There is a connection between these two types of process since in any given interaction there is usually an immediate appearance both of kinetic energy and of scattered quanta. Since however scattered quanta may not be absorbed again in the scatterer it is useful to make a distinction between the two processes and to write

$$\mu = \mu_a + \mu_s \qquad (5.73)$$

The coefficient μ_a then gives the *deposition of energy* in a medium, as distinct from the diminution in the number of photons (given by μ) and is important in assessing radiation hazards.

The coefficients μ, μ_a and μ_s depend on the atomic number of the absorbing material and on the energy of the incident quanta in a way determined by the details of the interaction processes. These are:

   a) elastic scattering (Rayleigh, Thomson and nuclear resonant),
   b) photoelectric effect,
   c) Compton scattering,
   d) pair production for photon energies above 1 MeV,

of which the last three are usually stated to be inelastic. The Compton effect is actually elastic in the sense of Sect. 5.1.1 since there is no loss of kinetic energy, but there is a wavelength change and the scattered radiation is essentially incoherent with the incident beam. In addition nuclear inelastic scattering, the nuclear photoeffect and photomeson production are absorption processes which are important and interesting in detail but do not normally contribute essentially to the observed values of attenuation coefficients. Of the elastic processes Rayleigh scattering (Sect. 5.4.2) is usually by far the most important, but in special circumstances (Mössbauer effect, Sect. 13.6.3) nuclear attenuation may exceed that due to electronic processes.

If cross-sections σ_R, σ_{PE}, σ_C and σ_{PP} are assigned to the individual processes the linear attenuation coefficient for removal of photons from a homogeneous beam may be written*

$$\mu = N(\sigma_R + \sigma_{PE} + \sigma_{PP}) + ZN\sigma_C \qquad (5.74)$$

where N is the number of atoms of absorber per cm³. The atomic number Z multiplies the cross-section σ_C because the Compton effect takes place with individual electrons rather than with atoms as a whole. From μ, the mass attenuation coefficient μ_m is obtained by dividing by the density of a particular absorber; Fig. 5.18a, b show the variation of μ_m with energy for aluminium and lead over the region of the electromagnetic spectrum of main interest for nuclear physics. The figure shows that the energy is not a single valued function of the attenuation coefficient, because the pair production cross-section σ_{PP} increases with energy while the photoelectric and Compton cross-sections decrease. Measurement of attenuation

---

* In most practical cases the term σ_R may be omitted (Sect. 5.4.2).

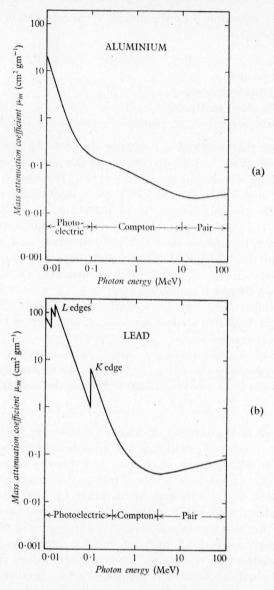

Fig. 5.18. Mass attenuation coefficients for electromagnetic radiation in aluminium and lead. The regions over which the photoelectric effect, Compton effect and pair production are important are indicated (Ref. 5.1).

coefficient near minimum absorption is therefore not an unambiguous method of determining photon energy in this region
of the spectrum.

The wavelength of a photon of energy 10 MeV is
0.12×10^{-10} cm. For energies below this it is a good approximation to assume that the instantaneous electric field of the photon
does not vary over a typical nucleus. Variations over the *atom*
however must occur, and can be used for radiation of X-ray
wavelength to reveal details of atomic structure.

5.4.2 ELASTIC SCATTERING OF RADIATION. If a plane
polarized electromagnetic wave falls upon a free electron
(Fig. 5.19a), the charge receives an acceleration

$$\ddot{z} = \frac{eE_0}{m} \cos \omega t \qquad (5.75)$$

where the electric field of the incident wave is taken to be

$$E_z = E_0 \cos \omega t \qquad (5.76)$$

The solution of Eq. 5.75 is

$$z = -\frac{eE_0}{m\omega^2} \cos \omega t \qquad (5.77)$$

so that the electron moves in anti-phase with the electric
vector. This accelerated motion creates a time-varying dipole
moment $D = ez$, and according to classical electrodynamics, a
radiation field results, in which the amplitude of the electric
vector at a point P distant R from the dipole is

$$E_S = -\frac{e^2 E_0}{mc^2} \frac{\sin \Theta}{R} = \frac{f(\Theta)E_0}{R} \qquad (5.78)$$

where Θ is the angle between the polarization vector and the
direction of observation and $f(\Theta)$ is known as the *scattering
amplitude*. The time-averaged flux of radiation across a small
area dA perpendicular to R is (Eqn. 3.50)

$$dW = \frac{e^4 \sin^2 \Theta \, E_0^2}{8\pi R^2 m^2 c^3} \, dA$$

$$= \frac{e^4 \sin^2 \Theta \, E_0^2}{8\pi m^2 c^3} \, d\Omega \text{ erg sec}^{-1} \qquad (5.79)$$

The incident intensity of radiation is

$$I = \frac{cE_0^2}{8\pi} \text{ erg sec}^{-1}\text{cm}^{-2} \tag{5.80}$$

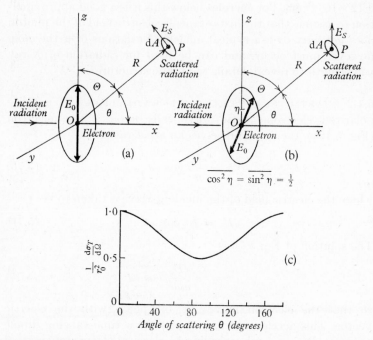

$$\overline{\cos^2 \eta} = \overline{\sin^2 \eta} = \tfrac{1}{2}$$

Fig. 5.19. Thomson scattering of radiation from a free electron, observed in plane xOz. (a) Plane polarized wave, (b) unpolarized wave, (c) angular distribution of scattered radiation from unpolarized wave.

From the considerations of Sect. 5.1.3 (see also Ref. 5.1, p. 821) we may relate the radiation dW scattered by a *single electron* to the incident radiation intensity through the concept of cross-section, and write

$$dW = I \, d\sigma_T = I\sigma_T(\Theta) \, d\Omega \tag{5.81}$$

whence

$$\sigma_T(\Theta) = \left(\frac{e^2}{mc^2}\right)^2 \sin^2 \Theta = |f(\Theta)|^2 \tag{5.82}$$

If the incident radiation is unpolarized an average over the possible orientations of the incident electric vector must be made, and by resolving this vector parallel and perpendicular to the scattering plane xOz (Fig. 5.19b) we obtain

$$
\begin{aligned}
dW &= \frac{e^4 E_0^2}{8\pi m^2 c^3}\, d\Omega\, [\sin^2 \Theta \,\overline{\cos^2 \eta} + \overline{\sin^2 \eta}] \\
&= \frac{e^4 E_0^2}{8\pi m^2 c^3}\, d\Omega\, \frac{1 + \sin^2 \Theta}{2} \\
&= I \left(\frac{e^2}{mc^2}\right)^2 d\Omega\, \frac{1 + \cos^2\theta}{2}
\end{aligned}
\tag{5.83}
$$

where θ is the angle of scattering. The differential cross-section for scattering of unpolarized radiation through angle θ by a *single electron* is thus

$$
d\sigma_T = \left(\frac{e^2}{mc^2}\right)^2 \frac{1 + \cos^2\theta}{2}\, d\Omega
\tag{5.84}
$$

and the total cross-section, obtained by writing $d\Omega = 2\pi \sin \theta\, d\theta$ and integrating between the limits $\theta = 0$ and $\theta = \pi$ is

$$
\sigma_T = \frac{8\pi}{3} \left(\frac{e^2}{mc^2}\right)^2 = \frac{8\pi}{3}\, r_0^2
\tag{5.84a}
$$

where $r_0 = e^2/mc^2$ is the classical electron radius. This cross section, first calculated by J. J. Thomson and now known after him, is independent of primary frequency and enters into all more accurate expressions for the scattering of electromagnetic waves. It is also valid quantum mechanically in the non-relativistic limit ($h\nu \ll mc^2$) for scattering of radiation by free electrons. Fig. 5.19c shows the angular distribution of the Thomson scattering of unpolarized radiation, as given by 5.84.

When radiation is incident on an atom containing Z bound electrons and a nucleus of charge Ze, elastic scattering can take place:

a) from the bound electrons (*Rayleigh scattering*), providing that the electrons do not receive sufficient energy to eject them from the atom,

b) from the nuclear charge (Thomson scattering).

Nuclear resonant scattering (Sect. 13.6.3) and scattering of the photons by the electromagnetic field of the nucleus (potential or Delbruck scattering) can also take place but will be disregarded in this chapter. The Rayleigh scattering by the bound electrons acting together is calculated by assuming that each electron scatters a wave with amplitude at unit distance given by the Thomson factor $\dfrac{e^2}{mc^2}\sin\Theta$ and that a coherent superposition of these amplitudes for a given direction of scattering must be made. An integration over the electron distribution then leads to an *atomic scattering factor* f_θ in terms of which the differential cross-section for Rayleigh scattering may be written

$$d\sigma_R = \left(\frac{e^2}{mc^2}\right)^2 |f_\theta|^2 \frac{1+\cos^2\theta}{2}\, d\Omega \qquad (5.85)$$

In the limit of very long wavelengths $f_\theta \to Z$, but as the wavelength decreases (and the non-relativistic approximation becomes worse) the Rayleigh scattering from an atom is concentrated into forward angles as expected from simple diffraction theory. The Rayleigh scattering from atoms arranged in a regular crystal structure is responsible for X-ray diffraction phenomena.

The Thomson scattering by the nuclear charge Ze is well described by the classical theory because the nuclear mass M must replace the electron mass in Eq. 5.75 and the condition $h\nu \ll Mc^2$ is amply fulfilled. Thomson and Rayleigh scattering are coherent since they arise from the motions of complementary charges in the same electric field, although this may vary over the atom for the shorter X-rays and gamma rays. The theoretical values of Rayleigh and Thomson scattering for 411 keV gamma rays are shown in Fig. 5.20a, given by Moon.* This figure also gives for comparison the cross-section for incoherent scattering due to the Compton effect (Sect. 5.4.4) which gradually replaces the coherent Rayleigh scattering as the photon energy increases and electrons are increasingly removed from their bound states. For very small angles the Rayleigh scattering, then proportional to Z^2, exceeds the Compton scattering, but since it is so strongly peaked forward it contributes little to the attenuation of a beam, and is not included in Fig. 5.18. The variation of the Rayleigh cross-section for lead with energy is shown in Fig. 5.20b.

---

* P. B. Moon, *Proc. phys. Soc. Lond.*, **63**, 1189, 1950.

5.4.3 PHOTOELECTRIC EFFECT; AUGER EFFECT. A free electron cannot wholly absorb a photon because it is impossible simultaneously to conserve both energy and momentum. Quanta of energy greater than an atomic ionization potential may however eject a bound electron from a free atom (Fig.

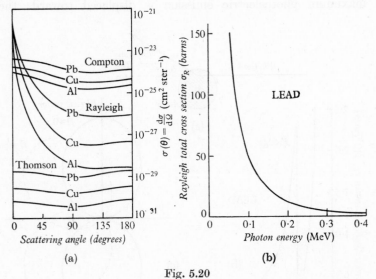

Fig. 5.20

a) Scattering of 411 keV radiation by atoms of Al, Cu, Pb (Moon, *Proc. phys. Soc.*, **63**, 1189, 1950).
b) Variation of Rayleigh total cross-section σ_R with energy for lead (Ref. 5.1).

5.21a) because the residual ion is able to take up the balance of momentum. The probability of this photoelectric absorption is greater the more tightly bound the electron and hence chiefly involves the K-shell, if sufficient energy is available, so that the energy of the emitted photoelectron is

$$T = h\nu - E_K \tag{5.86}$$

where E_K is the ionization energy of the K electron.

The theoretical treatment of this effect is only simple if the electron energy is small compared with mc^2, so that non-relativistic wave functions may be used. It is then found that most of the photoelectrons are emitted in the direction of the electric vector of the incident radiation, so that the angular distribution about the beam is as shown in Fig. 5.21c. The cross-section, and hence the absorption coefficient, is roughly given by

$$\sigma_{PE} \approx Z^5 \lambda^{7/2} \text{ (sometimes given as } Z^4 \lambda^3) \qquad (5.87)$$

As the primary quantum energy increases the direction of maximum photoelectric emission is displaced towards the

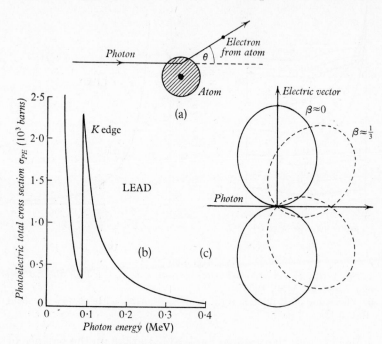

Fig. 5.21. Photoelectric effect.
a) Interaction of photon with an atom.
b) Variation of photoelectric total cross-section σ_{PE} with energy for lead (Ref. 5.1 and 5.10).
c) Polar diagram showing angular distribution of photoelectrons with respect to electric vector of incident radiation.

forward direction (Fig. 5.21c) and in the extreme relativistic region the cross-section varies more nearly as

$$\sigma_{PE} \approx Z^5 \lambda \qquad (5.88)$$

The theoretical variation of σ_{PE} with energy for lead is shown in Fig. 5.21b; there is a sharp increase in cross-section with increasing quantum energy at the ionization potentials of successive atomic shells. The process is important for absorption at energies below 0·5 MeV.

The photoelectric effect essentially gives no scattering of the incident radiation in the sense discussed in Sect. 5.4.1 because the small amount of energy which does not appear directly in the photoelectron is emitted as X-radiation and Auger electrons resulting from the atomic vacancy and these radiations are usually easily absorbed.

The Auger effect is the emission of low energy photoelectrons as an alternative to X-rays after the creation of a vacancy in one of the atomic shells by photoelectric effect, nuclear electron capture or other transition. If the K-shell is excited, the Auger electron may then originate in the L-shell and its energy is

$$T = h\nu_K - E_L = E_K - 2E_L \qquad (5.89)$$

where ν_K is the frequency of the K X-ray line, and E_L is the energy of the L-edge. The Auger process is sometimes described as internal conversion of X-rays although it is strictly an alternative process for removal of energy. The relative probability of Auger emission and X-radiation is measured by the *fluorescence yield*

$$W_K = \frac{\text{number of } K \text{ quanta}}{\text{number of } K \text{ shell vacancies}} \text{ (for the } K\text{-shell)} \qquad (5.90)$$

and the empirical variation of this quantity with Z is shown in Fig. 5.22. For heavy atoms radiation is the more probable because of the high nuclear charge which effectively increases the coupling of the system to the radiation field; for light atoms the Auger effect is predominant. The effect was discovered by the observation of short electron tracks associated with the emission of longer photoelectrons along the path of a beam of X-rays in an expansion chamber, cf. Plate 3. It has been possible to give an accurate theoretical treatment of the process and in particular to predict the curve shown in Fig. 5.22. The Auger effect is also important in transitions between the levels of mesonic atoms (Sect. 11.2.3).

5.4.4 COMPTON EFFECT. Neither the Rayleigh elastic scattering nor the photoelectric absorption cuts off sharply at any particular quantum energy, and both depend upon the reaction of an atom as a whole. As the quantum energy increases the wavelength becomes shorter and there is a greater tendency for interaction to take place with individual electrons, providing always that the energy exceeds the ionization potential. Since, however, relativistic effects also become important as the wavelength decreases, the simple Thomson theory of free

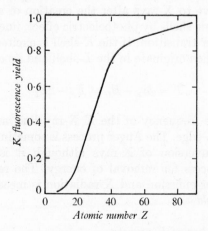

Fig. 5.22. K-shell fluorescence yield (Ref. 5.1).

electron scattering is inadequate and the interaction must be regarded as the collision of a photon with an electron. This process is known as the Compton effect and is the most important mechanism of energy absorption for radiation of energy between, say, 0·5 MeV and 10 MeV. It differs most markedly from the Thomson scattering because the scattered radiation is of longer wavelength than the incident beam, and its wavelength depends on the angle of scattering. At each angle the Compton-scattered (modified) radiation is accompanied by a Rayleigh-scattered (unmodified) component, and the ratio between the two depends on the atomic number of the scatterer, which determines the ratio of effectively free to effectively bound electrons. These effects are illustrated in Fig. 5.23a.

The energy and momentum relations for the Compton effect follow from Fig. 5.23b. For conservation of linear momentum

$$\frac{h\nu_0}{c} = \frac{h\nu'}{c} \cos\theta + p \cos\phi$$

$$0 = \frac{h\nu'}{c} \sin\theta - p \sin\phi \qquad (5.91)$$

where p is the (relativistic) momentum of the recoil electron and for conservation of energy

$$h\nu_0 = h\nu' + T \qquad (5.92)$$

where T is the kinetic energy of the electron, related to its momentum p by the equation

$$p^2 c^2 = T(T + 2mc^2) \qquad (5.93)$$

From these equations, which must hold whatever the details of the scattering process, by elimination of ϕ and p the change in frequency or wavelength of the scattered photon is found to be

$$\frac{c}{\nu'} - \frac{c}{\nu_0} = \lambda' - \lambda_0 = \frac{h}{mc}(1 - \cos\theta) \qquad (5.94)$$

The Compton shift in *wavelength* $\lambda' - \lambda_0$ is thus

a) independent of the incident *wavelength*, so that photons of high energy (short wavelength) lose a large amount of energy in the scattering,

b) independent of the material of the scatterer,

c) dependent on angle in a way which is found to agree with experiment if m is taken to be the mass of an electron

d) expressible in terms of a fundamental constant h/mc, the Compton wavelength of a free electron, which is the wavelength of a photon of energy equal to mc^2, the electron rest energy.

The energy of the scattered quantum is

$$h\nu' = \frac{h\nu_0}{1 + \dfrac{h\nu_0}{mc^2}(1 - \cos\theta)} \qquad (5.95)$$

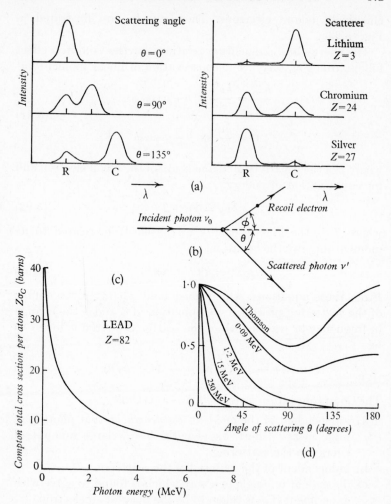

Fig. 5.23. Compton effect.

a) Qualitative dependence of Compton scattering (C) on angle and atomic number of scatterer, in relation to Rayleigh (unmodified) scattering (R). The intensity scales are arbitrary.

b) Interaction of photon with free electron.

c) Variation of Compton total cross-section per atom of lead ($Z\sigma_C$) with energy (Ref. 5.10, Table XIV).

d) Angular distribution of Compton scattered radiation; the intensity at angle θ is proportional to $\nu'\,\mathrm{d}\sigma_C$ (Ref. 1.6).

and the kinetic energy of the recoil electron is then

$$T = h(v_0 - v') = hv_0 \frac{\dfrac{hv_0}{mc^2}(1 - \cos\theta)}{1 + \dfrac{hv_0}{mc^2}(1 - \cos\theta)} \qquad (5.96)$$

which is zero for $\theta = 0$ and a maximum for $\theta = \pi$, as might be expected. For $hv_0 \gg mc^2$ the Compton scattered photons at $\theta = 90°$ always have the energy mc^2 (511 keV).

These consequences of the photon hypothesis and of the laws of collision have been verified with great quantitative detail. The simultaneity of the emission of the scattered quantum and recoil electron, which now tends to be implicitly assumed, is of great importance for the photon hypothesis and has not remained unquestioned. The early experiments of Geiger and Bothe, in which the quantum and recoil electron were recorded in counters, and of Compton and Simon, in which tracks of recoil electrons and of photoelectrons from scattered γ-rays were observed in an expansion chamber, have, however, been abundantly confirmed by more recent work.

The probability of Compton scattering cannot be calculated simply, since it depends on details of the photon-electron interaction, e.g. the relation between the direction of polarization of the radiation and the direction of spin momentum of the scattering electron. A full discussion of the Klein–Nishina formula, which gives the differential cross-section for Compton scattering, is given by Evans (Ref. 5.1, p. 677). The fundamental expression for the differential collision cross-section per electron for polarized radiation is

$$d\sigma_C = \frac{r_0^2}{4} d\Omega \left(\frac{v'}{v_0}\right)^2 \left(\frac{v_0}{v'} + \frac{v'}{v_0} - 2 + 4\cos^2\Theta\right) \qquad (5.97)$$

in which r_0 is the classical electron radius and Θ is the angle between the polarization vectors of the incident and scattered radiation. This formula gives the probability of the scattering of a photon into the solid angle $d\Omega$ with energy hv'; if the solid angle element is $2\pi \sin\theta\, d\theta$, corresponding to scattering through angle θ, then θ is given in terms of v' by Eq. 5.95. It may also be shown (Ref. 5.1) that the scattered photon and recoil electron tend to lie in a plane perpendicular to the electric vector of the incident radiation. This fact is utilized in the design of polarimeters for studying nuclear gamma radiation. Circularly polarized radiation would have no preferential scattering plane, but the scattering of this type of radiation is sensitive to the direction of the electron spins in the scatterer, and iron magnetized to saturation can be used as a polarimeter in this case. For unpolarized incident radiation, averaging of 5.97 over all incident and scattered polarizations gives for the differential collision cross-section for deflection θ

$$d\sigma_C = \frac{r_0^2}{2} \, d\Omega \left(\frac{\nu'}{\nu_0}\right)^2 \left(\frac{\nu_0}{\nu'} + \frac{\nu'}{\nu_0} - \sin^2\theta\right) \tag{5.98}$$

This formula can be used to calculate the *number* of photons observed at a scattering angle θ. Since the energy of the scattered photon varies rapidly with θ, the *intensity* of radiation or energy scattered through the angle θ, is proportional to $\nu' \, d\sigma_C$. Fig. 5.23d shows the relative intensity of Compton scattering as a function of angle; for small angles and for small incident energies it approaches the value predicted by the Thomson formula.

The *total* collision cross-section σ_C is obtained by integrating 5.98 over all angles θ from 0 to π. This gives the probability of removal of a photon from the beam by a Compton process and is shown for a particular case in Fig. 5.23c; it also appears directly in the attenuation coefficient μ shown in Fig. 5.18. The Klein–Nishina theory has been exhaustively and successfully tested by measurements of Compton total and differential cross-section for a wide range of atomic numbers and energies; as shown in Fig. 5.23c the cross-section decreases with quantum energy.

5.4.5 PAIR PRODUCTION. Dirac's relativistic wave equation, which gives such an excellent description of the properties of the electron and of the fine structure of the hydrogen spectrum, leads to the conclusion that electrons possess states of negative energy. From the relativistic formula connecting energy and momentum of a particle of rest mass m we have for the total energy

$$E^2 = (T + mc^2)^2 = p^2c^2 + m^2c^4$$

whence $\qquad\qquad E = \pm\sqrt{p^2c^2 + m^2c^4} \tag{5.99}$

This means that the states of energy for an electron are as shown in Fig. 5.24a, extending positively from mc^2 to $+\infty$ and negatively from $-mc^2$ to $-\infty$. Classically the negative energy states* could be excluded as having no physical meaning, but quantum mechanically an external field can cause transitions to these states which must therefore be accommodated in the theory. The derivation of the Klein–Nishina formula for the Compton effect is based on Dirac's theory and explicitly involves transitions of this kind in which momentum, but not energy, is conserved. Such processes are permitted within the limits of the uncertainty principle; energy need not be conserved in an intermediate state if it is sufficiently short-lived. The exact quantitative success of the Klein–Nishina formula is strong evidence for the existence of negative energy states.

In order to avoid the difficulty that the ordinary electrons of experience should all make transitions to negative energy states Dirac put forward his theory of 'holes' according to which in the absence of an external field all negative energy states are filled with electrons and there can be no transitions to these occupied states. This sea of electrons is supposed to give no contribution to the total energy and momentum of a system. If now an electron is removed from the distribution by the action of an external field, creating a hole, the system acquires an energy $-(-E)$, a momentum $-(-p)$ and a charge $-(-e)$, that is to say it behaves as an electron of ordinary momentum and energy but with positive charge. Since the electron elevated by this transition must finally occupy a state of total energy greater than mc^2, it is clear from Fig. 5.24a that the external field, which may be that of γ-radiation or that of a charged particle, must supply an energy greater than $2mc^2$ to induce the transition. The elevated electron and the 'hole' together form an electron–positron pair and the process, which obviously has a threshold energy of $2mc^2$, is known as pair production. In order to satisfy the conservation laws, pair production must take place in the field of an electron or a nucleus, which can absorb linear momentum. Positrons were discovered in cloud

---

* In a negative energy state acceleration would be in a direction opposite to the applied force.

7*

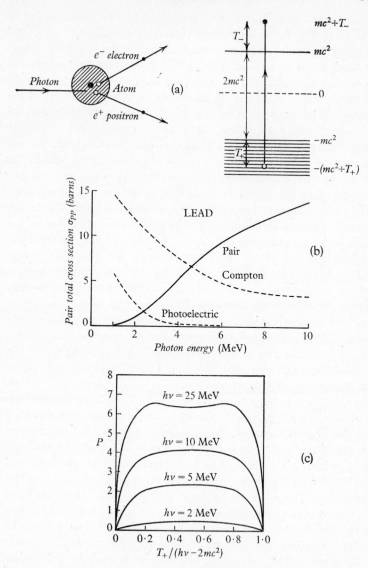

Fig. 5.24. Pair production.
a) Mechanism; the energy absorbed in the process is $2mc^2 + T^+ + T^-$.
b) Variation of pair total cross-section σ_{PP} with energy for lead. The Compton and photoelectric cross-sections are indicated for comparison (Ref. 5.10, Table XIV).
c) Distribution in energy between electrons and positrons (Ref. 5.1).

chamber photographs of cosmic radiation by Anderson* in 1932 and are now familiar particles, of common occurrence in nuclear β-processes (ch. 16); a picture of a positron track, distinguished by its curvature, is given in Plate 6.

The interaction between electrons and positrons includes, in addition to ordinary scattering, the possibility of annihilation. This is the process inverse to pair production, and in it the electron makes a transition to the vacant negative energy state corresponding to the positron. Both particles disappear and there is an appearance of an energy of $2mc^2$ as electromagnetic radiation. In the annihilation of free positrons at rest by free electrons conservation of momentum requires that this energy shall appear as two oppositely directed quanta of energy $mc^2 = 0.511$ MeV, the so-called *annihilation radiation*, but in the field of a nucleus one quantum annihilation is also possible, with absorption of an electron. If a positron is annihilated by collision with a moving electron the angle between the two annihilation quanta becomes less than $180°$ and observation of these angles is an important means of learning about the distribution of electron momenta in matter. Annihilation of positrons in flight is possible, and has been observed; the single quantum process yields homogeneous γ radiation.

Annihilation of positrons is formally equivalent to the production of bremsstrahlung in the collisions of fast electrons with nuclei. The only difference is that in the former case the electron makes a transition to a state of negative, instead of positive, energy. The theory of both processes was given by Bethe and Heitler, who also deduced the cross-section for the inverse process of pair production from the same calculation. For creation of pairs by a gamma ray in the field of a nucleus the differential cross-section for the production of a positron of kinetic energy T_+ (and an electron of energy $h\nu - 2mc^2 - T_+$) may be written (Ref. 5.1, p. 703)

$$\mathrm{d}\sigma_{PP} = \frac{\sigma_0 Z^2 P}{h\nu - 2mc^2}\,\mathrm{d}T_+ \qquad (5.100)$$

where
$$\sigma_0 = \frac{1}{137}\left(\frac{e^2}{mc^2}\right)^2 = 5.8 \times 10^{-28}\ \mathrm{cm}^2$$

---

* C. D. Anderson, *Phys. Rev.*, **43**, 491, 1933.

and P, shown in Fig. 5.24c, is a slowly varying function of $h\nu$ and Z. The figure implies symmetry in the distribution of energy between electrons and positrons in pair production; in fact this is disturbed by the nuclear charge, which slightly accelerates the positrons and retards the electrons.

The variation of the total cross-section for pair production in lead with quantum energy is shown in Fig. 5.24b. This is obtained by integrating the expression 5.100 over the energy spectrum. The cross-section increases at first with energy, as the pair production takes place at larger and larger distances from the nucleus, but a limit is set to the increase by the screening of the nuclear charge by the atomic electrons. In the absence of screening the pair cross-section is proportional to Z^2; it is therefore, as shown in Fig. 5.18, the predominant effect at high energies and for heavy nuclei in comparison with the Compton scattering and photoelectric effect. The electron pairs are mainly confined at high energies within a small forward cone of semi-angle mc^2/E, and play an essential role in the building up of the cascade showers of cosmic radiation.

The theory of pair production has been successfully tested experimentally both by direct observation in the expansion chamber and by determination of absorption coefficients for high energy gamma radiation. As explained in Sect. 5.4.1, a distinction can be drawn between pair absorption σ_{Pa} and pair 'scattering' σ_{Ps}, which may be taken to refer to the production of annihilation quanta by ultimate disappearance of the positron. The total pair cross-section is then

$$\sigma_{PP} = \sigma_{Pa} + \sigma_{Ps}$$

as before, where $\qquad \sigma_{Ps} = \sigma_{PP} \cdot \dfrac{2mc^2}{h\nu_0}.$

This effective additional scattering of high energy gamma radiation was observed by Meitner and Hupfeld, and by Gray and Tarrant, before its origin as annihilation radiation was understood.

The pair production discussed in this section is not a nuclear phenomenon, although a nucleus may be involved in the momentum balance. It is therefore known as *external* pair production to distinguish it from *internal* pair production

(Sect. **13.3**) which is a process alternative to radiative emission from an excited nucleus. Theoretically external production is treated as a *plane* wave phenomenon; internal production however depends markedly on the multipolarity (Sect. 3.9.2) of the radiative transition and hence on the *spherical* wave representation of the radiative field.

References

5.1   R. D. Evans, *The Atomic Nucleus*, McGraw Hill, 1955.

5.2   J. V. Jelley, *Cherenkov Radiation and its Applications*, Pergamon Press, 1958.

5.3   E. Rutherford, J. Chadwick and C. D. Ellis, *Radiations from Radioactive Substances*, Camb. Univ. Press, 1930.

5.4   S. K. Allison and S. D. Warshaw, 'Passage of Heavy Particles Through Matter', *Rev. mod. Phys.*, **25**, 779, 1953.

5.5   B. T. Price, 'Ionization by Relativistic Particles', *Rep. progr. Phys.*, **18**, 524, 1955.

5.6   H. A. Bethe and J. Ashkin, 'The Passage of Radiations Through Matter', in *Experimental Nuclear Physics*, ed. E. Segrè, Vol. I, Wiley, 1953.

5.7   M. S. Livingston and H. A. Bethe, *Rev. mod. Phys.*, **9**, 245, 1937.

5.8   W. Whaling, 'The Energy Loss of Charged Particles in Matter', *Encyclopedia of Physics*, **34**, 193, Springer 1958.

5.9   R. D. Evans, 'Compton Effect', *Encyclopedia of Physics*, **34**, 218, Springer, 1958.

5.10 C. M. Davisson and R. D. Evans, 'Gamma Ray Absorption Coefficients', *Rev. mod. Phys.*, **24**, 79, 1952.

5.11 W. Heitler, *The Quantum Theory of Radiation*, Clarendon Press, 3rd ed., 1944.

5.12 G. D. Rochester and J. G. Wilson, *Cloud Chamber Photographs of the Cosmic Radiation*, Pergamon Press, 1952.

6. NUCLEAR DETECTORS

One of the most important applications of knowledge of the passage of radiations through matter has been in the design of detecting instruments. The availability of a new type of detector, such as the Geiger-Müller counter (Sect. 6.1.4) or the expansion chamber (Sect. 6.2.1) or the sodium iodide crystal (Sect. 6.1.6) has sometimes greatly enlarged experimental possibilities in nuclear physics, and much work is continually being undertaken to improve existing instruments. In the present chapter the main types of nuclear detectors are surveyed, with particular attention to the specific applications for which they are best suited; in the following chapter the general problem of the measurement of the energy and intensity of ionizing radiations will be discussed.

6.1 Detecting instruments (electrical)

6.1.1 IONIZATION CHAMBERS. In its simplest form the ionization chamber is a gas-filled metal vessel into which is inserted an insulated electrode (Fig. 6.1a); under the influence of ionizing radiation the application of a potential difference of a few hundred volts between the electrode and the wall causes a current to flow through the gas. If the insulated electrode is charged and then disconnected from the voltage source, the ionization current discharges the capacity of the electrode, and the fall in potential may be displayed as motion of a leaf or fibre as in an electroscope, rather than as continuous current. In both cases the chamber is responding smoothly to the integrated effect of a large number of ionizing events, and such *current chambers* are extensively used for flux determination or source intensity measurement for all types of radiation. In some applications the parallel plate type of chamber (Fig. 6.1b) is more convenient.

It has been long known from experiments with X-rays, that for a steady rate of primary ionization the current reaches a

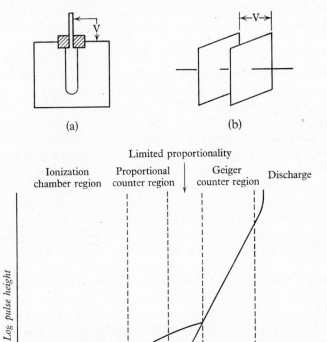

Fig. 6.1

a), b) Simple forms of ionization chamber or counter.

c) Pulse size obtained from a counting chamber as a function of voltage applied. Curves are drawn for a heavy initial ionization, e.g., from an α-particle and for a light initial ionization, e.g., from a fast electron. For voltages less than V_p only the primary ion pairs are collected; for $V > V_p$ ionization by collision takes place and the counter ceases to be a conventional ionization chamber. Very roughly the electric field in argon at atmospheric pressure corresponding to V_p is 10,000 V cm^{-1} (from Korff, *Electron and Nuclear Counters*).

saturation value when all ion pairs are collected before recombination. If q ionizing events each producing n ion pairs take place per second in the chamber, the saturation current is

$$i_s = qne \qquad (6.1)$$

where e is the electronic charge, and under these conditions the chamber can give an indication which accurately determines the primary ionization. The ionization current is usually measured electronically by observing the voltage developed by the current across a resistance of value of $10^{10}-10^{13}$ ohms; alternatively the output may be converted into a.c. by a vibrating-reed electrometer, which is effectively a condenser whose capacitance is varied at a frequency of about 300 c/s. This provides a stable, high impedance input and permits measurement of currents of the order of $10^{-14}-10^{-16}$ amp. Such ionization chambers for detection of γ-radiation are usually filled with high pressure argon, for fast neutron detection with hydrogen, and for slow neutron detection with boron trifluoride (BF_3). In all these cases a secondary effect is detected, i.e. either electron conversion of photons, or recoils from nuclear elastic scattering or transmutation in the case of neutrons.

The development of high-gain pulse amplifiers has made it possible to use ionization chambers as *counting instruments* for single particles. An α-particle of energy 6 MeV wholly absorbed in a gas will produce about 2×10^5 ion pairs, equivalent to positive and negative charges of 9.6×10^{-5} e.s.u. In a chamber of capacitance 10pF such a charge causes a change of potential of 3.2 millivolts which is much larger than the input noise voltage of a typical amplifier. It is in fact possible to distinguish the pulse due to as few as 1000 ion pairs and hence, by means of a shallow chamber, to study in detail the variation of ionization along the track of a single α-particle.

The output pulse height from a counting chamber varies with applied voltage as shown in Fig. 6.1c. In the region OV_p all the primary ions are collected and the pulse height has a saturation value. For higher voltages, ionization by collision occurs and the pulse height increases; counters operating in these regions will be described later (Sect. 6.1.3, 6.1.4). In the ionization chamber region OV_p the operation of a pulse chamber may be understood from Fig. 6.2a, b, in which a charged particle is supposed to traverse the chamber along the path AB in a time of perhaps 10^{-9} sec, leaving a track containing about 15,000 ion pairs per cm. In gases such as pure hydrogen, nitrogen and argon, which do not readily form negative ions, the initial effect is the production of positive ions and electrons. If an electric field of about 100 volts cm^{-1} is maintained across a chamber of 1 cm depth, and if the argon is at atmospheric pressure, the electrons will move towards the plate O with a

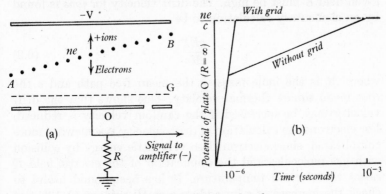

Fig. 6.2. The ionization chamber.

The collector potential for ordinary and gridded chambers is shown as a function of time, neglecting increased collector capacity due to the grid.

velocity of about 5×10^5 cm sec^{-1} and the positive ions will move towards plate $-\mathrm{V}$ with a velocity of about 140 cm sec^{-1}. If the plate is insulated from earth its potential immediately following the burst of ionization varies as shown in Fig. 6.2b. The sharp rise is due to collection of the fast moving electrons in a time of the order of 10^{-6} sec; the positive ions move much more slowly, and until they have all reached the plate $-\mathrm{V}$ the potential of O continues to rise since the ions induce a negative charge on O which is not released until they are collected. The pulse is not complete until a time which may be considerably greater than 10^{-3} sec and the magnitude of the initial sharp rise, for a given primary ionization, is dependent on the position of the ionizing track AB in the chamber. These undesirable features of 'slow' ionization chambers are removed in the *gridded chamber* (Fig. 6.2a) in which the plate O is shielded by a mesh of wires G held at a potential intermediate between zero and $-$V. The capacity between a track of ions and the collector O is then very much reduced and only the fast electron pulse, of size independent of the position of the track in the chamber (neglecting wall effects), is obtained. The gas filling such 'fast' ionization chambers must not form negative ions and in order to sharpen the electron pulse as much as possible the uni-directional drift velocity of the electrons through the gas in a given field E must be high. The drift velocity for *ions* is found by an elementary calculation to be

$$\frac{eE\lambda}{Mc} \tag{6.2}$$

where M is the ionic mass, λ the mean free path and c the root mean square thermal velocity. This shows that the drift velocity may be increased if the random velocity is reduced. For electrons the calculation of drift velocity is somewhat more complicated, since electrons lose very little energy by collision with gas molecules and the application of the electric field E raises the electron temperature. It has been found useful to check the increase of c by adding a small amount (2–10%) of carbon dioxide or methane to the argon usually employed in ionization chambers. These molecules have many low-lying excited states and inelastic collisions continually remove the energy gained by the electrons from the field E, so that the drift velocity is increased. It is customary to allow a suitable mixture of gases to flow through the ionization chamber, so that electron-capturing impurities do not accumulate.

The pulse from an ionization chamber is detected by connecting the collector plate O (Fig. 6.2a) to earth through a high resistance R (10^{10}–10^{13} ohms) which together with the capacity C of the chamber forms part of the input circuit of an amplifier (Sect. 6.1.8). If an argon filling is used in the chamber the amplifier time constants may be set to reproduce only the sharp rise of voltage resulting from electron collection. Fast counting of particles is then possible, and, in addition, low frequency microphonic disturbances are entirely eliminated.

Counting ionization chambers are not used for electrons because of the low primary ionization of these particles; for lightly ionizing events a counter providing either gaseous

multiplication or a long path length is required. The parallel
plate chamber has been much used for determination of the
energies of radioactive α-particles, and offers a moderate energy
resolution.* Fig. 6.3a shows a spectrum obtained using an α-
particle source in a gridded parallel plate chamber filled to an
argon pressure sufficient to stop the α-particles within the
chamber. For a 6 MeV α-particle the statistical fluctuation

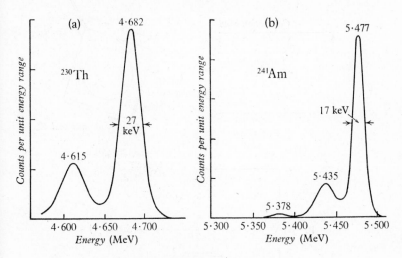

Fig. 6.3. Alpha-particle groups.
a) ^{230}Th in gridded ionization chamber (Engelkemeir and Magnusson,
Rev. sci. Instrum., **26**, 295, 1955).
b) ^{241}Am in solid-state ionization chamber (Dearnaley and Whitehead,
Nucl. instrum. and Methods, **12**, 205, 1961).

(Sect. 6.1.9) in the number of ion pairs is $\sqrt{(2 \times 10^5)}$ and this
indicates that a homogeneous group of this energy would have
a width at half-height of about $\frac{1}{2}\%$ of its energy. When care is
taken to minimize amplifier noise, and thin, clean sources are
used, this figure can be approached.

6.1.2 SOLID-STATE IONIZATION CHAMBERS. Gas-filling is
not an essential part of an ionization chamber. It has been
known since 1945 that semi-conducting crystalline materials
such as diamond, zinc sulphide and silver chloride will respond

---

* The term 'energy resolution' is defined in Sect. 6.1.9, see Fig. 6.18.

to the ionization produced by particles, and the conduction mechanism is well understood; Fig. 6.4a illustrates the general principle. Ideally the crystal has a low conductivity because the conduction band is empty and a high collecting field can then

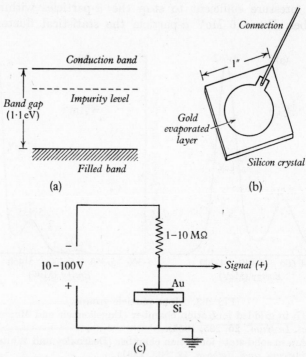

Fig. 6.4. The solid-state ionization chamber or semi-conductor counter (Dearnaley and Whitehead, *Nucl. instrum. and Methods*, **12**, 205, 1961).
    a) Bands and impurity level in semi-conductor.
    b) Construction of silicon surface-barrier detector.
    c) Circuit arrangement.

be maintained across a block of material without causing excessive current. Electrons released by an ionization process can enter the conduction band and move through the crystal under the applied field. In practice it is found that for most materials the number of electrons released by an ionizing process is considerably less than the number of charged carriers (electrons or positive holes) already present in the semi-

conductor. These arise because of thermal excitation of electrons from the filled band across the band gap and because of
the presence of impurities which provide electron-donating
levels near the conduction band (Fig. 6.4a). In addition the
presence of impurities creates trapping centres which may
seriously impede the conduction process and lead to storage of
charge and ultimate polarization of the crystal. These difficulties
have recently been overcome in *bulk conductor counters* employing extremely high purity silicon, germanium or synthetic
semi-conductors such as gallium arsenide. The residual conductivity is reduced by operation at low temperatures or by
controlled 'doping' with impurities chosen to compensate the
existing donor or acceptor levels. In this way it seems likely
that satisfactory bulk detectors of high stopping power for
charged particles (≈ 1 cm of silicon) will ultimately become
available; counters of thickness equal to the range of 30 MeV
protons have already been operated.

An alternative (and highly successful) method of eliminating
mobile charged carriers from a *limited* volume of semi-conductor
is based on the properties of the *p–n* junction. In an *n*-type
semi-conductor conduction is due to the motion of electrons in
the conduction band and in *p*-type material the process is
effectively a motion of positive holes left by electrons which
have been removed from a previously filled band; the two
materials are prepared from the intrinsic (*i*) semi-conductor by
the controlled addition of electron-donating or electron-
accepting elements. At a junction between *p*- and *n*-type
materials electrons migrate from the *n*-region to the *p*-region
and a shallow layer at the interface (known as the depletion or
barrier layer) is cleared of carriers. The resulting space charges
create a small potential difference across the depletion layer,
and the thickness of this layer may be increased (up to ≈ 1 mm)
by application of an external voltage of the same sign. The
depletion layer, although charged, is effectively an intrinsic
semi-conductor and if electron-hole pairs are produced by an
incident ionizing particle they will be rapidly swept away by
the externally applied field and a pulse will be detected in the
external circuit (Fig. 6.4c). Two types of *p–n* detector have been
developed, the *diffused junction detector* in which a donor
impurity, usually phosphorus, is introduced into *p*-type

(boron-doped) silicon to form a depletion layer at the diffusion depth, and the *surface barrier detector* (Fig. 6.4b) in which a p-type layer is formed on the surface of n-type silicon by oxidation. Contact is made to the active face of these detectors by means of a thin evaporated layer of gold through which incident particles can pass. Silicon-based counters operate well at room temperature, but germanium has more thermally-excited carriers and must be cooled to liquid air temperatures.

Solid-state counters, especially the p–n and p–i–n* types, have rapidly become of outstanding importance in low energy nuclear physics. The energy required to release an electron-hole pair is only about 3 eV, compared with 30 eV per ion pair for a gaseous detector, and the energy resolution (Sect. 6.1.9) therefore intrinsically better than that of the gas ionization chamber. In practice the resolution of α-particle groups of about 8 MeV energy has been brought to about 0.3% which is better than the value obtained with the best gridded chamber; Fig. 6.3b shows the spectrum of ^{241}Am obtained in a silicon detector of area 30 mm^2 and resistivity 3000 ohm-cm. The detectors have a linear energy characteristic and this combined with their high intrinsic resolving power and small size makes them admirable as spectrometers for particles of range not exceeding the depth of the depletion layer (≈ 20 MeV protons). Pulses with a rise-time of a few millimicroseconds can be obtained and fast counting is possible although it should be noted that the detector itself provides no multiplication and a high-gain amplifier is required. The junction detectors are relatively insensitive to γ-rays and neutrons and are therefore useful for heavy particle spectroscopy under conditions of high background. When bulk detectors of large volume are perfected the semiconductor counter will also offer the possibility of high-resolution electron and γ-ray spectroscopy.

6.1.3 PROPORTIONAL COUNTERS.

If the voltage applied to a gas-filled ionization chamber is increased beyond the point V_p in Fig. 6.1c, the current begins to increase owing to ionization by collision. The field E necessary for ionization by electrons

---

* A more recent type of junction detector, which offers the possibility of large sensitive depths is the p–i–n structure obtained by diffusing lithium into p-type silicon.

starting from rest in argon at atmospheric pressure is of the order of 10,000 V cm^{-1}; if the pressure p of the gas is reduced, the mean free path increases and the field required decreases, in such a way that E/p is approximately constant.

The field required is most conveniently, although not necessarily, developed in a counter of the form shown in Fig. 6.5a, employing cylindrical geometry. The field at radius r is given by the formula (Fig. 6.5b).

$$E = \frac{V}{r \log_e \dfrac{b}{a}} \qquad (6.3)$$

where a is the radius of the central wire and b is the inner radius of the cathode cylinder. For a counter with $a = 0.01$ cm, $b = 1$ cm and $V = 1000$ volts the field required for ionization by collision in argon at atmospheric pressure is reached at a radius $r = 0.02$ cm. The electrons from ion pairs produced anywhere in the counter volume move towards the positively charged wire and produce further electrons, which build up into an 'avalanche' of ionization in the central region. The gas multiplication m is the number of electrons reaching the wire for each initial electron and is usually between 10 and 10^3. Although these avalanche electrons are collected rapidly, the electrical pulse in an external circuit obtained from the collector wire is due to the drift of the residual positive ions away from the wire to the outer cylinder, since while the positive ions are close to the wire they neutralize the effect of the electrons.

The shape of the pulse from a proportional counter is independent of the position of the ionizing track in the chamber because the main multiplication always occurs in the high field region. Fig. 6.5c shows the pulse shape calculated for the counter specified earlier in the section; the pulse rises to half its final height in 2·5 μsec, although before this rise commences there may be a time-lag of perhaps 1 μsec while the initial electrons drift towards the wire. This lag may be reduced by the addition of carbon dioxide to the counter filling. Fast pulses may be obtained by using a short time constant of differentiation in a following stage of amplification.

The high multiplication available in proportional counters renders them suitable for the study of lightly ionizing particles, such as β-particles, mesons, and fast protons. Slow heavy particles are also readily detected and external amplification in

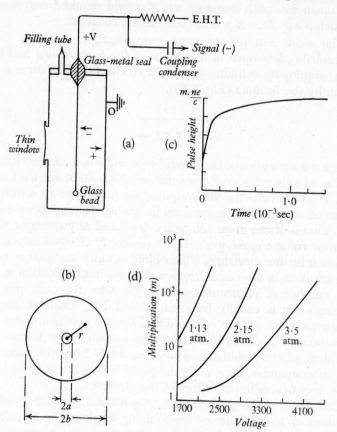

Fig. 6.5. The proportional counter.

a) Construction. The glass bead prevents sparking from points at the end of the wire.

b) Cross-section, cylindrical geometry.

c) Pulse shape (Ref. 6.7).

d) Dependence of multiplication on voltage for a cylindrical counter filled to the pressures indicated (Ref. 6.7).

such cases need only be very small. For this reason the proportional counter was historically the first type of counting tube to be used, before the development of pulse amplifiers permitted the application of ionization chambers to particle detection. It is however desirable whenever possible to keep the gas multiplication of a proportional counter low in the interests of stability even at the expense of loss of resolution. The proportional counter loses its proportionality for high initial ionizations or high multiplications owing to space-charge effects in the avalanche and in the limit of high multiplications the output pulse height becomes independent of the primary ionization; this is the so-called *Geiger* region (Fig. 6.1c).

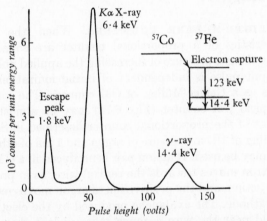

Fig. 6.6. Pulse height distribution for 14.4 keV γ-radiation and iron K X-radiation from a source of ^{57}Co (decay scheme inset) observed in a krypton-filled proportional counter. When a 14.4 keV photon produces a photoelectron in the krypton a K-shell vacancy usually results. If a K X-ray quantum is emitted it may escape from the counter. The total energy deposited in the counter is then 14.4 keV − 12.6 keV (the krypton K_{α}-energy) = 1.8 keV (Lemmer *et al.*, *Proc. phys. Soc.*, **68**, 701, 1955).

Methane is better than argon as a filling for proportional counters to be used at high multiplication because of its ability to absorb photons which might provoke catastrophic breakdown. The gas is usually allowed to flow at atmospheric pressure through the counter in order to preserve purity and to facilitate the introduction of samples for counting. Typical proportional counter characteristics are shown in Fig. 6.5d.

Proportional counters are of particular service in measuring the energy of low energy radiations which can be absorbed wholly in the gas filling of the counter. Gaseous β-emitters of low energy such as ^{3}H (18 keV) ^{14}C (155 keV) or ^{35}S (168 keV) have been studied extensively in this way and the counter is also widely applied in the determination of the energies of X-rays and low energy γ-rays by pulse-height analysis; for this purpose its resolution is considerably better than that of the alternative scintillation counter (Sect. 6.1.6). Fig. 6.6 shows the spectrum of low energy radiations from a source of ^{57}Co, decaying into ^{57}Fe, obtained in a krypton-filled proportional counter. The energy scale may be calibrated using X-rays of known energy.

6.1.4 GEIGER-MÜLLER COUNTERS. When the discharge characteristics of a proportional counter are so altered, by reducing the gas pressure or increasing the applied voltage, that the output pulse is independent of initial ionization the tube operates as a Geiger-Müller, or GM counter. The construction of a typical GM counter (Fig. 6.7a) may be almost identical with that of the proportional counter described in Sect. 6.1.3; a gas filling of 10 cm pressure of argon and 1 cm of ethyl alcohol vapour may be used. If an ion pair is produced in a GM counter, the electron moves towards the central wire, as in proportional counter action, and the positive ion of argon moves more slowly to the cathode. The avalanche produced by the electron in the high field near the wire is much more violent than in a proportional counter and secondary ultra-violet photons are produced in sufficient number to convey the discharge down the whole length of the wire of the counter. The velocity of propagation is about 10^6–10^7 cm sec^{-1} and as a result of this spread of the avalanches the charge available for collection by the wire has a constant value, independent of the magnitude and location of the initial ionization. When the electrons from the avalanches have been collected the slowly moving sheath of positive ions acts as a partial electrostatic screen and reduces the field at the wire below the value necessary for ionization by collision so that the discharge should cease. This simple expectation is however modified by the fact that the positive ions can eject electrons from the cathode when they reach it and since the field at the wire is then no longer reduced, avalanches can once more occur and a single ionizing event can therefore lead to multiple or continuous discharges. It is the function of the alcohol in the gas filling to 'quench' the discharge and this it does because of its low ionization potential (11·3 eV). The argon ions (ionization potential 15·7 eV) on their journey to the cathode are practically all neutralized by acquiring an electron from the alcohol molecules. The ions reaching the cathode are

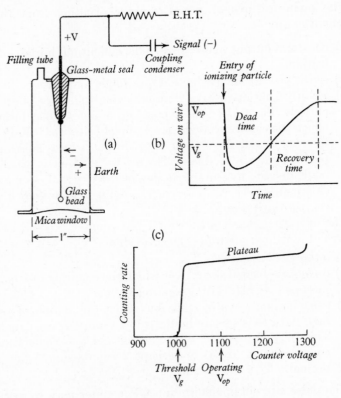

Fig. 6.7. The Geiger-Müller counter.

a) Construction.

b) Voltage on wire immediately following entry of an ionizing particle. The dead time and recovery time are each approximately 100-200 μsec.

c) Counting rate of GM tube exposed to constant source, as a function of applied voltage.

then alcohol ions and although they are themselves neutralized at the cathode, the energy available is absorbed in dissociating the alcohol molecule rather than in producing further electrons from the cathode. The discharge thus ceases when the central field has fallen sufficiently. The alcohol vapour will also absorb the ultra-violet photons emitted during the avalanche stage, and prevent them from ejecting photoelectrons from the cathode although not from causing propagation of the discharge down the central wire.

The main features of a GM counter resulting from this mechanism are:

a) constant output pulse size, independent of initial ionization,
b) sensitivity to the production of a single ion pair,
c) a fairly long insensitive time following the entry of each particle (Fig. 6.7b). This is made up of a *dead time* during which the counter voltage has dropped below the counting threshold, and a *recovery time* during which pulses of reduced size are produced. The insensitive time is usually made definite by suitable design of the external electrical circuit (see Sect. 6.1.8, quench unit); it is then known as the *paralysis time*.

The operating characteristics of a GM counter exposed to a source of ionizing radiation (Fig. 6.7c) shows:

a) *a threshold voltage* V_g,
b) *a plateau* of small slope, over which the counting rate only increases slightly with operating voltage,
c) *a background counting rate* due to contamination of the materials, to cosmic radiation and to spurious discharges. This may be reduced by screening and anti-coincidence counters (Sect. 6.1.8) to perhaps 2 counts min^{-1} but is normally 7–20 counts min^{-1}.

The pulse size obtainable from a GM counter may be many volts, depending on the operating voltage. The pulse rise time is slower than that of a proportional counter and the dead time is far longer owing to the propagation of the discharge along the wire and to the large reduction of field by the positive ion sheath. The lifetime of a self-quenched counter is limited by the existence of the quenching agent, which in the case of argon–alcohol mixtures is dissociated after about 10^9 counts. Counters filled wholly with argon–halogen mixtures in which the halogen acts as quencher, have an indefinite lifetime. The characteristics of two commercial GM tubes are shown in Table **6.1**.

TABLE 6.1   Characteristics of GM counters

| TYPE | PLATEAU | | OPERAT-ING VOLT-AGE V_{op} | LIFE NO. OF COUNTS | SIGNAL DE-VEL-OPED ON 1MΩ | DEAD TIME μ sec. | RE-COVERY TIME (μ sec.) |
	Length (volts)	Slope (per volt)					
GM4 Argon–Alcohol Type	250	0·05%	1300	6×10^8	2·5 V	100	250
MX123 Halogen Type	150	0·07%	675	$> 10^{11}$	5 V	85	250

There is obviously no energy sensitivity in the response of a GM counter. The tube responds to every charged particle which enters its sensitive volume and produces an ion pair there. The efficiency for counting photons depends upon the conversion of the radiation into electrons in the counter walls and is normally about 1% for photons of energy 1 MeV for a counter of the type shown in Fig. 6.7, so that the GM counter is useful for counting charged particles in the presence of γ-radiation. Geiger-Müller counters, like proportional counters, are available with a wide range of physical dimensions.

6.1.5 ELECTRON MULTIPLIERS. The gaseous counters for individual particles so far described are all limited in response time by a discharge process, and in many applications they must be separated from the origin of the particles which they detect by a thin window so that some limitation on the minimum detectable energy may be imposed. The solid state ionization chamber does not suffer from these disadvantages, but it provides no amplification of signal and owing to its high capacity can detect only particles of energy sufficient to produce about 10,000 electrons. For the simple counting of particles without energy discrimination, all these restrictions are eliminated in the electron multiplier (Fig. 6.8) in which an incident photon or charged particle ejects an electron from a plate placed at the beginning of a specially shaped series of secondary emitting electrodes (dynodes). Application of a positive voltage between successive dynodes focuses the electrons from one dynode to the next and at each impact 2–5 secondary electrons per primary may be produced so that for 10 stages gains of the order of 10^6 in the current pulse may be obtained. The dynode surfaces are typically of beryllium-copper with a thin layer of oxide.

The electron multiplier needs no gas filling and may be mounted directly on a vacuum system for the detection of particles whose energy need only exceed the work function of the first dynode. The multiplication process is extremely rapid

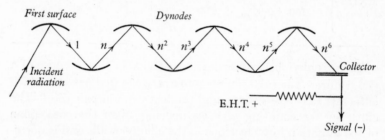

Fig. 6.8. Electron multiplier (vacuum envelope omitted).

($\approx 10^{-9}$ sec) and by increase of dynode voltage and of number of stages may, with proper attention to considerations of space charge, be made to yield an output pulse amplitude of many volts, so that external amplification is unnecessary.

6.1.6 SCINTILLATION COUNTERS. The scintillation screen, a thin layer of zinc sulphide or barium platinocyanide viewed by a low-power microscope for the observation of light flashes, is historically important as the first detector of individual nuclear particles. It was used in many of the classical researches of Rutherford and was employed as late as 1932 by Cockcroft and Walton to demonstrate the disintegration of lithium by protons. The present extensive use of the scintillation method is due partly to the application of the photo-electron multiplier (photomultiplier) to the detection of the light flashes (Curran and Baker, 1945) and partly to the discovery of new scintillating materials or phosphors such as anthracene and the alkali halides (Kallmann) which are transparent to their own radiations and can therefore be used in the form of thick slabs.

In both types of phosphor the first result of the passage of a charged particle is the production of a trail of ionization in a time of the order of 10^{-10}–10^{-9} sec. If we consider a particle of energy 1 MeV which stops in the scintillator, about $10^6/30 \approx 30,000$ ion pairs are produced. The next stage depends on the type of phosphor concerned. In inorganic crystals containing impurity (or activator) ions it is known that luminescence centres exist; these are atomic or molecular groups in which energy of excitation is liberated by a radiative transition rather than by direct mechanical interaction with the crystal lattice. The initial ionization process releases electrons from the various electron bands of the solid and some of the resulting holes are filled by electrons from the luminescence centres; when this happens, a photon is emitted. The efficiency of conversion of the initial energy deposited in the scintillator into energy of radiation thus depends on the density of luminescent centres in the crystal in comparison with other non-radiative centres, and is usually 5–10%. About 20,000 photons may thus result from the absorption of a 1 MeV particle, and these will be emitted over a time (≈ 1 μsec) determined by the delay in transfer of energy to the luminescence centres and the decay time of the centres themselves. In organic scintillators similar processes take place but the energy transfer mechanisms are different.

The scintillators which have been chiefly used for particle and photon detection are listed in Table 6.2. The particular properties of these phosphors which may be emphasized are:

a) *Sodium iodide* (*thallium-activated*). This is the most versatile of all the phosphors, and is of outstanding importance for the study of γ-radiation, but it has the disadvantage that it is hygroscopic and must be sealed in an aluminium can (Fig. 6.10) with reflecting or diffusing walls. The efficiency for γ-ray detection is many times greater than that of a Geiger counter because of the effective thickness of the converter.

b) *Caesium iodide*. This material is not hygroscopic and it is frequently used in preference to sodium iodide for the detection of low energy charged particles. It may be mounted in the vacuum system of an accelerator, and is available in thin plates, which can act as energy loss (dT/dx) counters.

c) *Zinc sulphide.* This is an excellent phosphor for particles of short range, but cannot be used in thick layers since it rapidly becomes opaque to its own radiation.

d) *Anthracene and stilbene.* Organic phosphors have a faster decay time than the inorganic phosphors but a poorer efficiency, especially for heavy particles. Since they contain only light elements they are useful for counting β-particles in the presence of γ-radiation. For fast counting they have been largely superseded by

e) *Plastic and liquid scintillators.* These are readily obtainable in very large volumes and can be adapted to many different geometrical arrangements. Energy of excitation in this case is transferred from the solvent to the solute, which then re-emits radiation in a wavelength range for which the solvent is transparent. Plastic scintillators form the detectors in the multiple counter 'telescopes' used in high energy physics to define the path of a particle.

f) *Gases.* Xenon is particularly useful when heavy charged particles are to be counted in the presence of γ-radiation. The main emission of light takes place in the ultra-violet and a wavelength shifter (often a film of grease) is necessary to convert the energy to a wavelength suitable for detection by a standard photomultiplier.

The linearity of response of a scintillator depends on the density of initial ionization in comparison with the number of luminescent centres and differs between organic and inorganic materials. High density of ionization impedes the processes of energy transfer in organic phosphors and the light output for heavy particles is suppressed with respect to that for electrons. The inorganic crystals suffer less from this disadvantage, and it does not occur at all in gaseous scintillators. Fig. 6.9 shows the relative scintillation responses as a function of incident energy for two widely used phosphors and for different types of particle. The linearity frequently obtainable and the high intrinsic efficiency are responsible for the wide use of scintillation spectrometers for determining the energy of individual particles or photons.

Table 6.2 Characteristics of scintillators

MATERIAL	FORM	DENSITY g cm⁻³	REFRACTIVE INDEX	MAIN EMISSION WAVE-LENGTH	INTRINSIC EFFICIENCY (per cent)†		DECAY TIME μsec.
					protons	electrons	
ZnS–Ag*	Powder	4·1	2·4	4500	20	13·5	>10
NaI–Tl*	Crystal	3·7	1·7	4100	20	20	0·25
KI–Tl*	Crystal	3·2	1·65	4000	5	5	>10
CsI–Tl*	Crystal	4·5	1·75	white	—	—	>1
Anthracene	Crystal	1·25	—	4450	—	10	0·03
Stilbene	Crystal	1·16	—	4000–4200	0·8	6	0·008
Terphenyl in xylene	Solution	0·86	1·5	3200–4000	—	5–10	0·002
'Pamelon'	Plastic	—	1·5	—	—	5–10	0·006
Xenon gas						10	0·01–0·1

* The concentration of activator is usually about 0·1% (molar).

† The intrinsic efficiency is the ratio of energy emitted as radiation to the energy absorbed in the scintillator. The figures depend considerably on the preparation of the phosphor and should be taken as a rough guide only.

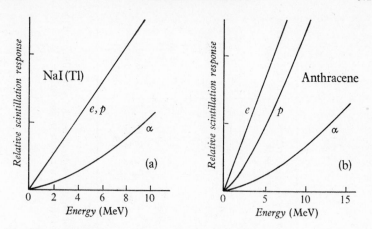

Fig. 6.9. Scintillation response of phosphors for electrons, protons and
α-particles.

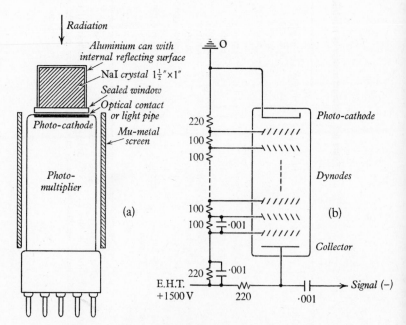

Fig. 6.10. Scintillation counter.
a) Arrangement of sodium iodide crystal on photomultiplier.
b) Circuit diagram, showing potentiometer chain for supplying dynode
potentials. The resistance values are given in kilo-ohms and the condenser capacity values in microfarads.

In such instruments the light output of the scintillator must be conveyed to the photo-sensitive cathode surface of a sealed-off photomultiplier tube. Many problems arise in obtaining efficient optical transfer; whenever possible the scintillator is mounted directly on the photomultiplier envelope with a suitable sealing liquid to ensure good optical contact, but in many applications some kind of Perspex light guide is necessary, with consequent reduction in efficiency owing to absorption in the Perspex. Fig. 6.10 shows a typical photomultiplier arrangement. The photo-cathode of the multiplier tube should have a good response over the wavelength of the luminescence emission and a low 'dark current', i.e. spontaneous noise generation due to random emission of electrons from the cathode surface. The most frequently used surface is an antimony–caesium coating, which may have a quantum efficiency (number of photo-electrons produced per photon incident) of up to 20%. High quantum efficiency is important for the study of low energy radiations because the spread in output pulse height is generally determined by the statistical fluctuation in the electron emission from the photocathode. Since the number of these electrons is proportional to the energy E of the particle incident on the scintillator, the fluctuation is proportional to $E^{1/2}$ and the percentage spread of pulse height therefore varies as $E^{-1/2}$ (Sect. 6.1.9).

Photomultiplier characteristics for a number of tubes in common use are given in Table **6.3**.

TABLE 6.3   Characteristics of photomultiplier tubes

TYPE	EMI 6097	Dumont 6292	RCA 6810
Cathode area cm^2	15	15	14·2
Cathode sensitivity μA lumen^{-1}	20	60	60
Number of stages	11	10	14
Maximum voltage per stage	200	145	500
Overall gain	10^7	2×10^6	$1·25 \times 10^7$

The RCA multipliers employ an electrode (or dynode) structure in which electrons from one dynode are focused electrostatically on the next. In the EMI 'venetian blind' type of tube there is no focusing and the electrons spend some time in relatively low field regions between the slats, so that greater transit time variations are observed than with the RCA tubes. All photomultipliers are to a greater or less degree sensitive to

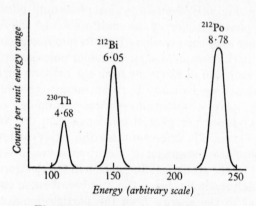

Fig. 6.11. Scintillation spectrometry.
Pulse height distribution from α-particles, observed in CsI (Tl-activated) crystal. The peak energies in MeV are indicated (Bartolini *et al.*, *Nucl. instrum. and Methods*, **7**, 350, 1960).

magnetic fields and must normally be heavily screened with iron or mu-metal if magnetic fields are likely to be present. The circuit arrangements for supplying dynode potentials and for developing the output signal are shown in Fig. 6.10b.

The use of the scintillation spectrometer in energy measurements is illustrated in Figs. 6.11 and 6.12. For heavy particles, a scintillator is 100% efficient, and a resolution of about 4% for α-particles of energy 5 MeV is easily obtained with caesium iodide (Fig. 6.11). For γ-radiation, the efficiency of detection depends on the size of the crystal and for a $1\frac{1}{2}$ in. diameter by 1 in. high cylinder of sodium iodide is as shown in Fig. 6.12a. The efficiency varies with energy in accordance with the variation of the linear attenuation coefficient for γ-radiation. The pulse height distribution for homogeneous γ-radiation observed in a single crystal scintillation spectrometer depends on the quantum energy. For $E_\gamma < 250$ keV (Fig. 6.12b) the photo-electric effect predominates, and a strong full energy peak is observed (with a lower energy 'escape' peak corresponding to events in which the K X-ray photon of iodine has emerged

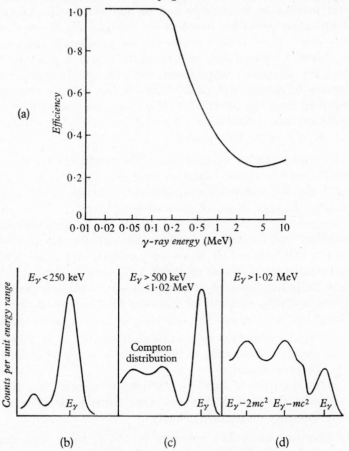

Fig. 6.12. Scintillation spectrometry.

a) Calculated efficiency of NaI crystal ($1\frac{1}{2}'' \times 1''$) with source mounted directly on the crystal, for γ-radiation of homogeneous energy (Siegbahn, *Beta and Gamma Spectroscopy*).

b), c), d) Pulse spectrum of homogeneous γ-radiation of energy corresponding to interaction mainly by photoelectric effect, Compton effect and pair production. In each case there is a full energy peak due to capture of all radiations by the crystal but the height depends markedly on the relation between the crystal size and the γ-ray energy.

from the crystal). For $E_\gamma > 500$ KeV (Fig. 6.12c) the Compton effect is also important, and the full energy photoelectric peak is accompanied by a broad distribution of recoil electrons, with a well marked 'Compton edge'. For $E_\gamma > 1 \cdot 02$ MeV (Fig. 6.12d) pair production is possible and in addition to the Compton distribution peaks are found at the energies E_γ, $E_\gamma - mc^2$, and $E_\gamma - 2mc^2$. These arise because in pair production the energy $E_\gamma - 2mc^2$ is shared between an electron and a positron; the positron ultimately annihilates with the production of two quanta of energy mc^2 each of which has a finite chance of escaping from the scintillator. If neither escapes, a full energy pulse appears. A resolution of about 8% at 600 keV is obtainable in a crystal of the size quoted.

6.1.7 CHERENKOV COUNTERS. The conditions for the production of Cherenkov radiation were given in chapter 5, Sect. 5.2.3. Eq. 5.51a shows that a relativistic particle of unit charge passing through 10 cm of glass or Perspex gives rise to about 2500 photons in the visible wavelength range. If these are all collected and focused on to the photocathode of a multiplier tube a few hundred electrons are produced and pulses with a statistical spread in size of about 10% may be detected. The light output of this type of counter is very much less than that of a *scintillating* material for the same total energy loss but the Cherenkov counter has the following important advantages:

a) rapid rise and decay of pulse (intrinsically $\ll 10^{-10}$ sec),
b) directional emission of light, with an angle dependent on particle velocity,
c) no emission of light for particles of velocity less than a critical value, and above this value a dependence of intensity on particle velocity.

In practical Cherenkov counters b) and c) have been chiefly exploited. Liquid and solid counters of large volume can be used as threshold detectors and another class of instruments with special optical systems can be employed to select particles with a narrow spread of velocity or of direction. These counters have been particularly useful in high energy physics. Fig. 6.13 shows the construction and performance curves of

a) a simple cosmic ray detector,
b) a conical counter used in work with 950 MeV protons.

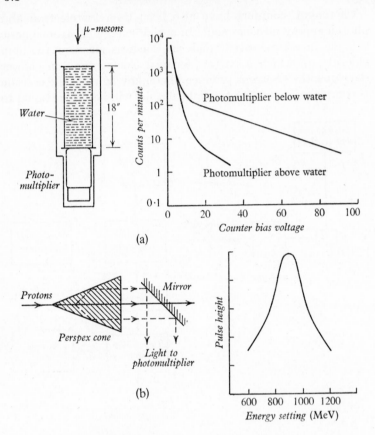

Fig. 6.13. Simple Cherenkov detectors.

a) Water tube used by Jelley (*Proc. phys. Soc.*, **64**, 82, 1951) for detection of μ-mesons in cosmic radiation. The whole detector could be inverted; the bias curves showed that more large pulses were recorded when the photomultiplier was in a position to receive the downward going Cherenkov light.

b) Conical detector used by Huq (*Nucl. instrum. and Methods*, **2**, 342, 1958) to detect 950 MeV protons. The Cherenkov light from axial particles is internally reflected and emerges as a parallel beam for a certain incident energy. The light from particles of other energies emerges as a divergent or convergent beam and can be rejected by a suitable optical system. The curve shows the response of the detector to 950 MeV protons when the optical system is set for the energies indicated.

Cherenkov counters have also been used for electron and photon energy measurement. In a high energy electromagnetic cascade in a transparent material, such as glass, or thallium chloride, in which a narrow forward electron-photon shower develops, the electrons produce Cherenkov light. If the cascade is completely absorbed the light output will be proportional to

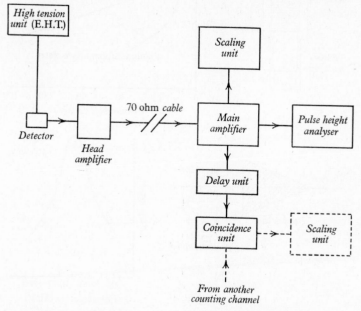

Fig. 6.14. Block schematic of nuclear detection equipment.

the energy of the primary, cascade-producing photon and may be determined, after calibration with known-energy particles, by pulse height analysis.

The extensive evolution of Cherenkov counters is described in Ref. 6.9.

6.1.8 ELECTRICAL CIRCUITS USED WITH TYPICAL NU-CLEAR DETECTORS. The elements of a typical circuit assembly used with a nuclear detector are shown in block schematic form in Fig. 6.14.

The *high tension unit* for supplying the potentials for the detector is normally designed for an output of 0–4 kV, 1 mA.

It must be stabilized, but the degree of stabilization depends on the detector and is less important with an ionization chamber or Geiger counter than with a scintillation or proportional counter in which the gain is a sharp function of anode voltage. Commercial units achieve a stability of 0·02% in output voltage.

The *head unit* is either an amplifier or a cathode follower (Ref. 6.11) designed specifically with the object of presenting a high impedance, low capacity input to the signals from the detector, which are usually developed over a high load resistance. The output impedance of the head unit is low, so that signals may be fed into 70-ohm coaxial cable and conveyed to a main amplifier at a considerable distance from the detector and head unit. This is usually necessary in the operation of counting equipment near large accelerating machines. Typical performance figures are: Head amplifier gain = 45, cathode follower gain = 1/10.

Geiger counter pulses do not need amplification but a 'quench unit' is used to render the counter inactive for a definite period of a few hundred microseconds following each pulse. Uncertainties in dead time are thus eliminated.

The *main amplifier* is used to convert the signal of perhaps 10 millivolts from a typical detector plus head unit into a pulse of 50–100 volts amplitude. The gain is therefore at least $\times 10^4$ (80 db) and time constants are introduced to control the shape of the pulse. Each detector may be regarded as a current source of high impedance, which charges up the total capacity C of the collecting electrode and of the input circuit (Fig. 6.15a). The rise time of the voltage pulse (Fig. 6.15b) is determined by transit times in the detector and, in the case of scintillators, by the decay times of the luminescent centres. The collector and input capacity are shunted by the EHT load resistance R_1, and the input resistance R_2 of the head amplifier and this combination restores the collector voltage to its original value with a time constant CR where $R = R_1 R_2 / R_1 + R_2$. The decay time of the pulse is thus determined by CR, and the overall width τ by the combination of CR and the 'internal' rise time. The main amplifier time constants may be set to reproduce this waveform, or they may be used to alter it. It is usual to keep the detector time constant fairly long and to shorten the pulse

8*

length by a differentiating time constant T_1 in the amplifier; these measures minimize noise originating at the input. An integration time constant T_2 can be used to increase the pulse rise time if desired.

The electronic noise in amplifiers, which determines their sensitivity, arises from thermal agitation in the input circuit, shot noise in the first valve and other circuit fluctuations. The noise voltage is approximately proportional to the square root of amplifier bandwidth and signal-to-noise ratios may be improved by narrowing the frequency band. This however may

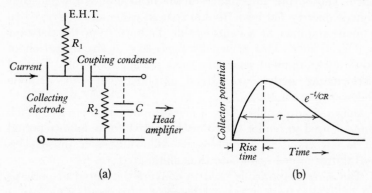

(a)   (b)

Fig. 6.15

a) Amplifier input circuit.

b) Waveform presented to first valve of the head amplifier.

spoil the pulse shape since a voltage waveform with large Fourier components of frequency up to ω c/s requires an amplifier bandwidth of ω c/s at least for satisfactory reproduction. The tendency in modern photomultiplier circuits is to obtain as large a pulse as possible from the collector and to reduce external amplification to a minimum.

Gain stability and linearity of response are important in most applications of pulse amplifiers. These characteristics are obtained by the use of negative feed-back (Ref. 6.12) which also provides a convenient method of gain control. The output pulses from the amplifier may be observed visually by an oscilloscope and recorded photographically or counted by a *scaling unit*. Such units derive historically from the scale-of-two circuit of Wynn-Williams (Fig. 6.16) in which the arrival of a pulse changes the state of a bi-stable pair of thyratrons. These tubes are gas-filled triodes in which a negatively biased grid can hold off a much larger anode voltage. If a positive pulse is

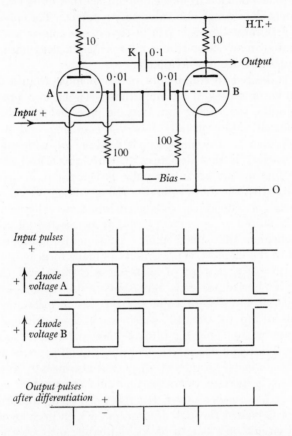

Fig. 6.16. Basic scale-of-two thyratron circuit; resistances in kilo-ohms, condenser capacities in microfarads. The waveforms show that as a result of the transition of the circuit from one stable state to the other, the number of positive-going pulses on the anode B is half that of the positive-going impulses applied to the pair of grids.

applied to the grid of a thyratron (Fig. 6.16) the tube conducts and the grid becomes surrounded by a space charge sheath as a result of which it can no longer exercise any influence on the anode current, even if it is driven hard negatively. The current in thyratron A may be interrupted if thyratron B is triggered, since the voltage drop of the anode of B lowers the potential of the anode of A through the coupling condenser K. The circuit AB has then changed from the one to the other of its two stable states in each of which one valve only conducts. The waveforms in Fig. 6.16 show how this pair of thyratrons acts as a scale-of-two counter; many circuits of similar principle using hard valves and transistors are now available.

If it is desired to count only pulses of more than a certain amplitude, or pulses of an amplitude between two pre-determined limits, the scaling unit may be preceded by a *discriminator* circuit. More usually however counting and analysis are combined in the *pulse-height analyser* of which a well-known variety is that designed by Hutchinson and Scarrott. In this instrument an input pulse is compared in size electronically with the amplitude of a rising voltage wave, so that pulse height is effectively converted into time. The coincident signal is stored in a memory circuit consisting of a delay line in which the timed pulses continually circulate. The content of the memory is presented in binary form by intensity modulation of a pattern of spots on a cathode ray tube, in which the horizontal axis represents pulse height and the vertical axis number of counts. In a recent instrument 100 channels of up to $1 \cdot 6 \times 10^7$ pulses each are available and a maximum mean counting rate of 1600 pulses per second is possible. The result of analysis is printed out on paper in decimal form; an analogue (graphical) display is also usually available.

In many experiments the correlation between two or more nuclear radiations is studied. For this purpose a pulse from the amplifier is passed through a *delay line*, which may be either a lumped circuit or a length of coaxial cable, into a *coincidence unit* (Ref. 6.11). This unit also receives pulses from a second counting channel. If the two pulses overlap in time an output pulse is generated; single pulses produce only small output signals which may be rejected by a biassing arrangement at the output. Multiple coincidence units are of extreme importance in high energy physics in which beams of particles are defined by passage through a series of scintillators (counter telescope). The delay unit is of importance when time correlations, such as nuclear lifetimes or times of flight are studied. The combination of coincidence counting and multi-channel pulse analysis is a powerful tool in nuclear spectroscopy. Similar circuits may also be used in *anti-coincidence* in which the signal from a counter B is *not* accepted if there is simultaneously a signal in a counter A; such circuits are useful in discriminating between effects due to fast protons and fast neutrons.

6.1.9 STATISTICAL EFFECTS IN NUCLEAR DETECTORS.

a) *Counters and coincidence circuits.* Nuclear processes such as radioactive decay, or the emission of particles from a target under bombardment are essentially random in character. The verification of the Poisson distribution for the number of α-particles received from a constant source in a given time interval has already been mentioned (Sect. 2.3.4 and Eq. 2.8). In any counting experiment the number of particles or events recorded in a given interval will be distributed about the mean number N with a mean square deviation or *variance* given by

$$\sigma^2 = \sum_0^\infty (n-N)^2 \, \frac{N^n e^{-N}}{n!} \quad \text{from (2.8)}$$

$$= N \tag{6.4}$$

The standard deviation σ in a count of N particles for N large is thus $\sqrt{N}$ and the observation is usually quoted as $N \pm \sqrt{N}$.

If a nuclear counter or recorder remains insensitive for a time τ_p (paralysis time*) after the entry of a particle and if recovery is not affected by the entry of further particles, there will be a counting loss because of the occurrence in a random series of events of a certain number of intervals less than τ_p. If the observed counting rate is n counts $\sec^{-1}$ the apparatus is insensitive for a time $n\tau_p$ in each second and $N n \tau_p$ of the true counts are missed. It follows that

$$n = N - N n \tau_p$$

or $$N = \frac{n}{1 - n\tau_p} \approx n(1 + n\tau_p) \tag{6.5}$$

This formula is used for correcting Geiger counter observations;

---

* In many counters this is just the pulse length, as defined by the fundamental mechanism or by amplifier constants.

for a counter with an imposed paralysis time of 200 μsec. and $n = 1000 \ \mathrm{sec}^{-1}$ the true rate is $N = 1200 \ \mathrm{sec}^{-1}$.

In coincidence counting, the *resolving time* is defined as the minimum time separation for which two pulses are not recorded as a coincidence. If the pulse outputs from the individual counting channels are each of duration τ (which may be very much less than the paralysis time τ_p), then the coincidence resolving time is also τ (Fig. 6.17a) in an ideal case. For two

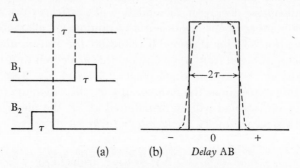

(a)   (b)   *Delay* AB

Fig. 6.17. Coincidence resolving time.
a) Limiting times of pulses $B_1 \ B_2$ from counter B which just form a coincidence with the pulse from counter A.
b) Coincidence count for simultaneous events as a function of delay inserted in the channels. The dotted lines show the type of curve obtained with actual pulses.

truly coincident radiations a plot of the number of coincidences as a function of delay inserted in one of the channels would give the coincidence curve shown in Fig. 6.17b. If the two channels contain independent events (such as background events) arriving at rates N_1 and $N_2 \ \mathrm{sec}^{-1}$ there will be a random coincidence rate

$$N_r = 2\tau N_1 N_2 \qquad (6.6)$$

since this is the number of the N_2 counts which fall within $\pm \tau$ of the N_1 events.

b) *Energy sensitive detectors.* Even if counting statistics are unimportant, because of high counting rates, an energy sensitive detector will still give a distribution of pulse sizes for a homogeneous incident radiation of energy E (Fig. 6.18). This is due, apart from circuit noise, to the statistical nature of the basic ionization or photon production process, coupled with fluctuation in any subsequent multiplication which takes place. If a given event produces on the average m_0 electrons, and the detector provides a multiplication factor m_A then the variance of the final number of electrons may be shown (Ref. 6.13) to be

$$\sigma^2 = m_A^2 \sigma_0^2 + m_0 \sigma_A^2$$

where σ_0^2 and σ_A^2 are the variance of the distributions of m_0 and m_A. The final signal is proportional to $m_0 m_A$ and its

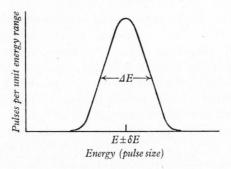

Fig. 6.18. Pulse-size distribution from an energy sensitive nuclear detector responding to homogeneous radiation of energy E. If the curve is approximated by a Gaussian error curve then the width ΔE at half maximum is 2·35 times the standard deviation. In Eq. 6.7, σ and $m_0 m_A$ refer to numbers of ion pairs; the corresponding energies are $\sigma \omega$ and $m_0 m_A \omega$.

The *resolution* $\Delta E/E$ is $2 \cdot 35 \sigma / m_0 m_A$. The *relative accuracy* $\delta E/E$ of the energy determination depends on calibrations.

spread to σ; the resolution $\Delta E/E$ of the detector is then proportional to

$$\frac{\sigma}{m_0 m_A} = \sqrt{\frac{\sigma_0^2}{m_0^2} + \frac{\sigma_A^2}{m_A^2}\frac{1}{m_0}}. \tag{6.7}$$

For ionization chambers and semi-conductor counters there is no multiplication so that $m_A = 1$ and $\sigma_A = 0$. For a Poisson distribution $\sigma_0^2 = m_0$ and the resolution is therefore proportional to $1/\sqrt{m_0}$. If ω is the energy required to liberate an electron, $m_0 = E/\omega$ and since $\omega \approx 30$ eV for the ionization chamber and only 3 eV for the semi-conductor, the latter detector should have intrinsically a resolution about 3 times better than the former for the same input capacity.

In proportional counters and photomultipliers m_A may be large. The relative variance σ_A^2/m_A^2 for the avalanche process in the proportional counter and for the electron multiplication in the photomultiplier have each been found experimentally to be approximately unity and for a Poisson distribution of initial events Eq. 6.7 then gives

$$\frac{\sigma}{m_0 m_A} \approx \sqrt{\frac{2}{m_0}} \qquad (6.8)$$

The resolution of the proportional counter should therefore be worse than that of the ionization chamber by a factor of $\sqrt{2}$ at least. The resolution of the scintillation counter is about a factor of 10 worse than that of the ionization chamber partly owing to the magnitude of the energy (50–100 eV) required to release a photon, but mainly owing to low photocathode efficiency and poor light collection.

For each energy sensitive detector the resolution varies inversely as $m_0^{1/2}$, i.e. as $1/\sqrt{E}$. This may be concealed by other instrumental sources of line-width such as circuit noise or crystal imperfections and the resolution may then appear less dependent on particle energy.

6.2   Detecting instruments (visual)

Electrical detecting systems have the advantage of rapid accumulation and display of information in an experiment. They are especially suitable in well-defined situations, as when the number of particles scattered from a beam at a given angle has to be found as a function of beam energy. Such counting systems are less suitable for the analysis of a complicated process in which several particles may be emitted and tests of momentum balance and coplanarity have to be applied in the analysis. In such cases visual techniques are necessary; in many of the simpler experiments such methods provide important confirmation of suggested mechanisms and at the very least, a considerable aesthetic satisfaction to the physicist.

6.2.1 THE WILSON EXPANSION CHAMBER. The cloud chamber owes its existence to the interest of C. T. R. Wilson in

(LEFT)
1. Expansion chamber tracks of α-rays from radium (C. T. R. Wilson, *Proc. roy. Soc.* A, **87**, 277, 1912).

(ABOVE)
4. Expansion chamber track of carbon ion, showing delta rays (J. C. Bower).

(BELOW)
2. Expansion chamber tracks of fast and slow β-rays (electrons) produced by hard X-rays (C. T. R. Wilson, *Proc. roy. Soc.* A, **104**, 192, 1923).

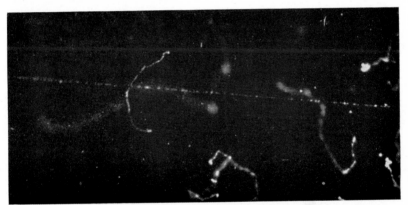

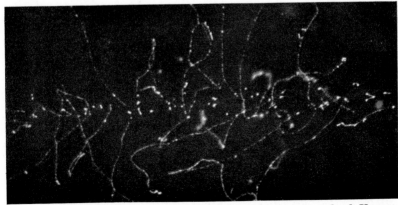

3. Expansion chamber tracks of recoil electrons due to beam of soft X-rays. Some of the short tracks are due to Auger electrons (C. T. R. Wilson, *Proc. roy. Soc.* A, **104**, 1, 1923).

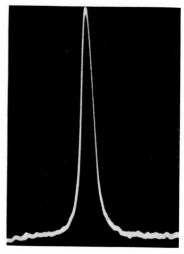

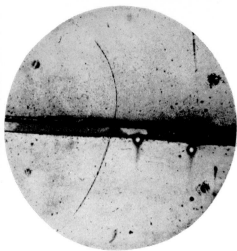

5. Nuclear resonance signal from protons in ferric nitrate solution (N. Bloembergen *et al.*, *Phys. Rev.*, **73**, 686, 1948).

6. A positron of energy 63 MeV passes through a lead plate and emerges with an energy of 23 MeV (C. D. Anderson, *Phys. Rev.*, **43**, 491, 1933).

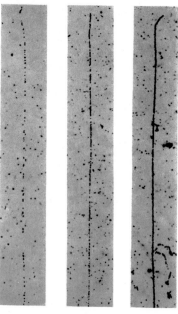

7. Hydrogen bubble chamber tracks of 1 GeV protons, showing a proton–proton collision (J. B. Kinson).

8. Tracks of protons in different emulsions. A Ilford Half-Tone, B Ilford C2, C Kodak NT4 (C. F. Powell, taken from Ref. 6.18).

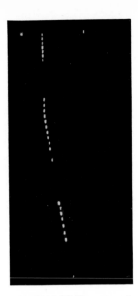

9. Track of 170 MeV proton, including a nuclear scattering, recorded in
a spark chamber (J. G. Rutherglen).

10. Expansion chamber photograph
showing ejection of a proton from
a nitrogen nucleus by an α-particle.
(P. M. S. Blackett and D. S. Lees,
Proc. roy. Soc. A, **136**, 325, 1932).

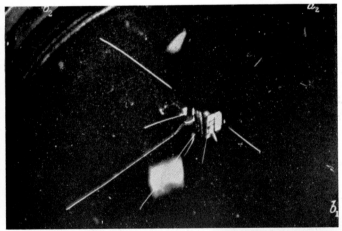

11. Expansion chamber photograph
showing disintegration of lithium by
protons with the emission of pairs of
α-particles in opposite directions.
(P. I. Dee and E. T. S. Walton,
Proc. roy. Soc. A, **141**, 733, 1933).

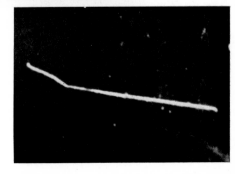

12. Expansion chamber photograph
of disintegration of nitrogen by neutrons (N. Feather, *Proc. roy. Soc.* A,
136, 709, 1932).

13. Expansion chamber tracks of fission fragments emerging from a uranium foil bombarded by slow neutrons (J. K. Boggild *et al.*, *Phys. Rev.*, **71**, 281, 1947).

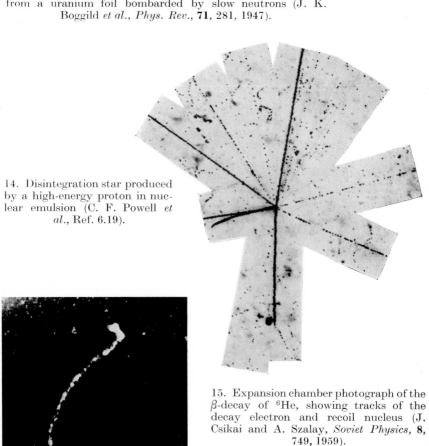

14. Disintegration star produced by a high-energy proton in nuclear emulsion (C. F. Powell *et al.*, Ref. 6.19).

15. Expansion chamber photograph of the β-decay of ^{6}He, showing tracks of the decay electron and recoil nucleus (J. Csikai and A. Szalay, *Soviet Physics*, **8**, 749, 1959).

meteorological phenomena on the mountain of Ben Nevis in 1894. The present form of the instrument differs hardly at all in essentials from the earliest models and tracks obtained by Wilson in 1911 are still among the best examples of performance of the chamber. The dramatic quality of the pictures obtainable

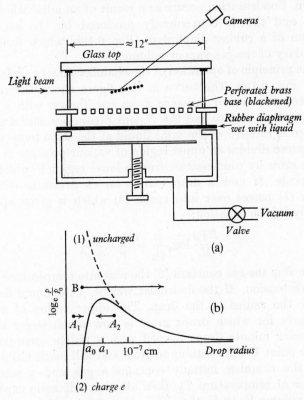

Fig. 6.19. The expansion chamber.

a) Outline construction.

b) Vapour pressure equilibrium curves for small droplets. Curve (1) is for uncharged drops and curve (2) for drops carrying one electronic charge (Ref. 6.14).

with the Wilson expansion chamber is well illustrated by the examples of events shown in Plates 1–4 and practically every nuclear phenomenon has come under the scrutiny of this powerful technique in the half century following its invention.

The expansion chamber, whose essential features are illustrated in Fig. 6.19a, causes condensation of a vapour into drops along the path of an ionizing particle passing through a gas. The gas and vapour are contained in a cylinder with suitable transparent windows, and the visible tracks are illuminated and photographed through the walls or top of the chamber as shown. Condensation occurs as a result of an adiabatic expansion, and this is conveniently produced by the controlled motion of a rubber diaphragm (Fig. 6.19a) which forms one boundary of the gas-vapour volume.

The principle of operation of the chamber may be understood from Fig. 6.19b. The curve in this figure shows the relation between the vapour pressure p_0 in equilibrium with a liquid with a plane surface and the vapour pressure p near a convex surface of radius r of the same liquid at the same temperature. The curve divides an upper region of vapour pressure in which drops grow by condensation from a lower region in which they evaporate. If now a drop carries an electrostatic charge q curve (1) passes over into curve (2) which is given approximately by the equation:

$$\frac{RT\rho}{M} \log_e \frac{p}{p_0} = \frac{2\gamma}{r} - \frac{q^2}{8\pi r^4} \qquad (6.9)$$

where R is the gas constant, T the absolute temperature, γ the surface tension, M the molecular weight, ρ the liquid density, and r the radius of the drop. The upper region of vapour pressures for which drops grow is now much larger and in particular minute drops formed with a radius corresponding to the point B will continue to grow and will reach visible size.

If the chamber initially contains a gas and a saturated vapour at temperature T_1, then after an adiabatic expansion from volume V_1 to V_2 the temperature is given by

$$T_2 = T_1 \left(\frac{V_1}{V_2}\right)^{\gamma-1} \qquad (6.10)$$

where γ is the ratio of the specific heats of the gas-vapour mixture. Initially the vapour pressure is p_1, corresponding to saturation at temperature T_1, but after the expansion it is

$$p = p_1 \left(\frac{V_1}{V_2}\right)^{\gamma} \qquad (6.11)$$

which is considerably greater than the saturation vapour pressure for temperature T_2. If the ratio p/p_2, known as the *supersaturation S*, exceeds the value indicated by the maximum of curve 2 in Fig. 6.19b condensation occurs on drops carrying a charge and these grow. For smaller values of S, small drops (A_1, A_2) grow or evaporate until they reach conditions specified by curve (2) for which they are stable, but too small to be seen. For water vapour at approximately 0°C the critical supersaturation is $S = 4·2$ and the drop radius corresponding to the maximum of curve (2) is 6×10^{-8} cm.

Condensation centres produced by ionization probably have a radius of the order of a_0 ($\approx 3 \times 10^{-8}$ cm) in the first instance. If a sufficient degree of supersaturation is existing at the time of ionization the drops grow to a diameter of about 3×10^{-3} cm in about 0·5 sec and during this time of growth may be photographed with a suitably phased flash of light. It is found that positive ions require a somewhat greater degree of supersaturation, and hence *expansion ratio* V_2/V_1, than negative ions. The interval after production of supersaturation during which ionization leads to track formation is known as the *sensitive time*; it is primarily determined by the warming up of the chamber from the temperature T_2 with consequent reduction of supersaturation. The expansion ratios used in practice are limited by the appearance of background condensation on uncharged centres.

A typical sequence of operations for the photography of charged particle tracks is as follows:

At zero time a fast adiabatic expansion occurs (in about 0·01 sec) with an expansion ratio of perhaps 1·30. The resulting temperature drop is about 28°C for a mixture of air and water vapour and a supersaturation of ≈ 6 is produced and persists for perhaps $\frac{1}{2}$ sec. During this time a burst of particles is admitted by a shutter mechanism and after about 0·2 sec for drop growth the tracks are illuminated by a short burst of light and photographed. The expansion ratio and timing sequence are adjusted for maximum clarity. The ions formed in the burst of particles must be removed after the photograph is taken and a potential of a few hundred volts supplies a clearing field to sweep the ions to the bottom of the chamber; the clearing field is removed during the expansion to minimize track broadening.

Even with this field some centres for condensation may remain after the adiabatic expansion but many of these may be removed by a subsequent slow expansion. The ideal timing sequence cannot always be achieved, particularly in the important case of a *counter-controlled chamber*. In this application the expansion is triggered by a particle which has passed into, or through the chamber, and in addition through one or more counters, and there is of necessity some diffusion of ions in the track before it is recorded. The broadening is minimized by making the expansion as rapid as possible.

Expansion chambers have been made in many different sizes and they operate with many different gases and vapours with pressures up to tens of atmospheres. Rapid chambers in which the resetting time is reduced by particular forms of pressure cycle, have been constructed to operate as frequently as once in every 10 sec. Large sensitive volumes are available and stereoscopic photography with twin cameras is usually possible. Tracks are examined in detail by reprojection on to a white surface through the cameras used for the photography.

6.2.2 THE DIFFUSION CLOUD CHAMBER. The expansion chamber has the limitation of a short sensitive time and the evolution of continuously sensitive diffusion chambers by Langsdorf in 1936 was a considerable step forward. A chamber of this type (Fig. 6.20) contains a mixture of a suitable gas and vapour and a thermal gradient is maintained between the bottom and top of the vessel by external heating or cooling. In a typical arrangement the chamber top is at about room temperature T_1 and the bottom is cooled by a mixture of methyl alcohol and solid carbon dioxide (or other suitable coolant) to a temperature T_0 of about $-60°C$. Methyl alcohol vapour is supplied from a tray containing the liquid near the top of the chamber, and this region is one of saturation vapour density. The vapour diffuses downward through the gas of the chamber into regions of lower temperature and towards the bottom of the chamber the resulting supersaturation may exceed the value necessary, according to Eq. 6.9, for drop formation. A track sensitive region then develops as shown in Fig. 6.20b.

Many varieties of diffusion cloud chamber have been constructed. The vertical diffusion mechanism leads to a sensitive depth of only 2–3 inches and the chamber is therefore not very useful for cosmic ray studies. The sensitive region is also rather easily depleted of vapour by intense ionization and after a burst of such ionization some 10–20 sec may be necessary for recovery; a clearing electrostatic field is usually applied during

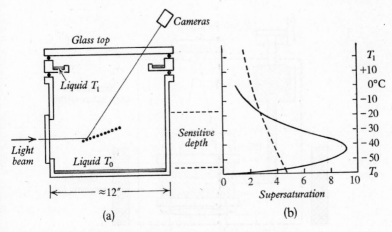

Fig. 6.20. The diffusion cloud chamber.
a) Outline construction.
b) Supersaturation as a function of temperature of gas vapour mixture. The dotted curve gives the critical value necessary for drop formation and the intersection of the two curves defines the sensitive region of the chamber (Ref. 6.15).

this time to help in the removal of ions. These features however make the diffusion chamber extremely suitable for use with pulsed accelerators, such as high energy synchrotrons or synchrocyclotrons, and a further advantage for this type of work is the fact that the operating pressure of the chamber can be increased to many atmospheres without greatly lengthening the re-cycling time, as would be necessary with an expansion chamber.

6.2.3. THE BUBBLE CHAMBER. The first few years of operation of hydrogen-filled diffusion chambers with high energy accelerators clearly exhibited the major limitation of the apparatus, namely the low stopping power of the gas even at the highest pressures feasible and the consequent slow rate of gathering information about high energy events. In a typical study of the proton–proton interaction under optimum conditions for track measurement, only about 1 picture in 30 taken with a 20 atmosphere chamber of 18 in. diameter contains an event.

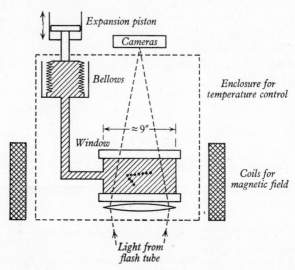

Fig. 6.21. Outline construction of a bubble chamber with glass windows and metal walls, of a type suitable for use with liquid hydrogen.

The limitation of track chambers was very considerably alleviated in 1952 by the invention by Glaser of the bubble chamber, in which the supersaturated gas–vapour mixture of the diffusion chamber is replaced by a superheated liquid. The passage of an ionizing particle through such a superheated liquid may cause bubbles to grow along the track to a size at which they may be photographed without first precipitating uncontrolled boiling throughout the volume of the fluid. Fig. 6.21 illustrates the construction and operation of the apparatus; a suitable liquid is heated above its normal boiling point and is maintained in the liquid phase by the application of a pressure above the saturation vapour pressure at the operating temperature. The pressure is then reduced by movement of a piston or diaphragm and the liquid becomes superheated and sensitive to the presence of ionization; after some seconds general boiling will occur unless a re-compression prevents it. The first theory of bubble formation followed the electrostatic theory of condensation in the expansion chamber (Sect. 6.2.1) very closely, and led to curves of the type shown in Fig. 6.19b for bubble radius. The charges required for this mechanism are however unrealistic and it is now considered that bubble development is a thermal effect due to the deposition of energy by short delta rays originating in the initial ionizing process.

Unless special care is taken to avoid roughness on surfaces, the sensitive time of bubble chambers after expansion (before uncontrolled boiling) is only a few milliseconds and entry of particles and photography must take place during this time. In this sense the bubble chamber has apparently lost the advantage of continuous sensitivity enjoyed by the diffusion chamber but this is not in practice so because (a) the continuity of the diffusion chamber is of limited use owing to vapour depletion, (b) the bubble chamber accumulates very few background tracks, (c) rapid cycling of the bubble chamber appears to be possible, and (d) the sensitive depth of a bubble chamber is not limited. When the increased yield of events due to increased density is taken into account the bubble chamber is operationally much the more economic. Bubble growth occurs in about 10^{-2} sec in an average chamber, and the centres on which the bubbles form seem to last for about the same time. It is therefore difficult to adapt the chamber for counter control since the centres produced by the triggering particle would have disappeared before the chamber could be expanded. Expansion must take place before particles enter the chamber.

Practical chambers have used pentane, propane, xenon and above all, because of their significance in high energy physics, liquid hydrogen, deuterium and helium. Table **6.4** gives typical operating conditions for these liquids.

The only limit to the size of such chambers is their cost and a liquid hydrogen chamber of dimensions 72 in. × 20 in. × 15 in. is working at the Radiation Laboratory, Berkeley. Plate 7 shows tracks obtained in a liquid hydrogen chamber; particles of minimum ionization may be detected, magnetic fields may be employed to determine momentum, and the range of the shorter secondary products may be determined directly.

TABLE 6.4   Operating conditions for bubble chamber fluids

FLUID	TEM-PERATURE °C	PRESSURE (atmo-spheres)	MEAN FREE PATH for 100 MeV γ rays (cm)	DENSITY g cm^{-3}
Hydrogen	− 246	5	2700	0·06
Deuterium	− 241	7	2000	0·13
Helium	− 269	1	1800	0·13
Propane	58	21	220	0·43
Pentane	157	23	—	0·5
Xenon	− 20	26	6·6	2·3

6.2.4 THE NUCLEAR EMULSION. Photographic methods have exerted a profound influence on the development of nuclear physics ever since the discovery of radioactivity. The passage of ionizing radiation through a photographic emulsion renders grains of silver bromide developable and this fact has been applied for many years in the detection of X-rays and γ-rays, and in the recording of beams of charged particles deflected by magnetic spectrometers. In this application the small grain size of the emulsion provides in principle extremely high resolution of recorded spectra. The use of the emulsion for the detection of single particles also dates from the early days of radioactivity and was slowly developed, by gradual improvement of the emulsion characteristics, until in the mid-1930s it was possible to distinguish under suitable magnification the tracks of both α-particles and protons as rows of individual grains. At about this time the rapidly increasing interest in nuclear transmutations and cosmic rays led to more detailed study of all types of nuclear detector and the Ilford and Kodak companies were soon success-ful, in collaboration with workers in Cambridge and elsewhere, in producing emulsions which, although relatively slow photo-graphically, had a small grain size and a tolerable density of 'background' grains on development. Techniques for processing and subsequent examination of the tracks by the binocular microscope were also evolved and by 1940 the nuclear emulsion was available as a new and promising detector of heavy charged particles, and of neutrons through the projection of recoil protons.

Although the simplicity and economy of the nuclear emulsion detector won early recognition, its reliability as a quantitative method was not widely accepted until the publication of the early work of Powell in which he demonstrated very convincingly that measurement of the length of tracks in Ilford emulsions could give reliable values for the energy of particle groups. The emission of protons and neutrons in the reactions

$$^{10}B + d \rightarrow {}^{11}B + p + 9.22 \text{ MeV} \qquad (6.12)$$

$$^{10}B + d \rightarrow {}^{11}C + n + 6.46 \text{ MeV} \qquad (6.13)$$

was studied and for the former reaction number-range curves agreeing well with those previously obtained by a counter method were found. The results for the neutron-producing reaction were even more promising. In an exposure of a few minutes made by placing a small photographic plate coated with nuclear emulsion near a boron target in a Cockcroft–Walton apparatus (Sect. 8.1.1), some 3000 recoil proton tracks were obtained in a few square centimetres of emulsion area. Subsequent microscope work led to a neutron spectrum of higher quality than that obtained from a similar experiment in which 20,000 expansion chamber photographs were taken.

This remarkable work, and parallel investigations in which the easily portable plates were exposed at mountain altitudes in a search for cosmic ray events, clearly demonstrated the great power of the emulsion method. The major limitations at this time seemed to be (i) the time consumed in scanning the emulsions and measuring tracks, (ii) the fact that owing to the very small length of most tracks no magnetic curvatures could be measured in the emulsion, and (iii) the fact that the emulsions were not sensitive to particles of minimum ionization. The first two points remain as limitations for some experiments at present but as a result of further work by Powell and his collaborators, and by the Kodak and Ilford companies, the Nuclear Research Emulsion, which can be made electron-sensitive, became available. In this emulsion the visibility of tracks is much improved over those obtained in earlier (half-tone) plates by an increase in the concentration of silver halide;

proton and α-particle tracks are dense, continuous lines and particles of minimum ionization including the readily scattered electrons also leave easily distinguishable tracks. Many beautiful examples of tracks in modern emulsions are now available; Plate 8 may suffice to show the improvement in technique obtained over a few years, and the potentialities of the present emulsions. The discovery* in 1947 of the π-meson by the exposure of concentrated emulsions to cosmic radiation at mountain altitudes stems directly from the technical improvements made in 1946 and from the simplicity and visual property of the method. The ability of the emulsion to store information was also vital in this discovery, and the important advantage of integration has been much deployed in subsequent years.

The composition of Ilford Nuclear Research Emulsions is approximately as shown in Table **6.5** (from Ref. 6.18).

TABLE 6.5   Composition of dry Ilford emulsion

Element	H	C	N	O	S	Br	Ag	I
g cm^{-3}	0·049	0·30	0·073	0·20	0·011	1·465	2·025	0·057
atoms cm^{-3} × 10^{22}	2·93	1·51	0·31	0·75	0·02	1·15	1·17	0·03

Mean density 3·9 g cm^{-3}

The size of the developed grains when examined under the microscope depends on the method of preparation; so too does the probability of a grain being rendered developable by the passage through it of a charged particle of given velocity, and the grain size and sensitivity (which may be defined quantitatively as the number of electrons required to render a grain developable) are interdependent. Table **6.6** (from Ref. 6.18) gives the characteristics of a few types of Ilford emulsion.

Of these emulsions the type C2 is most used for non-relativistic particles and the type G5 for studies of electron and high

---

* C. M. G. Lattes, G. P. S. Occhialini and C. F. Powell, *Nature*, **160**, 453 and 486, 1947.

TABLE 6.6 Characteristics of nuclear emulsions

Ilford Emulsion Type	D1	E1(K1)	C2(K2)	B2	G5
Mean grain diameter (microns)	0·12	0·14	0·10	0·21	0·18
Highest velocity detectable $\beta = v/c$		0·2	0·31	0·46	all
Highest detectable energy of protons (MeV)		20	50	120	all

energy tracks in general. All emulsions are sensitive in greater or less degree to the presence of γ-radiation, which causes an increase of background grains, or even the appearance of distinct tracks due to photoelectrons or Compton electrons.

Nuclear emulsion is usually supplied in the form of coated glass plates with emulsion thicknesses from 20 μ to 600 μ. Since the range of a proton of 10 MeV in emulsion is about 580 μ, and since in any case the tracks under investigation may often be produced tangentially in the plates, such thicknesses are generally adequate for nuclear reaction studies. In high energy, cosmic ray and meson physics, however, it is desirable to follow tracks of particles over very large distances and it is now possible to use large blocks of emulsion sheets several inches thick which form effectively a solid track chamber. After exposure to radiation these blocks are suitably marked with fiducial lines, divided up, processed, and mounted on glass backing plates for observation. Several laboratories can then participate in the examination of selected tracks.

The processing of nuclear emulsion is similar to that of ordinary photographic material, but is determined by fixed routines which ensure that the lower layers of thick glass-backed emulsions are not under-developed, or the top layers over-developed. Wet emulsion has about 2·3 times the volume of dry emulsion and distortion of tracks during shrinkage has to be avoided. The examination of the developed emulsion under the microscope is usually carried out with oil-immersion objectives ($\times 45$ or $\times 95$) and a total magnification up to $\times 1500$ dependent on the particular application; in 'area scanning', for outstanding events a relatively small magnification is used, but for 'along the track' scanning small deviations may be important and high magnification and precision stage movements are required.

The many applications of the nuclear emulsion technique fall into two broad classes: (a) the uses in which interactions originating in the emulsion are studied, and (b) the uses in which the emulsion is employed simply as a detector of charged particles. The study of interactions is somewhat complicated by the complex composition of the emulsion (Table **6.5**) which makes it difficult to identify the type of nucleus with which an incident particle, such as a proton or neutron, has interacted. An exception arises in the case of the hydrogen content when high energy protons are being used; the resulting collisions may be identified fairly easily because of the simple kinematics of the process. For collisions between high energy particles and the other emulsion constituents, assignment of observed stars (such as that shown in Plate 14) to the light or heavy elements of the emulsion must be based on detailed consideration of the prongs of the stars. In some cases specific effects may be observed when other elements are introduced into the emulsion either in manufacture or by impregnation; the best known example is the boron-loaded emulsion in which short α-particle tracks due to the reaction

$$^{10}B + n \rightarrow {}^7Li + \alpha + 2 \cdot 79 \text{ MeV} \tag{6.14}$$

may be seen after irradiating with thermal neutrons. Deuterium loading and uranium loading have also frequently been used in studies of photodisintegration and fission respectively. A further important feature of the emulsion for the study of interactions is the high resolution of distance provided by the small grain size. Distances of recoil or travel from a particular point, such as the location of a star, of the order of 1 μ or less can be estimated, and the possibility of the decay of unstable particles in this sort of distance can be assessed. This property, coupled with the high stopping power of the emulsion, has led to some evidence on the lifetime of the π^0-meson ($\approx 10^{-16}$ sec).

The identification of the nature and energy of charged particles from observed tracks in nuclear emulsions depends on knowledge of (a) range-energy relations, (b) grain density, (c) delta ray production and (d) multiple scattering properties. For heavily ionizing particles 'gap' density rather than grain density is used. In some cases, momentum may be known by deflection or selection in external magnetic fields. A single observed quantity usually depends on both e/m for the primary particles and on its velocity v and two independent observations are necessary to give full information. The methods used are fully described by Powell (Ref. 6.21) with particular reference to the π- and μ-mesons.

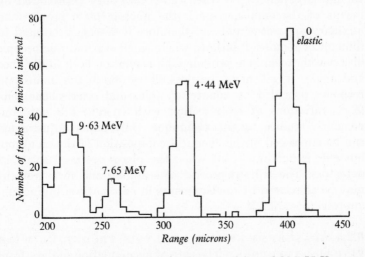

Fig. 6.22. Range distribution in nuclear emulsion of 38.1 MeV α-particles scattered by carbon nuclei. The groups marked correspond to elastic scattering and to inelastic scattering with excitation of the carbon nucleus to the levels indicated (Aguilar *et al.*, *Proc. roy. Soc.* A, **254**, 395, 1960).

The second main application of the emulsion technique is the integral recording of the number of charged particles originating in a given experiment, together with identification or selection by special characteristics, such as grain density or residual range. Nuclear plates are widely used for the recording of nuclear reaction products after high resolution magnetic analysis; the plates are examined only to yield the number of tracks per mm² as a function of angle to a primary beam, or as a function of some coordinate along the plate related to momentum or energy. The emulsion itself may be used to yield an energy spectrum of incident particles if ranges can be measured

(Fig. 6.22); absolute track counts in experiments of this sort yield reaction cross-sections.

It is clear that the nuclear emulsion provides a powerful and versatile detection technique, in which many of the properties of other detectors are combined. It records continuously and stores the recorded information; it has energy and velocity discrimination properties and high stopping power. Although large lengths of track can if necessary be followed by means of the emulsion stack the nuclear plate requires no auxiliary apparatus and can therefore if necessary be used in difficult or remote situations, where small size and microscopic observation technique provide high resolution both in distance and angle. It will never be possible to obtain the immediate response provided by counter systems and some phenomena (e.g., variations of cross-section with energy) are not conveniently studied by this technique. Only minor adjustments can be envisaged in the chemical composition of the emulsion, but this is not important when the plates are used solely as detectors. The tedious process of scanning and measurement may be alleviated by developments in automatic scanning and analysis (Sect. 6.2.5).

6.2.5 MEASUREMENT AND ANALYSIS TECHNIQUE WITH VISUAL DETECTORS. The rate of accumulation of data from modern track chambers, such as bubble chambers of large size, operated in conjunction with high energy nuclear accelerators with high repetition rates may approach a few events per second. The economic operation of large accelerators implies long runs and it therefore becomes necessary to have a rapid method of processing information. The usual method of reprojection of stereoscopic photographs on to a plane surface adjustable in 3 dimensions and subsequent measurement of range by ruler and of curvature by fitting to templates is obviously incapable of sufficient speed. Effort is therefore being devoted to methods in which reprojected tracks are followed by an optical system whose movements in space are accurately recorded by techniques such as the Moiré-fringe diffraction grating method developed for machine-tool control. The output of such a measuring unit representing track coordinates can be made available in digital form on punched tape for direct feed to an electronic computer. This in turn can be programmed to calculate curvatures or energies, to test for coplanarity or to solve any particular kinematical problem. The method is general and can be applied to tracks in nuclear emulsions as well.

6.3   The triggered spark chamber*

The visual techniques described in Sect. **6.2** provide excellent spatial resolution for particle studies, but poor or non-existent time determination. The counter techniques (Sect. **6.1**) on the other hand offer highly accurate time resolution but are unsuitable for the study of spatial distribution except in well-defined circumstances, such as a simple scattering or trans-mutation experiment. The first successful attempt to combine the two desirable features of high resolution both in space and time resulted in the counter-controlled cloud chamber, which had an important influence on cosmic ray physics. The re-cycling time of chambers however limits the efficiency of this type of detector.

Triggered visual detectors have been designed in which a bank of neon tubes is pulsed with a high voltage immediately after the passage of a primary ionizing particle through a counter telescope. The neon tubes through which the particle has passed then discharge and their glow may be photographed. A simpler form of detector operating in the same way is the triggered spark chamber (Fig. 6.23) in which an ionizing particle passes through a stack of thin metal plates contained in a vessel filled with a noble gas at about 1 atmosphere pressure. A signal from a counter telescope is used to trigger a voltage impulse of 10–15 kV which is applied to the plates within about $0 \cdot 3$ μsec of the primary event. The rise time of the voltage pulse is about $0 \cdot 025$ μsec and within $0 \cdot 1$ μsec of its appearance on the plates an electron avalanche builds up through a channel defined by what remains of the initial ionization. This gives a bright, well-defined spark, which may be photographed. Tracks due to unwanted particles are minimized by the application of a constant clearing field ($\approx 100 \, \text{V cm}^{-1}$) to the chamber to remove residual ionization and a sensitive time of about $0 \cdot 5$ μsec can be

---

* See E. F. Beall *et al. Nuovo Cimento*, **20**, 502, 1961.

obtained. The high voltage pulse is cut off abruptly by the discharge and terminates in 0·1 μsec; there is a dead time of 1–10 msec while the positive ions are being cleared from the spark channel.

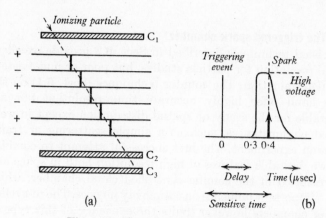

Fig. 6.23. The triggered spark chamber.
a) Construction; C_1, C_2, C_3 are counters forming a telescope.
b) High voltage pulse.

This detector is clearly capable of rapid operation, and because it provides excellent definition of direction, and may be operated in coincidence with other counters, it is rapidly becoming important in high energy physics. Plate 9 shows the quality of the information obtainable with the spark chamber.

References

6.1   J. Sharpe, *Nuclear Radiation Detectors*, Methuen, 1960.
6.2   H. Staub, 'Detection Methods', in *Experimental Nuclear Physics*, ed. E. Segrè, Vol. I, Wiley, 1953.
6.3   S. Fluegge (ed.), *Encyclopedia of Physics*, Vol. 45, Springer, 1958.
6.4   D. H. Wilkinson, *Ionization Chambers and Counters*, Cambridge University Press, 1950.
6.5   N. Cusack, *The Electrical and Magnetic Properties of Solids*, Longmans, 1958.
6.6   G. Dearnaley and A. B. Whitehead, 'The semi-conductor surface barrier for nuclear particle detection'. *Nucl. instrum. and Methods*, **12**, 205, 1961.
6.7   D. West, 'Energy measurements with Proportional Counters', *Progr. nucl. Phys.*, **3**, 18, 1953.

6.8   G. F. Garlick, 'Luminescent Materials for Scintillation Counters', *Progr. nucl. Phys.*, **2**, 51, 1952.

6.9   J. V. Jelley, *Cherenkov Radiation*, Pergamon Press, 1958.

6.10 W. B. Lewis, *Electrical Counting*, Cambridge University Press, 1948.

6.11 I. A. D. Lewis and F. H. Wells, *Millimicrosecond Pulse Techniques*, Pergamon Press, 1954.

6.12 A. B. Gillespie, *Signal, Noise and Response in Nuclear Counter Amplifiers*, Pergamon Press, 1953.

6.13 E. Breitenberger, 'Scintillation Spectrometer Statistics', *Progr. nucl. Phys.*, **4**, 56, 1954.

6.14 J. G. Wilson, *Principles of Cloud Chamber Technique*, Cambridge University Press, 1951.

6.15 M. Snowden, 'The Diffusion Cloud Chamber', *Progr. nucl. Phys.*, **3**, 1, 1953.

6.16 C. Dodd, 'The Bubble Chamber', *Progr. nucl. Phys.*, **5**, 142, 1956.

6.17 H. Slatis, 'On Bubble Chambers', *Nucl. instrum. and Methods*, **5**, 1, 1959.

6.18 J. Rotblat, 'Photographic Emulsion Technique', *Progr. nucl. Phys.*, **1**, 37, 1950.

6.19 C. F. Powell *et al.*, *The Study of Elementary Particles by the Photographic Method*, Pergamon Press, 1959.

6.20 D. M. Ritson (ed.), *Techniques of High Energy Physics*, Interscience, 1961.

6.21 C. F. Powell, 'Mesons', *Rep. progr. Phys.*, **13**, 350, 1950.

6.22 L. C. L. Yuan and C. S. Wu (ed.), *Methods of Experimental Physics*, Vol. 5A, Academic Press, 1961.

7. MEASUREMENT OF ENERGY AND INTENSITY OF IONIZING RADIATIONS

The radiations of nuclear physics are encountered as *single particles* or *photons*, as *collimated beams* of particles or photons with an intensity such that single members cannot be identified, or as *fluxes* in which the single particles or photons travel with a wide range of angles and the usual measure of intensity is the number crossing unit surface in unit time. All observations of radiation rely on some kind of detector, which, except in the case of a current-measuring instrument, will usually be one of those described in chapter 6. Energy measurements often involve the combination of an analysing instrument such as a magnetic spectrometer or a time-of-flight spectrometer with a detector for plotting a line profile, as in optical spectrometry, but many detectors are themselves energy sensitive and furnish information on energy and intensity simultaneously.

The object of intensity determinations in nuclear physics is usually to obtain the absolute yield of a particular process and from it the corresponding cross-section (Sect. 5.1.3). Absolute intensity determinations can be avoided in simple cases when a collimated beam is available and only one type of process is significant, since a transmission method may then be used to find the linear attenuation coefficient (Sect. 5.1.3) and the cross-section follows immediately. More usually, however, a beam or flux of particles or photons bombards a target and the intensity of a particular radiation, often in a particular direction, is estimated. When only a total cross-section is required, determinations of a specified residual activity may be sufficient (Sect. **7.1**).

7.1 Determination of disintegration rate of a radioactive source

The earliest accurate determinations of α-disintegration rate were made by Rutherford and Geiger, and have already been described in Sect. **2.2**; they form the basis of quantitative measurements of radioactivity. Similar methods of individual particle counting are now used extensively both in general radiochemistry (Ref. 7.1), and in specific problems, such as the determination of the intensity of a beam of neutrons or protons from the activity induced in a suitable detector. Standards of activity are discussed briefly in Sect. 2.5.2 and extensively in Ref. 7.2 and many standardized sources are now available for comparative measurements. Among the particular techniques which have been used in absolute activity determinations are

a) *Absolute β- (or α-) counting.* Two methods are used, *the defined solid-angle method* in which the fraction of particles entering a counter is determined, and the *4π counter method* in which the source is placed wholly within the volume of a Geiger or proportional counter. The main corrections in β-counting arise from the fact that the source is not usually weightless and that scattering and absorption occur even in the thinnest supporting foils (≈ 20 μg cm^{-2}).

b) *Coincidence methods.* If a nucleus disintegrates by emission of a β-particle, followed by a photon, or by a cascade of two photons, coincidences between two of the radiations may be observed. If the disintegration rate of a source is N per sec, the coincidence rate is

$$C = N\varepsilon_1\varepsilon_2 \qquad (7.1)$$

where ε_1, ε_2, are the efficiencies of the two counters for detection of the particular radiations (Fig. 7.1). The counting rate of the first counter is $C_1 = N\varepsilon_1$ and of the second $C_2 = N\varepsilon_2$ so that the ratio C/C_1 gives ε_2 and then $C_2/\varepsilon_2 = N$. Corrections must of course be made for random coincidences (Sect. 6.1.9) and for angular correlation between the radiations if this differs from isotropy.

c) *Positron emitters,* e.g.

$$^{11}\mathrm{C} \to {}^{11}\mathrm{B} + \beta^+ + \nu \qquad (7.2)$$

The necessity for β-counting may be avoided by stopping the positrons in a thin absorber surrounding the source. Two annihilation quanta, travelling in opposite directions, then arise for every positron stopped in the absorber and may be detected quantitatively in a scintillation spectrometer. Background can

be reduced by the use of two counters in coincidence at 180°
angular separation.

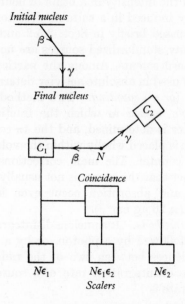

Fig. 7.1. Coincidence method of determining disintegration rate of
radioactive source.

d) *Tritium estimation*. The isotope ^{3}H decays by emission of
β-rays in a spectrum with an end point energy of about 18 keV.
This is very suitable for gaseous proportional counter determinations and the cross-sections for reactions producing ^{3}H
may be measured in this way.

7.2   Measurements of energy and intensity of charged particles

7.2.1 RANGE METHODS.   Precise measurements of the energy
of groups of natural α-particles were made by Rutherford
and his collaborators using shallow ionization chambers.
Number-range curves were obtained and the results were
reduced to mean range (Sect. 5.3.5) and then converted to
energy by use of the range-energy relation (Sect. 5.3.3). An
accuracy $\delta E/E$ of 1% is possible by this method, but it is
slow because the number-range curve must be plotted point

by point while source conditions are maintained constant and it is little used at present.

More extensive use has been made of the nuclear emulsion for range measurements, because the entire number-range curve can be obtained, as a histogram, by scanning a single photographic plate (Sect. 6.2.4 and Fig. 6.22). In typical experiments with 10 MeV protons an accuracy of 0·3% and a resolution of 2% have been obtained. The resolution is determined by range straggling (Sect. 5.3.5).

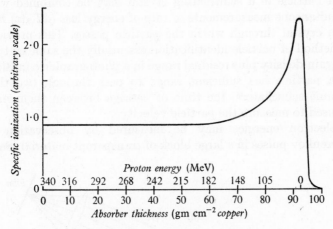

Fig. 7.2. Bragg ionization curve for 340 MeV protons stopped by copper (Bakker and Segrè, *Phys. Rev.*, **81**, 489, 1951).

In high-energy physics range measurements are often somewhat rough, and are only useful for energies at which *nuclear* processes do not significantly attenuate a beam of particles, e.g. $E < 500$ MeV for protons. Fig. 7.2 shows an accurate Bragg ionization curve for protons; such curves have been used to indicate the energies of protons and mesons to about 0·5%, using semi-empirical range-energy curves (Sect. 5.3.3).

7.2.2 TOTAL IONIZATION METHODS.
If the whole range of a charged particle can be contained within an ionization chamber or proportional counter, the resulting saturation pulse size is a measure of the energy of the particle. Examples of this use of nuclear ionization detectors are given in Sects. 6.1.1,

6.1.2 and 6.1.3; the solid state ionization chamber has the best resolution (0·3%) in the energy range for which it is suitable and is finding many applications.

7.2.3 LIGHT OUTPUT METHODS. The scintillation method is the most versatile of all energy measuring techniques of moderate resolution. A typical pulse height distribution for α-particles in a CsI crystal is given in Fig. 6.11; a resolution of 4% at 6 MeV is obtainable.

Measurements of total energy E based on complete absorption of a particle in a scintillating crystal may be combined with simultaneous measurements of rate of energy loss (dT/dx) in a thin crystal through which the particle passes. This provides a method of particle identification essentially the same as that of grain-density plus residual range in a photographic emulsion. If a particle has sufficient range to pass through two thin organic scintillators, the time of passage between them may be used to measure the particle velocity.

Electron energies may be measured by observation of Cherenkov pulses in a large block of transparent material (Sect.

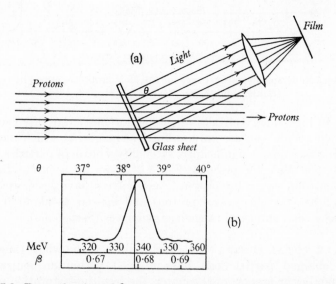

Fig. 7.3. Determination of $\beta = v/c$ for 340 MeV protons by observation of Cherenkov angle. (a) Principle of apparatus. (b) Microphotometer trace of photographic image. (Mather, *Phys. Rev.*, **84**, 181, 1951.)

6.1.7). If intensity permits, the angle of emission of Cherenkov light from a thin radiator traversed by a charged particle can give a very accurate determination of velocity. The principle of such an apparatus is shown in Fig. 7.3. From accurate measurements of the line image obtained, the energy of a beam of 340 MeV protons was determined to 0·2%. The resolution is of the same order of magnitude. This experiment employed an intense beam of protons, but similar, though less accurate energy measurements can be made on single particles using special types of Cherenkov counter with focusing attachments.

7.2.4 ELECTROSTATIC AND MAGNETIC SPECTROMETRY (GENERAL).

The deflection of charged particles by electrostatic and magnetic fields has been of outstanding importance in the development of physics since the first studies of the gaseous discharge. At the present time the theory of such deflections finds application in

a) energy or momentum measurements,
b) monochromators or steering magnets for particle beams,
c) mass spectrometry, and
d) accelerator design.

For heavy particles of energy above about 50 MeV accurate electrostatic and magnetic spectrometers are comparable in size with accelerators and very few have been constructed. Large magnets with or without double focusing properties are however widely used for deflecting and concentrating particle beams from synchrocyclotrons and proton synchrotons and are an essential part of the beam engineering installations. They usually have a long focal length and are not suitable for anything better than a crude estimate of particle energies. For such purposes they may be calibrated by the 'floating wire' technique,* but the information thus obtained is likely to be much inferior to that provided by knowledge of the properties of the accelerator itself.

---

* It is easy to show that a flexible wire under tension T and carrying current i takes up the path of a single charged particle of momentum p in a magnetic field H where $p = \dfrac{Te}{ic}$.

In low energy nuclear physics magnetic spectrometers give the most precise information available on nuclear energy changes in transmutations, and lead to a scale of atomic masses comparable with that based on mass spectrographic measurements (which are also made in essence with magnetic spectrometers). The development of β-ray spectrometers originated in the study of naturally occurring radioactive elements as a method of refining the crude data provided by absorption methods. Such instruments are now used for practically all β-spectroscopic measurements except in cases in which the low disintegration rate of the source under investigation demands the use of a large angle of collection.

The response of a spectrometer in which a radiation of homogeneous energy is being examined may often be represented as in Fig. 6.18, as for an energy-sensitive nuclear detector. In both cases we distinguish between ΔE, the full width of the response curve at half intensity and δE, the accuracy with which the energy E is known.* The width ΔE depends jointly on the properties of the particular instrument and on the size of the source and detector of particles used in the spectrometer; it determines the resolution $R = \Delta E/E$ of the apparatus. The accuracy δE depends on calibrations. In general, resolution can only be improved by some sacrifice of transmission (T), which is defined to be the fraction of particles of a given energy or momentum emitted by the source which is collected and focused on a detector by the spectrometer.

Heavy particle spectrometers have generally followed existing designs of β-ray instruments and present no new features except that much larger fields are required.

7.2.5 BETA SPECTROMETERS.

a) *Semicircular focusing spectrometer.* Magnetic deflection through 180° in a uniform field was first applied to beta rays by von Baeyer, Hahn and Meitner. If the electrons move in a plane perpendicular to the lines of force of the field there is first order focusing; particles of the same velocity passing through the slit AB from a point source (Fig. 7.4a) describe circles of

---

* In many cases it is more convenient to express the response in terms of momentum p, rather than energy E.

the same radius and converge to a focus F. The trace of such particles on a photographic plate in the focal plane has a sharp edge on the high energy side corresponding to rays emitted at right-angles to the diameter SF, and this permits accurate measurements to be made (Fig. 7.4b). If the slit AB (which may

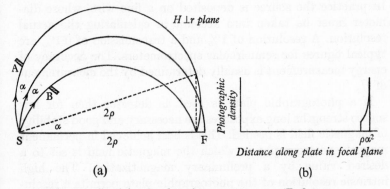

(a)   (b)

Fig. 7.4. Semicircular focusing spectrometer (Ref. 7.5).
a) First order focusing at F of particles of uniform energy from a point source S after 180° deflection in the plane of the diagram.
b) Microphotometer trace of line on a photographic plate placed in the focal plane.

be at any point on the trajectory) defines an angle of acceptance of 2α then the width of the image of a point source at the focus is approximately

$$s = 2\rho(1 - \cos \alpha) \approx \rho\alpha^2 \qquad (7.3)$$

where ρ is the radius of curvature for the given (relativistic) momentum p, i.e.

$$\rho = \frac{pc}{eH} \qquad (7.4)$$

The resolution in momentum, i.e. the relative change in momentum necessary to shift the line by its width s, is

$$R = \frac{\mathrm{d}p}{p} = \frac{\mathrm{d}\rho}{\rho} = \frac{s}{2\rho} = \frac{\alpha^2}{2} \quad \text{from 7.3} \qquad (7.5)$$

If now trajectories in other planes are considered, it is found that over a narrow range of angles α there is still first order

9*

focusing at F. The transmission factor in the case when AB is a circular hole subtending a solid angle Ω is

$$T = \frac{\Omega}{4\pi} = \frac{1}{4\pi} \cdot 2\pi(1 - \cos \alpha) \approx \frac{\alpha^2}{4} \qquad (7.6)$$

In practice the source is deposited on a fine wire, whose diameter must be taken into account in calculating the actual resolution. A resolution of 1% and a transmission of 0·1% are typical figures for semicircular spectrometers. The accuracy of energy measurement is usually determined by the measurement of H.

If a photographic plate is used as detector then for low source strengths long exposures are necessary and good stability of magnetic field is needed. This is best achieved in permanent magnet spectrographs in which the magnetic field is set to a desired value by a preliminary magnetization. The high intrinsic resolution of the photographic plate permits a resolution of about 0·25% in energy to be reached in 180° magnetic spectrographs. Photographic recording is not quantitative, unless individual tracks in nuclear emulsions are counted, and when intensity measurements are important a counter or scintillator may be used as detector. In this case the magnetic field is varied, and measured after each variation, and a momentum spectrum is obtained by plotting a corrected counting rate as a function of magnetic field. Since according to 7.5 the detector aperture will embrace a momentum interval dp proportional to p at any given setting, the corrected counting rate is obtained by dividing the observed rate by p.

b) *The magnetic lens spectrometer.* Consider a source S emitting electrons with homogeneous momentum p at a point on the axis of a homogeneous magnetic field produced by a solenoid (Fig. 7.5). The path of the electrons emerging at an angle α with the axis will be a helix which will intersect the axis again at the point F. To calculate the distance SF we note that the angular velocity of the electron about the lines of force is

$$\frac{v \sin \alpha}{\rho} = \frac{eH}{mc} \qquad (7.7)$$

and that in the time τ taken to describe an angle 2π the electron moves parallel to the field through a distance

$$SF = v \cos\alpha . \tau = \frac{2\pi mvc}{eH} \cos\alpha \approx \frac{2\pi pc}{eH}\left(1 - \frac{\alpha^2}{2}\right) \quad (7.8)$$

if α is small. Particles emitted with a range of values of α defined by the slit AB intersect the axis over the distance FF′; it may also be shown (Refs. 7.4, 7.5) that there is a *ring focus* F″ nearer to the source S.

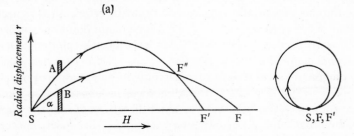

Fig. 7.5. Focusing of charged particles by a longitudinal field. F″ is the position of the ring focus. The circles represent the trajectories viewed in the direction of H (Ref. 7.5).

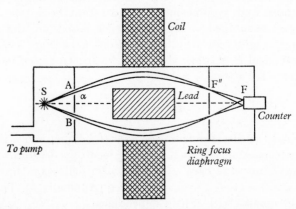

Fig. 7.6. Short lens spectrometer. The central lead block is to screen the counter from γ-radiation from the source (Ref. 7.5).

Spectrometers in which a strong axial field exists over the whole volume between source and detector (*long lens spectrometers*) have good transmission but require a large power supply if air-cored coils, for which H is accurately linear with current, are to be used. If linearity is not necessary iron may be used in the magnetic circuit; the field shape is then usually adjusted to minimize the axial focusing distance FF'. A more popular instrument is the *short lens* spectrometer (Fig. 7.6) in which the magnetic field is produced by an air-cored coil over a short central region of the trajectory. This spectrometer is analogous in principle to an optical lens with a power proportional to $(i/p)^2$, where i is the coil current and p the momentum of the focused particles. The resolution may be improved by placing an annular slit at the ring focus; typical performance figures for SF $\approx$ 100 cm are $R = 2\%$, $T = 1\%$ for a 6 mm diameter source.

The properties of the ring focus have been exploited to an extreme degree in the *intermediate image spectrometer* described by Siegbahn and Slätis. In this instrument, an example of which is sketched in Fig. 7.21, the ring focus is expanded so that electrons pass through it in an axial direction. It can then act as an object for a second lens section of the spectrometer, which is approximately the mirror image of the first, and focuses the electrons on the detector.

c) *Inhomogeneous field (double focusing) spectrometers.* The good transmission property of the lens spectrometer and the potentially high resolution of the constant field 180° instrument are combined in spectrometers based on the double focusing property of an inhomogeneous field (Fig. 7.7). If the magnetic field H between the poles of a spectrometer with axial symmetry is written

$$H = H_0 \left(\frac{r_0}{r}\right)^n \tag{7.9}$$

where r is the distance from the axis and H_0, r_0 and n the field index are parameters, then for $n = \frac{1}{2}$ electrons diverging from a point will converge back to a point after deflection through an angle $\sqrt{2}\pi (= 254 \cdot 6°)$ from the source (Appendix 5). This type of spectrometer with a field dependence

$$H \propto r^{-\frac{1}{2}} \tag{7.10}$$

was suggested by Svartholm and Siegbahn. An instrument with a radius of 50 cm and a pole gap of 2·8 cm had a transmission of 1% and a resolution of 0·9% with a source of 5 mm wide. The source and detector must be within the field if the instrument is to be used for absolute measurements. The spectrometer is non-linear because of the iron in the magnetic circuit, but shaped fields can also be obtained without iron by suitably arranged conductors if sufficient power is available.

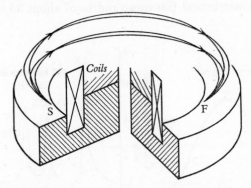

Fig. 7.7. Double focusing spectrometer. The top half of the annular magnet is largely cut away to show the orbits (Ref. 7.4).

d) *Performance.* A figure of merit for all types of spectrometer is the ratio T/R; it is a maximum for double focusing and intermediate-image instruments. The use of β-spectrometers in nuclear physics is illustrated in Fig. 7.8, which shows a typical β-spectrum, and homogeneous electron lines due to an internal conversion process (Sect. 2.2.2).

7.2.6 HEAVY PARTICLE SPECTROMETERS. The design of heavy particle spectrometers has generally followed that of β-spectrometers with the limitation that iron-free magnetic instruments cannot be used because of the high momenta involved.

The first *uniform field spectrometer* as distinct from magnetic deflection apparatus was designed by Cockcroft for the analysis of naturally occurring α-particle groups by Rutherford and his collaborators (1933). The magnet was of the 180° focusing type, and in order to use only a minimum of iron an annular gap was employed. The thin radioactive source and an ionization chamber or proportional counter as detector were immersed in the field at opposite ends of a diameter. For absolute measurements of the highest precision* the diameter must be compared directly with a standard metre by optical means, and the magnetic field must be measured by the nuclear resonance method (Sect. 4.4.3) and corrected (Hartree correction) for azimuthal variation. Under these circumstances the precision of energy measurement is about 1 part in 5,000 and the resolution of the instrument (for mean radius of about 35 cm) can be

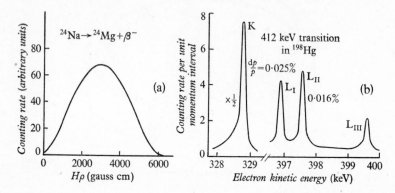

Fig. 7.8

a) Beta-spectrum of ^{24}Na observed in a lens-type instrument (Siegbahn, *Phys. Rev.*, **70**, 127, 1946).

b) Internal conversion lines observed in a double focusing spectrometer (Graham *et al.*, *Nucl. Instrum. and Methods*, **9**, 245, 1960).

about 0·1%. This performance is however combined with a small transmission of 0·005% and in the type of measurement in which the magnetic field is varied while a line profile is plotted from counter readings the exploration of a spectrum can be extremely tedious.

For experiments in which only a momentum distribution is required it is better to convert the spectrometer into a spectrograph by using a nuclear emulsion as a detector. Particles with a considerable range of momenta can then be recorded simultaneously, and immediate discrimination between singly and doubly charged particles is obtained from grain density on

---

* See, for example, E. R. Collins, C. D. McKenzie and C. A. Ramm, *Proc. roy. Soc.* A, **216**, 219, 1953; and the review by G. H. Briggs, *Rev. mod. Phys.*, **26**, 472, 1954.

examination. If a sector-shaped magnetic field with deflection angle less than 180° is used both source and detector can be some distance outside the magnetic field, and the arrangement is very convenient for transmutation work in which the source is a target bombarded by a beam of particles. This principle has been adopted by Buechner (Ref. 7.6) and by others in the 90° *broad-range magnetic spectrograph* (Fig. 7.9a) which is able to record an extensive spectrum at one exposure. Fig. 7.9b is typical of the work of this instrument, which has been responsible for the demonstration of many hundreds of nuclear levels. Sector-field instruments are neither absolute nor linear because of fringing field effects and must be calibrated with known particle groups over the range of energies required. Measurements are then possible to an accuracy 1 part in 1000 with a resolution of 0·06% at a radius of 50 cm.

In cases in which good transmission is more important than extreme resolution as in the study of the yield of a group of particles as a function of energy, the *inhomogeneous field spectrometer* may be used. If the deflection angle is less than the $\sqrt{2}\pi$ usual in double-focusing β-spectrometers, then again both source and detector may be placed outside the magnetic field, and the instrument becomes very suitable for nuclear reaction studies. In a small analyser of this type made by Snyder *et al.** for 2 MeV protons a resolution of 0·8% and a transmission of 0·06% were obtained with a detector dimension of 8 mm.

Accurate determinations of energy may also be made with the *electrostatic spectrometer*, which has been used in both cylindrical† and spherical form.‡

7.2.7 ABSOLUTE ENERGY DETERMINATIONS.   Primary standards of energy are based on instruments of simple construction, such as the uniform field magnetic spectrometer and the cylindrical electrostatic analyser, for which accurate calculations of energy may be made. In this way the energies of α-particle groups from Po (5.30 MeV), ThC′ (8·78 MeV) and ThC (6.04 + 6·08 MeV) have been found to an accuracy of the

---

* C. W. Snyder, S. Rubin, W. A. Fowler and C. C. Lauritsen, *Rev. sci. Instrum.*, **21**, 852, 1950.

† S. K. Allison *et al.*, *Rev. sci. Instrum.*, **20**, 735, 1949.

‡ C. P. Browne *et al.*, *Rev. sci. Instrum.*, **22**, 952, 1951.

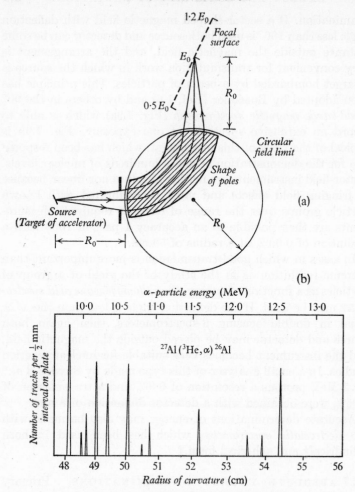

Fig. 7.9. The broad range spectrograph.
a) Geometrical arrangement. There is adequate focusing for particles of a range of energy about E_0, the energy for $90°$ deflection (Ref. 7.6).
b) Results for the $^{27}\text{Al}(^3\text{He}, \alpha)^{26}\text{Al}$ reaction (Hinds and Middleton, *Proc. phys. Soc.*, **73**, 501, 1959).

order of 1 part in 5000 (Ref. 7.2). The threshold energy for neutron production in the reaction

$$^7\text{Li} + p \rightarrow {}^7\text{Be} + n - 1\cdot6449 \text{ MeV} \qquad (7.11)$$

has been determined with the same precision and is given as $1880 \cdot 7 \pm 0 \cdot 4$ keV.

These standards can be used in the calibration of spectrometers for measurements of the energy of charged particles. Accurate measurements of energy release in nuclear reactions also require the use of thin targets and of beams of particles of accurately known energy. Absolute spectrometers may also be used as beam energy analysers.*

7.3   Measurement of energy and intensity of neutrons

Neutrons are produced only in nuclear reactions and they cannot in practice be accelerated or deflected by electric or magnetic fields. In consequence some of the methods (Sects. 7.3.1, 7.3.2) used for measuring neutron energy are also used to define it for experiments in which beams of homogeneous particles are required. The techniques of quantitative neutron physics depend markedly on the energies involved and it will be convenient to define the ranges shown in Table **7.1**.

TABLE 7.1   Classification of neutron energies

RANGE	DESCRIPTION	SUB-DIVISION
0–1000 eV	Slow	0–0·002 eV Cold $\approx 0 \cdot 025$ eV Thermal $\approx 0 \cdot 5$ eV Epithermal 1–100 eV Resonance
1–500 keV	Intermediate	—
0·5–10 MeV	Fast	—
10–200 MeV	High energy	—
above 200 MeV	Ultra high energy	—

The most generally useful technique over the whole range of energies is the time-of-flight method of energy definition; for near thermal neutrons crystalline diffraction also offers high precision.

The strength of a given neutron source is often related to a

* J. B. Marion, *Rev. mod. Phys.*, **33**, 139, 1961.

radon-beryllium standard; 1 mC of radon intimately mixed
with beryllium powder yields approximately $1\cdot3 \times 10^4$ neutrons
sec^{-1}.

7.3.1 THE TIME-OF-FLIGHT TECHNIQUE.

a) *Slow neutrons.* The neutron velocity spectrometer suggested by Alvarez (1938) has been continuously developed
since the early days of slow neutron studies, but the principle,
illustrated in Fig. 7.10 remains the same. A short pulse of
neutrons is produced at a source by suitable modulation, and
the neutrons are allowed to travel over an accurately known
flight path l before reaching a detector. The detector output

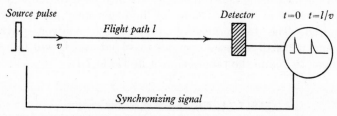

Fig. 7.10. Principle of time-of-flight technique using modulated source.

may be displayed on a time base which is synchronized with
the source modulation pattern, and if the source is monokinetic, signals are obtained only at the definite time delay l/v
after the source pulse. If the source is not monokinetic the
signals displayed on the time-base give a velocity spectrum of
the neutrons. Alternatively signals may be accepted from the
detector only through a 'gate' delayed by a variable time from
the source pulser. All such signals are then due to neutrons of a
given velocity, which may thus be selected from a continuous
distribution of source velocities. If a sample of material is
placed in the flight path the absorption for neutrons of the
selected velocity may be studied.

In the first successful application of this method at the
University of Columbia the source was a cyclotron in which
neutrons were produced by the deuteron bombardment of
beryllium as a result of the nuclear reaction

$$^9\text{Be} + d \rightarrow {}^{10}\text{B} + n + 4\cdot36\,\text{MeV} \qquad (7.12)$$

The ion source of the cyclotron was modulated and the fast neutrons emerging from the target were slowed down in a block of paraffin wax near by. The slow neutrons traversed a flight path to a boron-trifluoride ionization chamber. In experiments made with a path of 5.4 metres, pulses of length between 10 and

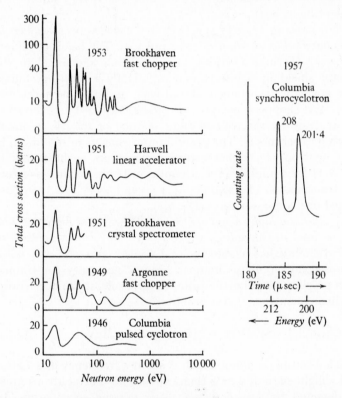

Fig. 7.11. Determination of total neutron cross-section for silver by time-of-flight methods, 1946–1957 (Rainwater, *Encyclopedia of Physics*, **40**, 373, 1957).

1000 μsec were used with repetition rates of 100–1000 pulses per second; the resolution was determined by the pulse lengths. The method has recently been developed at the University of Columbia by use of the 385 MeV proton synchrocyclotron to produce neutron bursts of 0·1 μsec duration at a rate of 60 pulses per second. A flight path of 35 metres was used and the yield of gamma radiation from neutrons interacting with a sample at the detector position was observed. Similar velocity spectrometers for slow neutrons have been based on electron linear accelerators as source, the neutrons being produced by (γ,n) reactions in beryllium as a result of bremsstrahlung pulses. The accelerator pulse length of about 1 μsec is very suitable for time-of-flight work.

Slow neutron velocity spectrometry has also been applied to the neutron beams from nuclear reactors. The beam of mixed, but near thermal, energies emerging from a channel in the reactor shielding is interrupted rapidly by a rotating shutter of a strongly absorbing material such as boron or cadmium. Such 'fast choppers' can provide pulses of about 1 μsec duration for analysis by the time-of-flight method or for use in transmission experiments. The general improvement in resolution in slow neutron spectrometry over a few years is illustrated in Fig. 7.11 for a number of well-known instruments; in this figure the transmission of a sample at a given energy has been converted into a cross-section (Eq. 5.8).

b) *Fast and high energy neutrons.* The time of flight method can be used in the energy range 0·5–10 MeV but a neutron of energy 1 MeV has a velocity of $1·4 \times 10^9$ cm sec^{-1} and milli-microsecond circuit techniques become necessary for timing. It is possible to pulse the beam of an electrostatic accelerator producing neutrons by the reaction

$$^3H + {}^2H \rightarrow {}^4He + n + 17·58 \text{ MeV} \qquad (7.13)$$

with a duration of about 2×10^{-9} sec at a frequency of 3·7 Mc/s and a flight path of 2 m is then convenient. The neutrons must be detected by fast counters using organic scintillators. In another variant of this technique a particle or photon associated with the neutron production, e.g. the α-particle in the reaction (7.13), provides the timing pulse and neutrons are observed in delayed coincidence with this signal. Cyclotrons and linear accelerators are also particularly suitable for this work because the beam is bunched during the acceleration process and arrives at the neutron producing target as a succession of short pulses in any case. Fig. 7.12 shows a neutron spectrum obtained with a pulsed electrostatic accelerator.

Neutrons of energy 15–150 MeV have been produced by using the time-of-flight technique with the Harwell 180 MeV synchro-cyclotron. A wide primary spectrum is provided by the reaction

$$^{9}\text{Be} + p \rightarrow {}^{9}\text{B} + n - 1 \cdot 85 \text{ MeV} \qquad (7.14)$$

and by suitable electrostatic deflection the proton beam can be brought to the beryllium target in short pulses. The neutron

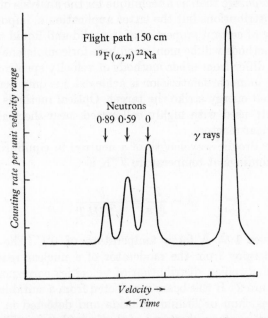

Fig. 7.12. Time-of-flight spectrum of neutrons from the reaction $^{19}\text{F}(\alpha,n)^{22}\text{Na}$. The large peak corresponds to γ-radiation (travelling between target and detector with the velocity of light). Three neutron peaks are shown, corresponding to formation of ^{22}Na in its ground state and in excited states of energy 0·59 and 0·89 MeV, giving neutrons of lower energy and longer flight time (Batchelor and Towle, *Proc. phys. Soc.*, **73**, 307, 1959).

energy required is then defined by the delayed timing method.

c) *General.* The resolution of time-of-flight methods of energy measurement is usually expressed in terms of a time spread per metre of flight path. For the Columbia (1957) results shown in Fig. 7.11 a resolution of $0\cdot01$ μsec m^{-1} is indicated corresponding to an energy resolution of about $0\cdot5\%$ at 150 eV. The method has been extensively applied to the study of spectra of inelastically scattered neutrons, which are detected with increased delay in the spectrometer.

7.3.2 DIFFRACTION METHODS FOR SLOW NEUTRONS.

Neutron diffraction has been more used as a method of studying crystal structure than as a technique for the analysis of neutron energy distributions but the latter application is important for the study of certain properties of the solid and liquid state and optical methods will be mentioned here for completeness. These methods differ from other methods of velocity spectrometry in that true monochromatization is achieved, i.e. only neutrons of the wanted energy strike the target. Optical methods are now exclusively used with highly collimated, near-thermal, beams from nuclear reactors.

The de Broglie wavelength of a neutron in equilibrium with its surroundings at temperature $T°K$ is

$$\lambda = \frac{h}{Mv} = \frac{h}{\sqrt{3MkT}} \qquad (7.15)$$

which gives $1\cdot55$ A for a temperature of $0°C$. The neutron beam emerging from the moderator of a nuclear reactor will have a Maxwellian distribution of velocities corresponding to temperature T. If this beam is reflected from a suitable crystal, such as calcium or lithium fluoride and detected in a boron trifluoride counter a spectrum of the form shown in Fig. 7.13 is obtained; if the crystal is left at a fixed setting, a monochromatic beam is obtained at the Bragg reflection angle with wavelength given by

$$\lambda = 2d \sin \theta \qquad (7.16)$$

where d is the spacing of the crystal planes. For LiF $d = 2\cdot32$ A and for neutrons of 'temperature' $0°C$, $\theta = 42°$; for neutrons of energy 1 eV however θ falls to $3\cdot5°$ and for higher energies still collimation of the beam is a serious obstacle to high resolving power. In practice the crystal monochromator is most satisfactory for thermal and resonance neutrons, of energies less than about 20 eV; in the thermal region a resolution of about 6% is possible with a continuous beam of about 10^4 neutrons cm^{-2} sec^{-1}.

7.3.3 MEASUREMENTS BASED ON RECOIL PROTONS. The energy of a proton recoiling at a laboratory angle ϕ with the direction of incidence of a neutron of energy E_0 is

$$E_r = E_0 \cos^2 \phi$$

from (5.2). If the neutron energy is less than about 10 MeV it is a good approximation to assume that the neutron–proton

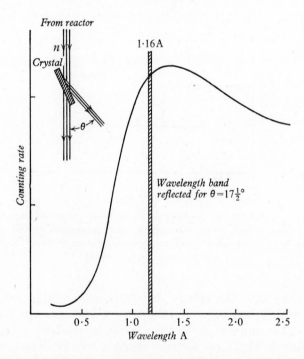

Fig. 7.13. Counting rate in collimated beam of slow neutrons reflected from a calcium fluoride crystal as a function of wavelength. The insert shows the geometrical arrangement (from Bacon, *Neutron Diffraction*).

scattering has an isotropic angular distribution in the centre-of-mass system. The differential cross-section for scattering of the neutron through an angle θ is then

$$d\sigma = \frac{\sigma}{4\pi} d\Omega$$

$$= \frac{\sigma}{2} \sin \theta \, d\theta \qquad (7.17)$$

By (5.4) the angles ϕ and θ are connected by the relation

$$\theta = \pi - 2\phi$$

so that

$$d\sigma = -2\sigma \sin \phi \cos \phi \, d\phi$$

$$= \frac{\sigma}{E_0} dE_r. \qquad (7.18)$$

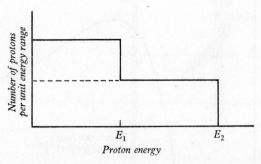

Fig. 7.14. Distribution of energies of protons projected from a thin hydrogenous target (or in a hydrogen-filled ionization chamber) by a neutron beam containing two homogeneous groups of energy E_1 and E_2 giving isotropic scattering.

It follows that the energy distribution of protons projected from a thin hydrogenous target by a homogeneous beam of neutrons is uniform up to the maximum available energy E_0, as shown in Fig. 7.14. Neutron energies may be determined by observing this distribution, or more usually, by observing the energy distribution of the protons projected within a small angular range near $\phi = 0$.

The first extensive survey of the energies of neutrons produced in nuclear reactions was made by determining the energy of forward recoils in hydrogen or helium filled cloud chambers (Sect. 6.2.1), but this method has now been superseded, except

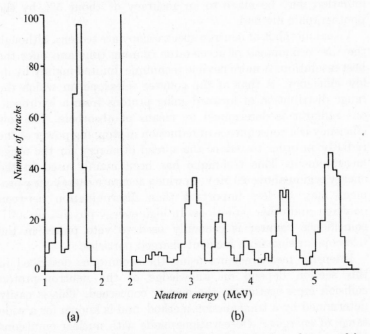

(a)   (b)

Fig. 7.15. Spectrum of recoil protons obtained in a nuclear emulsion irradiated by neutrons from the $^{13}C(d,n)^{14}N$ reaction. Sects. (a) (b) represent different areas scanned (Green *et al.*, *Proc. phys. Soc.*, **68**, 386, 1955).

in the case of extremely low energy neutrons,* by the observation of forward recoil protons in nuclear emulsions (Sect. 6.2.4). If good collimation is possible, as in the case of emulsions placed at a considerable distance from a point source, or viewing a source through a paraffin collimator, the resolution of the method is determined by the straggling of proton ranges, and

---

* A diffusion cloud chamber was used in a study of the neutrons emitted from the thermonuclear experimental apparatus ZETA.

the uncertainty in energy by the range-energy relation for the emulsion. Fig. 7.15 shows a typical neutron spectrum obtained by the photographic method applied to the $^{13}C(d,n)^{14}N$ reaction; the energies of the groups were determined to an accuracy of about 50 keV and with a resolution of about 3%. Flux determination may be made to an accuracy of about 5% by the photographic method.

Visual methods of neutron spectroscopy are tedious, although they are economical of accelerator running time and offer the best resolution. A more flexible technique, limited mainly by its low efficiency, is that of the counter telescope, in which the range distribution of forward-going protons from a hydrogenous radiator is determined by means of absorbers. The low efficiency is a consequence of reduction in stopping power of the radiator in order to reduce the spread of energy for the range measurement. This technique has been mainly used in the energy region above 20 MeV, in which accurate energy measurement may be less important than discrimination between neutrons and other radiations. In high energy physics, an anticoincidence counter is generally used to veto pulses in the telescope arising from incident charged particles.

Intensity measurements using the techniques described in this section depend on knowledge of the neutron–proton collision cross-section at the energy concerned. This is easily determined by a transmission method, and is known for a wide range of energies.* Observations made with nuclear emulsions must also be corrected for escape of recoil protons.

Energy determinations may be obtained from the pulse-size distribution in an ionization chamber or proportional counter which is predicted by Eq. 7.18 so long as the scattering cross-section is isotropic in the centre-of-mass system.

In flux determination by ionization chambers, either by counting recoils or by measuring ionization currents, corrections for wall effects are important. These can be eliminated in the current measuring chamber, as shown by Gray, if the walls of the chamber are of the same chemical constitution as the filling

---

* This cross-section and many others will be found in 'Neutron Cross Sections', by D. J. Hughes and R. B. Schwartz, Brookhaven Report BNL 325.

gas and are thick compared with the range of the recoil protons. An ethylene filled chamber lined with polythene is suitable (homogeneous ionization chamber). The ionization current from the hydrogen constituent may be written

$$i = n \frac{e\Omega}{w} \eta \sigma \bar{E} \qquad (7.19)$$

where n is the neutron flux density, $\bar{E}$ the mean recoil energy, Ω the volume of the chamber, η is the number of hydrogen nuclei per cm^3, σ the neutron–proton scattering cross-section at the incident neutron energy, and w is the energy required to form an ion pair. Alternatively, a high pressure hydrogen-filled ionization chamber (of counting or current type) may be used to minimize the wall effect.

The pulse height distribution from an organic scintillator irradiated by homogeneous neutrons is also described by Eq. 7.18. Since the scintillator, which may be anthracene, stilbene or a plastic phosphor, can be large, an efficient detector of fast neutrons is available. In high energy physics protons recoiling from neutrons of energies of a few hundred MeV may be able to produce light by the Cherenkov effect (Sect. 5.2.3) in a transparent medium. The special conditions necessary for this phenomenon provide a low energy cut-off and in practice counters of this sort are operated in conjunction with anti-coincidence counters to discriminate against primary charged particles.

7.3.4 REACTION, INDUCED ACTIVITY AND ASSOCIATED PARTICLE METHODS. The most satisfactory method of determining a flux of neutrons of mixed energies is that of *thermalization*; the neutron source is placed, if possible, in a large volume of water containing a suitable absorber such as $MnSO_4$. The neutrons are slowed down by the water to thermal energies and are then captured with high probability by the manganese yielding active ^{56}Mn by the reaction

$$^{55}Mn + n \rightarrow {}^{56}Mn + \gamma + 7 \cdot 27 \text{ MeV} \qquad (7.20)$$

In equilibrium the rate of absorption by the ^{55}Mn, which may be assessed by taking samples of the stirred solution and finding their activity, is equal to the rate of production by the source.

Thus if the source emits Q neutrons per second, and if the mean lifetime of a thermal neutron is τ, then in equilibrium

$$Q = \int \frac{\rho(r)}{\tau} \, dV = 4\pi \int_0^\infty \frac{r^2 \rho(r)}{\tau} \, dr \qquad (7.21)$$

where $\rho(r)$ is the slow neutron density at distance r from the centre. If the manganese captures with a cross-section σ at velocity v, and with cross-section σ_0 at a standard velocity v_0,

$$\tau = \frac{\lambda}{v} = \frac{1}{N\sigma v}$$

$$= \frac{1}{N\sigma_0 v_0} \qquad (7.22)$$

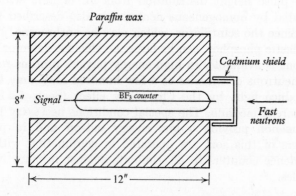

Fig. 7.16. Long counter (of Hanson and McKibben). Fast neutrons entering the counter are slowed down in the paraffin cylinder and are finally detected as thermal neutrons by the central counter at a distance from the front face dependent on the incident energy but with an efficiency which is roughly independent of energy over the range 2–5 MeV.

assuming that the capture cross-section obeys a $1/v$ law (Sect. 15.2.1); N is the number of capturing atoms cm^{-3}. Integration of 7.21 gives Q directly if $\rho(r)$ is determined absolutely from the induced activity, as described in Sect. (7.1). If two sources are compared it is not necessary to know τ, or absolute values of $\rho(r)$.

Another energy insensitive method of flux determination is

that of the *long counter*, Fig. 7.16. This is a boron trifluoride-filled counter surrounded by a paraffin wax cylinder of dimensions such that the response of the counter is energy independent (to about 5%) for neutrons of energies up to about 5 MeV, and is still sensitive, although less efficient, for neutrons of 20 MeV.

Energy measurements may also be based on suitable nuclear reactions. For energies up to 1 MeV, the ^{3}He proportional counter spectrometer is efficient and accurate; it depends upon the reaction

$$^3\text{He} + n \rightarrow {}^3\text{H} + p + 0.77 \text{ MeV} \tag{7.23}$$

and gives homogeneous groups of protons for each neutron group. Some use has also been made of the reaction

$$^6\text{Li} + n \rightarrow {}^4\text{He} + {}^3\text{H} + 4.64 \text{ MeV} \tag{7.24}$$

for fast neutron spectrometry. The lithium isotope is either contained in a nuclear emulsion or in a scintillating crystal such as lithium iodide. Neutrons of energies above 1 MeV may be investigated by means of threshold detectors relying upon reactions such as

$$\left.\begin{array}{l}
^{31}\text{P} + n \rightarrow {}^{31}\text{Si} + p - 0.7 \text{ MeV} \\
^{63}\text{Cu} + n \rightarrow {}^{62}\text{Cu} + 2n - 10.8 \text{ MeV} \\
^{12}\text{C} + n \rightarrow {}^{11}\text{C} + 2n - 18.7 \text{ MeV} \\
^{238}\text{U} + n \rightarrow \text{fission fragments}
\end{array}\right\} \tag{7.25}$$

Such reactions usually have excitation curves rising rapidly from threshold to a maximum, and may be used for flux measurement if the cross-section is known. The fission reaction is particularly suitable for counter detection owing to the high energy of the fragments (Sect. 14.1.6); in other cases it is usually necessary to make absolute measurements of the activity induced in the detector foils. A special case of this method arises in the determination of the flux from the frequently used lithium reaction $^7\text{Li}(p,n)^7\text{Be}$ by observation of the residual 50-day activity of ^{7}Be.

Similar methods are used in slow neutron studies. Accurate slow neutron spectroscopy is based on methods already described (Sects. 7.3.1, 7.3.2) but flux measurements demand only a detector of well-known properties. The most widely used slow neutron detector is the boron trifluoride ionization chamber (or the boron-loaded scintillator), in which neutrons induce the reaction

$$^{10}B + n \rightarrow {}^7Li + {}^4He + 2 \cdot 79 \text{ MeV} \tag{7.26}$$

which may be detected as an electrical pulse. The total cross-section for this reaction has been accurately measured as a function of energy by the crystal spectrometer method and has the value

$$\sigma({}^{10}B) = 3820 \pm 10 \text{ barns}$$

for a neutron velocity of 2200 m sec^{-1} ($E_n = 0 \cdot 025$ eV, $E_n/k = 293°$K). A $1/v$ dependence has been shown to hold in this region and probably up to energies of about 1000 eV. The boron chamber is thus extremely suitable for flux measurement since it effectively reduces an inhomogeneous neutron flux to the equivalent flux at standard energy.

Detectors based on the (n,γ) capture reactions are also important in the slow neutron region, but care must be taken in their use because the capture reaction shows sharp resonances. Table **7.2** gives a list of suitable materials, together with their cross-sections. The virtue of these detectors is that they can be prepared in a small size, e.g. as foils, and distributed throughout the volume of a large moderating system, as in the manganese-bath method already described.

Fission chambers based on the isotope ^{235}U are also extensively used as an alternative to boron trifluoride chambers when the falling sensitivity of the latter chamber at higher energies would be inconvenient (*cf.* Fig. A6.7a).

TABLE 7.2 Slow neutron detectors (β-activity)

TARGET NUCLEUS	HALF-LIFE OF ACTIVE PRODUCT	CAPTURE CROSS-SECTION (barns)
^{55}Mn	155 min	12·5
^{107}Ag	2·3 min	20
^{109}Ag	22 sec	40
^{115}In	13 sec; 54·5 min	190
^{127}I	25 min	7
^{164}Dy	140 min	790
^{197}Au	2·7 days	92

In all measurements of flux of neutrons of energy above thermal, care must be taken to exclude thermal neutrons from the detector because of the high cross-sections encountered in this energy region. This is normally done by enclosing the detector in a cadmium screen; cadmium has the very high cross-section of 2960 barns per atom for thermal neutrons and does not yield an active product after neutron absorption since the (n,γ) process leads mainly to stable isotopes. In addition all measurements of neutron flux must be examined carefully to see whether the detector disturbs the flux distribution under investigation.

In the *associated particle* method of neutron flux and energy measurement observations are made of charged particles emitted simultaneously with a fast neutron in reactions such as

$$^2\text{H} + {}^2\text{H} \rightarrow {}^3\text{He} + n + 3\cdot27 \text{ MeV} \qquad (7.27)$$

$$^3\text{H} + {}^2\text{H} \rightarrow {}^4\text{He} + n + 17\cdot58 \text{ MeV} \qquad (7.28)$$

It is only necessary to count the total number of recoil ^3He or ^4He particles emitted into a small solid angle in order to define the number and energy of the neutrons entering another small solid angle for experimental purposes. If necessary, observations can be conducted by requiring coincidences between the associated particles and effects produced by the neutrons, and in this way it is possible to reduce unwanted background counts. Flux determinations to 10% are possible by using the associated particle method.

7.4   Measurement of energy and intensity of photons

The most accurate measurements of γ-ray energies have been made by a development of one of the earliest methods to be used, the crystal diffraction technique of Rutherford and Andrade and of Frilley. Unfortunately, lattice spacings limit the application of this method to radiation of energy less than about 1 MeV, and for higher energies, magnetic spectrometers are used for high resolution measurements and inorganic scintillators for general work of high efficiency and moderate resolution. The characteristics of scintillation counters and proportional counters for photon energy measurement have already been discussed (Sect. 6.1.6), and only the more elaborate arrangements of such detectors will be discussed here.

7.4.1 ABSORPTION MEASUREMENTS. For homogeneous radiation, the attenuation coefficient (Sect. 5.4.1) gives a crude indication of energy, although ambiguity may arise at high energies because of the minimum in the absorption curve. The method is useful for weak sources.

If the quantum energy lies within the X-ray region, a critical absorption study may give results of much higher accuracy. Absorbers of different materials are tried until the unknown energy is bracketed by the K-absorption edge of two elements of adjacent atomic number.

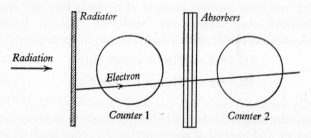

Fig. 7.17. Coincidence method of determining range of secondary electrons from γ-radiation (Bothe).

An extension of the absorption method to measure the range of secondary electrons ejected by gamma radiation was used by Bothe. Compton electrons produced in the radiator (Fig. 7.17) were detected by two Geiger counters operated in a coincidence circuit, and the coincidence count was plotted as a function of the thickness of absorber between the counters. In principle the count falls at the end point of each group of electrons corresponding to a particular photon energy in the incident radiation. In practice the method is difficult to employ if more than one energy is present.

7.4.2 THE CURVED CRYSTAL SPECTROMETER. Crystal diffraction has been developed for the spectroscopy of γ-radiation by DuMond and his collaborators. The main instrument is the transmission-type of bent crystal spectrometer first used by Cauchois and illustrated in principle in Fig. 7.18a,b. A thin cylindrical lamina of crystalline quartz, initially flat, is bent to have a radius $2R$ so that the diffracting planes intersect at distance $2R$ from the centre of the crystal. The source of radiation is placed either on the convex side of the crystal (Cauchois arrangement) or on the focal circle (DuMond arrangement). In each case the crystal picks out the wavelength λ appropriate for reflection at the Bragg angle θ given by

$$\lambda = 2d \sin \theta \qquad (7.29)$$

where d is the lattice spacing, and a real or virtual image is formed at the point V. In the DuMond arrangement the reflected beam diverging from the virtual image V is received by

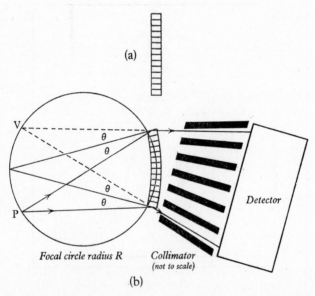

Fig. 7.18. Curved crystal spectrometer (Cauchois-DuMond); (a) crystal before bending, (b) ray diagram (DuMond, *Ann. Rev. Nucl. Sci.*, **8**, 163, 1958).

a scintillation counter shielded from the direct radiation from the source by a system of baffles or collimator. The source is moved mechanically with high accuracy along the focal circle to explore a range of wavelengths, and the crystal is automatically rotated as the source moves so that the detector and

collimator can remain in a fixed position. The grating constant
d for quartz is 1·178 A and the Bragg angle θ for $E_\gamma = 511$ keV
is 34 minutes of arc.

Fig. 7.19 shows the profile of the annihilation quantum line
at 511 keV obtained with a curved crystal spectrometer
(DuMond arrangement) using a quartz crystal 1 mm thick,
70 mm high and 50 mm wide, a radius of curvature R of 2
metres and a source strength of 2.5 curies of positron activity.
The wavelength was given as

$$\lambda = 0·024271 \pm 0·000010 \text{ A}$$

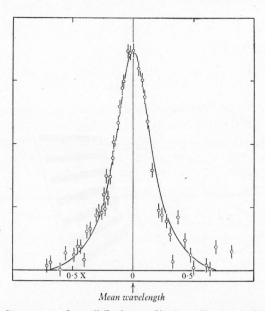

Fig. 7.19. Spectrum of annihilation radiation ($E = 511$ keV) obtained
with curved-crystal spectrometer $1X = 10^{-11}$ cm (DuMond *et al.*, *Phys.
Rev.*, **75**, 1226, 1949).

The resolution was approximately 1%, the accuracy of measurement 0·04%, and the efficiency of the instrument about 5×10^{-8}
counts per photon emitted from the source. The Cauchois
arrangement has been used by DuMond in a study of the γ-
radiation following inelastic scattering of protons from a cyclo-

tron in a variety of targets; exposures of many hours are necessary to obtain film records even using extremely high (≈ 5 ma) proton currents at 3·7 MeV.

The curved-crystal spectrometer has been used with great success for measurements of energies up to 500 keV and provides standards of γ-ray energy over this range (Ref. 7.2). Its main limitations arise from the fall of crystal reflecting power and the small angles of reflection at high quantum energies. The latter limitation has been overcome in a new type of two (flat) crystal spectrometer developed in the Chalk River laboratories in which neutron capture radiations of energy up to 2 MeV have been measured with a resolution of 0·4% at 1 MeV.

7.4.3 MAGNETIC SPECTROMETERS. The photoelectric effect, the Compton effect and pair production have all been made the basis of high resolution magnetic spectrometers for photon measurements. These instruments have now practically superseded the cloud chamber with magnetic field as a method for determining the momentum of electrons produced by photon interactions in thin radiators. The design of magnetic spectrometers for γ-radiation is obviously essentially the same as for β-spectrometers of a similar energy range but additional emphasis on transmission is desirable because of the loss of overall efficiency in the conversion of the photons into electrons. Gamma radiation arising from nuclear reactions may be accompanied by internal conversion electrons (Sect. 13.2) or by internal conversion pairs (Sect. 13.3) or both, and in such cases the photon energy is obtained directly from observations of the conversion spectrum. When internal conversion coefficients are low, a thin foil must be used as external radiator and the foil thickness must be taken into account in calculations of instrumental resolution and efficiency.

Lens spectrometers provide the best transmission. If a thin lead radiator is used in the source position, incident gamma radiation will give a spectrum of photoelectrons from the inner shells of the lead atom. These are accompanied, at a slightly lower energy, by a Compton spectrum due to interaction of the photons with the outer electrons of the lead atom. If a foil of a light element is used as radiator, the photoelectric peaks, of energy, $E_\gamma - E_{K,L} \dots$ may be suppressed with respect to the

Compton distribution, which for a photon energy E_γ gives a maximum electron energy of

$$\frac{E_\gamma}{\left(1+\dfrac{mc^2}{2E_\gamma}\right)} \tag{7.30}$$

from (5.96).

The photon energy E_γ may be obtained either from the photo-electric peak or from the upper limit of the Compton distribution. Fig. 7.20 shows a Compton spectrum obtained with a lens spectrometer.

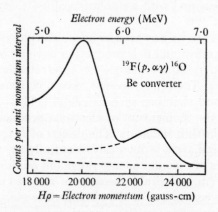

Fig. 7.20. Compton electrons from γ-radiation originating in the reaction $^{19}\mathrm{F}(p,\alpha\gamma)^{16}\mathrm{O}$, as observed in lens-type spectrometer (Rasmussen *et al.*, *Phys. Rev.*, **77**, 617, 1950).

The intermediate image lens spectrometer (Sect. 7.2.5) has been developed for use as a pair spectrometer. For high energy radiation the number of pairs $N(\theta)\,\mathrm{d}\theta$ emerging from a radiator with angle θ to $\theta+\mathrm{d}\theta$ between the photon and an electron is approximately

$$N(\theta)\,\mathrm{d}\theta \propto \frac{\theta\,\mathrm{d}\theta}{(\Theta^2+\theta^2)^2} \tag{7.31}$$

where $\Theta=mc^2/E_\gamma$. The average angle is $\theta_{\mathrm{av}}\approx\Theta$ and if this is small then the two components of a pair with equal energies may be focused simultaneously by the lens spectrometer, although they spiral in opposite directions round the lines of force of the lens field. If a suitably sectionalized scintillation detector is used at the second focus, about half of the pairs received will excite two sections simultaneously and a coinci-

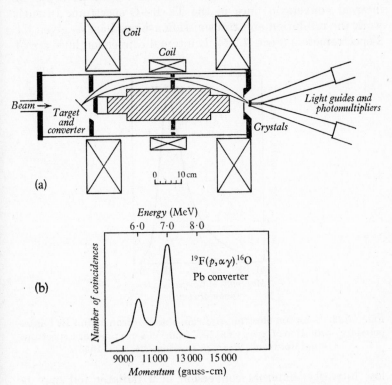

Fig. 7.21. Intermediate-image lens pair spectrometer.
a) General arrangement.
b) Positron-electron coincidence spectrum for γ-radiation from $^{19}F(p,\alpha\gamma)^{16}O$ reaction using a lead converter (Bent *et al.*, *Phys. Rev.*, **98** 1237, 1955).

dence output will be obtained. This permits an advantageous discrimination against background. Fig. 7.21a shows the layout of a pair spectrometer of this type and Fig. 7.21b pair lines obtained with the instrument. Resolutions of the order of 2·0% with an acceptance solid angle of 4% of the total sphere are obtainable when the spectrometer is used to study internal conversion pairs.

Deflection (*prismatic*) *spectrometers* were the first precision instruments used in the study of γ-radiation. Ellis (1932) used a 180° semicircular-focusing permanent magnet spectrometer with photographic recording for accurate measurements of internal conversion lines in the Th B+C spectrum. In such work the resolution and transmission achieved are as given for β-spectrometers (Sect. 7.2.5). If internal conversion lines are of

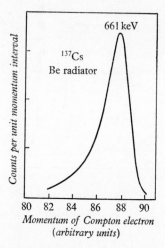

Fig. 7.22. Compton-electron spectrum obtained from a thin Be foil exposed to γ-radiation of energy 661 keV from ^{137}Cs in a prismatic spectrometer (Motz *et al.*, *Rev. Sci. Instrum.*, **24**, 929, 1953).

low intensity, external conversion in a radiator foil may be employed; the resolution and sensitivity then depend on foil thickness in addition to instrumental factors. Photoelectrons from heavy radiators (Pb) and Compton electrons from light foils (Be) have frequently been used, usually with counter detection. Fig. 7.22 shows a Compton distribution obtained in a prismatic spectrometer. The overall detection efficiency of Compton and photoelectric spectrometers is low (about 10^{-11} counts per photon from a source for 1% resolution at 1 MeV) and strong sources are necessary.

For γ-radiation of energy above about 3 MeV the prismatic pair spectrometer is a powerful instrument. Fig. 7.23a illustrates the principle of this method. A thin radiator is used and

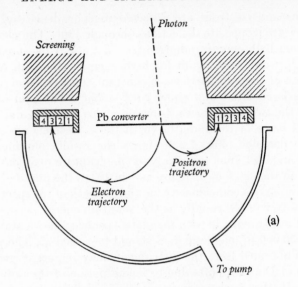

(a)

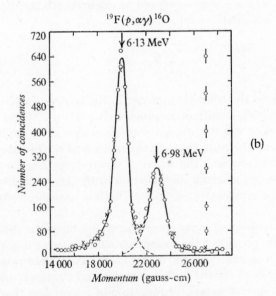

(b)

Fig. 7.23. Prismatic pair spectrometer.
a) Section through gap of magnet.
b) Pair spectrum for γ-radiation from $^{19}\text{F}(p,\alpha\gamma)^{16}\text{O}$ reaction (Walker and McDaniel, *Phys. Rev.*, **74**, 315, 1948).

positrons and electrons are detected in coincidence by fixed counters after opposite deflections through 180°. The electron pairs from high energy radiation (say $E \approx 5$ MeV) go predominantly forward, and, again for high energies, the sum of the momenta of the two particles is constant since the sum of the energies is constant and equal to $E_\gamma - 2mc^2$. The sum of the radii of the two trajectories is therefore also constant and pairs from all parts of the radiator (with the correct energy ratio) may be detected. Fig. 7.23b shows the results obtained by Walker and McDaniel in a study of (p,γ) capture reactions; the resolution was 6% but as many as 1 in 10^7 of the photons from the source gave a coincidence count at the peak of the spectrum. The sensitivity falls rapidly as the quantum energy decreases.

In all measurements with magnetic spectrometers a stability of 1 in 50,000 in magnetic field should be aimed at. The γ-ray energies obtained from the instruments may require correction because of Doppler shifts due to recoil motion of the radiating source. If the nucleus emitting the radiation moves with velocity v, the energy observed at angle θ with the direction of motion is shifted by an amount

$$E_\gamma \frac{v}{c} \cos \theta \qquad (7.32)$$

where E_γ is the transition energy in the centre-of-mass system. This can give a shift of as much as 1 part in 200 and it is not always clear whether such a correction should be applied. This depends on the ratio between the lifetime of the radiating nuclei for γ-emission and the slowing down time for these nuclei in the source material; observation of the Doppler effect has in fact been made the basis for lifetime measurements (Sect. 13.6.1).

The precision of γ-ray spectroscopy by magnetic deflection is now high, providing that adequate source strength is available, and approaches 0·2% in many cases. Pair spectrometers are normally used for the higher energies and Compton and photo-electron spectrometers for radiation of energy less than 2 MeV, although the division is not exclusive. Intensities are obtained by calculations based on elementary cross-sections and on the geometrical properties of the spectrometer.

7.4.4 SCINTILLATION AND TOTAL ABSORPTION SPECTRO-METERS.   Scintillation spectrometry, using thallium activated sodium iodide crystals, is the most widely used and versatile technique for studying gamma-ray energies and intensities. It combines high efficiency, resulting from the high stopping power of the iodide crystal, with moderate resolution and has the advantages of compactness and relative simplicity.

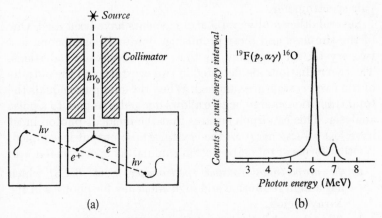

Fig. 7.24. Three-crystal pair spectrometer.
a) General arrangement of crystals.
b) Energy spectrum of radiation from $^{19}F(p,\alpha\gamma)^{16}O$ reaction (Bent and Kruse, *Phys. Rev.*, **108**, 802, 1957).

The performance of single crystal scintillation spectrometers has already been discussed (Sect. 6.1.6). The main disadvantage arises for γ-radiation of energy above about 2 MeV, when a single homogeneous line may give more than one peak in a pulse height spectrum from a typical crystal (Fig. 6.12d). The analysis of a complex spectrum then becomes difficult. This trouble has been overcome in the three-crystal spectrometer, which is arranged as shown in Fig. 7.24a. The incident radiation produces a pair in the centre crystal, and the positron and electron both stop in this crystal. The two oppositely directed annihilation quanta from the positron have a chance of escaping from the centre crystal and being detected, one in each side crystal. Triple coincidence counts are then taken between the crystals and the output is used to gate a pulse

10*

analyser recording the size of pulses from the centre crystal. A single peak, representing the kinetic energy of the pair, is then obtained for each quantum energy (Fig. 7.24b). With crystals of a size the order of a 1 in. cube, a resolution of 5% at 4·4 MeV has been obtained with a detection efficiency (which may be calculated from the cross-sections of sodium iodide) of one in 10^4 of the quanta from a suitably collimated source. This is several hundred times better than the performance of a magnetic pair spectrometer.

Several other multicrystal arrangements have been used. One of the simplest and most promising, due to Hoogenboom, is a two crystal spectrometer for the study of cascade radiations. The two radiations are detected in two crystals, and the outputs of the two crystals are summed. When the sum pulse equals the total transition energy, a gate allows one pulse to pass to a pulse analyser. This condition ensures that the incident photon must have lost all its energy in the crystal whose output is sampled.

Other forms of total absorption gamma-ray spectrometer are:

a) *the proportional counter spectrometer* (Sect. 6.1.3) which has a high resolution and high efficiency for photons in the X-ray region,

b) *The Cherenkov total absorption spectrometer* (Sect. 6.1.7).

Intensity calculations in all these cases must be based on known geometry and elementary cross-sections.

7.4.5 PHOTODISINTEGRATION METHODS. The cross-section for the photodisintegration of the deuteron

$$^{2}H + \gamma \rightarrow {}^{1}H + n - 2\cdot23 \text{ MeV} \tag{7.33}$$

has now been measured accurately at many points between the threshold at 2·3 MeV and an energy of several hundred MeV. A high pressure ionization chamber filled with deuterium is therefore a suitable instrument for flux measurement, and also for energy determinations if the photoproton range is small compared with the dimensions of the chamber.

Many other photodisintegration processes, leading to active products, can be used for relative flux measurements, e.g.

$$^{12}C + \gamma \rightarrow {}^{11}C + n - 18\cdot7 \text{ MeV}$$
$$^{63}Cu + \gamma \rightarrow {}^{62}Cu + n - 10\cdot8 \text{ MeV} \tag{7.34}$$

7.4.6 FLUX DETERMINATION BY IONIZATION CHAMBER.
Ionization chambers have three principal applications in determining photon flux:

    a) *for measurement of the relative yield* of γ-radiation in
       nuclear reactions as a function of bombarding energy,
    b) for *radiation monitoring* in health physics,
    c) *for monitoring the output* of electron accelerators such as
       betatrons, synchrotrons and electron accelerators.

The intensity of the photon beam from such machines is often
measured by the 'quantameter'* in which an electromagnetic
shower is produced in an ionization chamber containing
absorbing plates. The intensity may be expressed either as an
energy content U, deduced calorimetrically or directly from the
observed ionization, or as a total number of 'equivalent quanta'
Q given by

$$Q = \frac{U}{E_0} = \frac{1}{E_0} \int_0^{E_0} kn(k)\, \mathrm{d}k \qquad (7.35)$$

where E_0 is the maximum bremsstrahlung energy and $n(k)\,\mathrm{d}k$
is the number of photons with energy between k and $k + \mathrm{d}k$ in
the spectrum.

References

7.1   G. Friedlander and J. W. Kennedy, *Nuclear and Radiochemistry*, Wiley, 1955.

7.2   E. Segrè (ed.), *Experimental Nuclear Physics*, Vol. III, Wiley, 1959.

7.3   K. Siegbahn (ed.), *Beta and Gamma Spectroscopy*, North Holland Publishing Co., 1955.

7.4   P. E. Cavanagh, 'Spectroscopy of β- and γ-rays', *Prog. nucl. Phys.*, **1**, 140, 1951.

7.5   N. F. Verster, 'The Electron Optical Properties of Magnetic β-ray Spectrometers', *Prog. nucl. Phys.*, **2**, 1, 1952.

7.6   W. W. Buechner, 'The Determination of Nuclear Reaction Energies by Deflection Measurements', *Prog. nucl. Phys.*, **5**, 1, 1955.

7.7   D. J. Hughes, 'Reactor Techniques', *Encyclopedia of Physics*, **44**, p. 390, Springer, 1959.

7.8   G. Bäckstrom, 'Experimental methods for the study of neutron capture gamma-rays', *Nuclear instrum. and Methods*, **4**, 5, 1959.

7.9   L. Cranberg and L. Rosen, 'Measurement of Fast Neutron Spectra', in *Nuclear Spectroscopy, Part A*, ed. F. Ajzenberg-Selove, Academic Press, 1960.

7.10 W. D. Allen, *Neutron Detection*, Newnes, 1960.

---

* R. R. Wilson, *Nucl. instrum. and Methods*, **1**, 101, 1957.

8. THE ACCELERATION OF CHARGED PARTICLES TO HIGH ENERGIES

In the ten years following Rutherford's discovery of transmutation (1919) efforts were increasingly devoted to attempts to improve the intensity of the observed effects. A naturally radioactive α-particle source of 100 mC strength emits $3 \cdot 7 \times 10^9$ particles per second into a solid angle of 4π and therefore provides a flux density of 3×10^6 particles cm^{-2} sec^{-1} at a distance of 10 cm. A positive ion beam of $1 \mu A$, which may easily be collimated to a cross-sectional area of 1 cm^2, delivers 6×10^{12} singly charged particles per second. On the other hand the α-particles from radium and its products have velocities* corresponding to an energy of $5–8 \times 10^6$ eV (Table **2.1**) and the production of such energies by direct acceleration of positive ion beams entailed high-voltage apparatus of a type quite unknown at the time. Despite this, high-voltage development proceeded and by 1930, Cockcroft and Walton, in the Cavendish Laboratory, Cambridge, were able to announce the production of a beam of $10 \mu A$ of 280 keV hydrogen ions. Later the accelerating voltage was increased to 700 kV, and the successful transmutation of lithium in 1932, with protons of this energy (Sect. 14.1.2), gave great impetus to the rapidly developing field of accelerator technology.

Present-day accelerator design and construction is a major field of scientific effort in which vast sums of money are available. The enormous growth of this branch of physics in the last thirty years is due partly to a new awareness of the types of problem awaiting attack, and partly to technical progress in providing the necessary means. The problems are, briefly, the study of nuclear structure by means of nuclear reactions, and the study of the properties of elementary particles. The former

---

* A singly charged particle of mass M after falling through a potential difference V (volts) acquires a velocity v given by $\frac{1}{2}Mv^2 = eV/300$, where e is in e.s. units, and an energy of V electron-volts,

may be investigated with relatively modest machines, whose output energies match the potential barriers surrounding nuclei; the latter continues to tax experimental ingenuity to the utmost by demanding the highest possible energy or intensity, or both. It is in the latter field especially that progress depends mainly on new concepts and principles.

The division of the problems into two types also suggests a corresponding division of accelerators into direct current (d.c.) or pulsed (r.f.) machines. The latter class may be further subdivided into linear and orbital accelerators. The only exception from this division is the betatron, an orbital accelerator whose output appears in bursts, but which does not employ radiofrequency acceleration. The present account will adopt this classification, although it should not be inferred that the study of nuclear reactions is confined to d.c. machines.

8.1   High-voltage d.c. accelerators

Installations of this type always include an ion source, an accelerating tube, a method of generating high voltages for application to the electrodes of the accelerating tube, and an analysing system for selecting ions of a particular type after acceleration or for improving the energy homogeneity of the beams.

8.1.1 THE CASCADE GENERATOR. The circuit used by Cockcroft and Walton* for production of a steady terminal voltage of 700–800 kV was a two-stage doubling arrangement of transformer, rectifiers and condensers; Fig. 8.1 illustrates the principle. If the transformer develops a peak secondary voltage V, then condenser C_1 charges up to this potential difference through rectifier R_1 (load currents and rectifier voltage drops are neglected). The voltage across R_1 then varies from 0 to $2V$ sinusoidally during each cycle. This voltage is effectively applied to the circuit $R_2 C_2$ and charges up condenser C_2 to a potential difference $2V$, thus completing the first stage of voltage doubling. The voltage across R_2 also varies sinusoidally from 0 to $2V$ and by similar arguments it can be seen that C_3 and C_4 will also charge up to a potential difference $2V$. In the steady state condenser C_1 is charged to potential V, and C_2,

---

* J. D. Cockcroft and E. T. S. Walton, *Proc. roy. Soc.* A, **136**, 619, 1932.

C_3, C_4 to potential $2V$; C_1, C_3 are in series with the transformer secondary and their voltage *to ground* varies by $\pm V$ during each cycle, but C_2, C_4 have potentials fixed with respect to ground and final d.c. terminal voltage at P_4 is $4V$. The operation of the circuit may also be understood by regarding the rectifiers as switches through which the charge on C_1 is shared in successive a.c. cycles with the other condensers of the circuit. The number of stages of voltage doubling may be increased by adding more rectifiers and condensers and for a number $2n$ of

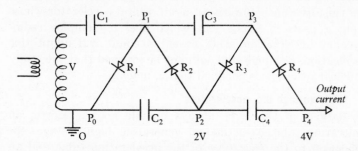

Fig. 8.1. Cascade generator circuit (2 stages of voltage doubling).

each of these components, the circuit is a n-stage voltage doubler providing a no-load output voltage of $2nV$. Each condenser must be rated for a voltage of $2V$, and each rectifier must withstand a reverse peak voltage of the same magnitude.

If a current i is drawn from the high-voltage terminal P_4 and if the frequency of the transformer mains supply is f cycles $\sec^{-1}$ then in one cycle the condenser C_4 drops in voltage by i/fC. This has to be made good by charge supplied by the sharing process from the rest of the circuit during the cycle and as a result both a *voltage drop* $\varDelta V$ from the no-load value and a *ripple* δV of supply mains frequency appear in the output. It may be shown that, for a n-stage voltage doubler, in which all condensers have the same capacitance C, and stray capacities are neglected

$$\delta V = \frac{n(n+1)}{2}\frac{i}{fC} \tag{8.1}$$

and

$$\varDelta V = \left(\frac{2}{3}n^3 + \frac{1}{2}n^2 + \frac{1}{3}n\right)\frac{i}{fC} \tag{8.2}$$

so that it is advantageous to use the smallest possible number of stages and the highest possible capacities and charging frequencies. Limits arise because of the voltage rating and frequency characteristics of the components.

Cockcroft and Walton used continuously pumped thermionic rectifiers erected in a tall glass column sealed by

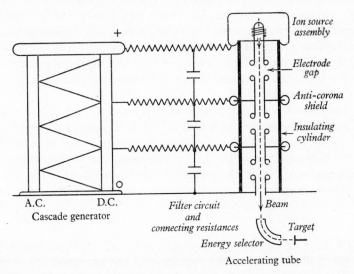

Fig. 8.2. General arrangement of cascade generator and accelerating tube.

Apiezon-Q compound. Modern cascade generators use high-voltage selenium rectifiers with a peak inverse rating up to about 200 kV.

Air-insulated cascade generators are reasonably convenient for voltages up to about 1000 kV, but beyond this, size is a major limitation, and techniques of pressurization and high-frequency operation have not yet been fully developed. A six-stage generator with $C = 0·02$ μF and $f = 200$ c/s has a voltage drop $\Delta V = 40$ kV mA^{-1} and a ripple $\delta V = 5$ kV mA^{-1}. The ripple may be reduced by use of a RC filter circuit on the output as shown in Fig. 8.2.

The cascade generator is connected to the continuously pumped accelerating tube (in which a pressure of 10^{-4}–10^{-5} mm is maintained), by high resistances (Fig. 8.2) through which the electrodes of the tube are kept at constant potential. Typical accelerating gaps are shown in the figure; the gaps are mounted in series and in operation constitute a succession of electrostatic lenses of long focal length. A focused beam of ions is delivered from an ion source (Sect. 8.1.3) through a small canal at the high voltage (positive) end of the accelerating tube and emerges at ground potential with a velocity corresponding to the accelerating voltage. The canal has a very low pumping speed and permits a much higher pressure in the ion source than in the accelerating tube. Power for the ion source is conveyed to the high-voltage terminal either by a belt driving a generator in the terminal, or by high-frequency currents circulating in the condenser stacks.

The main advantages of the cascade generator are that it uses standard components and that it has a large output; currents of up to 10 mA of positive ions (or electrons) are obtainable with an energy up to 3·0 MeV, if the apparatus is enclosed in a high-pressure vessel. Many more modest generators in the 200–300 keV range are in use for neutron production through the (d–T) reaction (Sect. **8.6**).

8.1.2 THE ELECTROSTATIC GENERATOR. This generator is a direct illustration of the definition of the potential of a conductor in elementary electrostatics as the work done in bringing unit charge from a standard reference point to the conductor. In the machine developed by Van de Graaff (1931) charge is sprayed from sharp corona points at a voltage of about 100 kV on to a moving insulating belt (Fig. 8.3). The belt conveys the charge to an insulated terminal electrode within which the charge is removed by collector points and allowed to flow to the surface of the electrode through a resistance R. If the capacity of the terminal is C to ground, the potential at any instant is

$$V = \frac{q}{C} \tag{8.3}$$

where q is the stored charge. If the belt delivers a current i to the terminal the rate of rise of terminal potential is

$$\frac{\mathrm{d}V}{\mathrm{d}t} = \frac{i}{C} \tag{8.4}$$

and this may be as much as 10^6 volts sec^{-1}. As the terminal
voltage increases, the current drain due to corona, losses

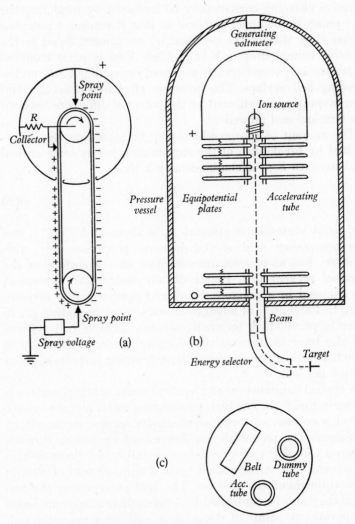

Fig. 8.3. Electrostatic generator.

a) Principle.
b) General construction of vertical generator showing accelerating tube
and equipotential plates.
c) Cross-section of generator stack.

through supporting insulators, and possible drain due to acceleration of ions or electrons, increases until an equilibrium
between load current and charging current is established. The
effective charging current may be increased by insulating the
belt pulley in the upper terminal so that it reaches a potential
higher than that of the terminal by an amount equal to the
resistive voltage drop in R (Fig. 8.3a). A spray point mounted
above the belt then deposits charge of opposite polarity on the
receding belt surface. The processes of charge collection and
charge spray are unaffected by the potential difference between
the terminal and ground.

The amount of charge which may be placed on the belt is
limited by breakdown of the surrounding gas at some critical
field strength E_c; the charge density is then

$$\sigma = \frac{E_c}{2\pi} \tag{8.5}$$

For air at atmospheric pressure E_c is about 30 kV cm^{-1}, and
this breakdown field should increase proportionately with
pressure, but in practice irregularities on the surface of the
terminal prevent this. Practically all electrostatic generators
are enclosed in a pressure vessel and operated at a pressure
of up to 400 lb in^{-2} of nitrogen or some other insulating gas in
order to permit high terminal voltages. Multiple belt systems
are also used to increase the charging current; speeds up to
8000 ft min^{-1} can be employed, with charging currents of about
400 μA per belt.

A typical construction of a vertical electrostatic generator is
shown in Fig. 8.3b. The high-tension terminal is mounted at the
top of a column of metal equipotential plates, separated by
insulators. The potentials are determined by corona currents
between the plates or by conduction through a chain of high
resistances. This arrangement gives a uniform field of electric
force throughout the column. The field surrounding the terminal may also be controlled by intermediate shields anchored
to appropriate points of the column, and the greater the uniformity achieved in the design, the greater will be the ultimate
breakdown potential. The belts run through slots cut in the
equipotential plates and further holes are provided for accelerating tubes. The radius of curvature of all high-potential

surfaces, including the terminal, is kept as large as possible to reduce field gradients. Although the weight of the top terminal is most easily supported in a vertical arrangement, many horizontally-mounted machines have been made.

Accelerating tubes used for ion beams in electrostatic generators are usually alternate sections of insulator and metal spaced to match the spacing of the equipotential planes. Such a tube has good breakdown properties, providing that the electrode structure is designed to prevent internal multiplication of small electron currents. The tube should not affect the convergence or parallelism of an ion beam and should be equally efficient at all terminal voltages. A vacuum of the order of 10^{-5} mm of mercury or better is maintained by pumps at ground potential. Ions enter the tube through a narrow canal from a compact source situated in the high-potential terminal and in order to prevent too much gas from the ion source entering the main accelerating tube, extra pumping near the canal may be provided via a dummy tube running through the column. For the more efficient ion sources, this differential pumping is unnecessary. Ion source power supplies are obtained from a small generator driven from the belt pulley; controls may be operated photoelectrically from ground potential.

The terminal voltage of an electrostatic generator (or the voltage of the outer corona shield) is usually measured by a generating voltmeter mounted at the top of the pressure vessel. This instrument has an insulated probe which is alternately exposed to and screened from the electrostatic field of the machine by a rotating electrode at ground potential. The currents induced in the probe circuit are rectified and the resulting steady current measures the generator potential on a scale which may be calibrated by observation of well-known nuclear resonance levels. The voltmeter output may be used to stabilize the generator voltage; control of the corona spray current is usually used. Another method which provides extremely fine control is to adjust the load current by means of a small and variable electron current travelling up the accelerating tube or the differential pumping tube; a stability of ± 150 volts in 10^6 volts has been claimed for this method.

The electrostatic generator has the great advantages of stability, ease of voltage control, and high voltage rating, which offset the apparent disadvantage of small output current in comparison with that given by cascade generators. The beams are highly homogeneous since there is no ripple voltage, and the residual spread of energy, due perhaps to the ion source, may be further reduced by magnetic or electrostatic analysis after acceleration. Such beams are admirable for nuclear resonance level work (Sect. **15.2**). By scrupulous attention to all points of design, the High Voltage Engineering Corporation has been able to raise the rating of recent generator columns to about 1 MeV per ft and a standard generator for 6–7 MeV, with a current output of 100 μA of hydrogen ions, is now available.

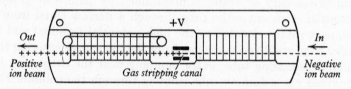

Fig. 8.4. Principle of tandem electrostatic generator.

A development of outstanding importance in the evolution of electrostatic generators is the introduction of the *tandem principle* (Fig. 8.4 and Ref. 8.14). Two insulating columns, mounted horizontally, are contained within one pressure tank, and the high voltage terminal at their junction is charged positively by a normal belt system within one column. There is no positive ion source in the terminal, but a *negative ion source* outside the pressure vessel supplies a beam of negative ions to the grounded end of the first accelerating tube. These ions are accelerated to about 7 MeV in their passage to the central terminal where they are stripped of electrons and converted to *positive ions*. The stripping is achieved by passage through a canal in which there is an increased gas pressure or through a thin carbon foil. The positive ions then enter the second accelerating tube in which they receive a second increment of velocity, so that for a single positive charge they emerge finally at a ground potential with a velocity corresponding to 14 MeV, i.e., twice the terminal voltage. The arrangement has most of the advantages of the normal electrostatic generator, together with the manifest improvement of having the ion source readily available. Beam currents of 1·5 µA of protons have been obtained, and although this is smaller than can be obtained from lower-voltage machines it is ample for most experiments of high resolution at 14 MeV. Further developments of the tandem principle, in which neutral as well as negatively and positively charged beams are used, may raise the effective output voltage for hydrogen ions to 20–30 MeV, which is comparable with the highest energy obtainable from conventional fixed frequency cyclotrons (Sect. 8.3.1). The machine has also been used to provide beams of heavy ions such as ^{12}C and ^{16}O.

8.1.3   ION SOURCES.

Practically all sources of positive ions used in accelerators rely on some form of gaseous discharge for ion production. The only exceptions are sources of lithium ions, which may be obtained thermionically from a heated salt. All discharge sources allow neutral gas molecules to stream into the accelerator vacuum together with the ions, and it is desirable to make the ratio of ion current to gas current as large as possible, particularly in the case of highly rated d.c. accelerating tubes, in which slight deterioration of vacuum may seriously lower the breakdown voltage. Most sources are designed for the production of beams of hydrogen ions, but there is also considerable interest in the use of heavier ions.

The two types of source now most widely used in high voltage d.c. accelerators are the PIG (Philips ionization gauge) source, and the radiofrequency source introduced in 1946 by Thonemann. *The PIG source** (Fig. 8.5a) has a cylindrical anode and a twin cathode and the whole assembly is mounted in a chamber within a solenoid providing an axial magnetic field. At a pressure of 20 µ of hydrogen, and with a magnetic field of about 500 gauss, a discharge takes place between the anode and cathode at a potential difference of about 500 volts. Electrons produced near one of the cathodes are accelerated towards the anode but are constrained by the magnetic field to move helically in the direction of the lines of force, and therefore pass through the (electric) field-free volume of the anode and out towards the

---

* See, for example, J. D. Gow and J. S. Foster, *Rev. sci Instrum.*, **24**, 606, 1953.

other cathode, where they are decelerated and reflected by the anode–cathode field. This process will continue until electrons have lost so much energy in collisions that they do not emerge from the anode volume and are finally collected. Before this happens, each electron may have created about 10 ion pairs in its long path, and these ions, together with the associated

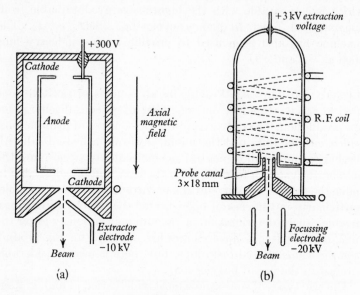

Fig. 8.5. Ion sources.
a) PIG type, the containing vessel forming the cathodes.
b) Radiofrequency type.

electrons, contribute to the formation of a plasma within the anode and out towards the cathodes. Ions emerge from this plasma under the influence of the field due to an extractor electrode which draws them down a canal into an electrostatic lens system (Fig. 8.5). The ions which do not pass through the canal strike the cathode surfaces, which are normally oxidized aluminium, and thus produce a further supply of electrons for the discharge, which builds up as far as is permitted by the external circuit. The electron and positive ion currents in this type of discharge are nearly equal and the source has the advantages of efficient operation at low pressures and small size.

Typical operating characteristics for a pulsed source of this type are shown in Table **8.1**. Continuous operation at lower ratings is possible. Ion sources using an oscillating electron beam have also been developed for the production of highly charged heavy ions.

In the *radiofrequency ion source** a plasma is produced in hydrogen or some other gas in a glass vessel (Fig. 8.5b). The electric field in the discharge is maintained by surrounding the glass tube by a solenoid excited from an oscillator with an output of about 300 watts at a frequency of 20 Mc/s. If the discharge volume, with the exception of the outlet to the probe canal (Fig. 8.5b), is entirely enclosed by glass, it is found that a high percentage of protons is obtained in the emergent beam; it is known that recombination of atomic ions to molecular ions or molecules is promoted by metal surfaces. The operation of this widely used source is characterized by the bright red glow of the Balmer series of atomic hydrogen and by positive ion densities in the plasma of about 10^{10} ions cm^{-3}. Optimum values for gas pressure and radiofrequency power input are usually established empirically; typical conditions for such a source are given in Table **8.1**.

TABLE 8.1   Ion source characteristics (hydrogen gas)

TYPE OF SOURCE	DUTY CYCLE	PRESS-URE (microns)	GAS FLOW $(cm^3\,hr^{-1})$	POWER INPUT (watts)	PROBE VOLT-AGE (kV)	CURRENT (mA) H_1^+	H_2^+	H_3^+
PIG	0·01%	20	26	600	15	1·5	0·9	0·3
RF	100%	35	20	300 at 20 Mc/s	3	4	0·3	0·15

In both PIG and radiofrequency sources the ions are extracted from a plasma under space charge limited conditions. The potential V of the probe electrode and hence of the plasma may have a considerable effect on the shape of the plasma boundary, so that in addition to the dependence of the current on

* P. C. Thonemann, J. Moffat, D. Roaf and J. H. Sanders, *Proc. phys. Soc., Lond.*, A, **61**, 483, 1948.

voltage given by a space charge formula, there is also a dependence of the divergence of the beam on the probe potential. This may be employed with advantage to direct the beam through the probe canal. It is usual to provide further electrostatic lenses after the probe electrode so that the beam can be varied by controlling the probe potential without destroying the focus of the final beam delivered to the accelerator. Notable improvements in radiofrequency ion sources have resulted from concentration of the beam on the canal by means of an auxiliary magnet.

Gas purity is of great importance in all ion sources. Hydrogen is most conveniently purified and admitted to the discharge simultaneously by allowing it to diffuse through a heated tube of palladium or nickel. Power supplies for the ion source are derived from a generator driven by the main charging belt in electrostatic machines but in cascade generator installations a capacitative feed of high-frequency power from ground to the high-potential terminal is often used.

Special sources have been developed for the efficient production of the negative ions required in tandem electrostatic generators (Sect. 8.1.2). It has been found that the charge state of atoms and ions can easily be altered by passing the beam through a narrow canal containing sufficient gas to ensure charge exchange. Such techniques are especially important for the production of beams of doubly charged helium ions (He^{++}) and for providing heavy ions in a highly charged state; the incident velocity must then be sufficient to permit removal of the necessary electrons. For the process $He^+ \rightarrow He^{++}$ an ion energy of about 400 keV is desirable.

8.1.4 ENERGY SELECTORS. The homogeneity of the beams provided by accelerators varies widely and for accurate definition (and measurement) of energy some form of post-acceleration resolution is generally necessary. This applies to all forms of accelerator but in practice energy selectors of the highest resolution are associated with electrostatic generators. The methods of electrostatic or magnetic deflection, familiar in the analysis of the energy of reaction products (Sect. 7.2.6) are also used for energy selection. It is obviously necessary to aim at comparable accuracy in the definition of beam energy and in the measurement of distintegration particle energy, since both contribute in similar degree to the determination of nuclear energy releases.

The existence of a number of well-defined and absolutely determined reaction thresholds, such as that for the ^{7}Li (p,n) reaction (Eq. 7.11) permits the energy setting of d.c. accelerators and their associated energy selectors to be related to an absolute *high voltage scale*.

8.2 Linear accelerators

In a linear accelerator, charged particles move down a vacuum tube under the influence of an electric field which either accompanies the particles as a travelling wave, or appears regularly, in correct phase, at a series of electrode gaps. In this way high velocities can be attained without the application of correspondingly high voltages and serious problems of insulation are avoided. Of the two types of accelerating structure used, the travelling wave accelerator, operating in the 3000 Mc/s frequency band, is particularly appropriate for electrons, while the sequence of gaps, separated by drift tubes, is useful for non-relativistic particles such as protons or heavy ions, and is excited at a lower frequency. All linear accelerators have the advantage over orbital accelerators (Sect. **8.3**) of providing an external beam without difficulty; they have the disadvantage that their accelerating fields are also defocusing, and special measures are necessary to concentrate the ion beam in the non-relativistic region of velocities.

8.2.1 DRIFT TUBE ACCELERATORS. The earliest accelerators (Wideroe 1928, Sloan and Lawrence 1931, Beams and Snoddy 1934) were of this type. The principle is illustrated in Fig. 8.6. In the Sloan-Lawrence accelerator, operated at approximately 30 Mc/s, a number of field-free drift tubes of length $L_1, L_2, \ldots, L_n$, separated by small accelerating gaps, were connected alternately to the output terminals of an oscillator of free-space wavelength λ. The length of the drift tubes is such that the field in a gap just reverses in the time that a particle takes to pass from one gap to the next. If the voltage across each gap at the time of passage of the particles is V then the particle energy at entry of the drift tube numbered n (Fig. 8.6) is neV (for initial energy eV) and the particle velocity is

$$v_n = \sqrt{\frac{2neV}{M}} \qquad (8.6)$$

where M is the mass of the particles being accelerated. The frequency of the oscillator is c/λ and, for a time of flight of half a cycle, the length of drift tube n must therefore be

$$L_n = \frac{1}{2} v_n \frac{\lambda}{c} = \frac{1}{2} \beta_n \lambda \qquad (8.7)$$

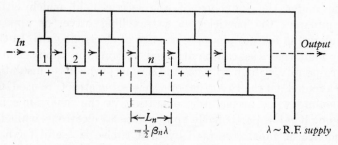

Fig. 8.6. Principle of the Sloan–Lawrence linear accelerator.

For non-relativistic energies it follows from Eqq. 8.6 and 8.7 that

$$L_n \propto \sqrt{n} \qquad (8.8)$$

It also follows from 8.7 that the size of a linear accelerator for a given output energy is determined jointly by the wavelength λ and the gap voltage V. If the energy gain per gap is held constant, the accelerator size is directly proportional to wavelength. The particles emerge in bunches corresponding to peak field at the gaps and resonance is only possible for particles passing at fields very close to this value.

In the method of excitation used by Beams and Snoddy the drift tube structure was connected to appropriate points of a loaded twin-wire transmission line. A voltage pulse was sent down the line and the loading was arranged so that the pulse travelled at the same speed as the particles, so that the two arrived at successive accelerating gaps in synchronism. The dimensions of the structure are given by 8.7.

The availability of high powers at short wavelengths as a result of radar transmitter development has enabled drift-tube accelerators to offer higher energies in a given length. More important, however, has been the realization that the accelerator need not be designed for exact resonance between the maximum accelerating field and the particles, since the motion can be *phase stable*. This discovery led, soon after its enunciation by McMillan and Veksler in 1945, to the design of an electron synchrotron, a synchrocyclotron and a linear accelerator at Berkeley. In its application to the linear accelerator (Alvarez, 1948) the principle of phase stability may be discussed as indicated in Fig. 8.7a, which shows the amplitude of the electric field across two successive accelerating gaps as a function of time. The drift tube structure is arranged so that a particle which crosses a gap with a phase angle ϕ_s (point A) with respect to the alternating field maintains this phase angle unchanged and is in exactly the same phase at the next gap transit. Particles with phase angles greater than ϕ_s (points B) will receive a larger acceleration in the gap, will traverse the drift tube more quickly and will move towards A in phase at the next gap; particles with phase angles less than ϕ_s (points C) will be less accelerated and will also move towards A in phase. Particles corresponding to point A thus have *stable phase*, and if ions of random phase with respect to the accelerating field are injected into the drift tube structure all particles within a certain phase range (Fig. 8.7a) will be trapped and will oscillate about the point of stable phase. If the point of stable phase is moved to the peak of the accelerating field, the possibility of oscillation about the point of stable phase disappears and trapping is much less efficient.

This desirable feature of phase (or axial) stability leads to radial instability because the stable phase point is on the rising part of the voltage wave. Fig. 8.7b illustrates this; the shape of the lines of force is such that a non-axial particle experiences a focusing force F_1 on entering the gap and defocusing force F_2 on leaving it. Since the overall field is increasing with time at the stable phase point the defocusing force predominates. In drift tube accelerators radial stability has been restored either by the use of grids across drift tube entrances to eliminate the unwanted curvature of the lines of force or by compensating the defocusing by means of quadrupole magnets within the tubes themselves.

The principle of the 32 MeV proton accelerator of Alvarez, which has been the pattern for all subsequent phase-stable

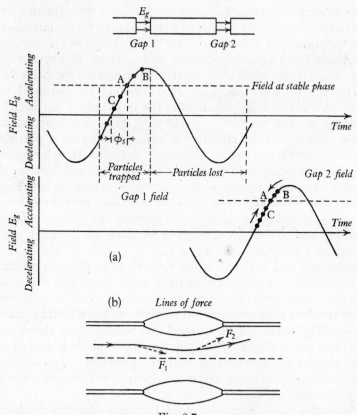

Fig. 8.7

a) Phase stability in a drift-tube ion accelerator. The dots show the phase angles with respect to the gap field of a bunch of particles of uniform velocity arriving at gap 1. At gap 2, there is increased bunching about the stable phase ϕ_s (45° in this particular example).

b) Radial defocusing of particles passing through a cylindrical gap in a field increasing with time.

heavy particle accelerators, is illustrated in Fig. 8.8. Basically the problem in design is the transfer of energy from an electromagnetic field to a charged particle, that is to say just the reverse of the problem of the design of a transmitter valve. At rather low frequencies, as in the Sloan-Lawrence accelerator, the particles pass essentially from one plate of a condenser forming part of an oscillatory circuit to another. At higher frequencies,

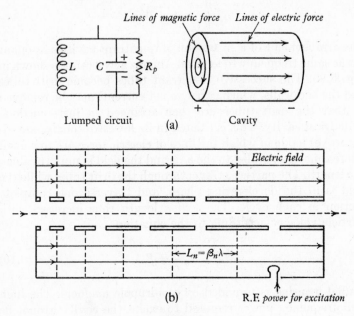

Lines of magnetic force   Lines of electric force

L C R_p

Lumped circuit   Cavity
(a)

Electric field

$\leftarrow L_n = \beta_n\lambda \rightarrow$

(b)   R.F. *power for excitation*

Fig. 8.8
a) Resonant circuits.
b) Alvarez resonant accelerator.

the LC circuit becomes a cavity resonator, excited by a magnetic loop. This is very similar to the resonance tube in sound, except that it is tuned by radius, rather than length variation. It is also very similar in performance to the LC circuit, and in particular may be represented at the resonant frequency by a shunt resistance R_p. The particles are accelerated by the electric field in the cavity and the energy gain in passage through the cavity, operated at power input W, is proportional to $V_{\max}$ where

$$\frac{V_{\max}^2}{2R_p} = W \qquad (8.9)$$

A single cavity could in principle be used for any specified final energy but it follows from 8.9 that it is more economical to divide the available power W between n similar cavities. The final energy is then proportional to

$$n \sqrt{\frac{W}{n}} = \sqrt{n\,W}$$

The arrangement of a succession of re-entrant cavities resonant at the same frequency to form an Alvarez accelerator is shown in Fig. 8.8b. The successive re-entrant tubes become drift tubes and the end walls, which carry no net current, may be removed so that the drift tubes are then arranged in just one long cylindrical cavity. This is excited in its lowest resonant (standing wave) mode in which the lines of electric force are to a good approximation parallel to the axis and the field is uniform along the length. The particles travel through the drift tubes while the field is in the decelerating phase, and traverse one complete section in each cycle. The *section* length thus increases with particle velocity according to the equation

$$L_n = v_n \frac{\lambda}{c} = \beta_n \lambda \tag{8.10}$$

Radial focusing is provided by quadrupole magnets. The high radiofrequency power required to excite the cavity cannot be supplied continuously and the accelerator is operated from a pulsed transmitter with a duty cycle (on-off ratio) of about 1%. A d.c. injector supplies ions of energy 500–4000 keV to the main accelerator, and an improvement in intensity is sometimes obtained by incorporating a special cavity to 'bunch' the injected beam at approximately the selected stable phase angle of the main radiofrequency field.

Linear accelerators have been built both for protons and for heavier ions; the principle is similar in each case. For a given structure and wavelength 8.10 requires that the velocity increments at each accelerating gap should be the same for each particle. A range of values of Ze/M, corresponding to different heavy ions, in different charge states, can therefore be accelerated by adjusting the radiofrequency voltage so that the gap field E is proportional to M/Z. In practice different structures are usually used for protons and heavy ions. The performance of the Alvarez proton accelerator at Berkeley is shown in Table **8.2**.

The main advantages of the linear accelerator as a source of nuclear projectiles are the good collimation, the high homogeneity, the relatively high intensity of the beam (Table **8.2**) and the possibility of extension of the machine to extremely high energies. A serious disadvantage for experiments requiring coincidence counting is the sharply bunched nature of the output, which increases the ratio of random to real coincidences in the counter systems. It is also difficult to vary the output energy except by the insertion of absorbing foils and in this and the preceding respect the linear accelerator is much inferior to the electrostatic generator. The major technical limitation in the extension of linear accelerators towards higher energies and higher intensities is in the development (and maintenance) of the necessary high-power oscillators.

TABLE 8.2   Performance of linear accelerators

MACHINE	BERKELEY PROTON ACCELERATOR	STANFORD ELECTRON ACCELERATOR
Energy	31·5 MeV	630 MeV
Sectionalization	47 drift tubes	22 coupled sections
Length	40 feet	220 feet
Frequency	202·5 Mc/s	3000 Mc/s
Pulse length	400 μsec	2 μsec
Pulse repetition rate	15 sec^{-1}	60 sec^{-1}
Peak power input	2·3 MW	22×9 MW
Shunt impedance	280 MΩ	47 MΩ metre^{-1}
Mean current	1 μA	—
Energy spread	0·5%	2%

The output of a linear accelerator is a succession of pulses within each of which is a fine structure due to the bunching properties of the radio-frequency system.

8.2.2 WAVE-GUIDE ACCELERATORS.   A standing wave pattern in a cavity, such as that developed in the ion accelerator (Sect. 8.2.1) may also be regarded as a superposition of two progressive waves moving in opposite directions. One of these waves travels with the particles and accelerates them. This suggests the feasibility of an equivalent form of accelerator in which bunches of particles are continuously accelerated by a progressive wave in a metal guide. This type of accelerator becomes particularly simple when the particles are moving with relativistic velocity, since the wavelength of the accelerating

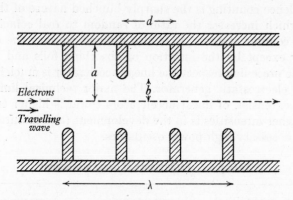

Fig. 8.9. Disc-loaded circular waveguide. The dimensions a, b, can be chosen to reduce the phase velocity of a travelling wave to the velocity of light (or lower).

field is then constant. Wave-guide accelerators are therefore especially suitable for electrons, since these particles have a velocity of $0.98c$ for an energy of only 2 MeV, which may easily be provided at injection by an electrostatic accelerator.

In familiar types of wave guide the phase velocity of the travelling wave is always greater than the velocity of light, but it may be reduced by loading the guide with a series of diaphragms, at a spacing giving 3 to 5 per free space wavelength (Fig. 8.9). Electrons are usually injected so that they travel in bunches near, but slightly earlier than the peak field of the travelling wave, as shown in Fig. 8.7. The electrons gain energy (i.e., increase in effective mass) continuously from the wave, rather than discretely at the gaps as in the drift tube accelerator. If the electron velocity is less than the velocity of light, there will be phase stability, as discussed in Sect. 8.2.1, and a wave guide section with variable disc loading ('tapered guide') can therefore be used to accelerate electrons over a certain range of non-relativistic velocities for feeding into a uniformly loaded guide. The radial defocusing which accompanies axial stability can be simply counteracted for electrons by applying a small axial magnetic field from an external solenoid. When the particle velocity becomes approximately c, the defocusing force vanishes (Ref. 8.7) and no focusing fields are necessary. There is also no definite axial stability and the mechanical construction of the loaded guide must be of high quality in order to ensure that the phase velocity of the wave does not deviate seriously from c.

Travelling-wave electron accelerators usually operate from pulsed magnetrons or klystron amplifiers with a wavelength of about 10 cm. In the successful and efficient 4 MeV accelerator constructed by Fry, Harvie, Mullett and Walkinshaw and developed commercially as an X-ray generator, the microwave power emerging at the end of the guide is returned to the beginning and recirculated. Electrons from a filament are injected at a voltage of about 50 kV and are accelerated in a guide section of variable loading so that the phase velocity increases to match the particle velocity. An axial magnetic field is provided throughout the 2 metre length. The electron beam itself absorbs about 30% of the power provided by the magnetron oscillator; the remainder is used to build up the fields in the guide. The figure-of-merit of such an accelerator is its 'shunt impedance' (see 8.9) per unit length which determines the ratio of the energy gain by an electron per unit length to the power dissipated in the guide in the same length. The shunt impedance is large when the energy losses in the guide walls are small, since the input power required to build up the accelerating fields is then correspondingly reduced.

An outstanding accelerator of the travelling wave type is the 600 MeV machine built at Stanford University under the general direction of W. W. Hansen.* In this remarkable instrument, whose characteristics are summarized in Table 8.2, power is fed to a disc-loaded wave-guide of high mechanical precision from 22 klystron amplifiers driven in synchronism from a tunable magnetron. Electrons are injected into a short tapered

---

* M. Chodorow and others, *Rev. sci. Instrum.*, **26**, 134, 1955.

11 + N.P.

section in which the phase velocity and longitudinal accelerating field both increase, and are bunched at a phase near the peak field of the travelling wave. Phase oscillations are damped by the effect of the rapidly increasing mass and the bunch moves through the main length of uniformly loaded guide with the velocity of light. No auxiliary focusing is used but despite this a beam is obtained, once perturbing magnetic fields have been neutralized, at the end of a 220-ft length of guide. This is possible because of the relativistic shortening of the guide in the electron frame of reference; from the point of view of an observer at rest with respect to the electron the guide appears to be only 26 cm long and there is not much time for lateral divergence. The machine is supplied with microwave power from the klystrons in pulses of 2 μsec length; a time of 1 μsec is consumed in building up the fields in the guide and electrons are injected in, and accelerated during, the remaining microsecond. The machine is heavily shielded against γ and neutron radiation from the guide sections, and provision is made for deflecting beams out of the guide at intermediate energies. Energy values are determined by magnetic deflection.

The Stanford linear accelerator has proved an extremely successful machine for the study of nuclear sizes by electron scattering (Sect. 11.2.1). No difficulties of principle arise in the upward extension of linear accelerator energies, in contrast with the situation with orbital electron accelerators for which radiative losses in the circular paths may become prohibitive.

8.3   Orbital accelerators 1930–53

If a particle of mass M and charge e moves in a plane perpendicular to the lines of force of a uniform magnetic field H the radius r of its path is related to its velocity v by the equation

$$\frac{Hev}{c} = \frac{Mv^2}{r} \tag{8.11}$$

The angular velocity of the particle is

$$\omega = \frac{v}{r} = \frac{eH}{Mc} \text{ radians sec}^{-1} \tag{8.12}$$

and its momentum is

$$p = Mv = \frac{eHr}{c} \tag{8.13}$$

from 8.11. These equations are true for relativisitic velocities, providing that the mass M is not the rest mass M_0 but is related to it by the equation

$$M = \frac{M_0}{\sqrt{1 - v^2/c^2}} \tag{8.14}$$

The *total* energy of the particle moving in the orbit of radius r is, by the formulae of the special theory of relativity,

$$\begin{aligned} E &= Mc^2 \\ &= \sqrt{p^2 c^2 + M_0^2 c^4} \\ &= \sqrt{(eHr)^2 + M_0^2 c^4} \end{aligned} \tag{8.15}$$

from 8.13. The *kinetic* energy T is given by

$$T + M_0 c^2 = E$$

or $$T(T + 2M_0 c^2) = p^2 c^2 = (eHr)^2 \tag{8.16}$$

In the non-relativistic approximation $T \ll M_0 c^2$ and then

$$T = \frac{p^2}{2M_0} \tag{8.17}$$

For extreme relativistic velocities $T \gg M_0 c^2$ and

$$E \approx T = eHr \tag{8.18}$$

Equation 8.15 gives the total energy of a particle moving at radius r in an orbital accelerator in which the magnetic field is H. If the speed of the particle is uniform, the orbit is a circle. The way in which the final energy is attained will now be described for the different types of accelerator.

8.3.1 THE STANDARD CYCLOTRON (fixed field, fixed frequency).   The first accelerator to produce high velocity protons without the use of correspondingly high voltages was the cyclotron described by Lawrence and Edlefsen in 1930 and developed by Lawrence and his collaborators, notably Livingston* in the succeeding years. The cyclotron was based on the principle of magnetic resonance, which is fundamental to the majority of present-day orbital accelerators and which subsequently also became important in the measurement of nuclear magnetic moments (ch. 4) and of fundamental constants. The principle is

---

* E. O. Lawrence and M. S. Livingston, *Phys. Rev.*, **40**, 19, 1932.

illustrated in Fig. 8.10a for a particle of mass M and charge e in a magnetic field H_0. In the non-relativistic approximation ($M = M_0 = $ constant) it is clear from 8.12 that the angular

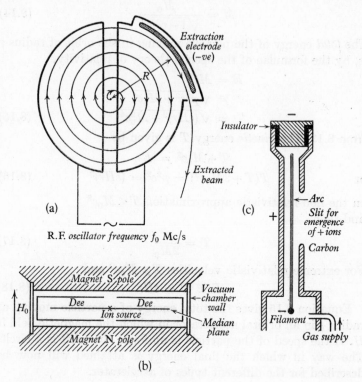

Fig. 8.10.

a) Path of ions in the fixed-frequency cyclotron from central ion source to extracted beam.

b Vertical section showing dees and walls of vacuum chamber in which they are supported.

c) Ion source construction. The arc is constrained to the vertical direction by the main magnetic field.

velocity is independent of the radius of the orbit. The 'cyclotron frequency' or number of revolutions per second is

$$f_0 = \frac{\omega}{2\pi} = \frac{eH_0}{2\pi M_0 c} \tag{8.19}$$

$$= 1 \cdot 525 \text{ Mc/s per kilogauss for protons.}$$

It follows from 8.19 that if the particle is accelerated while it is moving in the field H_0, then so long as the charge and mass remain constant, the cyclotron frequency will also be constant; it is this fact that makes the fixed-frequency cyclotron possible.

In the practical application, two dee-shaped electrodes are supported in a vacuum tank (Fig. 8.10b) leaving a fairly narrow gap between their opposing edges. The electrodes are excited from an oscillatory circuit at the cyclotron frequency f_0, so that an alternating electric field of this frequency appears across the dee-gap. The magnetic field H_0 is applied perpendicularly to the plane of the dee-electrodes and a source of ions (frequently a hot cathode arc source Fig. 8.10c) is placed centrally in the dee-gap. A positive ion of low velocity emerging from the source will be accelerated towards the negative electrode and will enter the field-free space within the electrode, in which it describes a circular arc. This returns it to the dee-gap, where it receives a further acceleration because of the synchronism between the applied voltage and the orbital frequency f_0. In the ideal case this synchronism is maintained and the particle describes a path consisting of semicircles of increasing radius until it reaches the maximum radius R permitted by the dimensions of the electrodes. The kinetic energy is then, according to 8.17 and 8.13,

$$T = \frac{p^2}{2M_0} = \frac{e^2 H_0^2 R^2}{2M_0 c^2}$$

$$= 2\pi^2 f_0{}^2 M_0 R^2 \qquad (8.20)$$

For normal operation of the cyclotron this means simply that the particle velocity at the final radius is equal to the circumference of the final orbit divided by the period of the radio-frequency voltage, i.e.

$$v = \frac{2\pi R}{1/f_0}$$

or $$f_0 = \frac{v}{2\pi R} \qquad (8.21)$$

In fact, the resonance condition 8.19 is fulfilled exactly at one particular radius only, because of the relativistic increase of mass of the ion as it is accelerated. For a *radially uniform field*

$H = H_0$ the resonant frequency when the particle velocity is v is

$$f = \frac{eH_0}{2\pi Mc} = f_0 \sqrt{1 - v^2/c^2} = f_0 \frac{M_0 c^2}{E} \qquad (8.22)$$

from 8.14 and 8.15. It follows that f should fall off as the particle energy increases, i.e. with increasing radius. For a *fixed frequency* $f = f_0$ the resonance condition may be preserved by letting H increase with radius from its low energy value H_0. From 8.12

$$H = \frac{2\pi Mcf_0}{e} = \frac{H_0}{\sqrt{1 - v^2/c^2}} = H_0 \frac{E}{M_0 c^2} \qquad (8.23)$$

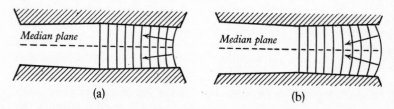

(a)   (b)

Fig. 8.11. Axial forces in radially varying field in a cyclotron.

where H_0 is given by 8.19. For a 10 MeV proton ($M_0 c^2 = 938$ MeV) the necessary increase in H is thus about 1%.

Unfortunately, if the cyclotron magnetic field is azimuthally uniform, it is not possible to allow it to increase radially without introducing a defocusing force. Fig. 8.11 shows the lines of force for radially varying fields and it is apparent that an ion beam circulating in the median plane of the field will only experience a force confining it to this plane in case (b) in which there is a radial *decrease* of field. A stabilizing force of this type is necessary to prevent the beam diverging and the resonance condition is therefore not met. This cannot be avoided in the simple type of cyclotron so far described and it is necessary to design the magnetic field* so that focusing is provided and to accept the fact that the ions will not be in synchronism with the accelerating voltage wave. In practice the radio-

---

* The required radial variation is obtained by a process of shimming, in which either thin iron rings or pole face conductors are used to adjust the field.

frequency is chosen to be slightly less than the resonant value at the centre so that the ions first of all revolve too rapidly and move ahead of the voltage. As they move out, however, they begin to lose phase in the radially decreasing magnetic field until they are about 90° behind (Fig. 8.12). This excursion over the accelerating phase range sets the practical limit to the energy obtainable from a fixed frequency cyclotron with a

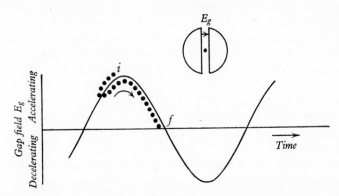

Fig. 8.12. Phase excursion in fixed-frequency cyclotron. The curve shows the time variation of the gap field on one side of the cyclotron. The dots represent the phase excursion of a bunched beam starting (i) at the centre at peak electric field with the radiofrequency lower than the resonant frequency. Subsequent motion takes place in a radially decreasing magnetic field. Acceleration ceases at a phase displacement of 90° (f) but an earlier phase is chosen for extraction.

given radiofrequency accelerating voltage. Higher energies may be obtained by increasing the radiofrequency voltage and thereby reducing the number of turns necessary for a given energy, but voltage breakdown soon becomes a limitation. The highest velocity obtainable is about $0·2c$, corresponding to deuterons of 35 MeV, but such energies are now more easily obtainable with azimuthally varying field machines (Sect. **8.5**).

The particles in a cyclotron perform vertical and horizontal oscillations about the mean orbits with frequencies given by (Appendix 5)

$$\left.\begin{array}{l} f_v = \sqrt{n}f \\ f_r = \sqrt{1-n}f \end{array}\right\} \tag{8.24}$$

where f is the orbital frequency and n is the field index (Sect.

7.2.5). In fixed-frequency cyclotrons n is small and the vertical oscillation period is much longer than the period of revolution, while the radial period is nearly equal to the revolution time. The vertical oscillation amplitude decreases as the beam moves outwards into regions of larger n, and the radial amplitude increases to instability; this aids the extraction of the beam.

There is no phase stability in the cyclotron, since although the particles traverse a considerable phase range in the progress of acceleration to extreme radius there is no effect tending to restore them to a stable phase. However, a marked bunching of particles occurs during the first half-turn and this bunching is maintained throughout the acceleration process. Investigations of cyclotron beam waveform show that the final high-velocity beam occupies about 10% of the radio-frequency cycle. This provides ready-made pulsing of the beam and time-of-flight measurements of particle energies (Sect. 7.3.1) can be based on this wave form.

The circulating beam of a cyclotron may be extracted at extreme radius by applying a negative voltage to an insulated deflecting electrode (Fig. 8.10). Extraction takes place in a region of rapidly falling magnetic field and the beam is well focused vertically but divergent horizontally. Quadrupole magnetic lenses are used to concentrate the beam on distant targets and auxiliary magnets may be used to improve the energy definition.

The fixed-frequency cyclotron has proved a valuable and versatile instrument. It can be made into a variable energy machine by changing the radiofrequency circuit, although it is not as flexible as a d.c. accelerator in this respect. The large beams available are useful for isotope production, while the quality of the external beams can be rendered high enough for precise nuclear reaction experiments. Many different types of ion can be accelerated by appropriate adjustment of magnetic field and if saturation effects result in defocusing fields at some particular radius, these can be corrected by pole-face conductors. The characteristics of a typical cyclotron are given in Table **8.3** (p. 347).

8.3.2 THE SYNCHROCYCLOTRON (fixed field, variable frequency). The limit on the energy obtainable in a fixed frequency cyclotron imposed by the relativistic increase of mass is removed in the synchrocyclotron by the introduction of frequency modulation. This is only possible in practice because of the existence of phase-stable orbits. Consider a bunch of ions crossing the dee-gap of a cyclotron (Fig. 8.13) with exactly

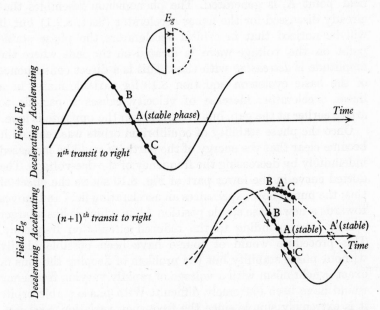

Fig. 8.13. Phase stability in a synchrocyclotron. The dots show the phase angles with respect to the gap field of a bunch of particles of uniform (resonant) velocity at a particular gap transit. At the next transit there is a further bunching towards the phase of zero field if the radiofrequency is constant. If the radiofrequency decreases (dotted curve) the bunch finds itself in an accelerating field.

the resonant velocity, but with a range of phase angles with respect to the radiofrequency voltage. Resonant ions (A) which cross the gap at zero field circulate indefinitely in this phase (if magnetic field and radiofrequency are maintained constant) and if the field index n is less than 1 the radial and vertical oscillations will be stable and the orbit will be in equilibrium. Ions B crossing earlier than A will be accelerated and according to 8.22 their revolution frequency will decrease,

11*

so that at the next gap transit they are delayed and move towards A in phase. Similarly ions crossing later than A are decelerated and, from 8.22, acquire an increased revolution frequency so that these also move towards the stable phase (A) at the next transit. It may be shown that a stable *phase oscillation* covering a large range of phase angles about the zero-field point A, is generated. The phenomenon resembles that already discussed for the linear accelerator (Sect. 8.2.1) but it will be noticed that in orbital accelerators the phase stable point on the voltage wave is located on the side where the amplitude is *decreasing* with time. This is a direct consequence of the basic cyclotron equation 8.19 for variable mass; in a linear accelerator, increase of velocity causes a particle to arrive earlier at the gap, but in a cyclotron the opposite is true.

Once the phase stability of equilibrium orbits was realized it became clear that the energy of the particles could be increased indefinitely by decreasing the frequency of the dee-voltage. The dotted curve in the lower part of Fig. 8.13 shows the effect of this; the bunch now experiences an accelerating field and moves towards a new phase stable position A', in which it has a larger energy, corresponding to the reduced circulation frequency. This procedure would of course have been possible ideally without phase stability but the problem of keeping the ions in exact synchronism with a voltage of rapidly varying frequency would have been extremely difficult. With phase stable orbits it is extremely simple since the frequency variation need not, and indeed must not, be rapid; the orbit expands until it reaches a limit set by the maximum radius available or by the onset of vertical instability due to increase of n-value. The particular limit encountered in synchrocyclotrons occurs at $n = 0·2$, when $f_v = 0·2^{1/2}f$ and $f_r = 0·8^{1/2}f$, so that $f_r = 2f_v$. Energy is then fed from the radial oscillations into the vertical oscillations and the beam diverges vertically. An n-value of $0·05$ is used throughout the main accelerating region to provide vertical focusing. The energy attained for a given field and fixed radius may be calculated from 8.15.

The existence of phase stability has the important practical consequence that many more turns may be described in a synchrocyclotron than in a conventional machine. It is therefore possible to use low dee voltages and to dispense with one of the dees, making the radio-frequency power requirement less, and access to the machine much better. The remaining dee may be supported and fed with power symmetrically and the vacant space opposite may be used for targets and for extraction channels. The frequency modulation necessary for operation is imposed by including a variable condenser, driven mechanically, in the resonant circuit. The frequency range necessarily depends on the final energy and on the magnetic field drop and may be calculated from 8.19; from about 20 Mc/s to about 15 Mc/s is typical for proton synchrocyclotrons. A linear fall of magnetic field is generally used, with extra iron near the edge to reinforce the field when leakage occurs. The property of phase stability makes 'shimming' for the correct field law much less critical than in the conventional cyclotron. Despite this, large variations in the field law are not tolerable and because of its size the synchrocyclotron cannot readily be converted into a variable energy machine, in which the different values of mean field would lead to different degrees of radial fall-off.

Ions are supplied from a source of the type (Fig. 8.10c) used in the conventional cyclotron. In typical operation, bunches of ions are accepted at the beginning of each modulation cycle over a period of 100 μsec and with a modulation frequency of 100 c/s so that both the duty cycle of 10^{-2} and the mean circulating current of about 1 μA are worse than those of the conventional cyclotron. They may be improved if the mechanical problems of high modulation frequency can be overcome. Beam extraction by deflection methods tends to be more difficult than in the cyclotron because the orbit spacing is much less (~ 0.1 mm instead of perhaps 5 mm) but this difficulty has been overcome by the ingenious peeler-regenerator technique developed by Le Couteur, Crewe and Gregory, working on the 410 MeV synchrocyclotron of the University of Liverpool. The principle, suggested by Tuck and Teng, is shown in Fig. 8.14 and is essentially to increase the amplitude of radial oscillation of the circulating particles until they enter the mouth of a magnetically screened channel through which they can be conducted away from the main magnetic field. This is mechanically impossible without special measures because of the small spacing of successive orbits. If, however, the particles are allowed to pass first through a region in which the field is made to decrease linearly with radius (peeler) and then through a second region in which the field increases linearly with radius (regenerator) the free radial oscillation can be augmented. Extraction by this process is arranged to start at a radius at which the field index for the main synchrocyclotron field is small; the frequency of radial oscillation $f_r = \sqrt{1 - nf}$ is approximately equal to the revolution frequency. A particle whose orbit

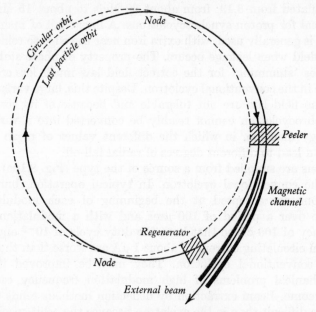

Fig. 8.14. Synchrocyclotron extraction system (Le Couteur, *Proc. roy. Soc.* A, **232**, 236, 1955).

has an antinode of radial oscillation (outward) between the peeler and regenerator receives an outward impulse in the former and an inward impulse in the latter and the oscillation amplitude builds up into radial instability. It was found that ultimately an increase in radius of 1 in. could be obtained after one turn and this is amply sufficient to bring the beam into a magnetic channel.

In the Liverpool experiments, 10% of the circulating beam of about 1μA entered the magnetic channel and 2% of the beam was subsequently focused by an auxiliary magnet in a spot of area $\frac{1}{2}$ in^2 nearly 40 ft from the cyclotron. Similar results have since been obtained with other machines; the performance in terms of particle flux is at least 1000 times better than that of extraction methods relying on scattering from foils, and has the great virtue of depending only on a static field system. It has been found that the extractor functions also as an energy selector and the homogeneity of the external beam is better than 0·5%.

The successful operation of the proton synchrocyclotron has been of the greatest importance for the development of high energy physics. The principle was tried successfully on the 37-in. cyclotron at Berkeley in 1946 and almost immediately the large 184-in. machine at Berkeley was also converted to frequency modulation. An astonishing number of important experiments, including artificial meson production, were carried out with the beams of 380 MeV alpha particles and 350 MeV protons which then became available. The only limit to the energy which may be reached by synchrocyclotrons is imposed by the cost of the magnet, and appears to have been reached at a proton energy of about 700 MeV. The performance figures for a well-known machine of this type are given in Table **8.3** (p. 347).

8.3.3 THE MICROTRON (fixed field, fixed frequency). The relativistic limitation of the standard cyclotron could be overcome if the increase of mass at each gap transit were so large that the revolution time increased by one radiofrequency period. The basic cyclotron equation 8.19 may be written

$$f_0 = \frac{ecH_0}{2\pi M_0 c^2} \tag{8.25}$$

and the increase of energy required at each gap therefore corresponds to one rest mass $M_0 c^2$. This is quite impossible to achieve for protons ($M_0 c^2 = 938$ MeV) but is practicable for electrons ($mc^2 = 511$ keV). The microtron (or electron cyclotron) is a multiple period accelerator based on this principle; it was suggested by Veksler and by Schwinger, and has been developed in a few laboratories (Ref. 8.13) but seems unlikely to compete with the electron synchrotron (Sec. 8.3.4) or the linear accelerator for high energy operation.

The principle of the microtron is illustrated in Fig. 8.15.

Electrons (produced conveniently by field emission from metal surfaces) pass through a cavity excited from a pulsed radio-frequency source of frequency 3000 Mc/s. The magnetic field H_0, from 8.25, is then 1070 gauss, and this field is maintained

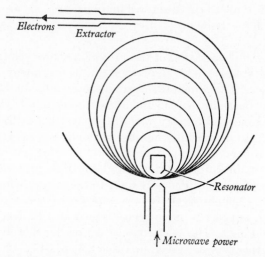

Fig. 8.15. Successive electron orbits in the microtron (Ref. 8.13).

over a large area bounded by the cavity. At each transit the electrons gain energy mc^2 so that the total energy E for the first orbit is $2mc^2$ and for the Nth $(N+1)\,mc^2$. Since the electron velocity rapidly approaches c the orbit radii are given by 8.11, as

$$R_N = \frac{(N+1)mc^2}{eH_0}$$

and the revolution times are

$$t_N = \frac{2\pi R_N}{c} = \frac{N+1}{f_0}$$

There is phase stability in the microtron but vertical stability may present a problem since the magnetic field must be sufficiently uniform to maintain the resonance condition. Extraction is relatively easy because of the wide spacing of the orbits, and the beam is monochromatic to about $0\cdot1\%$. Characteristics of a 29 MeV accelerator of this type are given in Table **8.3** (p. 347).

8.3.4 THE ELECTRON SYNCHROTRON (variable field, fixed frequency). For an electron accelerator the basic cyclotron equation 8.19 may be written, using 8.15

$$f = \frac{ecH}{2\pi E} = \frac{ecH}{2\pi\sqrt{m^2c^4 + (eHR)^2}} \qquad (8.26)$$

where R is the orbit radius and H the magnetic field. In the relativistic region of velocities (say above an energy of 1 MeV), we have $eHR \gg mc^2$ and

$$f \to \frac{c}{2\pi R} \qquad (8.27)$$

which means simply that the electrons move round a given orbit with constant frequency. If the electron energy E is increased by a radiofrequency electric field the orbit will expand, but if at the same time the magnetic field increases proportionately to E the orbit radius remains unchanged. The electron synchroton is based on this principle.

Fig. 8.16a, b shows the layout of a machine of this type. The magnetic field is annular and in small synchrotrons this leads to the construction shown in the figure in which the magnetic circuit has to be completed outside the vacuum chamber for reasons of space. In larger machines this arrangement, which results in inaccessibility to the vacuum chamber, can be avoided. The machine is operated with an a.c. field of a period of the order of 100 c/s and thin magnet laminations are therefore necessary. The vacuum chamber in the smaller synchrotons is a glass or ceramic 'doughnut' supported in the magnet gap. High resistance metallized surfaces are necessary in order to avoid storage of charge without excessive eddy currents.

Electrons are injected into the synchrotron from an electron gun just inside the chamber wall under the influence of a voltage of 50–100 kV. A surprisingly large fraction of these electrons is trapped into orbits in which acceleration can take place and the initial acceleration to about 2 MeV takes place as in the betatron (Sect. 8.3.6). When the magnetic field has risen to the value corresponding to this energy, saturation in the flux-bars (Fig. 8.16a) is arranged to occur and the conditions necessary for betatron acceleration are no longer satisfied. The electron velocity however is then $0.98c$ and the conditions necessary for

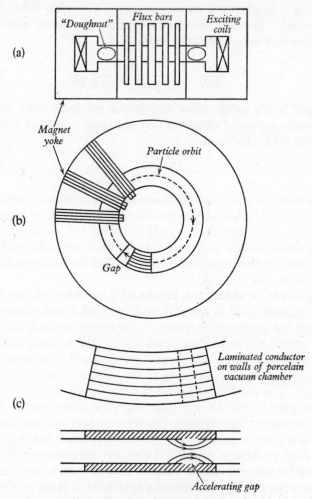

Fig. 8.16
a), b) Layout of electron synchrotron.
c) Synchrotron accelerating cavity (Ref. 8.8).

synchrotron action are fulfilled. A radiofrequency voltage is
applied to a resonator forming part of, or mounted in, the
vacuum system, and the particles receive an energy increment
per turn just sufficient to keep them near the equilibrium orbit
in the rising magnetic field. A stable oscillation about the

synchronous phase A develops as discussed in the case of the synchrocyclotron (Fig. 8.13); if an electron crosses the resonator too early (B) it receives extra energy and therefore moves to an orbit of slightly larger radius according to 8.15; since it is already moving with velocity c, its velocity does not alter but its orbit takes longer to describe and in the next transit of the resonator it will have moved towards the stable phase. Similar arguments apply to the electrons crossing too late (C). Both phase and free oscillations are damped as the magnetic field rises and the final cross-section of the beam can be very small. The final energy is given by 8.18 as

$$T \approx E = eH_{max}R \qquad (8.28)$$

where H_{max} is the peak field.

The magnet inductance forms part of an oscillatory circuit with a large condenser bank chosen to give the required repetition frequency. The energy oscillates between the inductive and capacitative form and only ohmic losses have to be supplied by the driving circuit. The frequency of the accelerating voltage is constant and the accelerating resonator is effectively a quarter-wave coaxial line, shorted at one end and developing a maximum voltage difference at the open end which forms the resonator gap (Fig. 8.16c). The resonator is bent into an arc of radius equal to that of the equilibrium orbit, and would in free space occupy an angle of 90° since the electrons are travelling with the same velocity as electromagnetic waves. The angular extent of the resonator may be reduced by filling the line with dielectric, e.g. the wall of the vacuum chamber.

The main emphasis in synchrotron experiments has been on photodisintegration. For this purpose it is unnecessary to extract the electron beam and it is normally allowed to expand outwards at the peak of the magnet cycle and strike a heavy target, from which the main bremsstrahlung spectrum originates. For this reason little work has been done on extraction problems in the electron synchrotron and none of the earlier machines of this type have straight sections. The availability of high-power sources for electron linear accelerators now makes it unlikely that much effort will be devoted to the production of external beams from constant n-value electron synchrotrons. The rate of expansion of the electron orbits can be controlled by suitably adjusting the radiofrequency cycle and pulse lengths between 1 and 1000 μsec can be obtained. The maximum energy can be varied by switching off the radiofrequency at a suitable point in the magnet cycle.

The major limitation of electron synchrotrons is one which is common and fundamental to all orbital electron accelerators. The electrons moving in circular orbits of radius R are under radial acceleration and must therefore radiate energy. The total loss increases as $\left(\dfrac{E}{mc^2}\right)^4 \dfrac{1}{R}$ for constant radius where E is the electron energy and this may amount to many hundred eV per turn in the larger synchrotrons. Some compensation for radiative loss occurs automatically as a result of phase stability, but ultimately it becomes impossible to supply the losses and no further acceleration can take place. In conventional electron synchrotrons this limit is in the region of 1000 MeV for available sources of power. The synchrotron radiation has a spectrum with maximum intensity in the far ultra-violet and a bluish glow originating from the orbit (and emitted at each point in a cone of angle $\approx mc^2/E$) is easily visible using suitable optical arrangements.

The successful operation of an electron synchrotron was first demonstrated by Goward and Barnes (1947) who converted a 4 MeV betatron into an 8 MeV synchrotron by the addition of an accelerating cavity. Many large machines of this type have now been built and provide extremely intense sources of bremsstrahlung; the performance of a typical machine is shown in Table **8.3**.

8.3.5 THE PROTON SYNCHROTRON (variable field, variable frequency). In the electron synchrotron, resonance between the orbital frequency of a charged particle in a rising magnetic field and a radiofrequency accelerating voltage permits acceleration to take place in an orbit of constant radius. This principle may also be applied to protons, and an annular magnet then suffices so that a proton synchrotron is a much more economical machine than the synchrocyclotron for the same final energy. Until the protons reach relativistic velocities, however, the orbital frequency in the proton synchrotron is energy dependent and provision for variation of accelerating frequency must be made.

Fig. 8.17a shows the main components of a proton synchrotron. The annular magnet may be a continuous ring or, more conveniently, an arrangement of quadrants with intervening

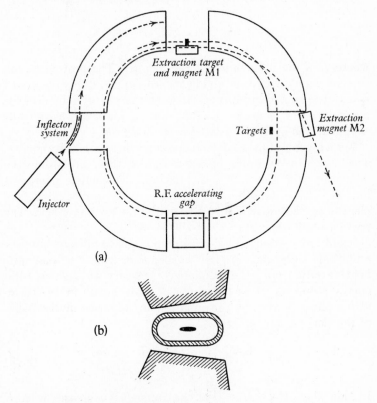

Fig. 8.17

a) Main components of proton synchrotron.

b) Cross-section of synchrotron magnet gap. In the initial stages of acceleration the beam fills the whole cross-section of the vacuum chamber. The magnetic field decreases with increasing radius.

straight sections. The cross-section of the magnet gap is shown in Fig. 8.17b; the pole tips are shaped to give a field index n of the order of 0·7, for which the radial and vertical oscillations are stable. The magnet is laminated to reduce eddy current losses. The vacuum ring, made of stainless steel, porcelain or plastic, is supported in the magnet gap.

The magnet current is supplied from a d.c. generator which develops an open circuit voltage V. When the contactor in the magnet circuit closes, the initial rate of growth of current i and of field H in the magnet gap is determined by the equation

$$V = L \frac{\mathrm{d}i}{\mathrm{d}t}$$

where L is the inductance of the magnet. The growth to full current takes about 1 sec and in the subsequent decay of current it may be arranged to return the inductive energy stored in the magnet to the generator, so that only ohmic losses have to be supplied. The cycle is repeated every 3–10 sec.

For a given radius, each field corresponds to a definite energy. The synchrotron must be so designed that, accepting the magnetic field law as a basic datum, the particle energy is increased by a radiofrequency electric field applied along the orbit in just the way required to match the magnetic field. The particles will then stay near the same orbit throughout the acceleration period. The minimum radiofrequency voltage amplitude necessary can be worked out from the magnetic field variation, and the frequency necessary at a given total energy E in order that the particles shall remain in an accelerating phase is given by the equation already used in discussion of the electron synchrotron,

$$f = \frac{ecH}{2\pi E} = \frac{ecH}{2\pi \sqrt{M_0^2 c^4 + (eHR)^2}} \tag{8.29}$$

In this case $eHR \approx M_0 c^2$ and the frequency increases with E (i.e. with H) in contrast with the case of the synchrocyclotron. The final energy E is given by 8.15.

The acceleration is in principle phase stable as shown in Fig. 8.13, although this stability may be impaired if the frequency variation is imprecise. A bunch of particles moves round near the equilibrium orbit with an azimuthal spread determined by the limits of phase stability and particles move from end to end of this bunch as it revolves in consequence of the phase oscillation. The phase range contracts from about 180° to about 90°

during acceleration and the superimposed free oscillations are
also damped so that the beam shrinks in cross-section.

The accelerating voltage is supplied from a tubular electrode
in the vacuum system (Fig. 8.16b) or from a magnetic toroid
through which the vacuum box passes (Fig. 8.17a). In the
former case the electrode forms part of an oscillatory circuit
which must be kept in tune by inductance variation over the
considerable range of frequency necessary for the acceleration.
In the latter method the toroid forms effectively the core of a
transformer of which the exciting circuit is the primary winding
and the equilibrium orbit the secondary.

The beam is injected from a pulsed electrostatic generator or
linear accelerator before the radiofrequency voltage is switched
on at a time determined by the rising magnetic field. Some form
of electrode structure is necessary to guide the beam towards
the equilibrium orbit and the capture of the beam into this orbit
depends on the orbit radius shrinkage during the first turn
since this will determine the fraction of beam which succeeds
in avoiding the guide electrodes after one circuit. Injection
continues until the first orbits, contracting in the rising magnetic
field, have reached the centre of the vacuum box; the radial
oscillation amplitude of newly injected particles is then equal
to half the box width and further injection merely results in a
loss of particles to the walls. The radiofrequency power is then
switched on and the process of acceleration, accompanied by
phase, radial and vertical oscillations, commences. The free
oscillations are stimulated at energies near injection by collisions with residual gas molecules and a serious loss of particles
to the walls of the vacuum box may occur at this stage. It is
desirable for this reason to use as large a vacuum chamber and
as low a pressure as possible and, for the same reason, no
projections such as targets must be left in the chamber at the
time of injection since these in effect reduce the dimensions of
the box in both directions by the amount of intrusion and may
have a serious effect on the magnitude of beam. Gas scattering
is less serious at high injection energies but the orbit shrinkage
is relatively also less and it is not clear that the beam necessarily improves with the use of higher injection voltage.

At the end of the acceleration period the beam has con-
tracted to dimensions much smaller than those of the vacuum

box owing to damping of the free oscillations and a target may be inserted through the wall of the vacuum system. If the radiofrequency voltage is switched off while the magnetic field is still rising the beam spirals inwards and may strike a target placed on the inside wall; if the acceleration is continued until the magnetic field reaches its maximum the particles will spiral outwards to a target placed on the outside wall. Similar operations may also be carried out at any time during the acceleration period and the synchrotron is thus able to provide a beam of variable energy in a direct and natural way. The radiofrequency timing may also be adjusted to yield a long target pulse which is useful for counting experiments.

A considerable fraction of the circulating beam may be extracted from the vacuum system by inducing a radial oscillation by means of a thin foil (Fig. 8.17a) on to which the circulating beam is allowed to shrink at the end of the accelerating cycle. A suitable foil will cause a small energy loss which shifts the centre of the orbit and brings the beam into the field of an extracting magnet M1 placed together with the foil target in one of the straight sections. Further deflection is provided if necessary by a second magnet M2 in the following straight section. An extraction efficiency of up to 50% has been claimed for this method.

Three large proton synchrotrons were under construction by 1948 and several other similar or larger machines have since been completed. The characteristics of one of them are shown in Table **8.3**. Until 1953 these synchrotrons, with their azimuthally constant field gradients, represented the most advanced phase of accelerator design, and in the years that followed, such machines have yielded an enormous amount of information on the physics of nucleons, antinucleons, mesons and strange particles. The beam currents are small compared with those of synchrocyclotrons owing to the small repetition rates and to the difficulties associated with injection, but adequate yields of high-energy events have usually been obtained. The yield of secondary particles of all kinds from beam stoppage is very large and extensive biological shields are necessary. The low repetition rate and high pulse yield make the track chamber an especially suitable detector for use with proton synchrotrons.

8.3.6 THE BETATRON. The possibility of accelerating charged particles by means of the electric field surrounding the lines of force of a changing magnetic field has long been realized. The early work of Wideroe (1928), Breit and Tuve (1928) and Walton showed how this principle might be applied in practice but experimental attempts at acceleration were unsuccessful, probably owing to difficulties in magnet design, until 1941. The 2 MeV betatron designed by Kerst and operated in that year is an instrument of historical importance because not only was it the first successful electron accelerator which gave promise of extension to high energy, but also it stimulated the development of the theory of orbit stability which is fundamental to cyclic accelerators of all types. The betatron is the only orbital accelerator that does not depend on the principle of magnetic resonance.

The construction of a betatron is illustrated in Fig. 8.18. Electrons move in an annular chamber or 'doughnut' made of glass or ceramic with a conducting coating and supported in the gap of a specially shaped a.c. magnet. The magnet is built of thin iron laminations and is operated in an LC resonant circuit at about 100 c/s; the magnetic flux crossing the vacuum chamber and passing through the centre section then alternates with this frequency. If the electrons move in an equilibrium orbit of radius R (Fig. 8.18) the electromotive force $\mathbf{E}$ acting tangentially round the orbit when the flux linking the orbit is changing at a rate $\dot{\Phi}$ given by

$$2\pi R\mathbf{E} = \frac{1}{c}\,\dot{\Phi} \qquad (8.30)$$

This is the e.m.f. which would be found in an open loop of wire surrounding the betatron magnet, just as in a transformer. If H is the magnetic field at the equilibrium orbit and p the electron momentum at any time then, as in 8.13,

$$p = \frac{eHR}{c} \qquad (8.31)$$

and

$$\dot{p} = \mathbf{E}e \qquad (8.32)$$

so that by combining these equations

$$\dot{\Phi} = 2\pi R^2 \dot{H} \qquad (8.33)$$

This is the betatron condition for acceleration at constant radius R; the electrons will stay near the orbit providing that the flux linking the orbit is changing at twice the rate corresponding to a uniform field H throughout the betatron gap. It is therefore necessary to increase the central accelerating field above the value used for the guide field which maintains the particles in orbit. Core saturation occurs first in the central region of the magnet and the highest fields are not available for

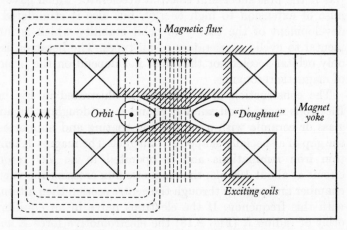

Fig. 8.18. Vertical section of construction of betatron, showing magnetic circuit with increased flux linking the particle orbit.

constraining the electrons. The betatron therefore tends to give lower output energies than electron synchrotrons of comparable size although electron currents are rather larger because of different injection behaviour. Injection phenomena in the betatron are complex, and the main difficulty in the machine construction is the ensuring of adequate uniformity in the low injection fields.

The acceleration process in a betatron is continuous while the condition 8.33 is satisfied and an energy increment of about 1000 V per turn can be obtained. No relativistic limits arise because the mass is eliminated between eqq. 8.31 and 8.32. Orbital stability requires that the magnetic field index n shall lie between 0 and 1 as in other orbital accelerators. The electrons are injected at an energy of about 50 keV from a gun and are delivered to a final target, as the magnetic field approaches its maximum value, as a sequence of pulses at the magnet repetition rate.

Since the condition 8.33 usually fails because of lack of accelerating flux the electrons, losing energy rapidly by radiation, usually spiral to an inside target. Special techniques such as scattering from targets must be used to obtain an external beam; the time of revolution is far too short ($\approx 0 \cdot 1$ µsec) to permit pulsed deflection in a single turn.

It has been possible to save some of the large amount of iron necessary in a betatron by providing separate excitation for the accelerating and guide fields. The former can then be operated with a negative bias so that the field changes from $-H$ through zero to $+H$ while the guide field is always of the same sign. Despite such economies the betatron seems unlikely to compete well with the synchrotron for high electron energies for which the loss of energy by radiation becomes appreciable but in the 0–50 MeV region the induction accelerator is a powerful and useful generator of short wavelength radiation. The function of the betatron principle in the early stages of synchrotron operation has already been mentioned (Sect. 8.3.4).

Performance figures for a typical betatron are given in Table **8.3**.

8.4   Alternating gradient (strong focusing) accelerators

All the orbital accelerators so far described have been of the constant gradient, weak focusing type. For these machines, the field index n lies between 0 and 1 so that any arc of the machine produces a damping of both radial and vertical oscillations, i.e. a net focusing effect in both directions. In 1952, at Brookhaven, Livingston considered the possibility of building a synchrotron with successive magnetic sectors facing inwards to and outwards from the centre in order to compensate for the effects of magnetic leakage. This led to the occurrence of a reversed n value in alternate sectors and Courant therefore studied the effect of this on orbital stability. It was soon found that there was net focusing after a pair of positive and negative sectors, and more important still both n-values could be made extremely large with great advantage. The general theory of this type of focusing was given by Courant, Livingston and Snyder in 1953; it was subsequently found that it had been enunciated two years earlier by Christofilos in Athens.

The principle of alternating gradient focusing is simply that with a large value of n, alternately positive and negative, there will be strong vertical focusing and radial defocusing in the sector with positive n and the converse in the sector with negative n; while overall, for a large range of n values, there

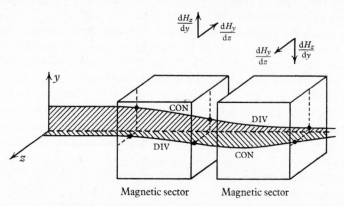

Fig. 8.19. Passage of two rays, representing charged particles, through magnetic sectors with reversed field gradients. There is net focusing after the two sectors (Ref. 8.3).

will be net convergence (Fig. 8.19). This result has now become familiar as the basis of magnetic quadrupole lenses; it is also the principle of the converging-diverging achromatic lens combination in optics. The advantage of AG focusing for accelerators is that because the free oscillation periods become much shorter, the amplitudes of oscillation are much smaller and there is a notable saving in the necessary magnet aperture and associated expenditure. Phase oscillation amplitudes are also reduced, and a considerable spread of momentum can be accommodated in a small radial space.

The original proposal envisaged the use of n values of about 3600. Unfortunately this was found later to demand an impossible accuracy in magnet construction in order that perturbations due to misalignment should not set up instabilities. In practice therefore n values have been reduced to about 300, but there is still an enormous saving in magnet costs for a given energy and the two large proton accelerators now operating in the 25–30 GeV energy region are AG machines. The main properties of the CERN proton synchrotron, which came into operation at Geneva on 24 November 1959, are included in Table **8.3**.

TABLE 8.3 Performance of orbital accelerators

Machine	Particle energy (MeV)	Maximum or stable orbit diameter	Radio-frequency (Mc/s)	Pulse repetition Rate	Output current or particles per pulse	Magnet weight (tons)
Fixed Frequency cyclotron (Birmingham)[1]	20 (d)	60 in.	10·3	C.W.	500 μA	250
Synchrocylotron (Liverpool)[2]	410 (p)	156 in.	29·2–18·9	110	1 μA	1650
Microtron (Univ. Coll., London)[3]	29 (e)	80 in.	3000	100	—	—
Electron synchrotron (Glasgow)[4]	340 (e)	250 cm	38·2	5/sec	About 10^8 equivalent quanta/sec	80
Constant gradient synchrotron (Birmingham)[5]	1000 (p)	32 ft.	330 kc/s –9·3 Mc/s	6/min	5×10^9	810
Betatron (Illinois)[6]	300 (e)	244 cm	—	6/sec	—	341
Alternating gradient synchrotron (CERN)[7]	28,000 25,000 (p)	200 m	—	12/min 20/min	6×10^{10} 10^{11}	3400

All accelerators operating with radiofrequency fields exhibit a fine time structure of the beam on a scale determined by the radiofrequency.

NOTES p = protons, d = deuterons, e = electrons

1. *Nature*, **169**, 476, 1952
2. M. J. Moore, *Nature*, **175**, 1012, 1955
3. Ref. 8.13.
4. W. McFarlane *et al.*, *Nature*, **176**, 666, 1955
5. *Nature*, **172**, 704, 1953
6. D. W. Kerst *et al.*, *Phys. Rev.*, **78**, 297, 1950
7. J. B. Adams, *Nature*, **185**, 568, 1960.

The characteristics of strong focusing accelerators have been intensively studied theoretically. One of the interesting features of the stability in phase of the circulating particles is that there is a critical energy E_c at which the position of stable phase moves from the rising voltage part of the radio-frequency cycle to the falling part. The former mode of acceleration is similar to that in the linear accelerator (Fig. 8.7) but the associated electric defocusing is a small effect in comparison with the strong magnetic focusing; the latter mode is as in the CG synchrotron or synchrocyclotron (Fig. 8.13).

The alternating gradient principle is being applied to linear accelerators by enclosing quadrupole lenses in the drift tubes. Some of the problems connected with AG focusing are less severe in this type of machine owing to the relatively short, non-repetitive path.

8.5 Survey and future prospects

The history of accelerator development is summarized in Fig. 8.20. From 1930 onwards it seems that at each point as a particular accelerator appeared to have reached its limiting performance, either fundamentally or for economic reasons, a new principle has emerged permitting further progress. An excellent account of the sequence of advances is given in Ref. 8.11; the number of high-energy accelerators (excluding cascade generators and electrostatic machines) existing or projected in 1958 is shown in Table 8.4.*

TABLE 8.4

High energy accelerators (1958)

Fixed frequency cyclotron	76
Synchrocyclotron	18
Proton synchrotron	17
Electron synchrotron	11
Electron linear accelerator	4
Proton linear accelerator	10
Heavy ion linear accelerator	4

* Taken from ORNL 2644, *Cyclotrons and High Energy Accelerators*, by F. T. Howard.

Electrostatic accelerators are numerous and popular and their maximum energy will be extended to 20–30 MeV by the tandem principle. They are pre-eminently suitable for the study

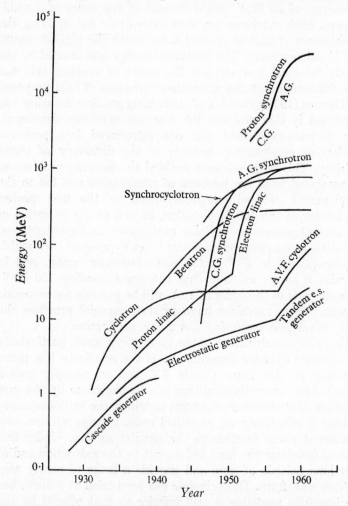

Fig. 8.20. Accelerator development, 1930 onwards. The figure shows the trend of energies reached by different machines (adapted from Ref. 8.3).

of individual nuclear energy levels and the general problem of the structure of complex nuclei. The apparent limitation of output energy associated with d.c. machines was removed by the evolution of resonance acceleration, which was already being tried at the time of Cockcroft and Walton's original experiment. The fixed frequency cyclotron rapidly advanced to an energy of 25 MeV and a current of the order of a milli-ampere. Such machines are used extensively for studying the mechanisms of nuclear reactions, for which the highest resolution is not necessary. The cyclotron energy was limited by the relativistic mass increase, but the means of avoiding this was soon forthcoming in the azimuthal variations of field proposed by Thomas (1938); the idea of alternating gradient focusing was contained in this proposal but was not explicitly developed. The Thomas-type field was not introduced into post-war accelerator construction because of the discovery of phase stability. This basic advance enabled the focusing problem to be separated from the problem of acceleration and led to the development of the synchrocyclotron as the first proton accelerator of the 100 MeV region, as well as the evolution of the present generation of linear accelerators and synchrotrons. The limit to synchrocyclotron size is set by magnet cost, which is proportional to $E^{3/2}$ in the non-relativistic region, and in practice it seems unlikely that energies exceeding 750 MeV, with currents of the order of $1\mu A$, will be possible for economic reasons. These machines have as their especial province the study of nucleon scattering and meson production.

The main disadvantage of the synchrocyclotron, particularly for accurate counter experiments, is the relatively low mean intensity of the beam (Table 8.3) and its sharply pulsed nature. The latter disadvantage can be overcome by the new principle of *stochastic* acceleration in which the radiofrequency voltage is effectively an amplified noise voltage without any considered phase relation to the circulating ions. Under this type of influence the ions diffuse out to the extraction radius over long periods of time and provide a beam of nearly continuous waveform. The principle has been tried at 5 MeV, but the intensity available is still inferior to that offered by the fixed-frequency cyclotron. The present likely replacement for the synchrocyclotron is in fact by a return to the Thomas principle, in the form of the *azimuthally varying field* (AVF) cyclotron. In this type of machine the mean field is allowed to increase with radius and vertical focusing is obtained by radial or spiral ridges built on to the poles to create alternate high and low field sectors. Focusing forces giving axial stability arise at each sector boundary. The AVF cyclotron (fixed frequency) gives a better performance than the standard cyclotron because the particles no longer lose phase as shown in Fig. 8.12, and acceleration continues to the limit defined by the magnet size. This will probably be about 750 MeV, as for synchrocyclotrons.

After the evolution of the synchrocyclotrons the next step in progress towards higher energies was the construction of the constant gradient proton synchrotron, with a probable limit of 15 GeV and a current which may ultimately reach 1 μA. The discovery of the antinucleon, and K-meson and hyperon properties are triumphs for these machines. Hardly had the proton synchrotron limit been brought in view when it was extended by a factor of 2 or 3 by the discovery of AG focusing, on which present accelerators of the 20–30 GeV class are based. Electron synchrotrons of this type are probably limited by radiation losses to about 6 GeV. Despite their economy of magnet space, these are vast machines, possible only under the aegis of a national or international organization.

The parallel developments of the betatron and the linear accelerators are limited mainly by cost; in the former case of the magnet and the latter of the klystron amplifiers or other power sources. It should be noted that the wartime development of high-power centimetre transmitters was in itself an important advance in accelerator technology.

The limit to the energies obtainable by accelerators is hard to define, but some there must be, whether physical or economic, and it is probable that 300 GeV is further than accelerator physics can advance under the principles known at present. There is always an urge to attain the highest possible energy in the hope of the discovery of new phenomena not so far observable with clarity in the cosmic ray field. This demand will probably be supplied by AG synchrotron type machines. An unfavourable return in centre-of-mass energy in a moving proton/stationary proton collision for increasing accelerator expenditure has not escaped attention,* and it is possible that

---

* The total energy in the cm system is $\sqrt{2m_pc^2(E+m_pc^2)}$ where E is the total laboratory energy of the incident proton.

the ultimate answer is some form of colliding beam experiment. Magnetic storage rings in which beams of electrons and positrons circulate in opposite directions have already been tried successfully and offer an enormous advantage in available energy. Their extension to protons is a problem for the future, but whatever success is achieved, the effective energy obtained is still likely to be low from the point of view of the cosmic-ray physicist. Ultra-high energy particles, as far as can be foreseen, will always have to be accelerated in the cosmos, and studied perhaps at the top of the earth's atmosphere.

8.6 Neutron and photon sources

a) *Neutrons* cannot be accelerated directly and must be produced in some primary nuclear reaction with an energy at least equal to that required. Many of the techniques for production of homogeneous neutrons are also used in neutron energy measurement, and have already been discussed in Sect. **7.3**, e.g. the time-of-flight technique and neutron diffraction methods. The most important source of thermal neutrons is, of course, the nuclear reactor (Appendix 7); for fast neutrons the following nuclear reactions have been much used:

i) photonuclear reactions in beryllium or deuterium, using fission product γ-ray sources.

$$^9\text{Be} + \gamma \rightarrow {}^8\text{Be} + n - 1 \cdot 67 \text{ MeV}$$
$$^2\text{H} + \gamma \rightarrow {}^1\text{H} + n - 2 \cdot 23 \text{ MeV}$$

(8.34)

Energies of the order of 100 keV are available from these sources with yields of the order of 2×10^5 neutrons sec^{-1} per curie of radioactive source.

ii) The $(d\text{--}T)$ reaction, which has a high maximum yield for about 140 keV deuterons and yields neutrons of energy 14 MeV

$$^2\text{H} + {}^3\text{H} \rightarrow {}^4\text{He} + n + 17 \cdot 58 \text{ MeV}$$

(8.35)

This is a popular reaction for small generators using electrostatic or cascade voltage units and simple accelerating tubes. Neutron yields of more than 10^9 sec^{-1} are possible.

iii) The threshold reaction

$$^7\text{Li} + p \rightarrow {}^7\text{Be} + n - 1 \cdot 64 \text{ MeV}$$

(8.36)

which provides neutrons of variable energy above about 50 keV with a yield of about 5×10^7 neutrons sec^{-1} per microampere of protons.

iv) The $(d-d)$ reaction,

$$^2\text{H} + {}^2\text{H} \rightarrow {}^3\text{He} + n + 3 \cdot 27 \text{ MeV} \qquad (8.37)$$

much used with electrostatic machines and cyclotrons for neutrons of variable energy up to about 10 MeV.

v) The (α, n) reaction on beryllium

$$^9\text{Be} + \alpha \rightarrow {}^{12}\text{C} + n + 5 \cdot 70 \text{ MeV} \qquad (8.38)$$

the classical reaction by which the neutron was discovered, which furnishes a useful compact laboratory source.

b) *Photons* must also be produced directly with the required energy. The strongest available source of high-energy photons is the *bremsstrahlung* (Sect. 5.2.3) in the forward direction when high-energy electrons strike a target, preferably of high atomic number. This is a continuous distribution of photons with energies extending up to the incident electron energy T_0; the corresponding energy distribution is shown in Fig. 5.5. The electrons may be produced by a Van de Graaff generator, or betatron or electron synchrotron. The total photon intensity in a bremsstrahlung distribution is specified by the number of 'equivalent quanta' Q (Sect. 7.4.6).

Monoenergetic photons may be selected from a bremsstrahlung spectrum by imposing the requirement of coincidence with an electron of reduced energy. This usually entails a low available intensity. It is more usual in photon experiments, such as photodisintegration, to use the whole available continuous spectrum and then to observe the alteration of the particular effect under investigation when the electron energy, and hence the maximum photon energy is varied. Using this 'photon difference' method cross-sections for effects due to homogeneous radiation can be deduced. In other experiments the photon energy may be deduced from the particular event studied, thus the (γ, p) reaction in the gas of a track chamber gives characteristic prongs for both proton and recoil nucleus with an energy determined by that of the quantum.

Line sources of electromagnetic radiation may be obtained from radioactive nuclei, from proton capture reactions and from X-ray generators. Energies up to about 20 MeV are available from capture processes of the type

$$\left.\begin{array}{l} {}^{7}\text{Li} + p \rightarrow {}^{8}\text{Be}^{*} \rightarrow {}^{8}\text{Be} + \gamma \\ {}^{3}\text{H} + p \rightarrow {}^{4}\text{He}^{*} \rightarrow {}^{4}\text{He} + \gamma \end{array}\right\} \qquad (8.39)$$

The capture processes are usually, but not always, sharply resonant as a function of the incident proton energy and the homogeneity of the line from a thick target is determined by the width of the resonance level and by Doppler effects due to motion of the recoiling excited nucleus. These radiations are of somewhat limited intensity because of target problems. Radioactive sources with simple decay schemes, prepared in great strength in nuclear reactors or cyclotrons, are also used to provide homogeneous gamma radiation, although usually in a lower energy range, up to ≈ 3 MeV. In suitable cases the absolute yield is known from β–γ coincidence measurements (Sect. **7.1**).

References

8.1 S. Fluegge (ed.), 'Nuclear Instrumentation I', *Encyclopedia of Physics*, Vol. 44, Springer, 1959.

8.2 *The Acceleration of Particles to High Energies*, The Institute of Physics, London, 1949.

8.3 M. S. Livingston, *High Energy Accelerators*, Interscience Publishers, 1954. M. S. Livingston and J. P. Blewett, *Particle Accelerators*, McGraw-Hill, 1962.

8.4 R. J. Van de Graaff, J. G. Trump and W. W. Buechner, 'Electrostatic Generators for Charged Particles', *Rep. progr. Phys.*, **11**, 1, 1946.

8.5 R. L. Fortescue, 'High Voltage Direct Current Generators', *Progr. nucl. Phys.*, **1**, 21, 1950.

8.6 P. C. Thonemann, 'The Production of Intense Ion Beams', *Progr. nucl. Phys.*, **3**, 219, 1953.

8.7 D. W. Fry and W. Walkinshaw, 'Linear Accelerators', *Rep. progr. Phys.*, **12**, 102, 1949.

8.8 J. H. Fremlin and J. S. Gooden, 'Cyclic Accelerators', *Rep. progr. Phys.*, **13**, 295, 1950.

8.9 T. G. Pickavance, 'Cyclotrons', *Progr. nucl. Phys.*, **1**, 1, 1950.

8.10 T. G. Pickavance, 'Focusing in High Energy Accelerators', *Progr. nucl. Phys.*, **4**, 142, 1955.

8.11. D. L. Judd, 'Conceptual Advances in Accelerators', *Ann. Rev. Nucl. Sci.*, **8**, 181, 1958.

8.12 E. M. McMillan, 'Particle Accelerators', in *Experimental Nuclear Physics*, Vol. III, ed. E. Segrè, Wiley, 1960.

8.13 R. E. Jennings, 'The Microtron', *Contemp. Phys.*, **2**, 277, 1961.

8.14 R. J. Van de Graaff, 'Tandem Electrostatic Generators', *Nucl. instrum. and Methods*, **8**, 195, 1960.

8.15 J. J. Livingood, *Cyclic Particle Accelerators*, van Nostrand, 1961.

Part C

STATIC PROPERTIES OF NUCLEI

9. NUCLEAR MODELS (I), THE NUCLEAR GROUND STATE AND THE NUCLEAR LEVEL SPECTRUM

A nucleus, like other quantum mechanical systems, possesses a set of characteristic energies, or excited states. Of these the most stable state, or *ground state* is that in which nuclei are normally found, and it is for the ground state that the most extensive survey of nuclear properties has been made.

The purpose of a nuclear model is to provide a practical means of predicting nuclear properties. Ideally the problem of calculating nuclear structures should be based on a knowledge of the law of force between nuclear constituents. Some progress has indeed been made in this way but only for the simplest nuclei, as will be seen in chapter 18; for most nuclei heavier than the α-particle it is necessary to make some form of model calculation. In such calculations our knowledge of the fundamental laws of force is incorporated in a general or phenomenological way rather than in complete detail.

In the present chapter we shall mainly consider the nuclear shell model, which has been outstandingly successful both in predicting the static properties of the ground state (ch. 10, 11) and in indicating the broad structure of the nuclear level spectrum. In chapter 12 we shall see how structure models of this type can be extended to give quite detailed predictions of the level spectrum, and how other features of nuclear behaviour such as collective motion can be introduced. We shall also defer, except for a brief preliminary mention, all consideration of models primarily designed to describe nuclear reactions. These are important for the determination of the characteristics of nuclear levels, and some unification with the structure type of model has in fact been possible.

9.1 The first nuclear models
One early nuclear model postulated an interacting assembly of electrons and protons as reasonable to describe a nucleus

capable of spontaneous emission of both α- and β-particles. Such a structure is consistent with the observation (ch. 10) that nuclear masses are approximately integral multiples of the mass of the proton. This model fails for many reasons, chief among which are that:

a) the observed spins and statistics of many nuclei disagree with the model. Even-mass nuclei of odd charge, e.g. ^{2}H, ^{14}N obey Bose statistics and have integral spin, which cannot be explained on the proton–electron model,

b) the observed nuclear magnetic moments are of the order of the nuclear magneton $eh/4\pi m_p c$ rather than the Bohr (electron) magneton $eh/4\pi mc$,

c) an electron confined within nuclear dimensions $\approx R$ would, in accordance with the uncertainty principle, have an uncertainty of momentum of about $\hbar/R$. The corresponding kinetic energy $\hbar c/R$ is ≈ 30 MeV and a potential energy many times greater than this would be necessary to contain the electron constituents of a heavy nucleus. This is inconsistent with what is known of nuclear potentials (ch. 11),

d) it is no longer necessary, in view of the success of Pauli's neutrino hypothesis and Fermi's theory of beta decay to postulate the emission of pre-existing electrons in β-radioactivity.

The discovery of the neutron in 1932 (Sect. 14.1.3) made it possible to avoid the difficulties of the electron–proton model and a neutron–proton model is the basis of modern theories of nuclear structure. The first task of the neutron–proton model was to give some account of nuclear binding energies and for this purpose several specific versions of the model have been widely discussed. These are:

a) *The Fermi-gas model*, in which neutrons and protons, existing independently but attracting in pairs are confined within a cube of volume equal to the nuclear volume and are described by plane waves. This is exactly as in the electron theory of solids, and as in that theory, the total energy of such a system may easily be calculated. For a nuclear dimension R and for A particles of mass M the de Broglie wavelength must be $\lambda \approx R/A^{\frac{1}{3}}$ and the corresponding momentum p is then given by

$$p = \frac{hA^{\frac{1}{3}}}{R}$$

The kinetic energy per particle will be proportional to $p^2/2M$, i.e., to $A^{\frac{2}{3}}/MR^2$ and for the whole nucleus to $A^{\frac{5}{3}}/MR^2$. The potential energy on the other hand is proportional to the number of interacting pairs, i.e. to $\frac{A(A-1)}{2}$ and for A large enough the potential energy is the main term. The nucleus would therefore collapse according to this model and properties of the neutron–proton interaction (ch. 18) must be postulated to prevent this. The Fermi-gas model is particularly useful in describing collision phenomena in high-energy nuclear processes because the idea of occupied states of low momentum explains the long mean free path that is observed, and the maximum allowed momentum determines the energy spread of particles after collision. The model obviously applies best to heavy nuclei.

b) *The liquid droplet model*, (N. Bohr and F. Kalckar) which essentially starts from the idea of continuous nuclear matter. This model concentrates on the strong interaction between the neutrons and protons of a many-body system and predicts the existence of the many closely spaced levels actually found by experiment. Bohr's compound-nucleus theory of nuclear reactions (ch. 15) receives a natural interpretation by this type of model. The outstanding success of this concept shows that strong interaction is a feature which must appear in some way in more general theories of wider application. The liquid drop model may also be adapted to predict nuclear binding energies and forms the basis of the semi-empirical mass formula; like the Fermi gas model it is best applicable to heavy nuclei, and predicts no discontinuities of nuclear binding energy with N or Z.

c) *The quasi-atomic or shell model*, which antedated the Bohr droplet model and offered, particularly for the lighter nuclei, the possibility of simple prediction of many nuclear properties in addition to binding energy. It differs from the Fermi-gas model in using instead of plane waves the wave functions of a particle moving in a spherically symmetrical potential, and because of the significance of angular momentum in this problem, the model offers the possibility of a spectroscopic classification of nuclear properties and interpretation of observed periodicities. The existence of such periodicities is considered, together with the present development of the single particle shell model, in Sections **9.2** and **9.3**.

9.2 Empirical evidence for the regularity of nuclear properties

Periodicity in atomic properties such as valency and ionization potential has been known for well over a century and forms the basis of the familiar periodic classification of the elements due to Mendeléev. It receives a natural interpretation in terms of the filling of the successive levels of a screened Coulomb potential by electrons whose number in a given sub-level is limited to 2 by the Pauli exclusion principle. A typical graph of an atomic property (ionization potential) as a function of atomic number (Z) is given in Fig. 9.1a.

It was early proposed from a consideration of nuclear binding energies and abundances (Elsasser, Guggenheimer and others, 1934) that a similar periodicity should exist in nuclear properties. Speaking before the Chemical Society on April 19, 1934, the centenary of the birth of Mendeléev, Rutherford concluded "It may be that a Mendeléev of the future may address the Fellows of this Society on the 'Natural Order of Atomic Nuclei' and history may repeat itself." but it was not until the late 1940s, when sufficient nuclear data had accumulated, that the detailed nature of the nuclear periodicity began to emerge. Fig. 9.1b shows a typical nuclear property (neutron capture cross-section) plotted against neutron number (N) and evidence for regularity is obvious.

Historically the development of the shell model in its modern form was retarded because it seemed difficult to envisage any nuclear structure of strongly interacting particles which could provide a strong central potential of the sort known in the atom. The feature of strong interaction was fundamental to the successful liquid droplet model (Sect. **9.1**) and this model seemed to exclude the possibility of the long mean free path for a nucleon in nuclear matter required by the shell model. Recently it has been realized that the Pauli principle operates to lengthen mean free paths because collisions in nuclear matter cannot take place if they lead to states of motion which are already occupied by other nucleons. It has also been found experimentally that nuclear reactions at energies higher than those considered by Niels Bohr do exhibit resonance phenomena of exactly the sort

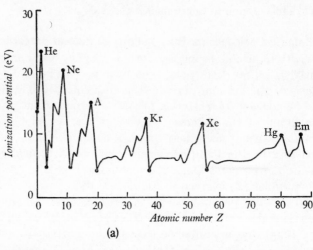

(a)

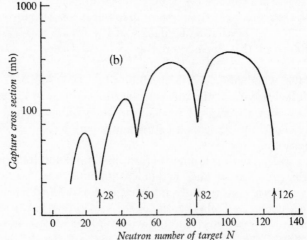

Fig. 9.1

a) Periodicity of an atomic property—the first ionization potential—as a function of atomic number Z.

b) Periodicity of a nuclear property—capture cross-section for neutrons in a reactor—as a function of neutron number N (Codd *et al.*, *Progress in Nuclear Energy*, **1**, 296, 1956).

predicted by the simple one body type of interaction with a potential well originally suggested by Bethe as a reaction mechanism and embodied in the shell model. Another objection, that nuclear binding energies were badly predicted by shell model calculations, has also been removed by recent advances in our understanding of the nature of the shell-model potential.

We now list for convenience the main nuclear properties on which the idea of the shell model rests; most of these will be discussed in more detail in subsequent chapters. They are:

a) Discontinuities of nucleon binding energy, especially the neutron binding energy as measured by the (n,γ) or the (d,p) reaction (Sect. **10.3**).

b) Anomalies in both total abundance and relative abundances of isotopes and isotones as a function of nucleon number, N or Z (Sect. **10.5**).

c) Excitation energy of the first excited state of nuclei, particularly even N–even Z nuclei (Fig. 9.8).

d) Energies of α- and β-decay (ch. 16).

e) Nuclear reaction cross-sections and level densities, as shown in Fig. 9.1b.

These properties are connected with irregularities due to shell closures in the mass formula based on the liquid drop model (Sect. **10.3**). In addition there are other properties connected with the regular sequence of available orbits for nucleons which is also a consequence of shell filling. These are:

f) the ground state spins of both stable and unstable nuclei,

g) the parity of nuclear ground states,

h) the magnetic dipole and to some extent electric quadrupole moments of nuclear states,

i) the comparative half-lives of β-emitters,

j) nuclear isomerism.

The properties (a)–(e) suggest that nuclei containing 2, 8, 20, 50, 82 or 126 neutrons or protons are particularly stable. Some phenomena also suggest the addition of the number 28. We now consider how the shell model suggested by Mayer and by Haxel, Jensen and Suess is able to predict these 'magic numbers'.

9.3 The single-particle shell model

The starting point of all shell models is the solution of the Schrödinger equation for a particle moving in a spherically symmetrical *central* field of force, i.e. in a field of force in which the potential energy V of the particle with respect to the centre is a function $V(r)$ of its radial distance r only. The origin of the field of force in a nucleus is not essential to the argument; it is sufficient that it exists. This problem has been discussed in general terms in Sect. **3.2**, and in connection with the hydrogen atom in Sect. **3.3**, where it is pointed out that the solutions to the three-dimensional Schrödinger equation may be written

$$\Psi = R_{nl}(r) Y_l^m(\theta,\phi) \tag{9.1}$$

where $Y_l^m(\theta,\phi)$ are the spherical harmonic functions discussed in Appendix 2. The total, azimuthal and magnetic quantum numbers n, l, m have also been discussed in Sect. **3.3**. The azimuthal quantum number l of a single particle state determines the *parity* of the wave function as $(-1)^l$ (Sect. **3.4**).

The spherical harmonic functions are of general application, but the radial functions $R_{nl}(r)$ can only be obtained if $V(r)$ is specified. For $V(r) = -Ze^2/r$ we have the case of the hydrogen atom and, allowing for electron spin, atomic shells containing $2\sum_0^{(n-1)}(2l+1) = 2n^2$ electrons arise. These consecutive shells contain

$$2, 8, 18, 32, 50\ldots$$

electrons if they fill regularly. In fact the higher shells begin filling before the lower ones are complete and the atomic 'magic' numbers correspond in some cases to the completion of subshells. From Fig. 9.1, the main atomic shell effects occur at the atomic numbers

$$2, 10, 18, 36, 54, 86\ldots$$

These are of course quite different from the nuclear magic numbers.

The hydrogen-like degeneracy of the atomic levels with respect to l is removed when the central field becomes non-Coulomb. In the alkali atoms for instance the potential has the 'screened Coulomb' form $(Ze^2/r)e^{-Kr}$ and since this falls off with r more rapidly than in the unscreened case, the wave functions with high l-values, for which the electrons are further away from the nucleus, are less strongly bound. This effect can be seen in the levels of the helium atom shown in Fig. 3.8.

In the case of a nucleon of mass M moving in a static, spherically symmetric potential field $V(r)$ with angular momentum $l\hbar$, the radial part of the Schrödinger equation may be written (cf. 3.12)

$$\frac{\mathrm{d}^2}{\mathrm{d}r^2}(rR_{nl}) + \frac{2M}{\hbar^2}\left\{E_{nl} - V(r) - \frac{l(l+1)\hbar^2}{2Mr^2}\right\}(rR_{nl}) = 0 \qquad (9.2)$$

where the suffix nl envisages a dependence of both the eigenfunction R and the energy eigenvalue E on total quantum number and angular momentum. The radial shape of the nuclear field is now well known from scattering experiments (ch. 11) but the form of $V(r)$ is not suitable for simple solution of 9.2. Since, however, the shell model is not primarily concerned with total binding energies, but only with levels corresponding to the states of motion of nucleons, it is sufficient to consider only simple forms of potential function, such as those already introduced in Sect. **3.2**. The range of the potential is taken to be short so that the energy levels are well spaced, as shown in Fig. 3.2a. We then find the following results:

a) *The square well potential* (Fig. 3.1b). Qualitatively the effect of an attractive force of this sort is just opposite to that of a screened Coulomb potential. The square well has no singularity at the origin, and the s-states, which have wave functions finite at the origin, are less strongly disturbed. For a given n-value, states of high l-value are found to be more strongly bound than those of lower l.

The radial wave functions in this case are analytically of the form

$$R_{nl}(r) = \frac{A}{\sqrt{Kr}} J_{l+\frac{1}{2}}(Kr) \qquad (9.3)$$

where A is a constant, $J_{l+\frac{1}{2}}$ is a Bessel function, and the wave number K is defined by the equation

$$K^2 = \frac{2M}{\hbar^2}(E_{nl} - V) \qquad (9.4)$$

where E_{nl} is the total (negative) energy and $V\ (= -U)$ is the well depth. It will be convenient to measure energies from the bottom of the well and then

$$K^2 = \frac{2M}{\hbar^2} E'_{nl} \qquad (9.4a)$$

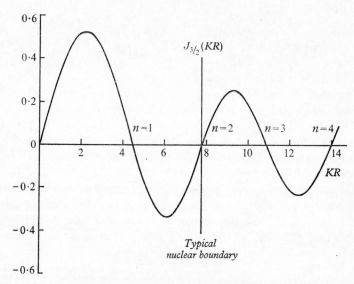

Fig. 9.2. Graph of the Bessel function $J_{3/2}(x)$ against x, where $x = KR$.

where E'_{nl} is positive. The permitted values of K are selected by a boundary condition. In the simple case of a well of infinite depth the wave function has to vanish at the nuclear boundary $r = R$, i.e.

$$R_{nl}(R) = 0 \qquad (9.5)$$

Fig. 9.2 is a graph of a typical Bessel function $J_{l+1/2}(KR)$ for $l = 1$. There is a succession of zeros at $KR = X_{nl}$ numbered serially $n = 1, 2 \ldots$ and these values differ for different l. For a given nuclear radius R it will be possible to satisfy the boundary condition 9.5 by choosing K so that $1, 2 \ldots$ oscillations of the Bessel function take place within the distance R. The more oscillations that are included, the larger must be K and the larger is the energy according to 9.4. The level energies are given by putting

$$KR = X_{nl} \tag{9.6}$$

i.e.,

$$E'_{nl} = \frac{K^2\hbar^2}{2M} = \frac{X^2_{nl}\hbar^2}{2MR^2} \tag{9.6a}$$

For $R = 8 \times 10^{-13}$ cm the quantity $\hbar^2/2MR^2$ is 0·34 MeV.

The X_{nl} values defining the first few states of the square well potential are shown in Table 9.1. The number n, giving the number of zeros of the radial part of the wave function (not counting the origin) is known as the *radial* quantum number. It differs from the *principal* quantum number of atomic spectroscopy since the latter counts all the nodes of the total wave function, angular as well as radial, and is of major importance for specifying the energy of the corresponding state. For the short range potentials of nuclear physics the effect of change of l on the energy is comparable with that of change of n.

TABLE 9.1 Single particle states of the infinite square well

	X_{nl}		
l	1ST ZERO $n = 1$	2ND ZERO $n = 2$	3RD ZERO $n = 3$
0	3·14	6·28	9·42
1	4·49	7·72	10·90
2	5·76	9·09	12·32
3	6·98	10·41	

The levels (9.6a) are shown in Fig. 9.3a; it will be seen that the order from the bottom of the well is

$$1s \ 1p \ 1d \ 2s \ 1f \ 2p \ 1g \ 2d \ 1h \ 3s \dots$$

where $1f$, for instance, means the first level of orbital momentum 3, i.e., the first zero in the Bessel function $J_{7/2}$. If 2 nucleons occupy each of these states (i.e., with opposite spins) the occupation numbers $2(2l+1)$ predict shell closures at total particle numbers (neutrons or protons):

$$2, 8, 18, 20, 34, 40, 58, \dots$$

These are not the nuclear magic numbers. The situation is not altered by calculating the levels for a finite rather than infinite well since the level *order* is found to be the same although the excitations alter.

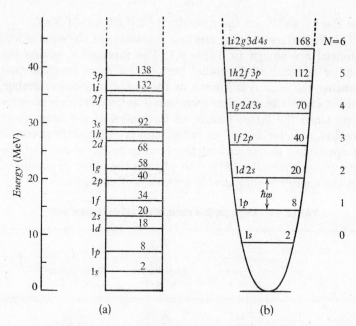

Fig. 9.3. Level sequence for nucleons in a potential well, showing spectroscopic classification of levels and total number of nucleons which may be accommodated up to the indicated excitation.
a) Infinite square well potential, radius 8×10^{-13} cm.
b) Oscillator potential, showing uniform spacing of levels. The levels are of even (odd) parity when the oscillator number N is even (odd).

b) *The harmonic oscillator potential* (Fig. 3.1c). For this well the potential energy may be written

$$V(r) = -U + \tfrac{1}{2}M\omega^2 r^2 \qquad (9.7)$$

where ω is the frequency of the corresponding simple harmonic oscillations of the particle. The solution of 9.2 for an infinite well may be expressed in Hermite polynomials. In the one dimensional case it is well known that the energy levels (again measured from the bottom of the well) are given by

$$E'_n = (n + \tfrac{1}{2})\hbar\omega \tag{9.8}$$

and in the general three dimensional case by

$$E'_{n_1 n_2 n_3} = (n_1 + n_2 + n_3 + \tfrac{3}{2})\hbar\omega \tag{9.9}$$

or

$$E'_N = (N + \tfrac{3}{2})\hbar\omega$$

where n_1, n_2, n_3 are integers specifying the wave functions and $N = n_1 + n_2 + n_3 \ (\geqslant 0)$ is the oscillator quantum number. When the angular dependence of the wave functions is examined, it is found that for each N value there is a degenerate group of levels with different l-values such that $l \leqslant N$ and even (odd) N corresponds to even (odd) l. Thus for $N = 2$ both s and d states occur, with the same energy. The number of nucleons which may be accommodated in the levels described by the oscillator number N is found to be $(N+1)(N+2)$. The levels are shown in Fig. 9.3b, and in Table **9.2**. It will be seen that the order is

$$1s;\ 1p;\ 1d, 2s;\ 1f, 2p; \ldots$$

TABLE 9.2   **Single particle states of infinite oscillator well**

N	E'_N	l-values	$(N+1)(N+2)$
0	$\tfrac{3}{2} \times \hbar w$	0	2
1	$\tfrac{5}{2}$	1	6
2	$\tfrac{7}{2}$	0, 2	12
3	$\tfrac{9}{2}$	1, 3	20
4	$\tfrac{11}{2}$	0, 2, 4	30

and shell closures occur at particle numbers

$$2, 8, 20, 40, 70, 112 \ldots$$

which again is not the series of nuclear magic numbers.

c) *The spin-orbit coupling model.* Several attempts have been made to modify the potentials to yield the observed magic numbers. The most successful is that proposed by Mayer and by Haxel, Jensen and Suess in 1949 according to which a *non-central component* should be included in the force acting on a nucleon in a nucleus. If this non-central force is an interaction depending on the relative orientation of the orbital angular momentum and the spin momentum of the nucleon (so far neglected except for its role in prescribing only two particles per orbital state) then a different periodicity can easily arise. It is assumed in this model that the *spin-orbit force* separates the motion of a nucleon with orbital momentum l into sub-states with total angular momentum quantum number $j = l \pm \frac{1}{2}$ and that the level with the higher spin is the more stable. With this assumption the levels of the oscillator potential are enumerated as follows

$$1s_{1/2}; \quad 1p_{3/2} \, 1p_{1/2}; \quad 1d_{5/2} \, 2s_{1/2} \, 1d_{3/2}; \quad 1f_{7/2}; \quad 2p_{3/2} \, 1f_{5/2} \, 2p_{1/2} \, 1g_{9/2}; \quad \ldots$$

allowing that some anharmonicity of the well or tendency to square well shape already lowers the states of high angular momentum for a given oscillator number. Each state of given j may accommodate $2j + 1$ neutrons or protons. If now the $g_{9/2}$ level (for $N = 4$) is lowered so much by the spin-orbit potential that it merges with the levels of oscillator number $N = 3$, and similarly for higher N-values, the shell closures occur at particle numbers

$$2, \, 8, \, 20, \, 28, \, 50, \, 82, \, 126$$

exactly as required by experiment. The sequence of levels is shown in detail in Fig. 9.4. The order of sub-levels such as $s_{1/2}$, $d_{3/2}$ may be altered, without affecting the magic numbers, by adjusting the strength of the assumed spin-orbit force.

The origin of the spin-orbit coupling employed in this version of the shell model is not yet clear. The attractive interaction potential is usually written

$$V_S(r)\mathbf{s}.\mathbf{l} \tag{9.10}$$

where $\mathbf{s}$ and $\mathbf{l}$ are the spin and orbital vectors for the nucleon. This form ensures that the orbits are split by an energy which increases with l-value, as required by the model. The potential resembles that which would arise from a simple magnetic effect but such effects are much too weak to give the necessary splitting. There is evidence for the existence of a strong spin-orbit force between nucleons from high energy polarization experiments (ch. 17).

To summarize, the single-particle shell model or quasi-atomic model with spin-orbit coupling, provides a sequence of nuclear energy levels classified according to orbital momentum

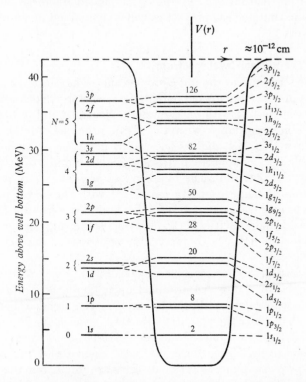

Fig. 9.4. Energy levels in a nuclear potential well, allowing for spin-orbit coupling. The basic states, shown on the left, correspond to a potential $V(r)$ of the form shown, which is intermediate in shape between an oscillator and square well potential. The oscillator numbers are shown and it is evident that if the spin-orbit effect is sufficient to overcome the oscillator spacing then the observed magic numbers result.

quantum number l (i.e., parity) total angular momentum j, and radial quantum number n. There are $2(2l+1)$ nucleon states for given l, and $(2j+1)$ states for given j. If there are x states of given nlj filled with nucleons we speak of a *configuration*

$(nlj)^x$. The final total wave function of the nucleus will of course depend on the coupling of the individual angular momenta of the nucleons in the configurations and we neither expect nor find that the single particle model provides good wave functions in all cases. The important fact is that it sets up a plausible set of single particle levels; the vital part played by these levels in coordinating nuclear properties will be examined in subsequent chapters.

9.4   The nuclear level spectrum

The structure of the succession of nuclei may be envisaged in terms of a single particle potential of constant depth and of a radius increasing with mass number. Neutrons and protons are added in accordance with the Pauli principle, to the levels shown in Fig. 9.4, and as the radius increases, so it becomes possible for single particle states of higher n and l to be bound within the potential. The binding of a new level may produce a change in some property associated with the single particle motion such as ground state spin, and this accounts for the observed periodicities. Changes in scattering or reaction cross-section (Fig. 9.1b) may also be observed for the same reason.

If we consider one specified nucleus with given R, then the levels shown in Fig. 9.4 are filled up to the level indicated by the known neutron and proton numbers. The higher unoccupied levels defined by the potential also exist, either bound or virtual (Figs. 3.2 and 9.5), and the shell model thus defines a set of single particle levels. These form the basic elements of the *nuclear level spectrum*; many additional states are found but the single particle states have an especial character because of the appaparent simplicity of the corresponding nuclear motion. All nuclear levels, except the ground state,* can in principle emit radiation, leaving the nucleus in a less highly excited state, and virtual levels can in addition emit particles. For any level it is possible to define a mean life τ equal to the reciprocal of the probability of decay by all processes per second. The mean life

---

* The terms 'state' and 'level' are used synonomously, although in principle the former should be reserved for the motion of a nucleon and the latter for the excitations of a nucleus.

in turn defines a *total width* Γ as discussed in Sect. 3.9.1. For bound levels, neglecting internal conversion (Sect. **13.2**)

$$\Gamma = \Gamma_\gamma \text{ the radiative width} \tag{9.11}$$

but for virtual levels

$$\Gamma = \Gamma_\gamma + \Sigma\Gamma_{\text{particles}} \tag{9.12}$$

where the summation includes the widths corresponding to the emission of certain energetically allowed particles as alternatives

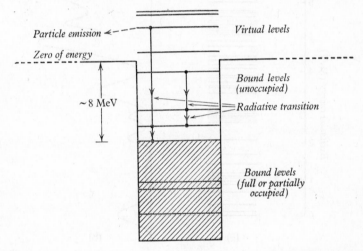

Fig. 9.5. Schematic diagram of occupied and unoccupied single particle levels in a nucleus.

to radiation. The widths Γ_γ and Γ_{particle} are partial widths. For the ground state

$$\Gamma = 0 \tag{9.13}$$

if we neglect the possibility of β-decay to a more stable isobar.

It will be seen that nuclear levels are strictly speaking not stationary states in the quantum mechanical sense, as in the case of the ground state of a stable nucleus. Providing however that the widths Γ are not too great these *quasi-stationary states* may be considered to live long enough to permit the definition (and sometimes measurement) of the properties which may be ascribed to the ground state, namely angular momentum, parity, electromagnetic moments; in addition the excited states exhibit the dynamical properties of radiative and particle widths. Determination of these properties for nuclear levels, as well as observation of level spacings and excitations, is clearly of importance for testing models of nuclear structure.

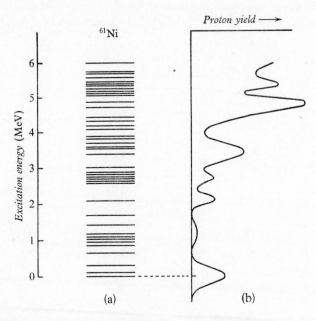

Fig. 9.6

a) Level spectrum of ^{61}Ni determined by high resolution magnetic analysis of proton groups from the ^{60}Ni$(d,p)^{61}$Ni reaction (Paris, *M.I.T. Report*, May 1959).

b) Proton groups from ^{60}Ni$(d,p)^{61}$Ni reaction examined under low resolution, showing relative probability of exciting various groups of fine-structure levels (Dalton *et al.*, *Proc. phys. Soc.*, **77**, 682, 1961).

The level spectrum of the nucleus ^{61}Ni, determined by a method of high resolution, is shown in Fig. 9.6a. The character-istic features of this and similar level systems are (a) a level spacing of a few hundred keV near the ground state, and (b) an increase of level density with increasing excitation energy. The levels shown are discrete, i.e., the width Γ is very much less than

the level spacing D, although as the excitation energy increases
beyond the value shown in the figure this is no longer true
because of an increase of Γ due to increasing probability of
particle emission and a decrease of D in accordance with the
general trend already shown in the figure. Level spectra of the
general type shown in Fig. 9.6a are found for all nuclei although
the precise level density at a given excitation depends on the
mass number. Such spectra are essentially those of a many-
body nuclear model, as was first pointed out by Niels Bohr;
they stand in sharp contrast with expectation from the single-
particle shell model, according to which only a few widely
spaced levels are expected in the range of energy shown in
Fig. 9.6a (cf. Fig. 9.4). If, however, the nuclear level spectrum
is examined by methods of low resolution, which average over
the narrow levels, and if the *probability* of exciting levels in a
reaction is plotted rather than the actual level positions, the
result shown in Fig. 9.6b is obtained. This shows exactly the
features expected from the single particle model, namely well-
separated peaks, whose behaviour in many cases agrees with the
angular momentum values suggested by the model. The interpretation of the *gross structure* indicated by Fig. 9.6b in terms of
the *fine structure* of Fig. 9.6a is one of the current problems of
nuclear theory.

It is not possible to give a detailed theoretical account of
individual levels in regions of high level density. Level densities
can be predicted under particular assumptions, such as that of
the Fermi-gas model (Sect. **9.1**), and compared with experimental measurements, but this is more useful to the theory of
nuclear reactions than to models of nuclear structure. The
ground state and the well-separated low-lying levels, up to
perhaps a few MeV in excitation, are likely to be described by
the simpler types of nuclear motion; they are well-known
experimentally and have been surveyed for an extensive range
of nuclei, both stable and unstable, throughout the periodic
system. As a result of these surveys the following important
regularities in the low-lying levels have been observed:

a) *Isomeric states* (Sect. **13.5**) are found in groups of nuclei
   with neutron or proton numbers just below the magic
   numbers. These are bound states of long life, for which

the expected radiative transition is slow because of a large spin change. Fig. 9.7 shows the distribution of known isomeric states for nuclei of odd mass number. The single particle shell model is able to account for this pattern if it is supposed that successive single-particle levels lie rather close together towards the end of a shell so that the first excited state of a nucleus may well have a spin considerably different from that of the ground state.

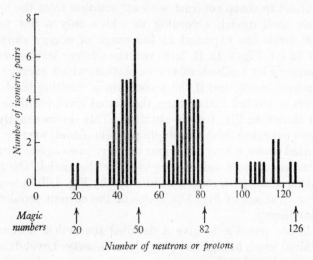

Fig. 9.7. Frequency distribution of odd-A isomeric nuclei (Ref. 1.7).

Usually the isomeric state is one which has moved down from a higher oscillator level because of the spin-orbit effect, and this leads to a parity change in addition to the large spin change (e.g. $g_{9/2} \rightarrow p_{1/2}$ in Fig. 9.4). Isomeric transitions of $E3$ and $M4$ type (Sect. 3.9.2) are therefore frequently found.

b) *The first excited states of even–even nuclei* show a systematic behaviour. These excited states usually have spin 2 and even parity and their excitation energy reaches a series of maxima at closed shells (Fig. 9.8). Between closed shells the energy varies in a systematic way with mass number.

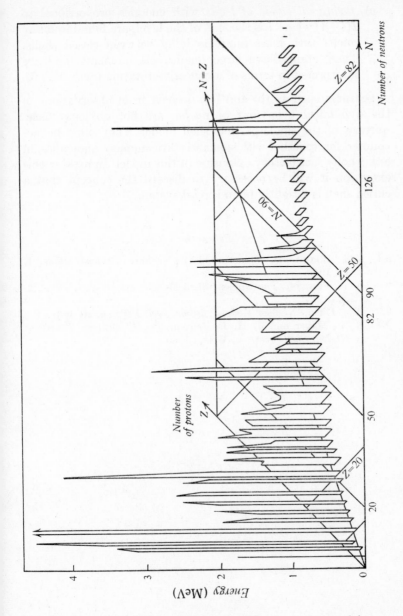

Fig. 9.8. Energy of first excited 2^+ state in even-even nuclei as a function of Z and N (Ref. 12.2).

c) *Rotational bands of levels* with energies proportional to $I(I+1)$ where I is the spin of the level, are found in many nuclei with mass numbers lying between closed shells. These states have large quadrupole moments, and are interpreted in terms of a collective rotation (Sect. 12.3.3).

Features such as (b) and (c), derived from observations of the dynamical behaviour of nuclei, are not obvious consequences of the single-particle shell model. They must be accounted for, together with spin and static moment anomalies, in any wholly satisfactory extension of this model. In making this extension it will be necessary to discard the concept that a closed shell is a tightly bound, rigid system.

References

9.1   R. J. Blin-Stoyle, 'Structure of the Nucleus', *Contemp. Phys.*, **1**, 17, 1959.
9.2   B. H. Flowers, 'The Nuclear Shell Model', *Progr. nucl. Phys.*, **2**, 235, 1952.
9.3   R. J. Eden, 'Nuclear Models', *Progr. nucl. Phys.*, **6**, 26, 1957.
9.4   M. G. Mayer and J. H. D. Jensen, *The Elementary Theory of Nuclear Shell Structure*, Wiley, 1955.

10. THE MASS AND ISOTOPIC ABUNDANCE OF NUCLEI

Mass and charge were the first properties to be determined for a wide range of atomic nuclei. Nuclear abundance, already known in part from chemical surveys, could be expressed as isotopic abundance as soon as mass spectrographic analyses were completed. Mass values are basic in any theory of nuclear structure but like many other nuclear phenomena can only be predicted accurately from the properties of nucleons if a complicated many-body problem is solved. In this chapter we first of all consider the inverse problem, namely the extent to which the existence of a range of stable nuclei, with known binding energy, can yield information on the nucleon–nucleon force. We then incorporate these general properties in a semi-empirical approach to the mass data, based on the idea of continuous nuclear matter, as embodied in the liquid drop model (Sect. **9.1**). The effects of shell structure are noted as relatively small but important corrections to the underlying mass sequence.

10.1 The mass tables; binding energy

Three scales of atomic mass were recognized in 1958:

a) *The absolute scale*, related to the gram.

b) *The physical scale*, defined by setting the mass of one atom of the nuclide ^{16}O equal to $16 \cdot 0000 \ldots$ atomic mass units (a.m.u.).

c) *The chemical scale*, defined by taking the average atomic mass of the normal isotopic mixture of oxygen as equal to $16 \cdot 0000 \ldots$ mass units. This scale differs from the physical scale because of the existence of the isotopes ^{17}O and ^{18}O and there is some arbitrariness in the scale because of small global variation of the isotopic constitution of oxygen gas.

Recently an important step towards the unification* of the

---

* T. P. Kohman, J. H. E. Mattauch, and A. H. Wapstra, *Science*, **127**, 1431, 1958.

physical and chemical scales has been taken by basing the former on carbon rather than oxygen. In mass tables published since 1960, the unit of atomic mass (m_u or u) is defined by setting the mass of 1 atom of ^{12}C equal to 12.000. . . . such units. The mass values quoted in this book (in particular in the table of Fundamental Constants, p. 728) are however still based on the older definition.

The absolute mass scale is rarely used because of its numerical inconvenience and because it conceals the physical content of the results of mass measurements. For the purpose of nuclear physics all masses are based on the physical scale; they are given for *neutral atoms* rather than for stripped nuclei mainly because in effect these are the masses that are determined directly by mass spectrometry. The mass $M(A,Z)$ of a nuclide of mass number A and atomic number Z is related to the nuclear mass M_N by the equation

$$M(A,Z) = M_N + ZN_0 m - B(Z) \tag{10.1}$$

where N_0 is Avogadro's number, m is the mass of an electron and $B(Z)$ is the total electron binding energy, expressed in atomic mass units. In this equation $B(Z)$ is only about $10^{-4}\%$ of the mass $M(A,Z)$ and its effect is therefore usually negligible. Although mass tables give the atomic masses of neutral atoms, the term 'nuclear mass' is often used. This will normally mean the neutral atom mass unless especially qualified.

The physical and chemical mass scales are by definition relative rather than absolute. A relative scale has the advantage that atomic masses may be expressed more accurately in relative units (a.m.u.) than in absolute units (g) because mass spectrometry is normally based on comparative rather than absolute measurements.

The masses of all stable isotopes have now been determined accurately by the refined techniques of mass spectrometry. For unstable isotopes the determination of energy releases in nuclear reactions and in decay processes provides information of comparable accuracy, and also connects together many mass values through consecutive processes. The combination of this body of data in such a way as to minimize errors (Ref. 10.3) leads to the present mass tables, of which a small section is presented in Table **10.1**. The accuracy claimed in masses of the order of 30 a.m.u. is better than 1 part in 10^6, corresponding to a determination of Q values to a few keV. Nuclear mass changes are linked to energy releases in nuclear reactions through Einstein's equation

$$\Delta E = c^2 \Delta M \qquad (10.2)$$

and it is one of the functions of the mass tables to predict such energy changes where they have not been determined experimentally.

TABLE 10.1   Atomic mass table ($^{16}O = 16$)

(From W. H. Johnson and A. O. Nier, *Phys. Rev.*, **105**, 1014, 1957.)

ISO-TOPE	ATOMIC MASS a.m.u.	$B(A, Z)$ MeV	B/A MeV per nucleon	$S_n (A, Z)$ MeV	$P_n (A, Z)$ MeV
$^{131}_{54}$Xe	130·94670 ±4	1103·1	8·41	6·6	—
$^{132}_{54}$Xe	131·94611 ±5	1112·0	8·42	8·9	2·3
$^{133}_{54}$Xe	132·94784 ±7	1118·7	8·40	6·7	—
$^{134}_{54}$Xe	133·94799 ±5	1126·9	8·40	8·2	1·5
$^{135}_{54}$Xe	134·94993 ±10	1133·4	8·39	6·5	—
$^{136}_{54}$Xe	135·95042 ±3	1141·3	8·38	7·9	1·4
$^{137}_{54}$Xe	135·9546 ±11	1145·7	8·35	4·35	—

The errors in the mass values (a.m.u.) refer to the last significant figure.

The first obvious conclusion to be drawn from an inspection of the mass tables is that the atomic masses of the isotopes are nearly whole numbers when expressed in terms of $^{16}O = 16·000$ ... or $^{12}C = 12·000$...; the more obvious choice of taking $^1H = 1·000$... does not yield atomic masses so near to whole numbers for other isotopes. Despite this, the isotopic masses are sufficiently near to multiples of the mass of the hydrogen atom to suggest that nuclei are built up of particles of mass comparable with that of the proton. The neutron mass had to be determined by reaction methods; its similarity to the proton mass renders the neutron–proton type of nuclear structure an obvious hypothesis. The masses are not in fact exact multiples of any combination of the neutron and proton mass, and they are not whole numbers. The difference between the exact atomic mass of an isotope $M(A,Z)$ and its mass number A is known as the *mass defect*, i.e.,

$$\Delta = M(A,Z) - A \qquad (10.3)$$

and the mass defect per unit mass number or *packing fraction* was defined by Aston, long before the neutron–proton model of the nucleus was known, as

$$P = \frac{\Delta}{A} = \frac{M(A,Z) - A}{A} \qquad (10.4)$$

If the neutron–proton model of the nucleus is assumed, it is possible to calculate the *total binding energy B* of the nucleus. This is the work required to break down the nucleus into its constituent nucleons, or alternatively, the energy released in the building up of the nucleus from these constituents. Thus

$$B(A,Z) = ZM_{\mathrm{H}} + (A - Z)M_n - M(A,Z) \qquad (10.5)$$

where M_{H}, M_n and $M(A,Z)$ are the masses of the hydrogen atom, the neutron and the nucleus in a.m.u., i.e., including sufficient electron masses to ensure neutral systems in each case. The binding energy B obviously measures nearly the same quantity as Aston's mass defect Δ and the *average binding energy per nucleon B/A* conveys for the neutron–proton model, the same information as Aston's packing fraction. Table **10.1** shows the total binding energy $B(A,Z)$ and the binding energy per nucleon for the xenon isotopes.

It is often useful experimentally to refer to the binding energy of a specific nuclear particle, such as a proton, neutron or α-particle, which may be detached or absorbed in a nuclear reaction. If a neutron is added to a nucleus $(A-1,Z)$ in a (n,γ) capture reaction for example, an energy equal to the binding energy of the neutron in the nucleus (A,Z) is evolved. This energy is also known as the neutron *separation energy*

$S_n(A,Z)$. The separation energy S_n or neutron binding energy B_n (strictly the binding energy of the last neutron) is related to the total binding energies of the nuclei concerned by the equation

$$\left.\begin{aligned}
S_n(A,Z) &= B_n(A,Z) \\
&= B(A,Z) - B(A-1,Z) \\
&= M(A-1,Z) - M(A,Z) + M_n
\end{aligned}\right\} \qquad (10.6)$$

It will be noted that the neutron binding energy or separation energy refers to the most easily detached neutron of the nucleus and is not in general the same as the average binding energy per nucleon.

The separation energies for protons and neutrons are greater for even Z or N than for odd Z or N, as may be seen for neutrons in Table **10.1**. This is due to attractive forces between pairs of nucleons, with opposite spin, occupying the same level. The *pairing energy* which thus arises may be defined for neutrons as

$$P_n(A,Z) = S_n(A,Z) - S_n(A-1,Z) \quad \text{for } N \text{ even} \qquad (10.7)$$

Pairing energies for the even–even xenon isotopes are shown in Table **10.1**.

10.2 Survey of nuclear binding energies

The results of the mass spectrometry of the stable nuclei were expressed by Aston (1927) not only in a table of masses, but also in a graph of the packing fraction as a function of mass number. It is now more usual to present this information as a graph of the average binding energy per nucleon as a function of mass number (Fig. 10.1). The main features of this diagram are:

a) A positive binding energy for all nuclei, which means that any nucleus is more stable than an unconnected assembly of its constituent neutrons and protons. This will be so if there are attractive (nuclear) forces between these constituents within the nuclear volume, as indicated also by scattering experiments (ch. 5). Since nuclei do not collapse these forces must in effect become repulsive for very close distances of approach of the nuclear particles.

b) A rapid increase of binding energy per nucleon for the light nuclei with a notable peak at $A = 4$ (^{4}He) and further peaks at $A = 4n$ (^{8}Be, ^{12}C, ^{16}O, ^{20}Ne, ^{24}Mg). This reflects the peculiar stability of the α-particle structure. Such stability arises naturally in any theory of nuclei in which a given orbital state may contain just two protons and two neutrons, with opposite spins in each case.

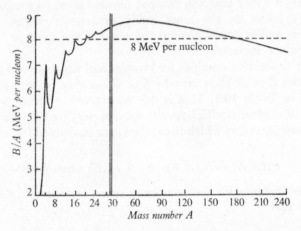

Fig. 10.1. Average binding energy per nucleon of the stable nuclei as a function of mass number (Ref. 10.4).

c) Approximately the same binding energy per nucleon (7·5 to 8·5 MeV) for all nuclei with A greater than 16, so that for all but the lightest nuclei it is a good approximation to suppose that B is proportional to A. For a nucleus in which each particle interacted with every other particle the total binding energy B would be proportional (Sect. 9.1) to A^2 approximately and the experimental facts therefore show that the nuclear constituents interact with only a limited number of their neighbours. This phenomenon is known as the *saturation of nuclear forces* (ch. 18). The peak in binding energy at $A = 4$ suggests that a neutron interacts strongly with one other neutron and two other protons; the fifth, sixth and seventh particles, in ^{5}Li, ^{6}Li, ^{7}Li for example, are less strongly bound. The maximum binding energy per nucleon occurs for A about equal to 60 (Fe, Ni, Co).

d) A gradual decrease in B/A from a maximum of 8·7 MeV per nucleon at $A = 60$ to 7·3 MeV per nucleon at $A = 238$. This is associated with the disruptive effect of the nuclear charge, which ultimately sets a limit to the number of elements which can be formed.

e) The absence of large magic number effects (except for the four-structure noted in (b)) in the *average* nucleon binding energy. This is in agreement with the ideas of the shell model because the large binding energies of the inner shells will submerge the discontinuities of the binding energy of the last nucleon. Closer observation does reveal significant changes in the general trend of B/A at N and $Z = 82$.

Points (a), (b) and (c), which imply saturating attractive forces between nucleons, are of basic importance and form a prime requirement to be imposed on any theory of the nucleon–nucleon interaction (ch. 18). They suggest strongly that in respect of binding energy at least a heavy nucleus behaves in analogy with a drop of liquid, in which as a result of the short range of the intermolecular forces each molecule experiences only attractions from its nearest neighbours and thus acquires a fixed potential energy.

10.3 The semi-empirical mass formula

There is no detailed theory of the binding energy of nuclei, except for a few of the lightest, but many attempts have been made to express the main features of Fig. 10.1 analytically. The mass formulae which have been set up have proved useful in predicting the binding energy of unstable nuclei and in evaluating the energy release to be expected in particular processes of nuclear division such as fission or α-particle emission. The earliest formulae, developed by Weiszäcker and by Fermi, included no terms to represent shell structure, and the effects of shell closure may be exhibited by comparing experimental data with the predictions of the mass formula. Later formulae have included shell model terms.

The mass formula is constructed as follows:

i) A neutron–proton liquid drop model of constant density is assumed. The volume is then proportional to A and the nuclear radius to $A^{\frac{1}{3}}$, i.e.,

$$R = r_0 A^{\frac{1}{3}} \tag{10.8}$$

where r_0 is a constant now usually taken to be about $1 \cdot 2 \times 10^{-13}$ cm (ch. 11).

ii) The first term in the mass formula is the sum of the atomic masses of Z hydrogen atoms and $(A - Z)$ neutrons.

iii) The neutrons and protons are held together by short-range attractive forces. These forces contribute the main binding term and reduce the mass of the nucleus below that of its constituents by an amount proportional to the number of nucleons, since the binding energy per nucleon is constant. The second term is known as the *volume energy* and is written $-a_v A$ where a_v is about 14 MeV per nucleon in unlimited nuclear matter.

iv) As in the theory of liquids, this simple expression neglects the surface in which nucleons are less effective for binding than in the interior of the nucleus. The main binding term must therefore be corrected by a disruptive term proportional to surface area, i.e., $+a_s A^{2/3}$ (*surface energy*).

v) There is, from Fig. 10.1, clearly a tendency to maximum stability when the number of neutrons and protons in a light nucleus is equal. This means that if $Z \neq A/2$ the nucleus is less strongly bound than it might be. Since protons and neutrons are equally effective in this connection it is reasonable to suppose that the 'asymmetry' energy is proportional to $(A/2 - Z)^2$. It may be shown that a reasonable form is $\dfrac{a_a}{A} (A - 2Z)^2$ (*asymmetry energy*).

vi) The nuclear charge Ze is confined within a volume $\frac{4}{3}\pi R^3$. A simple calculation of the potential energy of such a charge distribution gives a disruptive potential energy of approximately $\frac{3}{5}(Ze)^2/R$ or, alternatively, $+a_c(Z^2/A^{1/3})$ (*Coulomb energy*).

vii) For nuclei of even A, Z and N may be both even or both odd. If these numbers are even, the nucleons may be grouped into stable pairs, with spins opposed, and the nucleus will be correspondingly more stable than in the case Z, N odd. A term $\delta(A,Z)$ approximately equal to half the pairing energy $P(A,Z)$ (10.7), corrects for this effect.

If all these terms are collected together the atomic mass may be written

$$M(A,Z) = ZM_H + (A - Z)M_n - a_v A + a_s A^{2/3}$$
$$+ \frac{a_a}{A}(A - 2Z)^2 + \frac{a_c Z^2}{A^{1/3}} + \delta(A,Z) \text{ a.m.u.} \quad (10.9)$$

with $\delta(A,Z)$ negative for A even, Z even, positive for A even, Z odd, and zero for A odd. The average binding energy per nucleon may be obtained directly from this formula using 10.5, and a graph of this quantity against A gives a curve of the general shape of that given in Fig. 10.1. The coefficients in 10.9 may be calculated theoretically, as in the case of a_c, under certain simplifying assumptions, but with such values the equation would have little practical value. It is better to determine values for the coefficients empirically by fitting the equation to known masses, and by insisting that it should predict the correct proton to neutron ratio (or Z/A value) for the medium weight and heavy elements. Fermi proposed the formula

$$M(A,Z) = 0.99391A - 0.00085Z + 0.014A^{2/3} + \frac{0.021}{A}(A - 2Z)^2$$
$$+ 0.000627\frac{Z^2}{A^{1/2}} + \delta(A,Z) \text{ a.m.u.} \quad (10.10)$$

with $\delta(A,Z) = -0.036A^{-3/4}$ for A even, Z even,
$\quad\quad\quad\quad\ = 0$ for A odd,
$\quad\quad\quad\quad\ = +0.036A^{-3/4}$ for A even, Z odd.

If the coefficients in 10.9 are expressed in MeV the Fermi formula requires $a_v = 14.0$ MeV, $a_s = 13.0$ MeV, $a_a = 19.3$ MeV, $a_c = 0.58$ MeV, $\delta = 33.5A^{-3/4}$MeV.

Tables of $M(A,Z)$ based on the semi-empirical mass formula have been prepared and cover a wide range of A and Z; they should of course not be used when accurately measured mass values are available, which is now the case for the majority of stable nuclei.

A good example of the use of 10.10 is in the demonstration of shell closure effects in the neutron separation energy. The radiative capture of a slow (thermal) neutron by a nucleus A

$$A + n \rightarrow (A + 1) + \gamma + S_n(A + 1, Z) \quad (10.11)$$

releases a total energy per capture equal to the neutron separation energy for the nucleus $(A + 1)$. The same quantity may be measured by determining the energy release Q in the (d,p) reaction with nucleus A as target.

$$A + d \rightarrow (A + 1) + p + Q \tag{10.12}$$

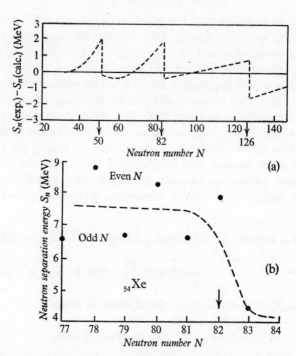

Fig. 10.2

a) Difference between observed and calculated neutron separation energies as a function of neutron number (Ref. 10.4).

b) Variation of neutron separation energy in Xe isotopes with neutron number, showing drop in S_n for the 83rd neutron.

Since the deuteron is equivalent to a neutron and proton bound together with an energy $\varepsilon \; (= -2\cdot23 \text{ MeV})$, comparison of 10.11 and 10.12 shows that

$$S_n = Q + |\varepsilon| = Q + 2\cdot23 \text{ MeV} \tag{10.13}$$

Many measurements of energy releases in (n,γ) and (d,p) reactions have been made. Fig. 10.2a shows the results obtained for nuclides with a neutron number N between 40 and 140; the quantity plotted is the difference between the observed separation energy and the smoothly varying separation energy predicted from the semi-empirical mass formula. There is clear evidence for breaks at the magic numbers $N = 50$, 82 and 126. It should be noted that the separation energy for the nucleon which completes a closed shell is not markedly greater than that of the two or three nucleons which precede it. The shell

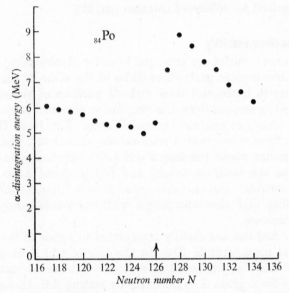

Fig. 10.3. Alpha-disintegration energy of isotopes of polonium.

closure is seen particularly as a sharp drop in the separation energy for the (magic + 1) and (magic + 2) nucleons (Fig. 10.2b).

Binding energy discontinuities have been found for other particles. In the region of the rare earth elements neutron-deficient isotopes formed in nuclear reactions are found to be α-active. If the energy of the α-particles is examined for a particular series of isotopes of a given element it is found to show a maximum for $N = 83$ or 84, suggesting that after $N = 82$ the next two neutrons are less tightly bound than for $N \leqslant 81$. At neutron number $N = 126$ the same effect appears clearly, as is seen in Fig. 10.3 which shows the α-decay energy for the isotopes of polonium ($Z = 84$) plotted as a function of neutron number. The most recent data of mass spectroscopy for the heavy stable nuclei show anomalies in pairing energy near the neutron numbers $N = 90$ and 116. Other nuclear properties, such as electric quadrupole moments and the pattern of excited states also change at these numbers. These discontinuities differ from those at the magic numbers of the shell model and represent a transition from a nuclear structure in which collective vibration is the dominant mode of motion to one characterized by collective rotation (ch. 12).

10.4 Nuclear stability

If the known nuclei are arranged in order of increasing N and Z on a rectangular grid, all nuclides of the same N (isotones) appearing in horizontal lines and all nuclides of the same Z (isotopes) in vertical lines, the diagram so obtained is known as a Segrè chart, or neutron–proton diagram (Fig. 10.4). On this diagram lines of constant A intersect the axes at 45°. The stable nuclei cluster about the line $N = Z = A/2$ for small mass numbers, but the medium weight and heavy nuclei have many excess neutrons. The unstable nuclei form a fringe to the band of stability and also intermingle with the stable isotopes for many elements.

These features are readily interpreted in terms of the semi-empirical mass formula 10.9. In the case of odd-A nuclei, for which δ may be put equal to zero, the nucleus of maximum stability for a given A is obtained by setting dM/dZ equal to zero. This gives

$$Z = \frac{A}{1\cdot98 + 0\cdot015A^{\frac{2}{3}}} \qquad (10.14)$$

if Fermi's constants are used, and shows that Z falls short of $A/2$ as A increases. Physically this is due to the fact that Coulomb repulsion between protons is a long-range force and becomes increasingly important with respect to the short-range nuclear forces as the nuclear charge increases. The repulsive effect has to be balanced in a stable nucleus by the presence of extra neutrons to provide extra attractive interactions. Isobars of odd A, with Z different from the integer nearest to the value predicted by 10.14, are expected to be unstable.

If a third coordinate representing the atomic weight $M(A,Z)$ is added to the neutron–proton diagram a three-dimensional region known as the mass surface is obtained. Stable nuclei then group round the bottom of a valley or trough in this surface.

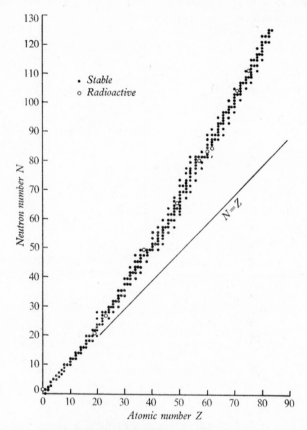

Fig. 10.4. Neutron–proton diagram (Segrè chart) of the naturally occurring nuclides with Z less than 84 (Ref. 10.4). The present diagram may not be found accurate in all details.

Intersections of the mass surface by planes of constant A define groups of isobars comprising both stable and unstable nuclei. Formula 10.9 shows that for A constant $M(A,Z)$ is a quadratic function of Z so that the curves of intersection are parabolas. For odd A one parabola only is obtained (Fig. 10.5a) but for even A the term $\delta(A,Z)$ in 10.9 must be included and the masses lie alternately on two distinct parabolas (Fig. 10.5b) separated by an energy $2\delta(A,Z)$. (A closer examination shows that there are two parabolas for odd A, corresponding to Z even and Z odd. The difference is smaller than in the case of even A and will be disregarded.)

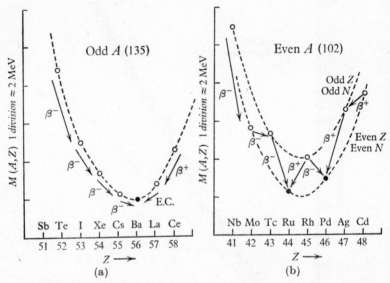

Fig. 10.5. Stability of isobars, showing atomic mass M plotted against atomic number Z. Open circles represent unstable, and full circles stable nuclei.

a) Odd A (135), for which there is one stable nucleus, $^{135}_{56}$Ba.

b) Even A (102), for which there are two stable isobars $^{102}_{44}$Ru and $^{102}_{46}$Pd, both of even–even type (Ref. 10.4).

It is clear that for odd A there will be one stable nucleus, although exceptionally (^{113}In, ^{113}Cd; ^{123}Sb, ^{123}Te) two isobars of adjacent Z may have so closely similar a mass that transitions between them are unobservable because of their low probability. For even A there may be two or even three stable isobars. Transitions between isobaric nuclei take place in the direction of increasing stability by positron or negatron (β) emission or by electron capture (Sect. **16.6**) as shown in Fig. 10.5a, b. The atomic mass $M(A,Z)$ of a neutral atom undergoing a decay process of this type is related to the mass $M(A,Z\pm1)$ of the product by the inequalities:

$$
\left.
\begin{array}{ll}
M(A,Z) \geqslant M(A,Z+1) & \text{for electron decay to} \\
 & (A,Z+1) \\
M(A,Z) \geqslant M(A,Z-1)+2N_0m & \text{for positron decay to} \\
 & (A,Z-1) \\
M(A,Z) \geqslant M(A,Z-1)+E_e & \text{for electron capture} \\
 & \text{decay to } (A,Z-1)
\end{array}
\right\} \quad (10.15)
$$

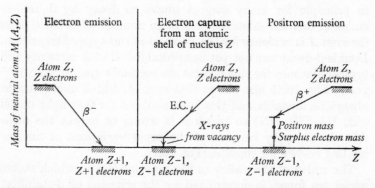

Fig. 10.6. Beta-decay processes for an atom (A,Z). In electron emission and electron capture (from an atomic shell), the total number of electrons always matches the nuclear charge. In electron capture the nuclear transition must provide the energy of ionization for the absorbed electron.

where N_0 is Avogadro's number, m is the electron mass and E_e(a.m.u.) is the ionization energy for the electron captured in the neutral atom of charge $Z-1$. In positron decay the formation of a neutral atom implies the release of an atomic electron as well as the emission of a positron and the atomic mass change must supply the mass of both of these particles. The relationships 10.15 are illustrated in Fig. 10.6, in which energies associated with the rearrangement of outer atomic electrons are neglected.

It is also assumed that no particle of finite rest mass other than an electron is emitted in β-decay, i.e., that the neutrino rest mass is zero. When the transition energy becomes very small it may be that only one of the lightly-bound outer

13*

electrons can be captured. If there is insufficient energy even for this, then both odd isobars (A,Z) and $(A,Z-1)$ may be stable; the rarity of this occurrence is good evidence for the zero rest mass of the neutrino since a finite rest mass for this particle would obviously widen the β-stability limits. The lifetime associated with very low β-transition energies may be extremely long even on a geological time scale and if so the corresponding nuclei are found in nature. Examples are given in Table 2.4.

For even-A nuclei it is possible for a nucleus (e.g., ^{40}K, ^{64}Cu) to exhibit both positron and negatron decay. It is also possible in principle for many even-A nuclei to decay by double β-emission but the existence of a large number of isobaric pairs for even A is evidence for the slowness of this type of transition. Double β-decay has not yet been established with certainty and typical lifetimes for this process are certainly greater than 10^{17} years. Fig. 10.5b also shows that even-A, odd-Z nuclei should always be unstable and this is true except for four light nuclei (^{2}H, ^{7}Li, ^{10}B, ^{14}N) to which it is wrong to expect the mass formula to apply because of the rapid variations of nuclear binding energy for small A (Fig. 10.1).

The width of the valley in the mass surface in which stable nuclei are found is determined by the criterion of β-stability. Other types of spontaneous decay, such as α-particle emission or fission may be energetically possible, but are impeded for the majority of nuclei by the Coulomb barrier. This barrier also affects positron decay but when its effect becomes serious, e.g., for heavy nuclei, electron capture provides an alternative and rapid means of decay. The stability limits predicted by the semi-empirical mass formula for various types of decay are shown in Fig. 10.7 in which the neutron–proton ratio N/Z is plotted against the mass number A. The line of maximum stability predicted by 10.14 is surrounded by the region of stable isobars determined by diagrams of the type 10.5a, b or eqq. 10.15.

The β-stable nuclei are stable against proton or neutron emission but for considerably larger or smaller values of N/Z emission of one or other of these particles becomes energetically possible. At such extreme values of the neutron–proton ratio, however, the β transitions become very rapid and neither proton nor neutron radioactivity is observed as a competitive mode of ground state decay.* The β-stable nuclei with $A > 150$ are unstable with respect to the emission of α-particles, but for low mass numbers the ratio of disintegration energy to potential barrier is unfavourable for α-emission. The main importance of α-decay as a stability limit occurs for $Z > 83$, where the nuclei expected to be β-stable are α-active. The only elements in this region found in nature are those such as uranium and thorium which have lives comparable with the age of the earth.

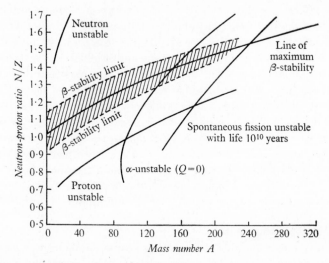

Fig. 10.7. Nuclear stability limits predicted by the semi-empirical mass formula (Segrè, *Experimental Nuclear Physics*, Vol. III).

The fact that there is a maximum in the binding energy curve at $A \approx 60$ suggests that the spontaneous splitting or 'fission' of heavy nuclei into two fragments of nearly equal size may be energetically possible. It may be shown from the semi-empirical mass formula that the critical parameter for such a process in a nucleus (A,Z) is the parameter Z^2/A; spontaneous fission may be expected to occur with a lifetime of about 10^{10} years if the numerical value of Z^2/A exceeds 37. This value is

* The emission of nucleons from highly excited nuclear states is of course a familiar phenomenon of nuclear reactions. The possibility of observing true proton radioactivity is discussed by V. I. Goldansky, *Nucl. Phys.*, **19**, 482, 1960.

already exceeded for some nuclei with $Z > 92$ and for the heaviest nuclei spontaneous fission competes successfully with α-emission as a mode of decay. The probability of fission increases rapidly with Z and is usually taken to be the factor that limits the number of transuranic elements that may be prepared to those with $Z < 104$.

Shell closure effects are seen in the energy release in β-decay just as they are in particle separation energies, since discontinuities in the mass surface are involved in a similar way. These effects are shown clearly if the energy of β-disintegration is plotted against neutron number for nuclei with a given value of the *isotopic number* $I = N - Z = A - 2Z$. Such nuclei have the same excess of neutrons over protons and might be expected to show a regular dependence of decay energy on mass number. In fact there are irregularities near the magic numbers. The yields of fission products, which are mainly electron emitters, are also enhanced at $N = 82$ and 83, perhaps because the energy available for the formation of these products in the fission process is slightly larger than for adjacent neutron numbers. Delayed neutron emission is observed in some fission products because of the unusually low binding energy of a neutron in members of β-decaying fission chains which pass through magic numbers.

10.5   Isotopic abundance

Naturally occurring nuclei are either stable or unstable with a half-life of the order of 10^9 years or longer. The naturally occurring radioactive elements with shorter periods derive from long-lived parents. The relative abundance of the observed stable species depends on the process of creation, which may have singled out particular nuclear types for preferential formation and on the nuclear stability limits discussed in the last section which may have caused the disappearance of some of the preferentially created species.

The elements of highest atomic abundance in the universe are hydrogen and helium, which are not retained gravitationally in the earth's atmosphere. The elements of the earth's crust (Table **10.2**) appear to represent very roughly the general cosmic abundance if this may be assessed by analysis of meteoritic material. The naturally occurring nuclides with $Z \leqslant 83$ are shown in Fig. 10.4 and the relative abundance of the lighter even–even nuclides in Fig. 10.8. These bodies form more than 85% by weight of the crust.

TABLE 10.2 Abundant nuclides of the earth's crust
(Ref. **10.4**)

NUCLIDE	$^{16}_{8}O$	$^{28}_{14}Si$	$^{56}_{26}Fe$	$^{40}_{20}Ca$	$^{24}_{12}Mg$	$^{27}_{13}Al$	$^{23}_{11}Na$	$^{39}_{19}K$
% abundance by weight	48	26	5	3·5	2·0	8·5	2·8	2·5

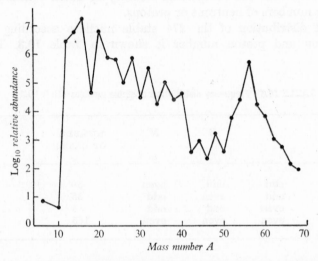

Fig. 10.8. Relative isotopic abundance in the universe of light even–even nuclei, taken from a larger diagram given by H. E. Suess and H. C. Urey, *Rev. mod. Phys.*, **28**, 53, 1956. The 'iron peak' near $A = 56$ is obvious.

In detail, isotopic abundances show anomalies at $A = 56$, 90, 135 and 200 and these mass values may be correlated either directly, or before decay of active parent nuclei, with the magic numbers $N = 28$, 50, 82 and 126. It is probable that nuclei containing these neutron shells were produced preferentially in the element-building reactions. Relative abundance of the isotopes of a given element (Z constant) and the isotones of a given neutron number (N constant) show the following main anomalies:

a) the number of stable and long-lived isotopes is greater for $Z = 20$, 28, 50 and 82 than for near-by elements,
b) the number of stable and long-lived isotones is greater for $N = 20$, 28, 50, 82 and 126 than for near-by N values,
c) the abundance of even Z, even N isotopes relative to the abundance of the other isotopes of a given element is greater for $N = 50$ (^{88}Sr) and $N = 82$ (^{138}Ba, ^{140}Ce).

These anomalies and a number of similar ones are clearly correlated with the exceptional stability of nuclei containing magic numbers of neutrons or protons.

The distribution of the 274 stable nuclides according to neutron and proton number is shown in Table **10.3**. The

TABLE 10.3   **Frequency distribution of stable nuclides** (Ref. 10.4)

A	Z	N	NUMBER OF CASES
odd	odd	even	50
odd	even	odd	55
even	odd	odd	4
even	even	even	165

approximate equality of number of odd Z–even N and even Z–odd N nuclides means that neutrons and protons behave in an equivalent way in nuclear structure and there is no reason for a nucleus with an odd proton to be more stable than one with an odd neutron. The preponderance of even Z–even N nuclides is explained by the strong tendency of nucleons to form stable pairs. The presence of two unpaired odd nucleons, as in nuclides of odd Z and odd N, results in instability in all but the lightest nuclei ^{2}H, ^{6}Li, ^{10}B and ^{14}N, for which space-exchange forces (ch. 18) are sufficiently strong to produce binding.

References

10.1   F. W. Aston, *Mass Spectra and Isotopes*, Arnold, 1933.
10.2   K. I. Mayne, 'Mass Spectrometry', *Rep. progr. Phys.*, **15**, 24, 1952.
10.3   J. Mattauch and F. Everling, 'Masses of Atoms of $A < 40$', *Progr. nucl. Phys.*, **6**, 233, 1957.
       H. E. Duckworth, 'Masses of Atoms of $A > 40$', *Progr. nucl. Phys.*, **6**, 138, 1957.
10.4   R. D. Evans, *The Atomic Nucleus*, McGraw-Hill, 1955.
10.5   N. Feather, *Nuclear Stability Rules*, Cambridge University Press, 1952.

11. NUCLEAR CHARGE, NUCLEAR RADIUS AND NUCLEAR MOMENTS

A nuclear charge value was first determined in the α-particle scattering experiments of Geiger and Marsden (ch. 2). The later and more accurate work of Chadwick showed that the nuclear charge was closely equal to Ze, and all subsequent experiments have confirmed this conclusion. The electrical neutrality of atoms and the neutron–proton nuclear structure are well tested hypotheses and together they imply that the charge of the proton and the electron are equal and opposite to a high degree of approximation. The exact equality of these charges has not remained unquestioned, particularly by the astrophysicist, but any difference appears to be beyond the present sensitivity of experimental investigation, and we shall assume that the nuclear charge is an integral multiple of the absolute charge of the proton.

As far as the early α-particle scattering experiments were concerned the nuclear charge could have been distributed through any volume of radius less than 10^{-12} cm; it could have been located at a structureless point, as appears now to be a good approximation for Dirac-type particles such as the electron or μ-meson. Extension of the α-particle experiments to light target nuclei (Sect. 5.3.1) first revealed deviations from inverse square law scattering which implied the existence of non-Coulomb forces at small distances or a finite nuclear size or both effects. Finite size is now an accepted and characteristic nuclear property and methods of determining it will be surveyed in the present chapter. Some evidence for shell effects in nuclear size has been found, but these are considerably less obvious than the effects in separation energy, since nuclear radii vary only as the cube root of the mass number.

The electromagnetic moments which arise as a result of the distribution of nucleons within a finite nucleus are not integral multiples of a fundamental unit, as is the case for angular momentum. These moments (ch. 4 and Appendix 3) are determined in a very direct way from the nuclear wave function, and if this wave function is essentially that of a single nucleon moving in a spherical field, then a simple and accurate prediction of moments may be expected. The single-particle shell model also offers precise information on parity and angular momentum.* From Fig. 9.4 there should be a change of ground state spin of odd mass nuclei at the completion of each sub-shell with given (l, j) and there may also be a change of parity. The spin and parity of the sequence of single-particle excited states in an odd mass nucleus is also evident. If these predictions fail, it follows that the nuclear wave function must involve configurations other than that of a spherical core plus a single particle. If more than one particle is involved then the resultant *spin* may change as a result of a particular type of vector coupling, but so long as a sequence of shell model states is preserved the parity should remain predictable.

Nuclear statistics is invariably associated with the integral or half-integral nature of the nuclear spin (Sect. **3.6**). It depends only on the number of nucleons in the nucleus and not on their mode of motion, so that it offers no information on nuclear models beyond the simple and basic confirmation of the neutron–proton structure.

In this chapter we shall be primarily, though not exclusively, concerned with the properties of the nuclear ground state. Nuclear moments, nuclear radii and quantum numbers exist for unstable nuclei and for the excited states of all nuclei. In principle these are accessible to spectroscopic measurement and work of this sort is rapidly increasing. Most of the existing information on nuclear levels and unstable nuclei has come from a study of nuclear reactions including β-decay (ch. 16) and isomeric transitions (ch. 13).

11.1   The Coulomb barrier and the nuclear potential well

The nuclear potential wells considered in chapter 9 (Fig. 9.3) were invoked mainly to provide a set of single particle levels. The radius R is an important parameter of the square well, but

---

* We shall use the term spin for nuclear angular momentum for convenience, remembering that for a given nucleus it is a combination of the angular momenta of orbital motion and of intrinsic spin.

for the purpose of defining levels the 'external' features of the well are less important. The finite well shown in Fig. 9.4 should, however, be taken to refer specifically to neutrons, since it implies that a charged particle approaching a nucleus from infinity feels no force until it comes within the range of the assumed potential. This cannot be true, and although neglect of the Coulomb potential may have no large effect on the order

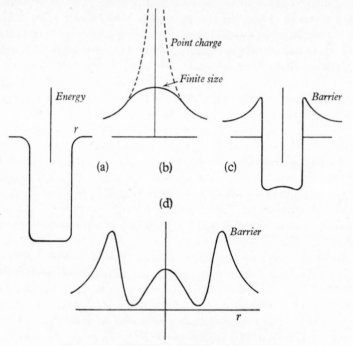

Fig. 11.1. Nuclear and Coulomb potentials.
     a) Nuclear well, for neutrons.
     b) Coulomb potential.
     c) Addition of (a) and (b) for $Z = 20$.
     d) Addition of (a) and (b) for $Z = 92$.

of single particle levels, this potential is extremely important for radioactive decay and for low energy nuclear reactions. From the point of view of an incident proton or α-particle, the nuclear potential must be represented as in Fig. 11.1, which shows (a) the finite attractive nuclear well appropriate for neutrons, (b) the repulsive Coulomb potential for a point charge, and for a finite charge distribution, (c) the combination of (a) and (b) for a fairly light nucleus ($Z \approx 20$) and (d) the combination of (a) and (b) for uranium ($Z = 92$). The combination of a long-range electric force with a short-range nuclear force of opposite sign is consistent with the α-particle scattering experiments, according to which the scattering first of all falls off as the incident energy increases.

The potential well for charged particles is often idealized for the purposes of calculation as shown in Fig. 11.2a. The radius R is then the distance from the centre at which the spherically symmetrical nuclear force becomes essentially zero and the height of the potential (Coulomb) barrier is given by

$$B = \frac{zZe^2}{R} \tag{11.1}$$

for an incident particle of charge ze. For a uranium nucleus R is about 8×10^{-13} cm and the barrier height is about 17 MeV per incident charge.* The α-particles from all naturally occurring radioactive bodies would therefore be scattered in accordance with the Rutherford law from this nucleus. Uranium itself, however, is an α-particle emitter and the observed particles of energy 4·2 MeV (^{238}U) must traverse the barrier. This is impossible classically but wave mechanically such penetration is reasonable and can be calculated (Fig. 11.2b and Sects. **14.2** and **16.2**). Classically, the α-particle has negative kinetic energy inside the barrier, but quantum mechanically the energy may be regarded as indefinite to an extent specified by the uncertainty principle during the time of passage through the barrier. At the point of emergence from the barrier (X in Fig. 11.2) the particle has zero kinetic energy but it is then accelerated by Coulomb repulsion from the nucleus until it attains its final energy at a large distance. The nuclear radius R in 11.1 is

---

* A crude but useful estimate of the barrier height is

$$B = \frac{Z}{A^{1/3}} \text{ MeV}$$

which corresponds to a radius

$$R = 1·4 \times 10^{-13} A^{1/3} \text{ cm} = 1·4 A^{1/3} \text{ fm}.$$

that already used in chapter 10 in discussion of the semi-empirical mass formula based on the liquid drop model of constant density and is written

$$R = r_0 A^{1/3} \qquad (11.2)$$

The implied assumptions of Fig. 11.2 and Eq. (11.2) that the nucleus has a sharp edge and that it is spherical have each had to be modified.

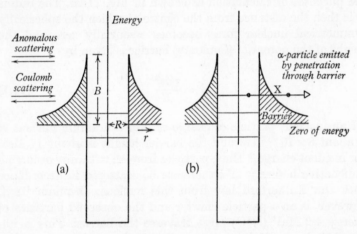

Fig. 11.2. Idealized potential well of radius R with barrier of height B, showing on the energy scale :—

a) Energies for which charged particles are scattered according to the Coulomb law and anomalously.

b) Emission of α-particles in a radioactive decay by tunnelling through the potential barrier.

The radius R indicated in Fig. 11.2 is known as a *potential radius* since it represents the distance at which nuclear forces are first felt by a proton or neutron. Because of the finite range of nuclear forces this radius is slightly larger than (a) *the radius of the mass distribution and* (b) *the radius of the charge distribution*. The mass distribution cannot be inferred from the potential radius since we do not know the details of the connection between these two quantities. The charge distribution on the other hand can be obtained directly by exploring the electromagnetic field of a nucleus with probes that are not sensitive to nuclear forces, such as high energy electrons or μ-mesons.

In this chapter we shall regard the spatial distribution of nuclear charge, i.e. the density of the nuclear protons, as the most important measure of nuclear size. This is not only because it is measurable with the greatest precision but because, owing to the strong attraction between neutrons and protons, it must be closely correlated with the total nucleon distribution. If the charge density is $\rho(r)$ (Fig. 11.5b) then the mean square radius of the distribution is given by

$$\overline{r^2} = \frac{\displaystyle\int_0^\infty r^2 4\pi r^2 \rho(r)\,\mathrm{d}r}{\displaystyle\int_0^\infty 4\pi r^2 \rho(r)\,\mathrm{d}r} \tag{11.3}$$

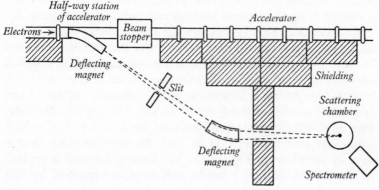

Fig. 11.3. Arrangement for observing scattering of 190 MeV electrons with the Stanford linear accelerator (Ref. 11.2).

Some experiments determine primarily this quantity rather than the detailed form of $\rho(r)$. If $\overline{r^2}$ is known then the radius of the equivalent uniform spherical distribution of charge ('square well') is given by

$$R = \sqrt{\tfrac{5}{3}}(\overline{r^2})^{1/2} \tag{11.4}$$

We shall assume for the purposes of comparison of experimental data for a range of mass numbers A that R is related to A by the constant density formula 11.2.

11.2 The radius of the nuclear charge distribution

11.2.1 ELASTIC SCATTERING OF FAST ELECTRONS. The reduced de Broglie wavelength $\lambda/2\pi$ of a 200 MeV electron is

10^{-13} cm and such particles, which interact strongly only with electric charges, are suitable for studying the nuclear proton density. Low-energy electrons have too long a wavelength to respond to structural details and higher energy particles will perhaps interact chiefly with individual nucleons.

The Stanford linear electron accelerator, which has been used by Hofstadter and his collaborators in a series of electron scattering experiments of outstanding importance, was described in Sect. 8.2.2. Beams of energy up to 550 MeV were used for work on the lightest nuclei while for most of the heavier nuclei energies between 100 and 190 MeV were used in the first instance. The experimental arrangement is shown in Fig. 11.3. Scattered electrons are detected, after momentum analysis by a double-focusing spectrometer, in a Cherenkov counter suitably screened from the intense background radiations produced by the accelerator. Fig. 11.4 shows the energy distribution of 185 MeV electrons scattered from carbon. For the purpose of charge density determination attention is concentrated on the absolute cross-section and angular distribution for the elastic peak; the inelastic scattering is important in the different context of the properties of excited levels (Sect. 13.6.2). The angular distribution of elastically scattered electrons for a carbon and a gold target are shown in Fig. 11.5a, and the corresponding charge density functions in Fig. 11.5b. The density for gold is typical of the results for heavy nuclei and may be expressed by the formula

$$\rho(r) = \frac{\rho_0}{1 + \exp \dfrac{r-c}{z}} \quad \text{(Fermi distribution)} \qquad (11.5)$$

where c and z are adjustable parameters.

The analysis of the observed angular distributions to give density functions was first approached in a way analogous to X-ray structure calculations. This is based on the Born approximation (Ref. 11.2) and gives a differential cross-section

$$\sigma(\theta) = \left(\frac{Ze^2}{2E}\right)^2 \frac{\cos^2 \theta/2}{\sin^4 \theta/2} F^2 \qquad (11.6)$$

where θ is the scattering angle (usually not corrected to the centre-of-mass system owing to the small mass of the electron, even at an energy E of 200 MeV, compared with that of the target) and F is a form factor. The quantity multiplying F^2 is the Mott expression for the scattering of a relativistic electron by a point charge, valid when $2Ze^2/\hbar c \ll 1$. If the charge is spread out into a finite volume the scattering is less because of interference of waves from different parts of the volume.

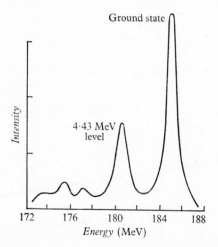

Fig. 11.4. Energy distribution of 185 MeV electrons scattered from carbon, showing elastic and inelastic peaks (Ref. 11.2).

The form factor $F (\leqslant 1)$ is an integral, in accordance with Huygens' principle, of the charge density times a phase factor over the nuclear volume. The scattering falls to a small value compared with the point charge value at a scattering angle θ for which the phase factor reaches the interference minimum and this gives an estimate of nuclear size in a familiar way $(\lambda/R \approx \theta)$. Experimental values of F obtained from observations such as those of Fig. 11.5a do not show sharp minima but can be compared with calculations for different charge distributions. Unfortunately, this relatively simple procedure is only suitable for light nuclei since for heavier targets the Born approximation using plane waves is invalid owing to distortion of the incident and scattered waves in the Coulomb fields. A full phase shift analysis (ch. 14) then becomes necessary; this does not give the sharp minimum of the plane wave approximation and is in better agreement with experiment.

The results of electron scattering experiments for a wide range of nuclei indicate that the half-way radius c (Fig. 11.5b) is proportional to $A^{1/3}$, that the surface thickness parameter z is approximately constant at about 2·25 fm, and that the radius R of the equivalent uniform distribution may be written in the form 11.2 with

$$r_0 = 1{\cdot}32 \text{ fm for } A < 50 \atop r_0 = 1{\cdot}21 \text{ fm for } A > 50 \Bigg\} \qquad (11.7)$$

The hypothesis of constant nuclear density $\left(\propto A \Big/ \dfrac{4\pi R^3}{3}\right)$ is verified.

An important application of high-energy electron scattering is the exploration of the electric and magnetic structure of the proton and the neutron.[*] The nucleons have a radius of about 10^{-13} cm and structure investigations demand the use of the highest possible electron energy; in the latest Stanford work energies up to 900 MeV have been used.[†] Electron scattering from a heavy nucleus is predominantly a charge effect but for a proton the scattering is due in comparable measure to the charge and to the magnetic moment. If the proton were a Dirac-type particle such as the electron or μ-meson the scattering of both types would be predictable but it is known that the magnetic moment of the proton is anomalous (2·79 nuclear magnetons). It is therefore usual, following Pauli, to assume that the proton dissociates itself into a nuclear core and a charged meson cloud surrounding it. Form factors can be extracted from the experimental results to show how the charge and magnetic moment distributions differ from points. Similar information can be obtained for the neutron by electron scattering in deuterium. Possible charge distributions[‡] for the two nucleons are shown in Fig. 11.6; these give, of course, unit

---

[*] R. Hofstadter and others, *Phys. Rev. Letters*, **5**, 263, 1960; **6**, 290, 1961. D. N. Olson and others, *Phys. Rev. Letters*, **6**, 286, 1961.

[†] About 1200 MeV has been reached by the A.G. synchrotron at Cornell University.

[‡] Work on the nucleons is continuing and these distributions must be regarded as provisional.

total charge for the proton and zero charge for the neutron, but in the case of the latter the mean square radius is also zero, as is required by experiments on the scattering of slow neutrons by electrons. The magnetic moment of the proton is μ_N from the unit charge, plus $1{\cdot}79\mu_N$ from the meson cloud; for the

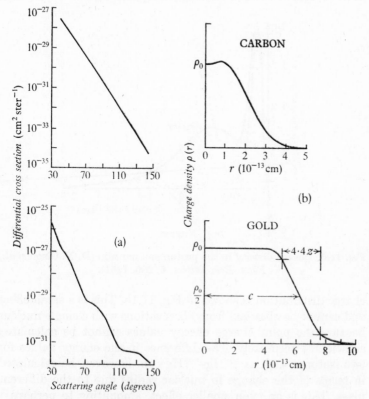

Fig. 11.5. Scattering of 183 MeV electrons from carbon and gold.
a) Differential cross-section per unit solid angle, showing diffraction features in the case of gold.
b) Density distribution $\rho\,(r)$ derived from scattering data (Ref. 11.2).

neutron the moment is $-1{\cdot}91\mu_N$ from the meson cloud only and this is approximately equal and opposite to the anomalous part of the proton moment.

11.2.2 BOUND ELECTRONS. The *optical isotope shift* has already been mentioned (Sect. 4.2.2) as an example of the effect of nuclear properties on atomic spectra. The penetration of the wave functions of optical *s*-electrons into the nuclear volume was shown in 1932 by Breit to result in a decrease in the electron binding energy by an amount depending on the spatial extent of the charge. The modified Coulomb potential due to the finite

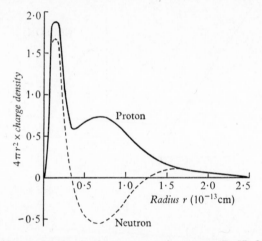

Fig. 11.6. Charge density in the proton and neutron (D. N. Olson *et al.*, *Phys. Rev. Letters*, **6**, 286, 1961).

charge distribution is shown in Fig. 11.1b. This is a small effect and cannot be obtained from observations with a single nucleus because the point charge energy values cannot be calculated sufficiently accurately. The difference in the energy values for two isotopes such as ^{196}Hg–^{198}Hg can, however, be calculated in terms of the change in nuclear radius due to the different mass. This is an even smaller effect, amounting to perhaps 1 part in 10^6 at the most, but the techniques of optical spectroscopy are sufficiently accurate to yield useful results, and have indeed been successful with sources of radioactive ^{197}Hg containing as few as 5×10^{12} atoms. The isotope shift essentially determines the change in $\overline{r^2}$ between the two nuclei compared; the shifts observed are consistent with $r_0 = 1 \cdot 2$ fm but are chiefly of interest for exhibiting the incidence of nuclear deformations at a neutron number $N = 90$.

The difficulty of point nucleus calculations is less in the case of *X-ray levels*, but it is still best to use comparative methods whenever possible. The fine structure of the K_α X-ray doublet due to the separation of the L_{II} ($p_{\frac{1}{2}}$) and L_{III} ($p_{\frac{3}{2}}$) levels can be calculated accurately and it is also possible to allow for the greater effect of nuclear size on the L_{II} level than on the L_{III} level. The experimental results are also consistent with the value $r_0 = 1 \cdot 2$ fm.

A change in nuclear radius also occurs when a nucleus is excited. For long lived isomeric states the corresponding change of frequency in optical lines (*isomer shift*) may be observed (e.g. in ^{197}Hg). The isomer shift may also be detected in special cases in the nuclear transition energy itself (e.g. in ^{57}Fe using the Mössbauer technique, Sect. 13.6.3).

11.2.3 BOUND μ-MESONS (MESONIC ATOMS).   The μ-meson, unlike its parent particle, the π-meson, is known experimentally to interact with nuclei mainly through the Coulomb force. Recent accurate measurements of the magnetic moment of the muon yield a value which is close to that expected for a Dirac particle of spin $\frac{1}{2}$, such as the electron. The electron and μ-meson are therefore both suitable particles for studying the nuclear charge distribution. Accurate muon scattering experiments have only recently commenced following the availability of high intensity, collimated beams of high energy μ-mesons from synchrocyclotrons. Intensities of lower energy muons sufficient to permit the observation of mesonic atoms have, however, been available for a number of years. A positive μ-meson approaching a nucleus is repelled and disappears by decay into electron and neutrinos with a mean life of $2 \cdot 2$ µsec. A negative μ-meson however can enter a bound state, losing energy by radiative transitions, in the same way that an electron is captured by a positive ion. The simple Bohr theory (Appendix 1, Eq. A1.9) shows that μ-mesonic orbits are smaller in radius than electronic orbits of the same quantum number by a factor $m/m_\mu = 1/207$, so that the μ-meson can exist in bound states whose wave functions lie mainly within those of the electrons of an ordinary atom. It may be shown that such a meson captured into an atom will pass rapidly, in perhaps 10^{-13}–10^{-14} sec, from loosely bound 'optical' levels to the tightly bound mesonic X-ray levels; the energy appears as radiation or Auger electrons from the ordinary outer shells of the atom. The binding energies of the mesonic levels are a factor $m_\mu/m = 207$ (Appendix 1, Eq. A 1.7) greater than those of the similar electron levels and the K_α X-ray line of a mesonic atom may have an energy of several MeV. The nuclear size effect, which is difficult to observe in the ordinary electronic transitions, is greatly magnified in the mesonic atom because of the proximity of the mesonic orbits to the nucleus; the

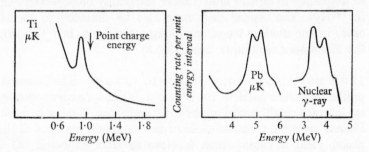

Fig. 11.7. Spectra of μ-mesonic K X-rays from titanium and lead. The figure for lead shows the spectrum of 4·43 MeV nuclear γ-radiation for comparison. The point charge energy for lead is 16·4 MeV (Ref. 11.5).

nuclear radius for $Z = 45$ is about equal to the Bohr radius for a μ-meson in the K-shell. In heavy atoms the K orbit may be entirely within the nucleus and such penetration greatly reduces the binding energy of the meson in the corresponding state. The reduction of energy in comparison with that expected for a point nucleus may be calculated for postulated charge distributions and compared with that deduced from the observed energy for the $L \rightarrow K$ X-ray.

In the work of Fitch and Rainwater* which established the value of the μ-mesons as a nuclear probe, π-mesons from a cyclotron decayed into μ-particles which were then allowed to enter a block of the material under investigation. The π-mesons were removed from the beam of incident particles by a suitably chosen copper absorber. The μK X-rays were detected in a

---

* V. L. Fitch and J. Rainwater, *Phys. Rev.*, **92**, 789, 1953.

sodium iodide crystal; typical spectra obtained in later work are shown in Fig. 11.7.

The lifetime of the mesonic $^2P_{3/2, 1/2}$ state is probably about 10^{-18} sec, corresponding to a natural width of 1 keV. The μ meson terminates its career either by normal decay in the K shell, or for penetrating orbits, occasionally by nuclear capture with star production. Pions also form mesonic atoms but are unsuitable for nuclear size determinations because of the effects of their strong nuclear interaction.

Observations of muonic X-rays determine the mean square radius $\overline{r^2}$, and the results are rather sensitive to the muon mass. With the most recent value of this quantity the equivalent uniform distribution has

$$r_0 = 1 \cdot 15 \pm 0 \cdot 03 \text{ fm} \tag{11.8}$$

11.2.4 COULOMB ENERGY OF NUCLEI.

The semi-empirical mass formula (Sect. **10.3**) contains a term

$$a_c \frac{Z^2}{A^{1/3}} = \frac{3}{5} \frac{e^2}{r_0} \frac{Z^2}{A^{1/3}} = E_c \tag{11.9}$$

representing the Coulomb potential energy due to the nuclear charge. Surveys of nuclear binding energies can therefore in principle lead to a value for r_0, but in practice ambiguity arises because of the presence of other adjustable constants in the formula. This difficulty can be avoided if binding energies of isobars are compared.

Fig. 11.8 shows schematically the structure of three nuclei; nucleus (a) contains equal numbers of neutrons and protons and nuclei (b) and (c) differ from (a) by the addition of a proton and neutron respectively. If the main binding energy of these nuclei is assumed to arise from (nn), (pp) and (np) interactions it is clear that nuclei (b) and (c) differ in this respect by the replacement of a number of (pp) bonds by the same number of (nn) bonds. If nuclear forces are *charge symmetric* the potential energies associated with (pp) and (nn) interactions with the nucleon pairs in the same spatial states are the same. The difference in binding energy between the odd mass isobaric nuclei (b) and (c), is then to a good approximation due to the difference in Coulomb energy arising from the nuclear charge.

This can be calculated with the assumption of a particular charge distribution; for a uniform spherical distribution of radius R the expression 11.9 may be used as a first approximation. The difference in binding energy between the two isobars shown in Fig. 11.8, which are known as *odd mirror*

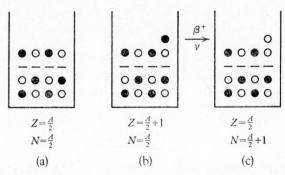

$$Z=\tfrac{A}{2} \qquad Z=\tfrac{A}{2}+1 \qquad Z=\tfrac{A}{2}$$
$$N=\tfrac{A}{2} \qquad N=\tfrac{A}{2} \qquad N=\tfrac{A}{2}+1$$

$$\text{(a)} \qquad\qquad \text{(b)} \qquad\qquad \text{(c)}$$

Fig. 11.8. Schematic representation of positron decay between odd mirror isobars. If nuclear forces are charge symmetric, the addition of a proton (●) to the nucleus (a) results in the same increase of binding energy as does that of a neutron (○).

nuclei since they differ merely by exchange of neutron and proton numbers, is

$$\Delta E_c = \frac{3}{5}\frac{e^2}{r_0 A^{\frac13}}[Z^2-(Z-1)^2]$$
$$= \frac{3}{5}\frac{(2Z-1)e^2}{r_0 A^{\frac13}} \tag{11.10}$$

For $A>3$ the nucleus of greater charge Z is unstable with respect to its mirror isobar and decays into it by positron emission or electron capture, e.g.,

$$^{13}_{7}\mathrm{N} \to {}^{13}_{6}\mathrm{C}+\beta^+(+\text{neutrino}) \tag{11.11}$$

and the maximum kinetic energy T_0 of the positron spectrum is determined by the Coulomb energy change ΔE_c and by the fact that a proton changes into a neutron and a positron. In terms of the *nuclear* masses of these particles

$$T_0 = \Delta E_c - (M_n - M_p) - mc^2$$
$$= \Delta E_c - 1.80 \text{ MeV} \tag{11.12}$$

and since $A = 2Z - 1$ for the mirror nucleus of greater charge this becomes, substituting from 11.10,

$$T_0 = \frac{3}{5} \frac{e^2}{r_0} A^{\frac{2}{3}} - 1 \cdot 80 \text{ MeV} \tag{11.13}$$

Experimental measurements of the decay energy T_0 of the odd mirror nuclei can therefore be used to obtain r_0.

Figure 11.9 shows the existing data, which verify the relation 11.13 in fair detail for nuclei up to $A = 40$. Close examination

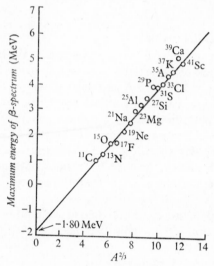

Fig. 11.9. Maximum positron energy for the light nuclei with $A = 2Z - 1$ (Ref. 11.6).

of the most accurate experimental information, including evidence obtained from even mass nuclei assuming charge independence (Sect. 12.1), reveals discontinuities in the Coulomb energies at major closed shells, e.g., at $N = Z = 2$, 8 and 20. Differences also appear between nuclei of mass number $4n + 1$ and $4n + 3$ which may be attributed to pairing energy effects. The method of this section has not so far been applied to nuclei with $A > 41$. In this region of mass numbers the odd mirror nuclei are both unstable and are found at an increasing distance from the line of β-stability so that their half-lives tend to be short and their decay schemes are not fully known. In addition the increasing Coulomb forces seriously disturb the neutron–proton symmetry of structure which is such a marked feature of lighter nuclei.

The first application of this method to the determination of nuclear radii gave $r_0 = 1.45$ fm which is in disagreement with electron scattering results. Corrections however must be introduced for the effect of the Pauli exclusion principle in keeping the protons apart and for $A < 50$ it now appears that

$$r_0 = 1.28 \pm 0.05 \text{ fm} \tag{11.14}$$

11.3 The potential radius

11.3.1 ALPHA PARTICLE SCATTERING. With the advent of strong beams of α-particles accelerated in cyclotrons to an energy of about 40 MeV, it has been possible to extend the classical experiments on α-particle scattering to the heaviest nuclei of the periodic table. The measurements usually made are (a) the energy variation of the scattering at a given angle, and (b) the angular distribution of scattering at a given energy. Fig. 11.10a, b shows the type of results obtained for heavy nuclei. Both experiments show that the scattering falls below the Coulomb value at an angle or energy corresponding to a certain critical distance of approach, at which it is assumed that strong absorption sets in. This distance is related to the nuclear radius.

For light nuclei, high energy α-particles are affected by the nuclear force even in glancing collisions and the angular distribution in this case gives a very convincing demonstration of the finite nuclear size. Fig. 11.10c shows that marked diffraction-like peaks appear and these may be simply (and indeed quantitatively) interpreted as in the case of electron scattering by multiplying the point charge scattering formula by a form factor which takes account of interference between waves scattered from different points of the nuclear volume. In the case of α-particle scattering the strong nuclear interaction confines interference effects to the rim of the nucleus, since α-particles which penetrate into the nucleus will not usually emerge without loss of energy, and it is therefore a good approximation to treat the scattering as diffraction from an

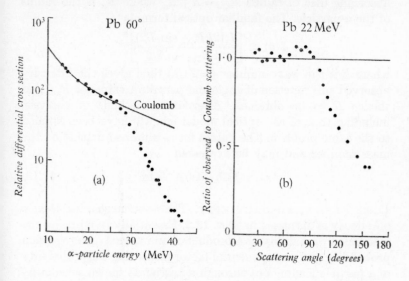

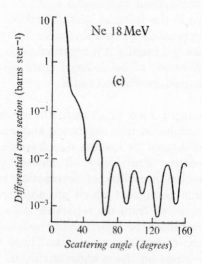

Fig. 11.10. Scattering of α-particles by nuclei.
a) Heavy nucleus, variation of scattering with energy.
b) Heavy nucleus, variation of scattering with angle.
c) Light nucleus, variation of scattering with angle.
(Eisberg and Porter, *Rev. mod. Phys.*, **33**, 190, 1961.)

absorbing disc of radius $R_{abs} = R + R_\alpha$ where R_α is the radius of the α-particle. The familiar optical formula

$$I(\theta) \propto \left[\frac{J_1(2kR_{abs}\sin\theta/2)}{2kR_{abs}\sin\theta/2}\right]^2$$

where k is the wave number $(= 2\pi/\lambda)$ then gives the intensity observed as a function of angle and permits a value for R_{abs} and thence R to be obtained. Alternative methods of analysis, including that of the optical model (ch. 15) have been applied to the same problem. The values for r_0 obtained depend on the mass number and may be expressed

$$r_0 \approx 1.35 - 1.0A^{-\frac{1}{3}} \text{ fm} \qquad (11.15)$$

11.3.2 ALPHA RADIOACTIVITY. The wave mechanical theory of α-decay is discussed in Sect. **16.2**. Essentially it expresses the α-emission probability as a product of an internal disintegration probability and an exponential factor measuring the probability of a particle leaking out through a barrier as shown schematically in Fig. 11.2. The penetrability factor is a rapidly varying function of the nuclear radius and could be used to determine this quantity if the internal distintegration probability were known. Unfortunately no reliable theoretical predictions for the quantity exist and usually it is regarded as the unknown in this type of calculation, to be deduced from penetrability values based on assumed interaction radii.

11.3.3 REACTION AND SCATTERING CROSS-SECTIONS IN GENERAL. Alpha-particle scattering and α-radioactivity have a special significance for nuclear size determination mainly for historical reasons. Practically all nuclear processes in fact similarly involve a radius of interaction and can provide values for this parameter which are comparable in accuracy with those obtained from the α-particle data. Analysis usually requires, in addition to penetrability calculations, some particular theory of nuclear reactions. These theories (ch. 15) depend very much on the energies involved.

The experiments which have been used to evaluate r_0 in 11.2 are:

i) *the total cross-section for the interactions of neutrons with nuclei.*

For neutrons of energy 10–20 MeV a simple classical argument (Sect. 14.2.2) suggests that the total cross-section should be:

$$\sigma_t = 2\pi R^2$$

or more accurately

$$\sigma_t = 2\pi(R+\lambda)^2$$

where λ is the reduced de Broglie wavelength of the incident particle. The absorption cross-section in the high-energy limit is:

$$\sigma_{abs} = \pi R^2$$

In these formulae R is a potential radius and includes a contribution due to the range of nuclear forces. Neglecting this correction it is found that

$$r_0 = 1\cdot25 \pm 0\cdot02 + (0\cdot6 \pm 0\cdot15)A^{-\frac{1}{3}} \text{ fm} \qquad (11.16)$$

At energies of 50 MeV and above nuclei become partially transparent to incident nucleons and the simple calculation must be replaced by an optical model analysis.

ii) *angular distributions for the elastic scattering of protons in the energy range 5–300 MeV.*

These give characteristic diffraction patterns on a scale determined by the ratio λ/R as in α-particle scattering. Very precise measurements in the region of 10–20 MeV show that the concept of a sharp nuclear boundary is unsuitable, since it leads to too much backward scattering. A diffuse nuclear edge, specified as a potential with a radial dependence

$$f(r) = \frac{1}{1+\exp\dfrac{r-R_1}{a}} \qquad (11.17)$$

where R_1 is the 'half-way' radius, gives good agreement with experiment. This radial dependence of the potential is similar to the electron scattering results for the charge density of the heavier nuclei (Eq. 11.5), and the surface thickness parameter a agrees closely with the quantity z found from electron scattering. The radius parameter for the equivalent square well is given by optical model analysis as

$$r_0 = 1\cdot33 \text{ fm} \qquad (11.18)$$

These determinations of potential radius usually involve some ambiguity since the quantity yielded by the analysis is $U r_0^n$ where U is the depth of the potential well assumed in the analysis and $n \approx 2$. The well depth and r_0 may be found separately when extra data, such as the energy variation of a cross-section, are available.

It has been pointed out (Ref. 11.7) that although the nucleon density cannot be directly inferred from the nucleon–nucleus potential, the high energy *absorption* cross-section should actually give the radius of the mass distribution.

11.4 Comparison of results on nuclear radii

In terms of the single parameter r_0 of the equivalent square well potential, the results for the nuclear charge distribution may be combined together to give

$$r_0 = 1 \cdot 19 + 0 \cdot 1 A^{-1/3} \text{ fm} \tag{11.19}$$

For the potential radius,

$$r_0 = 1 \cdot 25 + 0 \cdot 6 A^{-1/3} \text{ fm} \tag{11.20}$$

and from both types of experiment the surface thickness from 10% to 90% of the central density is about $2 \cdot 5$ fm for heavy nuclei.

There is so far no evidence to suggest that the radius of the neutron distribution differs from that of the proton distribution, but the potential radius exceeds both by an amount ($\approx 0 \cdot 7$ fm) due to the range of nuclear forces.

11.5 Parity of nuclear levels

The predictions of the single-particle shell model for the parity of many nuclear levels and in particular for that of the ground state, are unambiguous. Nucleons have even intrinsic parity by convention and the parity of a nucleon state in a potential well is determined immediately by the orbital motion. The angular part of the wave function (Appendix 2) is proportional to $P_l(\cos \theta)$ and the known properties of the Legendre polynomials show that the parity of the nucleon state is then $(-1)^l$. The parity of the Z protons of the nucleus is therefore even if only even-l states, or an even number of odd-l states, are occupied and is odd if an odd number of odd-l states are filled. The parity of the N neutrons is similarly determined. The parity of the nucleus as a whole is the product of the parities of the neutrons and protons, and since their motions are independent this parity is simply determined by the distribution of the A nucleons between even and odd orbital states. Thus we have

for $A = 6$,   configuration $1s^4 1p^2$, parity even $(+)$,
for $A = 7$,   configuration $1s^4 1p^3$, parity odd $(-)$,
for $A = 19$, configuration closed shell $+ 1d^2 2s^1$, parity even
$$(+).$$

This classification is independent of the intrinsic spin of the nucleons and of the total angular momentum quantum number I of the nuclear level. The parity of the nuclear ground state is thus predicted directly from the occupation numbers of the shell model states. For a given nucleus, excited states exist corresponding to the elevation of a nucleon from one single particle orbit to another, and the parity of this sequence of single particle states is immediately obvious. Thus for $A = 13(1s^4 1p^9)$ the ground state is of odd parity, but the configurations $(1s^4 1p^8 2s)$ and $(1s^4 1p^8 1d)$ with even parity should also be found at an excitation of a few MeV. The observed spectrum for ^{13}C and ^{13}N exhibits these states.

Methods of parity investigation strictly determine only change of parity between two states. The specific methods which have been much used are:

i) *Direct nuclear interactions*, and in particular the (d,p) stripping reaction (Sect. 15.4.3) of which a typical example is

$$^{16}O + d \rightarrow {}^{17}O + p + 1.92 \text{ MeV} \tag{11.21}$$

It has been found that a large number of nuclear reactions may be well described on the simple assumption that a nucleon taking part in the process enters or leaves a definite shell-model state of the target nucleus. Since such states have a definite orbital momentum l the process imposes a particular condition on the wave-function of the emitted particle, and the angular distribution of this particle has a characteristic form. From the position of the strong forward maximum in the diffraction-like pattern the angular momentum l taken into the target nucleus by the absorbed particle can be deduced. A great many examples of this type of reaction have been studied; the angular distribution analysis is above all a determination of *parity* change, although useful limits may also be set on nuclear angular momentum (I-value).

ii) *Resonance reactions, decay-scheme analysis and angular correlations.* Although direct interactions probably give the least ambiguous information on parity changes, practically every nuclear process is sensitive to this quantity. In heavy particle reactions the orbital quantum number of a particle may determine the ease with which it can penetrate a potential barrier and the yield is then determined by the parity change. Decay schemes involving electromagnetic radiation are a prolific source of information, since spin and parity changes determine multipolarity and the electric or magnetic character of the radiation (Sect. 3.9.2) which in turn determine observed conversion coefficients (ch. 13). Angular correlations between successive γ-quanta (Sect. 17.4.2) do not yield parities directly, but this information can be obtained from simultaneous measurements of polarization.

iii) *Electromagnetic moments.* As will be shown in Section **11.7**, the static magnetic moment of an odd-A nucleus often gives a clear indication of the l-value of the odd nucleon. Similar but more involved deductions can be made for even-A nuclei. Electric quadrupole moments can be used in the same way.

The results of a large number of investigations of this type confirm in detail the parities of the sequence of single-particle states predicted by the shell model. Many states besides single-particle states exist, and parity is also a good quantum number for these, but the corresponding nuclear motion is more complicated and involves the behaviour of more than one nucleon.

11.6   Angular momentum (spin) and statistics

The methods by which the spin and statistics of stable nuclei have been determined are listed in Table **4.1**. The spins of unstable nuclei and of the excited states of all nuclei are mainly inferred from nuclear reaction and decay scheme analysis, including angular correlation studies (ch. 17) although atomic beam methods are increasing in ability to deal with small quantities of radioactive material.

Nuclear spins are small integral multiples of the fundamental spin $\frac{1}{2}\hbar$, which is known experimentally to be the spin of both neutron and proton. This fact suggests that in the neutron-proton model the individual neutrons and protons in the same spatial state tend to pair off with opposite total angular momenta j, as expected for an assembly of particles obeying Fermi–Dirac statistics. Not all the protons and neutrons in a nucleus will be able to pair off into structures of zero resultant spin and there will be a number of unpaired nucleons outside the closed shells (with balanced angular momenta) constituting the nuclear core. The single-particle shell model predicts that odd-A nuclei *have a ground state spin given by the j-value of the last unpaired nucleon.* The spin sequence is then directly obtainable from Fig. 9.4 and the experimental values largely confirm this; spin values of odd *mass* nuclei are all odd multiples of $\frac{1}{2}\hbar$ and their values agree in detail with what is expected from the parities of the corresponding orbits and the spin-orbit coupling hypothesis. Allowance must be made in certain cases for the effect of the pairing energy in states of high j which, for example, makes the proton configuration $p_{3/2}^3 f_{5/2}^2$ (^{75}As, spin $=\frac{3}{2}$) more stable than the configuration $p_{3/2}^4 f_{5/2}$ (spin $=\frac{5}{2}$). Other exceptions to the simple sequence (e.g. ^{23}Na, $d_{5/2}^3$ spin $=\frac{3}{2}$) cannot be explained in this way, and make it clear that the simple shell model stands in need of extension. The statistics of odd mass nuclei has been determined in a number of cases and is always of the Fermi–Dirac type. This is expected for an odd number of nucleons obeying these statistics, since the complete exchange of nucleons between a pair of odd mass nuclei just multiplies the wave function of the system by $(-1)^4$.

Even-A nuclei have either Z, N both even, or both odd. The single-particle shell model (and all other nuclear models) predicts that:

even N–even Z nuclei have zero ground state spin

owing to the pairing effect. Experimentally, no exception is known to this rule. The even–even nuclides are the largest group of even-A nuclei; for the four stable odd–odd nuclei and for the much larger number of unstable nuclei of this class the single particle model makes no prediction because the angular moments of two unpaired nucleons must be combined in a way that is not specified by the model. Experimentally most odd–odd nuclei have $I > 0$, reflecting a tendency for the odd proton and neutron to align with parallel spins as in the deuteron. More detailed theoretical prediction requires an extension of the simple shell model. Even-A nuclei obey Einstein–Bose statistics; it was the experimental determination of this for ^{14}N which, among other reasons, rendered the proton–electron model of the nucleus untenable.

11.7 Nuclear magnetic dipole moments

The experimental determination of nuclear magnetic moments, like that of spins, has so far been mainly possible for the ground states of stable nuclei; the methods used, which generally give the nuclear g-factor g_I or the hyperfine interaction constant a in the first place are listed in Table 4.1. It has recently become possible in certain special cases to deduce magnetic moments of excited states of nuclei by observing the perturbation of angular correlations involving these states by a superimposed magnetic field (ch. 17). The most direct method of magnetic moment determination, the nuclear Zeeman effect, has in essence been used in a few favourable cases in which γ-ray lines of natural width are observed as a result of the Mössbauer effect (Sect. 13.6.3).

The single-particle shell model predictions for the magnetic moments of odd mass nuclei are not as simple as for spins because of the different g-factors g_s and g_l for intrinsic spin and orbital motion. For a single nucleon moving in a potential well with orbital angular momentum $\mathbf{l}$ and total angular momentum $\mathbf{j}$, where

$$\mathbf{j} = \mathbf{l} + \mathbf{s} \tag{11.22}$$

the calculation of the nuclear g-factor g_I $(I = j)$* follows that of the atomic g-factor for a single electron atom. By using vector diagrams of the type given in Fig. 3.7, it may be shown that

$$\mu_I = g_I \mu_N I \tag{11.23}$$

where

$$g_I = \frac{j}{2} \left[(g_l + g_s) + (g_l - g_s) \frac{l(l+1) - \frac{3}{4}}{j(j+1)} \right] \tag{11.24}$$

---

* For a single-particle nucleus the spin I is just the total angular momentum j of the odd particle.

This expression can now be evaluated for a single proton or neutron using known g-factors. Two cases arise, corresponding to the two possible orientations of the nucleon spin with respect to the orbital vector $j = l \pm \frac{1}{2}$.

For an odd *neutron* ($g_l = 0$, $g_s = -3.826 = 2\mu_n/\mu_N$, where μ_n is the neutron moment) we find

$$\left. \begin{aligned} \mu_I &= \tfrac{1}{2}g_s\mu_N = \mu_n & \text{for } I = j = l+\tfrac{1}{2} \\ \mu_I &= \frac{-j}{j+1}\,\tfrac{1}{2}g_s\mu_N = \frac{-j}{j+1}\,\mu_n & \text{for } I = j = l-\tfrac{1}{2} \end{aligned} \right\} \quad (11.25)$$

and for an odd *proton* ($g_l = 1$, $g_s = 5.585 = 2\mu_p/\mu_N$)

$$\left. \begin{aligned} \mu_I &= [(j-\tfrac{1}{2}) + \tfrac{1}{2}g_s]\mu_N \\ &= (j-\tfrac{1}{2})\mu_N + \mu_p & \text{for } I = j = l+\tfrac{1}{2} \\ \mu_I &= \frac{j}{j+1}\,[(j+\tfrac{3}{2}) - \tfrac{1}{2}g_s]\mu_N \\ &= \frac{j}{j+1}[(j+\tfrac{3}{2})\mu_N - \mu_p] & \text{for } I = j = l-\tfrac{1}{2} \end{aligned} \right\} \quad (11.26)$$

If a figure showing μ_I as a function of $I = j$ is drawn we obtain the *Schmidt* diagrams, as in Fig. 11.11. The lines drawn in this figure have a meaning only at the half-integral spin values corresponding to observed nuclear spins. Fig. 11.11 also gives observed values of μ_I for a number of nuclei with known spin; if these are truly single-particle nuclei, the magnetic moments should fall on the Schmidt lines.

Inspection of Fig. 11.11 shows that there is some correlation between observed moments and the Schmidt lines. In particular the magnetic moment follows the spin change at shell closure. With the exception, however, of a few single particle nuclei, such as ^{3}H, ^{3}He, ^{17}O, ^{39}K, observed moments tend to fall between the Schmidt lines, though rather nearer to one than to the other. It is this feature which enables magnetic moments to be used, with some confidence, in deducing the orbital quantum number, and hence the parity of the nuclear ground state. Thus we have, as an example of the method for odd proton nuclei:

$$\begin{array}{llll} {}^7_3\text{Li} & I = \tfrac{3}{2} & \mu_{\text{exp}} = 3.26 & \mu_{\text{calc}} = 3.79 \ (p\text{-orbit}) \\ & & & \phantom{\mu_{\text{calc}}} = 0.12 \ (d\text{-orbit}) \end{array}$$

14*

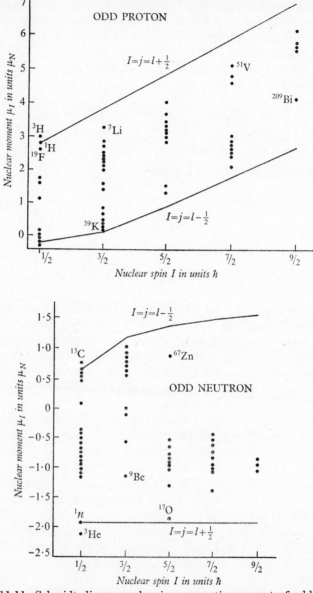

Fig. 11.11. Schmidt diagrams showing magnetic moment of odd-mass nuclei as a function of nuclear spin. The lines show the magnetic moments expected for a single nucleon at the spin values $j = l \pm \frac{1}{2}$, where l is the orbital momentum quantum number (Ref. 11.10).

in units of μ_N, so that a p-orbit is indicated, and

$$^{23}\text{Na} \quad I = \tfrac{3}{2} \quad \mu_{\text{exp}} = 2{\cdot}22 \quad \mu_{\text{calc}} = 3{\cdot}79 \; (p\text{-orbit})$$
$$= 0{\cdot}12 \; (d\text{-orbit})$$

so that some mixing of states is indicated, as is already expected since $I = \tfrac{3}{2}$ is a spin anomaly, and

$$^{39}_{19}\text{K} \quad I = \tfrac{3}{2} \quad \mu_{\text{exp}} = 0{\cdot}22 \quad \mu_{\text{calc}} = 0{\cdot}12 \; (d\text{-orbit})$$
$$^{45}_{21}\text{Sc} \quad I = \tfrac{7}{2} \quad \mu_{\text{exp}} = 4{\cdot}76 \quad \mu_{\text{calc}} = 5{\cdot}79 \; (f\text{-orbit})$$

which shows the transition between shells at magic number 20. For odd-neutron nuclei the evidence is not quite so clear but we note

$$^{129}_{75}\text{Xe} \; I = \tfrac{1}{2} \quad \mu_{\text{exp}} = -0{\cdot}78 \quad \mu_{\text{calc}} = -1.91 \; (s\text{-orbit})$$
$$^{137}_{81}\text{Ba} \; I = \tfrac{3}{2} \quad \mu_{\text{exp}} = 0{\cdot}94 \quad \mu_{\text{calc}} = 1{\cdot}1 \quad (d\text{-orbit})$$

Attempts have been made to modify the single particle model to account for the deviations from the Schmidt lines, but the only successful approach is the generalization of the model into the individual particle model or the collective model (ch. 12). The magnetic moments of even–even nuclei are zero as expected since the nuclear spin is zero and the charge distribution is spherically symmetrical.

11.8   Nuclear electric quadrupole moments

The existence of nuclear electric quadrupole moments (Appendix 3) was first demonstrated spectroscopically and spectroscopic methods of determining this quantity, which are mainly observations of the quadrupole coupling constant b, are listed in Table **4.1**. Nuclear methods of determining this moment, which is the lowest order electric moment observable as a static nuclear property, will be discussed in Sect. 12.3.5. For the purpose of comparing observed quadrupole moments with predictions of the single-particle shell model we require to know the quadrupole moment for a single proton moving in a shell model orbit; this has the same sort of significance for the electric moment as has the nuclear magneton for the magnetic dipole moment.

From the general definition of quadrupole moment (Appendix 3) we need to evaluate the averaged value of the quantity

$$(3z^2 - r^2) \tag{11.27}$$

for a proton of total angular momentum j. The calculation gives

$$Q_{Ip} = -\frac{2j-1}{2j+2}\,\overline{r^2} \tag{11.28}$$

where $\overline{r^2}$ is the mean square radius of the charge distribution as defined in Sect. 11.1. The single proton in orbital motion thus has a negative quadrupole moment, which corresponds pictorially to a disc-shaped charge distribution surrounding the axis Oz.

An odd neutron moving in a potential well has no electric quadrupole moment since it is uncharged. There is, however, a small quadrupole moment in an actual nucleus (A,Z) because of a recoil effect. If the neutron is considered to describe an orbit of radius δ about the centre, the Z protons of the nucleus describe an orbit of radius δ/A and the quadrupole moment expected is

$$Q_{In} = \frac{Z}{A^2}\,Q_{Ip} \tag{11.29}$$

which is of the same sign as the single proton moment but much less in magnitude.

Since $\overline{r^2} = \frac{3}{5}R^2$ where R is the radius of the equivalent uniform charge distribution, the quadrupole moment of odd proton nuclei should be of the order of the nuclear radius squared, i.e. $10^{-24} - 10^{-25}$ cm^2. The ratio Q_I/R^2 gives a useful estimate of the extent to which Q_I differs from the single particle value. The results of measurements of electric quadrupole moment are shown plotted against Z and N in Fig. 11.12; the moments change in sign at the magic numbers. Closed shell nuclei have zero quadrupole moment as would be expected from the symmetry of their nucleon orbits. Even–even nuclei in general also have zero quadrupole moment, but this must be so because they have spin $I=0$ and therefore a spherically symmetrical charge distribution. These general features are in agreement with the predictions of the single particle model. In detail, however, important deviations are found; these are:

a) the quadrupole moments of odd-neutron nuclei are

similar in magnitude to those of odd-proton nuclei instead of being much smaller, e.g.

$$^{35}_{16}\text{S} \quad Q_I = -0{\cdot}055 \times 10^{-24} \text{ cm}^2;$$
$$^{35}_{17}\text{Cl} \quad Q_I = -0{\cdot}078 \times 10^{-24} \text{ cm}^2$$

b) the magnitudes of quadrupole moments for nuclei with nucleon numbers between closed shells in the region $150 < A < 190$ are 10–20 times the single particle value, i.e., $Q_I/R^2 \approx 10\text{--}20$.

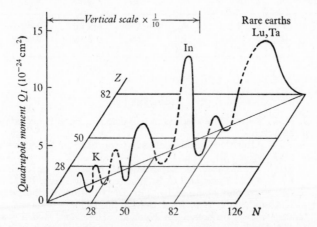

Fig. 11.12. Values of nuclear electric quadrupole moment Q_I as a function of N and Z. The values up to ^{115}In are multiplied by 10. Dotted lines show regions in which Q_I is not known. The moments are very large in the rare earth region (Ref. 11.11).

11.9 Summary

Table 11.1 is a small section of a typical table of data of nuclear moments, covering the whole range of stable nuclei. Such tables show that the single-particle shell model provides an excellent framework for a general description of the properties of the nuclear ground state. Nuclear radii are mainly properties of continuous nuclear matter and do not reveal inadequacies of the shell model. The deficiencies that have been noted in spin values, magnetic moments and electric quadrupole moments however are found to require extensions of the model to cover interactions between equivalent nucleons outside a closed core. We consider these extensions in the next chapter.

Table 11.1.   Data on nuclear moments

(From Ref. 11.11.) R is taken to be $1 \cdot 3 A^{1/3} \times 10^{-13}$ cm. The first three nuclei have an odd proton, the final two an odd neutron.

ELEMENT	A	Z	N	I	ASSUMED STATE OF LAST PARTICLE	$\dfrac{\mu_I}{\mu_N}$	SCHMIDT VALUE	Q_I $(10^{-24}$ cm)	$\dfrac{Q_I}{R^2}$
B	11	5	6	$\frac{3}{2}$	$p_{3/2}$	2·69	3·79	0·036	0·55
Cl	35	17	18	$\frac{3}{2}$	$d_{3/2}$	0·82	0·12	−0·079	−0·55
Ta	181	73	108	$\frac{7}{2}$	$g_{7/2}$	2·1	4·79	6·0	14
O	17	8	9	$\frac{5}{2}$	$d_{5/2}$	−1·89	−1·91	−0·004	−0·05
S	35	16	19	$\frac{3}{2}$	$d_{3/2}$	1·0	1·15	0.038	0·27

References

11.1   J. M. C. Scott, 'The Radius of a Nucleus', *Progr. nucl. Phys.*, **5**, 157, 1956.

11.2   R. Hofstadter, 'Electron Scattering and Nuclear Structure', *Rev. mod. Phys.*, **28**, 214, 1956; 'Methods of Measuring Nuclear Size', in *Methods of Experimental Physics*, Vol. 5, Part A, ed. L. C. L. Yuan and C. S. Wu, Academic Press, 1961.

11.3   K. W. Ford and D. L. Hill, 'The Distribution of Charge in the Nucleus', *Ann. Rev. Nucl. Sci.*, **5**, 25, 1955.

11.4   International Conference on Nuclear Sizes, *Rev. mod Phys.*, **30**, 412, 1958.

11.5   D. West, 'Mesonic Atoms', *Rep. progr. Phys.*, **21**, 271, 1958.

11.6   R. D. Evans, *The Atomic Nucleus*, McGraw-Hill, 1955.

11.7   L. R. B. Elton, *Nuclear Sizes*, Oxford University Press, 1961.

11.8   L. Wilets, 'Shape of the Nucleus', *Science*, **129**, 361, 1959.

11.9   M. G. Mayer and J. H. D. Jensen, *Elementary Theory of Nuclear Shell Structure*, Wiley, 1955.

11.10   R. J. Blin-Stoyle, *Theories of Nuclear Moments*, Oxford University Press, 1957.

11.11   H. Kopferman, *Nuclear Moments*, Academic Press, 1958.

11.12   K. F. Smith, 'Nuclear Moments and Spins', *Progr. nucl. Phys.*, **6**, 52, 1957.

NUCLEAR MODELS II

The earliest nuclear models (ch. 9) were of two types, those in which discrete nucleon states could be distinguished and those in which the emphasis was on the continuous properties of nuclear matter. Modern developments of models have proceeded on both lines and we now recognize:

a) models of the *individual particle type*, in which shell structure is a basic feature, and

b) models of the *strong interaction type*, such as liquid-drop models, in which there is much correlation between the motion of nucleons.

Each sort of model gives a more complete account of the nuclear level spectrum than does the single-particle shell model and this is achieved by allowing some degree of coupling between nucleons. In this chapter we examine the effects of introducing these interactions. Since internucleon forces are obviously involved, it will be convenient at the outset to introduce the formal concept of isobaric spin which makes possible a concise account of the effect of charge independence of forces and provides a new quantum number for nuclear states.

12.1 Isobaric (isotopic) spin*

The similarity of structure of the odd mirror nuclei due to charge symmetry of nuclear forces has been noted in Sect. 11.2.4. If we compare the level systems of even-A nuclei further similarities are apparent which suggest that disregarding Coulomb effects the neutron–proton force is the same as the neutron–neutron and proton–proton force for nucleons in the same state of motion. In Fig. 12.1a, the low-lying levels

---

* The original term isotopic spin is widely used but has little to commend it.

of the nuclei mass 10 (^{10}Be—^{10}B—^{10}C) are shown, and the ground states are placed at levels corresponding to the respective *nuclear* masses. Beta-decay takes place between the isobars as shown. If now the nuclear masses are corrected by subtracting the Coulomb energy (Sect. 11.2.4) which is greater for ^{10}C than for ^{10}B and greater for ^{10}B than for ^{10}Be, the relative level

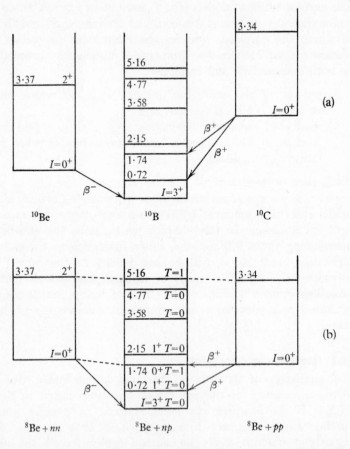

Fig. 12.1. Low-lying energy levels of the isobars of mass 10. Energies are marked in MeV and spins and parities are indicated by the symbols 0^+, 1^+, etc.

a) Masses of bare nuclei.

b) Nuclear masses corrected for Coulomb energy and for neutron-proton mass difference, showing isobaric triplet levels.

positions become as shown in Fig. 12.1b. It is then found that there is a well-marked correspondence of binding energy and other properties between the low levels of the even–even isobars ^{10}Be, ^{10}C and that these levels have counterparts in the odd–odd isobar ^{10}B, which has in addition many other levels.

This can be understood in terms of the *charge independence* of nuclear forces. If an isobar of mass 10 is considered as a core (^{8}Be) plus two nucleons in the $p_{3/2}$ shell, then identical levels will be expected in each isobar if the (nn), (pp) and (np) interactions are the same. Because of the Pauli principle, not all states of motion accessible to a neutron–proton system will be permitted for pairs of identical nucleons and fewer states are therefore found in the even–even nuclei. The states that are common between the isobars are those in which the motion is such that a proton may be changed into a neutron, or vice versa, without offending the Pauli principle. The ^1S state for instance, in which two nucleons with spins opposed move with zero relative orbital motion is permitted to the three pairs (nn), (pp) and (np) but the ^3S state is permitted only to the system (np).

The isobaric spin formalism describes the three pairs as a *charge triplet* and the (np) system associated with states such as ^3S as a *charge singlet*. An isobaric spin quantum number $T = 1$ is ascribed to the states of the triplet with components m_T (often written T_z) = 1, 0 −1 corresponding to the systems (pp), (np) and (nn), while for $T = 0$ only the (np) system exists, with $m_T = 0$. This concept, which will not be developed fully here (see Refs. 12.1 and 12.9), is only of value so long as the states of $T = 1$ have essentially the same binding energy, i.e. so long as nuclear forces are charge independent. There is then a degeneracy of the triplet states (Fig. 12.1.b) which is removed when electrostatic forces (Fig. 12.1.a) are allowed to act. This is in analogy with the removal of degeneracy connected with ordinary spin or orbital motion by the application of a magnetic field. We obtain a physical picture of the isobaric spin quantum number T by noting that $2T + 1$ is the number of isobaric nuclei in which the level of given T occurs. In Fig. 12, the states of ^{10}Be and ^{10}C are all of $T = 1$ and have $T = 1$ analogues in ^{10}B. States of $T = 0$ in ^{10}B cannot be found in the even–even nuclei.

The isobaric spin quantum number was first used in order to describe the neutron and proton as alternative states of the nucleon, distinguished only by charge. If we ascribe an isobaric spin $t = \frac{1}{2}$ to the nucleon then the components $m_t = -\frac{1}{2}$ and $m_t = +\frac{1}{2}$ may be taken† to denote the neutron and proton respectively. For a nuclear state there will be a total isobaric spin T with a component m_T ($\leqslant T$) given by

$$m_T = \frac{Z-N}{2} = \frac{A-2N}{2} = -\frac{A-2Z}{2}$$

where A is the mass number and N and Z the neutron and proton numbers of the nucleus in which the state occurs. For two nucleons, we obtain the results already quoted; in general T is integral for even A and half integral for odd A.

The concept of isobaric spin as a useful quantum variable under conditions of charge independence leads to selection rules for nuclear reactions which provide that this quantity shall be conserved. In the case of a scattering process such as

$$^{10}_{5}\mathrm{B} + {}^{2}\mathrm{H} \rightarrow {}^{10}_{5}\mathrm{B}^* + {}^{2}\mathrm{H}$$

the colliding nuclei have $T = 0$ and the isobaric spin selection rule therefore only permits the excitation of states of $T = 0$ in the $^{10}\mathrm{B}$ nucleus. For inelastic proton scattering on the other hand, e.g.

$$^{10}_{5}\mathrm{B} + {}^{1}\mathrm{H} \rightarrow {}^{10}_{5}\mathrm{B}^* + {}^{1}\mathrm{H}$$

this restriction does not apply, since the nucleon has $t = \frac{1}{2}$ and by combination of the corresponding vectors states of both $T = 0$ and $T = 1$ in $^{10}\mathrm{B}$ can be excited without violation of the conservation principle. Experimental results for these two reactions clearly indicate discrimination against the 1·74 MeV $T = 1$ state of $^{10}\mathrm{B}$ in inelastic deuteron scattering.

12.2 The individual (independent) particle model

The single-particle shell model assumes that nucleons outside closed shells, like those which make up the shells, pair off as far as possible with antiparallel spins and orbital momenta, i.e.

---

† The sign convention here is opposite to that used by Heisenberg in his discussion of exchange forces (Sect. 18.3) but is the more convenient in meson physics.

that there is a large pairing energy (Sect. **10.1**) in this state. Without some such assumption it is impossible to predict the ground state spin of a nucleus with several nucleons outside closed shells. In ^7_3Li for instance it is assumed that the two $p_{3/2}$ neutrons always couple to give a spin of zero, so that the resultant spin ($\frac{3}{2}$) is that of the odd proton. The neutrons may however couple to a spin* of 2 and resultant spin values between $\frac{1}{2}$ and $\frac{7}{2}$ are then possible. The corresponding states all have the same energy according to the simple potential well model and in theory this is a case of degeneracy. In fact although the general shell model potential must be due to the forces between nucleons, it may not be correct to place all their effect in this category, and if 'residual' inter-particle forces are allowed to act the degeneracy is lifted. The single particle model then develops into the *individual particle model* in which no specific assumption as to pairing energy need be made. In this model ^7_3Li is described as a nucleus with the configuration (closed shell plus $p^3_{3/2}$); the particles outside the closed shell are all in the same quantum state and are therefore *equivalent*.

In individual particle model calculations it is normally assumed that spin-orbit forces exist and that a potential energy

$$\xi(\mathbf{s.l}) \tag{12.1}$$

arises for each nucleon as a result of the interaction 9.10. This leads naturally to a classification of states in terms of j-j coupling (Sect. 3.7.2). The nucleon–nucleon force (which is deduced from two-body data, including high-energy experiments) contains a non-central term which is connected with the spin-orbit effect. There are also central force terms whose effect favours a coupling of the L–S type with which energies given by integrals of the form 3.30 arise. These may be conveniently specified by the exchange integral K. The predicted pattern of energy levels depends on the relative strength of the spin–orbit and central effects (ξ/K). For light nuclei the observed patterns favour an *intermediate coupling scheme* with $\xi/K = 1$ to 5. All calculations based on the individual particle model are much simplified if the charge independence of nuclear

---

* Spins of 1 and 3 are forbidden for identical nucleons by the Pauli principle.

forces is assumed. The total isobaric spin then provides a good quantum number T. In the L–S coupling scheme the total spin and orbital quantum numbers are also significant but in

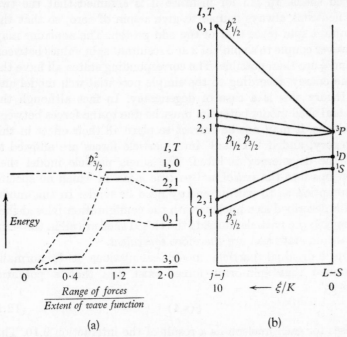

Fig. 12.2

a) States of the j–j configuration $p^2_{3/2}$ as a function of range of the interparticle forces. For zero range there are just two states, corresponding to good overlap and poor overlap of the wave functions. The assignment of isobaric spin T is in accordance with the requirements of the Pauli principle.

b) Transition from j–j to L–S coupling for the $T = 1$ states of the p^2 configuration. This includes the systems $p^2_{1/2}$ and $p_{1/2}p_{3/2}$ as well as $p^2_{3/2}$. States of $T = 1$ can be occupied by identical nucleons and the levels shown are expected in isobars in which two p-particles are found outside a closed core, e.g. ^{6}Li, ^{6}He; ^{10}Be, ^{10}B, ^{10}C. Two of these states will be noted in Fig. 12.1b (Ref. 12.1).

the j–j extreme these two numbers are meaningless and must be replaced by symbols showing the number of nucleons outside closed shells.

The order of energy levels expected in j–j coupling for the simple case of a nucleus ($^6_3$Li) with two $p_{3/2}$ nucleons outside a closed shell is shown in Fig. 12.2a, taken from the work of Flowers.* The level spacing is plotted against a parameter which compares the range of the residual forces with the extent of the shell-model wave-function (or nuclear radius) assumed in the calculation. For forces of zero range there is degeneracy, which is removed as the range increases; the levels are labelled according to the (I, T) values. It is seen that the level order depends on the range of the forces. If the spin–orbit coupling is weak, the L–S pattern of energy levels is approached. This is shown in Fig. 12.2b for two identical p-particles, which are allowed by the Pauli principle to form ^1S, ^1D, and ^3P states. The order of these states is generally such that the lowest states have the maximum spatial symmetery in their wave-function. This is because of the attractive nature of the forces, and gives a level order opposite to that found in atoms, in which the forces between electrons are repulsive. The ^1S and ^1D states pass over into the two $T = 1$ states of the $p_{3/2}^2$ configuration in j–j coupling, but the ^3P state, which is a triplet when resolved by a small spin–orbit interaction, leads to the $T = 1$ states of the $p_{1/2}^2$ and $p_{1/2}p_{3/2}$ configurations in the j–j limit. The $T = 0$ states may be similarly treated. For nuclei with more than two particles outside closed shells a similar discussion may be given, but extra quantum numbers are required.

The individual particle model, with short range forces, makes certain general predictions about spins of nuclear states, of which the most important are:

a) a configuration containing an even number of neutrons or protons has $I = 0$ in the ground state,

b) a configuration containing an odd number of particles of one kind has $I = j$ in the ground state,,

c) the states of a nucleus with a j^2 configuration of two like particles (e.g. the $T = 1$ states of p^2 shown in Fig. 12.2a) have spins $0, 2, 4, \ldots (2j - 1)$ in order of ascending energy.

Predictions (a) and (b) are also those of the single-particle shell model and are independent of the type of coupling assumed.

---

* A. R. Edmonds and B. H. Flowers, *Proc. roy. Soc.*, **A,215**, 120, 1952.

In the general case, when the classification in terms of quantum numbers (I,T) or (L,S,T) has been established, the order of the states must be found by solution of the Schrödinger equation. This type of calculation is familiar for the hydrogen atom (Sect. **3.3**) but must be generalized in the nuclear case because of the several particles outside closed shells.

The wave function of a given nuclear state obtained in this way may be quite complicated especially when different configurations are involved. For ^{19}F, for instance, in which there are three nucleons outside the ^{16}O core and the $1d$ and $2s$ shells are filling, the wave function of a typical low-lying state is 12% d^3, 59% d^2s, 0% ds^2 and 29% s^3. With this detailed knowledge it is possible to calculate the main nuclear properties and it is found that magnetic moments and electric quadrupole moments are both better predicted. Magnetic moments between the Schmidt values are obtained because the single particle moments are 'diluted' as a result of joint motion in the configurations of equivalent nucleons. The many-body description also explains the fact that odd neutron nuclei have appreciable quadrupole moments. There are however still deviations from experiment, of which the most obvious is the existence of the extremely large electric quadrupole moments for the rare-earth elements. Some improvement can be obtained by taking account of the mixing of effects due to different configurations, which adds extra coherence to the motion. A more appropriate description of these extreme moments appears however to be offered by the collective model.

12.3   The collective model

12.3.1   GENERAL.   If mixing of configurations in the shell-model sense is pushed to its extreme, the motions of all particles in the nucleus must be taken into account. This leads to a new type of model, in which the shape and angular momentum of the closed shells forming the nuclear 'core' play an important part. The significance of the shape of the nuclear core was first pointed out by Rainwater* and the quantitative development of the resulting 'collective' model was carried out by A. Bohr and Mottelson† using the analogy of the liquid drop, which had

---

* J. Rainwater, *Phys. Rev.*, **79**, 432, 1950.

† A. Bohr and B. R. Mottelson, *Dan. Mat. fys. Medd.*, **27**, No. 16, 1953.

been discussed much earlier by N. Bohr and Kalckar. Many other authors have contributed to the details of the model, and striking successes in prediction have been obtained.

The collective model starts essentially with the idea that in order to explain the extremely large static electric quadrupole moments of nuclei lying between closed shells some co-operative motion of nuclear matter, resulting in a 'permanent' nuclear deformation, is necessary. It is supposed that this deformation (which vanishes for closed-shell nuclei), is produced by a polarizing effect of the individual or intrinsic motion of the nucleons outside closed shells. It is vital to the detailed development of the collective model that it should be possible to envisage a clear separation between the individual motion of the 'loose' nucleons and the collective motion of the core. This means that the single-particle energies associated with the shell model states of the nucleons should be large compared with the rotational and vibrational energies of the core. It is then possible, by allowing some interaction between the two types of motion, to present a 'unified' picture of nuclear motion in which both shell-model and collective features appear. This approach is a combination of the individual particle type of model with the strong interaction type; it not only explains the large quadrupole moments but also predicts a fine structure of the nuclear level spectrum owing to energies associated with the vibrational and rotational motion of the core.

The origin of a stable deformation may be discussed as follows: suppose that a nucleus has an ellipsoidal type of deformation (Fig. 12.3a), symmetrical about an axis Oz' fixed in the body and specified by a deformation parameter β such that

$$\beta = \frac{\Delta R}{R_0} \tag{12.2}$$

where R_0 is the average nuclear radius and ΔR is the difference between the major and minor semi-axis of the ellipse.* The potential energy of the nucleus as a function of deformation may be represented as in Fig. 12.3b, in which the different

---

* Frequently β is defined by expressing the nuclear radius for an angle θ with the axis of symmetry as $R(\theta) = R_0[1 + \beta Y_2^0(\theta)]$. This is equivalent to (12.2) with the addition of a numerical factor of 1·06.

curves are plotted for different numbers of nucleons outside
closed shells. For nuclei near closed shells the pairing forces
(Sect. **10.1**) favour the grouping of these nucleons into pairs

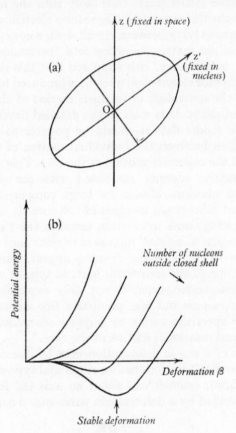

Fig. 12.3. Deformation of a nucleus.
a) Axially symmetrical deformed shape.
b) Potential energy of nucleus as a function of deformation (Ref. 12.2).

with zero angular momentum. The equilibrium shape is then
spherical, and the collective motion is a *vibration* about this
shape. As the number of loose nucleons increases, the effect of
longer range forces is felt more, the frequency of the collective
vibration decreases, and finally the spherical shape becomes
unstable and the nucleus acquires a permanent deformation.

This deformation appears both in the loose nucleons and in the nuclear core with which they interact, but for simplicity we shall consider it to be a property of the core alone. The collective motion now becomes a vibration about the equilibrium shape, and (more important for many nuclear spectra) a *rotation* of the nuclear orientation which maintains the deformed shape.

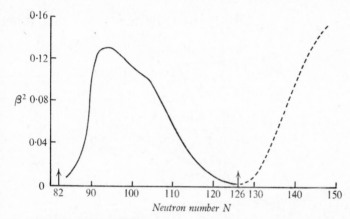

Fig. 12.4. Variation of the nuclear deformation parameter β (plotted as β^2) with neutron number in the range between the closed shells at $N = 82$ and 126. This includes the rare earth nuclei with their large quadrupole moments. The deformation disappears for the closed shell nuclei; at $N = 90$ a stable deformation suddenly appears (Ref. 12.4).

The deformation parameter β can be obtained from measurements of electromagnetic transition rates (Coulomb excitation and lifetime measurements), from the optical isotope shift and also from the pattern of rotational energy levels under certain assumptions as to moments of inertia. The general variation of β with neutron number between the magic numbers 82 and 126 is shown in Fig. 12.4. The jump in β between $N = 88$ and $N = 90$ is entirely unconnected with any features of the single-particle shell model and represents a transition between the vibrational and rotational type of collective motion.

The coupling of angular momenta in a deformed nucleus resembles the coupling scheme for molecules and is shown in Fig. 12.5. As in the molecular case there is no rotation about the symmetry axis in the lowest states, but the intrinsic motion of the loose particles takes place about this axis, with a component angular momentum $K\hbar = \sum K_p \hbar$ where K_p refers to a single nucleon. The collective angular momentum perpendicular to the symmetry axis is **R** and the total angular momentum is **I**. The component of **I** along the axis fixed in space is $M\hbar$ and the component of **I** along the symmetry axis is just $K\hbar$. The absolute value of **R** is given by

$$|\mathbf{R}|^2 = [I(I+1) - K^2]\hbar^2 \tag{12.3}$$

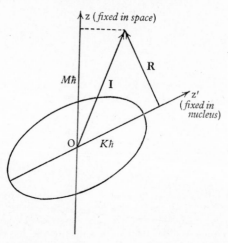

Fig. 12.5. Coupling scheme for angular momentum of deformed nuclei.

It is only possible to make a simple investigation of this complex situation if it is assumed that the motion can be separated into:

a) intrinsic nucleonic motion in the non-spherical potential,
b) collective rotation,
c) vibration about the static equilibrium shape.

The excitation energies corresponding to these motions increase in the order (b), (c), (a); we now consider each of these separately.

12.3.2 INTRINSIC STATES IN A SPHEROIDAL FIELD. The stable deformation β is produced by the polarizing action of nucleons moving in a spheroidal field, as distinct from the spherically symmetrical field assumed in the single particle shell model. The sequence of states of a single particle under these circumstances has been calculated by Nilsson* as a function of deformation for a stationary field of oscillator type.

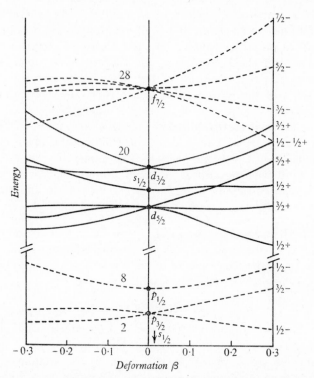

Fig. 12.6. Single particle states in a spheroidal potential as a function of the deformation parameter. The states are labelled by the quantum number $K_p(\leqslant j)$ and the parity (Ref. 12.5).

Results of the type shown in Fig. 12.6 are obtained; for zero distortion the normal shell model ordering appears but for large deformation this is drastically altered.

In a non-spherical field, total angular momentum is no longer a constant of the motion, but for an axially symmetric field the component of angular momentum along the axis is conserved. A particle which occupies a state l_j in a spherical field ($\beta = 0$)

* S. G. Nilsson, *Dan. Mat. fys. Medd.*, **29**, No. 16, 1955.

can occupy $(2j+1)$ states with component angular momenta $K_p = j, (j-1), \ldots -(j-1), -j$ along the symmetry axis in the non-spherical field. There is no energy difference between the states K_p and $-K_p$ so that each shell-model level splits into only $\frac{1}{2}(2j+1)$ levels in the spheroidal potential. These new single particle states are labelled by K_p and by the parity. In an actual nuclear spectrum, bands of rotational levels are built on the intrinsic levels defined by the number of particles in the nucleus and the deformation. In analysis of a spectrum the deformation may be estimated from the electromagnetic moments of the nucleus, and the intrinsic level order is then predictable.

The intrinsic states shown in Fig. 12.6 are populated by protons and neutrons independently in the building up of a stable nucleus, as in the single particle shell model. Two nucleons of each kind with oppositely directed orbital angular momenta $(\pm K_p)$ can be associated with each intrinsic state and the nth state is completely occupied in a nucleus of mass $A = 4n$.

12.3.3 ROTATIONAL STATES. For nuclei far from closed shells, the rotational motion of a deformed nucleus does not affect the internal structure of the system. The energy of the rotation may be written classically

$$E_{\mathrm{rot}} = \tfrac{1}{2}\mathscr{I}\omega^2 \qquad (12.4)$$

where ω is the angular velocity and $\mathscr{I}$ is an effective moment of inertia. The rotation is not simply that of a rigid body; it was at first regarded rather as due to a hydrodynamical wave moving round the nucleus considered as a liquid drop. Fig. 12.7, taken from an article by Bohr, shows how constituent particles of a nucleus in particular modes of oscillation can lead to a rotation of the geometrical shape. For the irrotational motion of the particles (Fig. 12.7b) the effective moment of inertia about an axis perpendicular to the symmetry axis is determined by the deformation and may be written

$$\mathscr{I} \approx \mathscr{I}_0\beta^2 = \mathscr{I}_0\left(\frac{\Delta R}{R_0}\right)^2 \qquad (12.5)$$

where $\mathscr{I}_0$ is the 'rigid' moment given by

$$\mathscr{I}_0 = \tfrac{2}{5}MAR_0^2 \qquad (12.6)$$

for rotation of a mass MA. If the rotational angular momentum $\mathscr{I}w = |\mathbf{R}|$ is inserted in 12.4 we find, using 12.3

$$E_I = \frac{\hbar^2}{2\mathscr{I}} [I(I+1) - K^2] \qquad (12.7)$$

For the value of K given by the intrinsic motion, this equation determines a rotational band of levels superimposed on the energies of the intrinsic motion. For $K = \frac{1}{2}$ a special formula is necessary (Ref. 12.2). The first term is already familiar as the rotational energy of a diatomic molecule (Sect. 3.8.3).

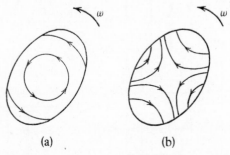

(a)   (b)

Fig. 12.7. Rigid and wave-like rotations of nucleus. In (a) the component particles move in circles round the axis of rotation. In (b) the particles oscillate along the paths shown and only the geometrical shape rotates (irrotational flow).

For *even–even nuclei* in their ground state, the particles fall alternately into states of opposite K_p and there is no contribution to the total angular momentum from the intrinsic motion ($K = 0$). There is symmetry about a plane perpendicular to the nuclear axis and hence, as in the case of the homonuclear diatomic molecule obeying Bose statistics,

$$I = 0, 2, 4, 6, \ldots \text{ (parity even)} \qquad (12.8)$$

in order that the wave function shall be invariant for a rotation of 180°. This type of rotational band is found in many nuclei in the known regions of deformation, $A \approx 24$, $150 < A < 190$ and $A > 200$. By putting $I = 0, 2, 4, \ldots$ in 12.7 it may be seen that the ratio of excitation of the successive states is $E_4/E_2 = 10/3$, $E_6/E_2 = 7$, $E_8/E_2 = 12$ and these characteristic values are verified for many even–even nuclei. Fig. 12.8a shows the predicted spacings of the levels of a rotational band, compared with observation for the nucleus ^{238}U (Fig. 12.8b).

The ground state of an even–even nucleus always has $I = 0$, and the first excited state usually has $I = 2^+$ in agreement with prediction. The systematic variation in energy of the observed 2^+ states in even–even nuclei is shown in Fig. 9.8; these states

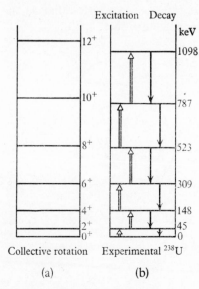

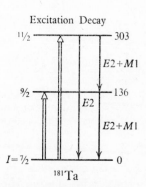

Fig. 12.8. Rotational band in a deformed even–even nucleus.
a) Theoretical series of levels.
b) Experimental results for ^{238}U obtained by Coulomb excitation (F. S. Stephens *et al.*, *Phys. Rev. Letters*, **3**, 435, 1959).

Fig. 12.9. Rotational states in odd-A nucleus showing radiative transitions upward (excitation) and downward (decay).

are usually strongly excited in $E2$ Coulomb transitions (Sect. 13.6.2), and have low energies between closed shells. The moments of inertia calculated from the level spacing can be used to obtain the deformation parameter β, from 12.5, but it is more instructive to use independent determinations of β (Sect. 12.3.5) to check the value $\mathcal{I}_0$. It is found that the collective rotation requires a moment of inertia which is less than the rigid body value 12.6 but greater than the hydrodynamical value.

In *odd-A nuclei* the last odd particle contributes an angular momentum K (which may be deduced from the Nilsson orbits, Sect. 12.3.2) along the nuclear axis and the allowed values of spin are

$$I = K, K+1, K+2\ldots. \text{ (half integral)} \qquad (12.9)$$

where K is then the spin of the ground (rotationless) state. The states of the rotational band have all the same parity, which is that of the intrinsic motion, and $E2$ Coulomb excitation can now populate two states ($K \rightarrow K+1, K+2$) instead of one only as in even–even nuclei. Energy values again agree with prediction from 12.7 and moments of inertia are similar to (though not identical with) those derived from nearby even–even nuclei. A typical spectrum is shown in Fig. 12.9.

12.3.4 VIBRATIONAL STATES. Nuclei with relatively few particles outside closed shells have a spherical equilibrium form, and the collective motion takes the form of an oscillation of the loose particles about the spherical surface. In this type of motion the nucleus possesses a certain number of vibrational quanta or 'phonons' of energy $\hbar\omega_l$ and angular momentum $l\hbar$ in accordance with the quantum mechanical picture of the harmonic oscillator. The level spectrum of such a nucleus is built upon these vibrational states in some cases by the addition of a rotational fine structure. Since there is no stable deformation for these nuclei the static moments are not enhanced, as in the case of nuclei far from closed shells.

The simplest vibrational spectra are found for even–even nuclei in which there is no contribution to the nuclear spin from the intrinsic motion. The basic vibrational spectrum is due to quadrupole 'phonons' and is given in Fig. 12.10 together with permitted spin values; in practice the degeneracy between the different levels is resolved and the expectation is a 0^+ ground state, and a 2^+ first excited state followed by a triplet of states 0^+ 2^+ 4^+ with energies of the order of twice that of the first excited state. The energies vary regularly according to the distance of the nucleus concerned from closed shells.

12.3.5 STATIC AND TRANSITION MOMENTS. The collective model gives a good account of static magnetic dipole moments in the regions of strong deformation. Gyromagnetic ratios for the core and for the intrinsic motion are necessary and with reasonable values for these quantities the Schmidt lines (Fig. 11.11) are shifted in the right direction. The large static electric quadrupole moments shown in Fig. 11.12 are naturally

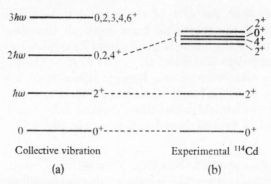

Fig. 12.10. Vibrational levels in even–even nuclei.
a) Theoretical series of levels.
b) Experimental results for ^{114}Cd. (Ref. 12.2 and H. T. Motz, *Phys. Rev.*, **104**, 1353, 1956.)

explained by the collective model as due to the equilibrium quadrupole deformation of the core. The moment corresponding to the deformation β for a nuclear charge number Z, is

$$Q_0 = \frac{4}{5} Z R_0^2 \beta \qquad (12.10)$$

but the spectroscopically observed ground state moment (Appendix 3) is only

$$Q_I = \frac{I(2I-1)}{(I+1)(2I+3)} Q_0 \qquad (12.11)$$

Radiative transitions between the levels of rotational bands of strongly deformed nuclei may be simply related to the static quadrupole moment Q_0. General expressions for these transition probabilities, which measure the lifetime of an excited state, are given in chapter 13. They contain, in addition to known energy

dependent factors, *reduced transition probabilities B* characteristic of the nuclear states concerned. Successive levels in a
rotational spectrum have spins differing by one unit (odd A)
or two units (even A) and since these levels have the same
parity, $M1$ and $E2$ transitions are expected. For even–even
nuclei, electric quadrupole excitations from the 0^+ ground
state to the 2^+ first excited state have a reduced transition
probability

$$B(E2) = \frac{5}{16\pi} e^2 Q_0^2 \qquad (12.12)$$

Observation of these probabilities, mainly by the method of
Coulomb excitation (Sect. 13.6.2) yield Q_0 values; it is not
possible to obtain these moments spectroscopically for even–
even nuclei since the moment Q_I cannot be observed in a
state of $I = 0$. For odd-A nuclei similar reduced transition
probabilities $B(E2)$ and $B(M1)$ may be obtained and these
exceed the single particle values (ch. 13) by a large factor.
They are, however, consistent with the values of Q_0 deduced
spectroscopically, as shown in Table **12.1** taken from Ref. 12.2.

TABLE 12.1   Quadrupole moments of odd A nuclei (10^{-24}cm^2)

NUCLEUS	I	Q_0 (COUL. EXCIT)	Q_0 (SPECT)
$^{153}_{63}$Eu	5/2	7·7	7·0
$^{175}_{71}$Lu	7/2	8·2	12
$^{181}_{73}$Ta	7/2	6·8	9·2

Similar measurements show the decrease of Q_0 as closed shells
of neutrons at $N = 82$ and $N = 126$ are approached (Fig. 11.12).
It may be concluded that the collective model gives a good
account of both static and transition moments of deformed
nuclei.

12.4   Prediction of nuclear level spectra

From the results outlined in Sections **12.2** and **12.3** it will now
be clear that there are two general models available for the
prediction of level spectra and other nuclear properties. One

of the most interesting results is the particular application of the two models to the level spectra of ^{19}F. This nucleus has been studied in detail by Elliott and Flowers* using the methods of the individual particle model, and the even–parity level spectrum predicted is shown in comparison with the experimental levels in Fig. 12.11a, b. By suitable choice of the two-body potential a very close correspondence can be reached.

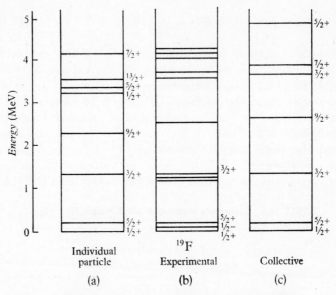

Fig. 12.11. Level system of the nucleus ^{19}F.

In Fig. 12.11c, however, are shown the results of an analysis by Paul† of the level system of the same nucleus in terms of mixed $K = \frac{1}{2}$ and $K = \frac{3}{2}$ bands of the collective model. The agreement is striking, and suggests that the two methods of approach are indeed equivalent. Similar rotational bands have been identified in other light nuclei such as ^{25}Al and ^{29}Si. In the case of mass 19 the two models also give equally good descriptions of the radiative transition probabilities, magnetic moments, β-decay probabilities and the detailed configuration of

---

* J. P. Elliott and B. H. Flowers, *Proc. roy. Soc.*, **A229**, 536, 1956.
† E. B. Paul, *Phil. Mag.*, **2**, 311, 1957.

the last three particles, i.e. the percentage of d and s states in the corresponding wave function. It is possible that the two models, which have been developed to account in each case for a specific set of phenomena, will ultimately be shown to be particular cases of a more fundamental theory of nuclear structure.

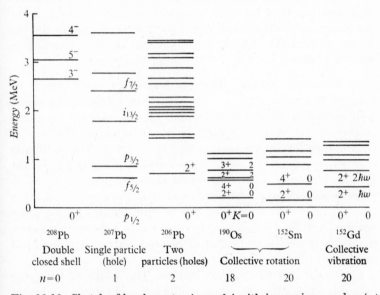

Fig. 12.12. Sketch of level spectra in nuclei with increasing number (n) of particles outside, or holes in, a closed core.

The most important parameter for an understanding of the general nature of nuclear spectra is the number (n) of particles outside a closed shell, or the number needed to complete a shell.* Fig. 12.12 illustrates the change of level spectra as n increases from the doubly magic nucleus $^{208}_{82}\text{Pb}$. In ^{207}Pb, single particle levels of the spherical potential are found, in ^{206}Pb there is a two-particle (hole) spectrum which can be treated by the individual particle model. From ^{190}Os to ^{152}Sm, the even–even

---

* The intrinsic states of even-A nuclei are not found within about 1 MeV of the ground state. The existence of this 'energy gap' has suggested a further important method, analogous to the theory of superconducting metals, of treating the residual interactions.

nuclei show the rotational spectra of the deformed shape, but at ^{152}Gd the deformation is small and the vibrational spectrum of the spherical shape is seen.

12.5   Study of the nuclear level spectrum

Frequent reference has been made in preceding sections to methods of studying the excited states of nuclei. These are collected together here for convenience, and to serve as an introduction to subsequent chapters. The properties of nuclear levels of interest, which have already been mentioned in Sect. **9.4**, are:

a) *Excitation energy.*   Discrete levels are best studied by nuclear reactions such as the deuteron stripping processes (especially for bound levels) and proton capture processes (especially for virtual levels). Level densities, in the case of overlapping levels, are also studied in this way. The particular reaction types most used are discussed in chapter 15. In the heavier elements, low-lying levels are often excited by α- or β-decay and these processes are treated in chapter 16. Indication or confirmation of level positions is often obtained from γ-ray spectra or from Coulomb excitation; these important electromagnetic processes and other associated matters are discussed in chapter 13.

b) *Partial and total width: lifetime.* The width of low-lying bound levels is often less than a millivolt and cannot in general be determined by direct observation of line homogeneity with the available resolution of spectrometers (ch. 7). The widths (and the corresponding transition probabilities) may however be obtained by lifetime measurements or from cross-sections for Coulomb excitation or resonant scattering (ch. 13).

Virtual levels have particle widths as well as radiation widths. The total width may be obtained from the observed shape of a resonance or transmission curve; partial widths, including radiative widths, may sometimes be derived from observations of absolute yield. Lifetime measurements are not usually possible for virtual levels, except indirectly by measurement of total width. Conditions are not usually favourable for Coulomb excitation or resonant scattering for these levels but observation of the associated γ-ray spectra gives relative widths and transition probabilities for the various possible electromagnetic radiations.

c) *Quantum numbers; spin, parity and isobaric spin.* Information on these quantum numbers comes in the first place from the operation of selection rules for intensity, angular distribution and polarization in the primary process leading to the level whose properties are desired. These are discussed for nuclear reactions and for α- and β-decay in chapters 15 and 16. The angular distribution of γ-radiation resulting from nuclear reactions, including α- and β-decay, is also discussed briefly in these chapters.

The de-excitation of a level excited in a primary process may involve competitive transitions of different multipolarity (Sect. 3.9.2) and energy, and also cascade transitions. Relative intensities, and angular correlations then depend on the quantum numbers concerned.

d) *Electric and magnetic moments.* The determination of the electromagnetic moments of excited states is difficult because of the short life of many of these states. Special methods, involving nuclear alignment and magnetic perturbation of angular correlation patterns, are discussed in chapter 17.

e) *Wave function.* It will be clear that for a given set of quantum numbers, a nuclear state has a wave function which differs for different nuclear models. A first test of the various models for a given state (as distinct from a comparison of a sequence of states) must then depend on quantities critically determined by the wave function. These are the electromagnetic moments and the absolute values of the transition probabilities included in the particle and radiative widths.

References

12.1 D. R. Inglis, 'Energy Levels and the Structure of Light Nuclei', *Rev. mod. Phys.*, **25**, 390, 1953.

12.2 K. Alder, A. Bohr, T. Huus, B. Mottelson and A. Winther, 'Coulomb Excitation', *Rev. mod. Phys.*, **28**, 432, 1956.

12.3 B. R. Mottelson, 'Collective Motion in the Nucleus', *Rev. mod. Phys.*, **29**, 186, 1957.

12.4 G. M. Temmer, 'Angular Shapes of Nuclei', *Rev. mod. Phys.*, **30**, 498, 1958.

12.5 A. H. Wapstra, G. J. Nijgh and R. Van Lieshout, *Nuclear Spectroscopy Tables*, North Holland, 1959.

12.6 J. P. Elliott and A. M. Lane, 'The Nuclear Shell Model', *Encyclopedia of Physics*, Vol. 39, Springer, 1957.

12.7 R. D. Lawson, 'The Nuclear Shell Model'; D. Kurath, 'Nuclear Coupling Schemes'; A. Bohr and B. R. Mottelson, 'Collective Motion and Nuclear Spectra'; in *Nuclear Spectroscopy, Part B*, ed. F. Ajzenberg-Selove, Academic Press, 1960.

12.8 D. H. Wilkinson, 'Molecules, Atoms and Nuclear Structure', *Science Progress*, **47**, 1, 1959.

12.9 J. P. Davidson, 'Isotopic Spin', *Amer. jnl. Phys.*, **27**, 457, 1959.

12.10 M. A. Preston, *Physics of the Nucleus*, Addison-Wesley, 1962.

Part D

DYNAMICAL PROPERTIES OF NUCLEI

13. RADIATIVE PROCESSES IN NUCLEAR PHYSICS

The emission and absorption of radiation by nuclei is of especial importance among the many types of nuclear reaction because the electromagnetic field is well understood. Corrections arising from field theory are negligible and observations of radiative processes can lead to reliable values for nuclear properties.

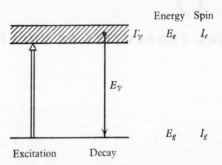

Fig. 13.1. Excitation and decay of a bound excited state at mean energy E_γ above a nuclear ground state. The width Γ_γ is shown greatly exaggerated.

Radiation itself is a property of two states as shown in Fig. 3.15; in order to avoid ambiguity in discussion we redraw this figure with an altered nomenclature (Fig. 13.1). The probability of both upward and downward transitions between the two states depends on (a) the multipolarities of the transitions allowed by the selection rules (Sect. 3.9.2); and (b) the wave functions of the states. Experimentally the multipolarity is determined if possible by conversion phenomena (Sects. **13.2**, **13.3**) and the change of spin and parity in the transition is then known. The wave functions determine the absolute transition probability $T(L)$ for a given multipolarity L and this may be calculated from detailed nuclear models for comparison with experiment. It gives information on nuclear structure similar to that obtained from the static moments discussed in chapter 12. The radiative transition probability is the reciprocal of the mean life τ_γ of the level concerned for emission of radiation and is therefore connected with the radiative width Γ_γ by 3.59, i.e.

$$T = \frac{1}{\tau_\gamma} = \frac{\Gamma_\gamma}{\hbar} \qquad (13.1)$$

where

$$\Gamma_\gamma \tau_\gamma = \hbar = 6{\cdot}6 \times 10^{-16} \text{ eV sec}$$

It is of course just equal to the 'radioactive' decay constant λ of the exponential decay of the excited state (Sect. 2.3.4).

The radiative width of bound levels is usually about $0{\cdot}1$ eV or less, corresponding to lifetimes of about 10^{-14} sec or more from 13·1. The decay rate of virtual levels depends on particle emission probabilities as well as radiative processes and may take place rapidly, in a time comparable with the time for a proton or neutron to cross the nucleus. This is typically $\tau \approx R/v \approx 10^{-21}$ sec and from 3.59 it follows that the total width (Sect. **9.4**) of such levels may be as much as $0{\cdot}5$ MeV.

We shall be concerned in this chapter with transitions between discrete nuclear states to which quantum numbers may be assigned, and with electronic phenomena in the radiating atom. Processes such as bremsstrahlung and external pair production will not be discussed.

13.1 The lifetime-energy relation

In Sect. 3.9.1 a semi-classical expression for the decay rate of an excited state emitting radiation was given. It was also stated that in the *long wavelength approximation* $(a \ll \lambda)$ it is possible to consider the total radiation from an oscillating charge distribution as a series of terms of increasing multipolarity and decreasing intensity. In most nuclear problems, since $a(\approx R) < 10^{-12}$ cm for all nuclei, this approximation will be valid.

A more detailed classical calculation for the transition probability for multipolarity L and energy E_γ (Fig. 13.1) gives (Ref. 13.1)

$$T(L) = \frac{8\pi(L+1)}{L[(2L+1)!!]^2} \frac{1}{\hbar} \left(\frac{E_\gamma}{\hbar c}\right)^{2L+1} B_{eg}(L) \text{ sec}^{-1} \qquad (13.2)$$

15*

where
$$(2L+1)!! = 1.3.5...(2L+1)$$

and $B_{eg}(L)$ is known as the *reduced transition probability*. It contains all specifically nuclear quantities and is obtained from experimentally determined $T(L)$ by dividing out the calculable energy-dependent factors shown in 13.2. The suffix indicates that the downward transition from the excited state to the ground state is considered. The reduced transition probability must be evaluated for a specified nuclear model.

In the *single-particle shell model* radiation may be considered to arise as a result of the transition of a single proton from one orbital state to another. This approach was adopted by Weisskopf[*] who shows that for this model a rough estimate for the case of zero orbital momentum in the final state is

$$B(EL) = \frac{e^2}{4\pi}\left(\frac{3R^L}{L+3}\right)^2 \qquad \begin{array}{l}\text{for electric}\\ \text{radiation}\end{array}$$

and   (13.3)

$$B(ML) = 10\left(\frac{\hbar}{M_p cR}\right)^2 B(EL) \qquad \begin{array}{l}\text{for magnetic}\\ \text{radiation}\end{array}$$

where R is of the order of magnitude of the nuclear radius. For electric quadrupole radiation, and for $R = 1\cdot 2A^{1/3}\times 10^{-13}$ cm $B(E2) = 6\times 10^{-4}A^{4/3}e^2 10^{-48}$ cm^4. The factor 10 in $B(ML)$ is introduced to allow for magnetic radiation originating from reorientation of intrinsic spins. The lifetime-energy relations based on these estimates have been very widely used; they are shown in Fig. 13.2. The formulae also give *single-particle radiative widths* directly, e.g.

$$\left.\begin{array}{l}\Gamma_\gamma(E1) = 0\cdot 07E_\gamma^3 A^{2/3}\\ \Gamma_\gamma(M1) = 0\cdot 021E_\gamma^3\\ \Gamma_\gamma(E2) = 4\cdot 9\times 10^{-8}A^{4/3}E_\gamma^5\end{array}\right\} \qquad (13.4)$$

where Γ_γ is the radiative width in eV, E_γ the transition energy in MeV and A the mass number of the nucleus. In the individual particle model radiative widths would be expected to be smaller, because of the sharing of the radiative moment among the several particles of the configuration.

---

[*] V. F. Weisskopf, *Phys. Rev.*, **83**, 1073, 1951.

The *collective model* also gives specific formulae for the reduced transition probabilities. For electric quadrupole radiation from the state of spin $I + 2$ to the state I

$$B(E2) = \frac{15}{32\pi} e^2 Q_0^2 \frac{(I+1)(I+2)}{(2I+3)(2I+5)} \qquad (13.5)$$

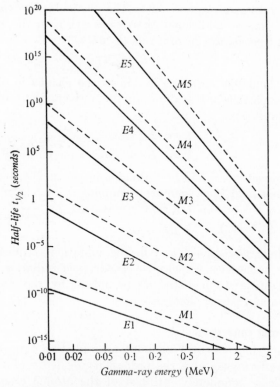

Fig. 13.2. Lifetime-energy relations for γ-radiation according to the single particle formula of Weisskopf (Ref. 13.2).

In this formula Q_0 is the static nuclear quadrupole moment, which has been seen (ch. 12) to be much larger than the single particle moment for deformed nuclei. In such nuclei the collective, in-phase motion of the protons thus gives radiative widths which are much larger than the single particle value.

The reduced transition probability B_{ge} for the upward excitation process shown in Fig. 13.1 is related to the downward probability by introducing the statistical weight $2I + 1$ of the states. This gives

$$B_{ge}(L) = B_{eg}(L) \frac{2I_e + 1}{2I_g + 1} \tag{13.6}$$

The general *selection rules* for emission of electromagnetic radiation were given in Sec. 3.9.2. The particular models now considered impose additional restrictions. Thus in the *single-particle shell model* the general rule (3.70)

$$I_e + I_g \geqslant L \geqslant |I_e - I_g|$$

must still hold but radiation is due to the change in orbital motion of a particle. If l_e and l_g are the initial and final orbital quantum numbers

$$|l_e - l_g| \leqslant L \qquad \text{for electric transitions}$$
$$|l_e - l_g| \leqslant L - 1 \quad \text{for magnetic transitions.}$$

The $M1$ transitions would be forbidden in this model, but the rule does not hold when spin-orbit coupling is introduced. For the *collective model* there is a rule

$$\Delta K \leqslant L$$

for rotational transitions, and in the vibrational transitions there is a preference for electric quadrupole radiation over magnetic dipole when both are permitted by the angular momentum and parity changes.

13.2   Internal conversion

The lifetime formula of Weisskopf for radiative transitions, and similar formulae, give the probability of decay of a bare point nucleus, completely stripped of the atomic electrons. Usually this is not the case, and since many electronic wave functions (in particular all wave functions of s-states) have finite amplitudes at or near the nucleus it is possible for nuclear excitation energy to be removed by the ejection of an atomic electron. The total probability per unit time of decay of the excited nucleus is then given by $\Gamma/\hbar$ where we write for a bound state

$$\Gamma = \Gamma_\gamma + \Gamma_e \tag{13.7}$$

in which Γ_e is the width for emission of electrons. In both cases the total energy of nuclear excitation is removed, but the electron emission process is generally described for historical reasons as internal conversion. This does not imply that the process follows the emission of radiation and the two processes must be regarded as competing alternatives. That this is so has been demonstrated conclusively[*] in the case of ^{99}Tc whose lifetime for isomeric decay (Sect. **13.5**) has been altered (by $0.30 \pm 0.01\%$) by changing the chemical nature of the Tc compound used and hence affecting the electron distribution surrounding the active nucleus. If the number of electrons observed per excited nucleus is N_e and the number of γ-rays is N_γ we define the internal conversion coefficient α as

$$\alpha = \frac{N_e}{N_\gamma} = \frac{\Gamma_e}{\Gamma_\gamma} \tag{13.8}$$

and α may have any value between 0 and ∞. From 13.7 it follows that if the total width Γ is determined then the radiative width Γ_γ is given by

$$\Gamma_\gamma = \frac{\Gamma}{1+\alpha} \tag{13.9}$$

or, in terms of mean lives,

$$\tau = \frac{\tau_\gamma}{1+\alpha} \tag{13.10}$$

The internal conversion process is responsible for the sharp homogeneous lines found in β-ray spectra. Fig. 7.8b shows a typical spectrum, obtained by magnetic analysis. From such results the energy E_γ of the nuclear transition may be obtained very accurately because the kinetic energy of an electron ejected from the K-shell, for instance is

$$E_\gamma - E_K \tag{13.11}$$

where E_K is the binding energy of an electron in the K-shell, which is known precisely.[†]

The magnetic spectra show that for each γ-ray there are in fact several conversion lines corresponding to the ejection of

---

[*] K. T. Bainbridge, M. Goldhaber and E. Wilson, *Phys. Rev.*, **84**, 1260, 1957.

[†] A table of $K, L, \ldots$ binding energies is given in Ref. 13.2.

electrons from different atomic shells, e.g. K, L_I, L_{II}, L_{III}, M_I, M_{II} ... and the total conversion coefficient is therefore

$$\alpha = \frac{N_K + N_L + N_M + \dots}{N_\gamma} \qquad (13.12)$$

$$= \alpha_K + \alpha_L + \alpha_M + \dots$$

The differences in energy between the various groups of internal conversion electrons corresponding to a single nuclear transition agree exactly with the energies of the lines of the X-ray spectrum of the atom containing the excited nucleus. The internal conversion electrons must be distinguished carefully from externally produced electrons arising from the photoelectric interaction of the alternative γ-radiation with matter through which it passes.

The emission from an atom of an internal conversion electron leaves a vacancy in one of the atomic shells. As in the case of the photoelectric effect with γ-radiation (Sect. 5.4.3) either K X-rays or Auger electrons may then be emitted. The fluorescence yield, which gives the probability of emission of K X-rays when a K-shell vacancy is created is shown in Fig. 5.22.

Internal conversion coefficients are determined by making absolute measurements of the intensity of γ-radiation and of the associated conversion electrons, X-rays or Auger electrons produced in radioactive decay or in nuclear reactions. Alternatively the intensity of any one of these radiations may be compared with that of a preceding or following nuclear transition. Magnetic spectroscopy may be used or the radiations may be detected in scintillation spectrometers. A typical example of the latter method is given in Fig. 13.3 which shows the pulse height spectrum of the radiations from ^{134m}Cs. The peaks are due to the nuclear γ-ray and to the K X-rays associated with the internal conversion electrons. Among the corrections to be applied in obtaining absolute yields is one for fluorescence yield.

The importance of the experimental study of internal conversion lies in the information which it may give about the multipolarity and parity change of the nuclear transition. The total conversion coefficient α is a ratio of intensities and if a nucleus of infinitesimal size is assumed, it does not depend on the actual value of the nuclear transition probability. The dependence on the multipolarity L arises because the amplitude of multipole fields near the nucleus is determined by L and is relatively higher for the higher multipoles. Extensive tables of K- and L-shell internal conversion coefficients, based on calculations with relativistic wave functions, now exist (Refs. 13.3, 13.4); Fig. 13.4a shows how the coefficient α_K varies with transition energy for a number of multipolarities in a typical nucleus*. The rapid decrease of α with transition energy

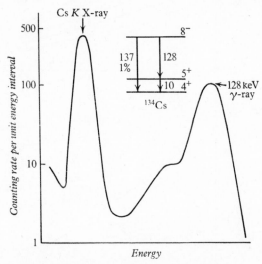

Fig. 13.3. Determination of K-conversion coefficient for the 128 keV transition in ^{134m}Cs by observation of relative intensity of K X-rays and nuclear γ-rays. The decay scheme is inset (Sunyar *et al.*, *Phys. Rev.*, **95**, 570, 1954).

and the relatively poor discrimination between different multi-polarities for high transition energies are made clear in this figure. The latter effect may be understood in view of the short wavelength of the radiation in comparison with *atomic* dimensions; internal conversion then involves electron densities at points many wavelengths distant from the nucleus and no dependence on L is felt. Internal conversion coefficients are small for light nuclei and the determination of these coefficients

---

* It is conventional to use α for electric transitions and β for magnetic transitions.

is therefore mainly useful for heavy elements and low transition energies.

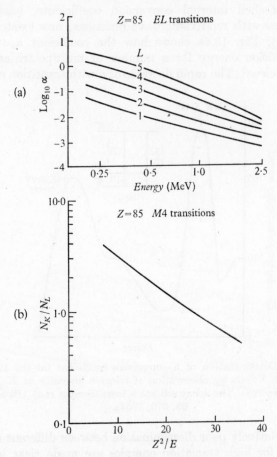

Fig. 13.4. Internal conversion.
a) Variation of K-conversion coefficient for electric multipoles (L) with energy for $Z = 85$.
b) N_K/N_L for $M4$ transitions as a function of Z^2/E for $Z = 85$ and E in keV (Ref. 13.4).

Although the emission of electrons from the K-shell is the most probable process of internal conversion when sufficient energy is available, because of the relatively greater electron density near the nucleus, the intensity of L and M electrons is usually easily observable. The ratio N_K/N_L of total emission of K-electrons to total emission of L-electrons also depends on multipolarity and nuclear transition energy and may be easier to measure accurately than conversion coefficients since it can be obtained directly from a high-resolution magnetic spectrum of the type shown in Fig. 7.8. The variation of N_K/N_L with transition energy in a particular case is shown in Fig. 13.4b.

The internal conversion coefficient gives no information about nuclear structure beyond that which is contained in the radiative lifetime if a point nucleus is assumed. This is not so if the finite size of the nucleus is taken into account since the conversion electron is affected by nuclear charge and current distributions. The corrections to computed conversion co-efficients can be made if particular distributions are assumed; they are important for the $E0$ monopole transitions between states of zero spin (Sect. **13.4**) for which internal conversion is the main mode of decay. These transitions may also compete with alternative transitions such as $M1$ or $E2$ when the spins of the initial and final states are the same.

13.3 Pair internal conversion

If the transition energy E_γ exceeds $2mc^2$, i.e. if $E_\gamma > 1$ MeV an excited nucleus may emit a positron-electron pair as an alternative to γ-ray emission and electron internal conversion. The theory of this process, which is electromagnetic in that it takes place in the Coulomb field of the excited nucleus, shows that the probability of pair internal conversion increases with transition energy, is greatest for small multipolarities and is almost independent of Z. These differences from ordinary internal conversion arise because the pair creation process requires only the elevation of an electron in a negative energy state to a positive energy and the supply of such electrons is unlimited, in contrast with the situation for ordinary electrons in an atom. Pair conversion thus becomes important under exactly the conditions under which ordinary internal conversion is becoming small and the phenomenon provides a powerful method of studying the radiative transitions of light nuclei. In such experiments care must be taken to distinguish between

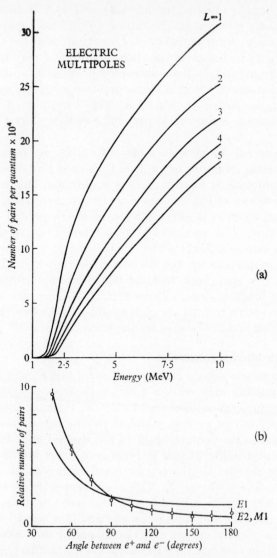

Fig. 13.5. Pair internal conversion.
a) Yield of pairs as function of energy for electric multipole radiation (Rose, *Phys. Rev.*, **76**, 678, 1949).
b) Angular correlation between positron and electron for the high energy transition in the $^7\text{Li}(p,\gamma)^8\text{Be}$ reaction. The full lines are theoretical curves (Devons and Goldring, *Proc. phys. Soc. Lond.*, **67**, 413, 1954).

internal pairs and ordinary pair production in matter by the competing γ-ray.

Fig. 13.5a gives the yield of internal pairs as a function of transition energy and multipolarity for electric transitions. It is clear that discrimination between the different multipoles is only good when the yield is poor (i.e. at low energy) and accurate experiments are necessary to distinguish between the multipoles by measurement of pair conversion coefficients. A more sensitive method is to measure the angular correlation between the positron and electron. This method has been extensively applied by Devons and his collaborators to determine multipolarities in the light nuclei; Fig. 13.5b shows results for the transition $Be^{8*} \rightarrow Be^8 + \gamma$ which determine the radiation to be of $M1$ or $E2$ type.

13.4 Zero-zero transitions

In general internal conversion proceeds because of the multipole field associated with the nuclear transition and if this field falls off with distance fairly slowly, contributions to the yield of internal conversion electrons come from all over the atom. In the particular case of $I = 0$ to $I = 0$ transitions, single quantum radiation is strictly forbidden (Sect. 3.9.2) and multipole fields do not exist outside the nucleus. The only contribution to internal conversion effects then involves electrons (such as the K-electrons) whose wave functions penetrate the nucleus, within which electromagnetic fields may still exist. *Total internal conversion* ($\alpha = \infty$) arising in this way is observed as a single homogeneous electron line, without associated γ-radiation, in the spectrum of RaC' (1·414 MeV level) and of ^{72}Ge (0·7 MeV level). The lifetimes of these levels are longer than would be expected for radiative transitions of the particular energy and both transitions are assumed to be of the monopole type $0^+ \rightarrow 0^+$. Pair internal conversion can also occur in $0^+ \rightarrow 0^+$ transitions and it is known for the first excited states of ^{16}O and ^{40}Ca.

Transitions of the form $0^+ \rightarrow 0^-$ cannot occur by any of the internal conversion processes just discussed. Two radiations are required, passing through a virtual state of suitable properties, e.g. $0^+(E1)1^-(M1)0^-$, with the emission of two quanta, would be a possible mode of de-excitation. Alternatively two conversion electrons or one conversion electron and one photon might be emitted. No clear example of this process of decay has yet been detected.

13.5 Nuclear isomerism

Fig. 13.2 shows that electromagnetic transitions of high multipolarity and low energy are relatively slow processes. Excited states of nuclei which can only decay by such transitions may therefore have a long life. Nuclei excited to these states will differ from unexcited nuclei only in their radioactive properties, and not in charge or mass number. Such excited nuclei are said to be *isomeric* with respect to their ground state.

Nuclear isomerism was first established for UX_2 and UZ (Sect. 2.4.3). Since this discovery, and since the suggestion of von Weizsäcker that the phenomenon of slow radiative decay might be associated with a high spin difference, many examples of nuclear isomerism have been found, both among the stable and radioactive nuclei. In the case of UX_2 the radiative transition is so slow that the energetically possible β-decay is able to compete with it; in β-stable nuclei an isomeric transition is usually accompanied by internal conversion electrons, since the conditions for isomerism are just those for high internal conversion coefficients. In this latter case the experimentally observed radiation is often an electron line of low energy decaying with a half-life short compared with that expected for a nuclear β-decay of the corresponding energy. The occurrence of internal conversion shortens the experimentally observed lifetime of a nuclear isomer, and the partial lifetime for the radiative transition is obtained by multiplying the observed lifetime by the factor $(1+\alpha)$ where α is the internal conversion coefficient. In the case of nuclear isomeric transitions the X-rays following conversion electrons are characteristic of the radiating atom, not of its daughter as in the case of β-decay or K-capture. There is no clear de-limitation of the range of isomeric lifetimes but it has been customary to regard them as measurable by the simpler techniques of radioactivity (Sect. 2.5.1). There is no essential difference between states with such lifetimes, of perhaps $t_{\frac{1}{2}} > 10^{-5}$ sec, and the much shorter-lived states which may be studied in special ways (Sect. **13.6**). A nucleus excited to an isomeric level which may be regarded as metastable is indicated by a superscript m, e.g. ^{80m}Br.

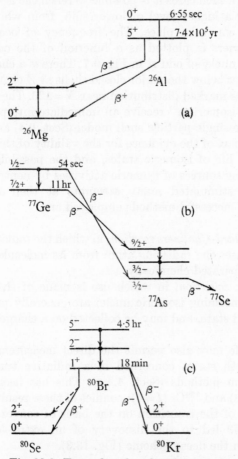

Fig. 13.6. Examples of nuclear isomerism.

a) ^{26}Al, in which the isomeric state decays by positron emission and the radiative transition is not seen.

b) ^{77}Ge, in which electron emission competes with γ-ray emission from the $\frac{1}{2}^-$ state.

c) ^{80}Br in which the 5^- state decays wholly by radiative transition.

Typical examples of isomeric transitions are shown in Fig. 13.6. Usually, but not always, the high spin level is the higher of the isomeric pair. Isomers may be produced in all types of nuclear reaction including β-decay but the yield may be low if the transference of a large amount of angular momentum is necessary. In such cases it is possible to reach the isomeric level by exciting a higher level of lower spin, from which cascade transitions can take place. The frequency of occurrence of nuclear isomers is plotted as a function of the odd nucleon number for nuclei of odd A in Fig. 9.7. There is a characteristic grouping just below the major closed shells at Z or $N = 50$ and 82 and a less marked distribution near $N = 126$. These so called "islands of isomerism" receive an immediate interpretation in terms of the single-particle shell model (Sect. 9.4) and form an important part of the evidence for the validity of this model.

The long life of isomeric states, and the possibility of producing strong sources of isomeric activities by neutron irradiation, have stimulated many attempts at their separation. Among the successful methods employed are

a) *the Szilard–Chalmers reaction*, in which the radiative transition releases the radiating atom from its molecule so that it can be separated chemically;

b) *electric collection*, in which use is made of the fact that atoms containing isomeric nuclei are generally produced in an ionized state, and may be collected on a charged plate.

The long life may also permit the direct measurement of the spins of both states concerned in a radiative transition by atomic beam methods (Sect. 4.4.4). This has been done for ^{134m}Cs $(I = 8)$ and ^{134}Cs $(I = 4)$; conflict of these results with the assignment of the transition on the basis of conversion coefficients as $E3$ led to the discovery of an extra low energy transition in the decay scheme (Fig. 13.3).

13.6 Determination of transition probabilities (Ref. 13.5)

13.6.1. LIFETIMES OF BOUND STATES $(\tau \leqslant 10^{-6}\ \mathrm{sec})$

a) *Comparison with alternative transitions*. The earliest estimate of the lifetime of radiative transitions was made by comparing the intensity of γ-radiation with the intensity of long-range α-particle emission in the decay of certain naturally occurring radioactive elements. Thus in the case of ThC' the main group of α-particles observed has an energy of 8·78 MeV but for every million such particles 170 α-particles of energy 10·54 MeV are emitted. These arise because the ThC' nucleus is formed in excited states, as well as its ground state, by β-decay from ThC and these excited states can either decay directly by γ-ray emission to the ground state of ThC' or by long-range α-particle emission to ThD. The competition between the long-range α-particle emission and the radiative process is determined theoretically by their respective lifetimes and the α-particle lifetime may be assumed to be given by the probability of penetration of the nuclear potential barrier (Sect. **14.2**). This is of course only a rough estimate since it neglects internal structure effects, but it was sufficiently good to indicate γ-ray lives of the order of 10^{-13} sec.

b) *Delayed coincidence method* ($\tau \approx 10^{-6}$ sec–10^{-11} sec). This method, which is described in Sect. 2.5.1 in connection with radioactive measurements, is also applicable using pulsed accelerators such as cyclotrons or betatrons, or accelerators whose output may be suitably modulated. In the isomeric region of lifetimes above 10^{-6} sec the duty cycle of a betatron (e.g. 1 μsec pulses at 180 c/s) provides a useful time reference and the detector may be a sodium iodide crystal with circuits pulsed to respond only for a short interval at a time T after the short pulses of bremsstrahlung from the accelerator. States excited by heavy particle bombardment may similarly be studied by modulating the output of an electrostatic generator with a radiofrequency voltage. In an experiment at Brookhaven a target of ^{10}B was bombarded by a proton beam modulated at a frequency of 7·8 Mc/s into bursts of 4×10^{-9} sec duration. Radiation from the first excited state of ^{10}B at 0·72 MeV was detected by a plastic scintillator in coincidence with a signal derived from the radiofrequency pulse circuit and delayed by a time T from the beam pulse; Fig. 13.7a shows the results, from which a mean lifetime of $1·05 \pm 0·10 \times 10^{-9}$ sec was obtained. In an alternative scheme for shorter lifetimes microwave modulation of a bombarding beam and of conversion electrons is employed.*

---

* A. E. Blaugrund, Y. Dar and G. Goldring, *Phys. Rev.*, **120**, 1328, 1960.

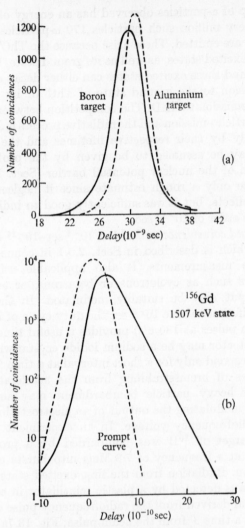

Fig. 13.7. Delayed coincidences.

a) Yield of coincidences between timing signal from a pulsed accelerator and γ-radiation from a target as a function of delay of the accelerator signal. The radiation from the aluminium target is taken to be emitted with effectively zero lifetime (Bloom *et al.*, *Phys. Rev.*, **105**, 232, 1956).

b) Coincidences between successive radiations in ^{156}Gd as a function of delay of first transition. The prompt curve is obtained with a ^{60}Co source for which the lifetime of the intermediate state is $\ll 10^{-10}$ secs (Bell and Jorgensen, *Nuclear Physics*, **12**, 413, 1959).

The delayed coincidence method has more often been applied to the successive transitions in a decay scheme recorded in separate counters, as shown in Fig. 2.10c. The main requirement of the counters and circuits used in this type of work is fast response, and by suitable design, by use of wideband amplifiers, and by choice of photomultipliers, Bell, Graham and Petch* were able to measure lifetimes down to 10^{-11} sec. The lifetime is found from the asymmetry of the curves showing number of coincidences between the counts of the two detectors as a function of delay inserted in one of the channels. Fig. 13.7b shows the results of a measurement for ^{156}Gd, from which a mean life of 2.7×10^{-10} sec was obtained.

c) *Recoil-distance method* ($\tau \approx 10^{-7}$–10^{-11} sec). This method, originally used by Jacobsen for measuring the lifetime of RaC′ (Sect. 2.5.1), overlaps the range of lives covered by the delayed coincidence method and is especially suitable when an excited nucleus is produced in a nuclear reaction with a high recoil velocity. Fig. 13.8a shows the principle of an apparatus used by Devons, Goldring and Lindsey to study transitions in ^{16}O. Excited states of this nucleus are produced in the reaction

$$^{19}\text{F} + p \rightarrow {}^{16}\text{O}^* + \alpha + 2.1 \text{ MeV} \tag{13.13}$$

and the recoiling ^{16}O nucleus leaves the thin target with an initial velocity of about 10^8 cm sec^{-1}. The collimator and counter define a narrow region of path from which radiative decay of excited nuclei which have travelled a certain distance from the target may be observed. This distance is adjusted and a curve showing the number of decays recorded as a function of target distance x is obtained; this is essentially given by

$$A_x = \text{constant} \times e^{-x/v\tau} \tag{13.14}$$

where v is the recoil velocity, and τ is obtained by comparison of the observed curve with curves calculated for the particular geometry used. In the experiments quoted a mean life of $7.2 \pm 0.7 \times 10^{-11}$ sec was measured for the 6.06 MeV (pair-emitting) state of ^{16}O and a life of $\leqslant 1.4 \times 10^{-11}$ sec for one of the γ-emitting states (6.13 MeV). The sensitivity of the method depends on the uniformity of the targets used and the accuracy of measurement of distances of about 10^{-4} cm.

---

* R. E. Bell, R. L. Graham and Petch, *Canad. J. Phys.*, **30**, 35, 1952.

d) *Recoil-Doppler method* $(\tau \approx 10^{-11}-10^{-15}$ sec). It has long been known that γ-radiation emitted from nuclei produced in a nuclear reaction may suffer a Doppler change in energy. In γ-spectroscopy it is often assumed that full correction for this effect should be made because radiation should take place before the recoiling nucleus has time to slow down. This is, however, not necessarily true and if the slowing down time is comparable with the mean life of the level a displacement in mean energy will be observed. If this can be reliably estimated and if the range-velocity relation for the recoiling ion is known, the mean life can be deduced. In a study of the $^{16}O^*$ levels by this method Devons, Manning and Bunbury used an apparatus of the type shown in Fig. 13.8b and recorded accurate energy spectra of radiation emitted in coincidence with an α-particle from the $^{19}F(p, \alpha)^{16}O^*$ reaction (13.13). The α-particle was detected in a proportional counter and the associated $^{16}O^*$ nucleus recoiled from the thin CaF_2 target into a stopping foil on the target holder. Spectra of the radiation were taken with the particle counter in positions A and B, and with the target rotated correspondingly. These positions correspond, in this coincidence technique, to emission of γ-radiation with and against the direction of motion of the $^{16}O^*$ nucleus into the stopping foil and from the difference between the two spectra a value $\tau \geqslant 2 \times 10^{-12}$ sec was found for the 6·13 MeV level of ^{16}O. This is consistent with the upper limit found for the same level by the recoil-distance method.

The accuracy of the recoil-Doppler method is limited by lack of knowledge of the range-velocity relations for slow heavy ions in solids and the method will not measure lives shorter than the time for the first collision of the recoiling nucleus (say $10^{-14}-10^{-15}$ sec) or longer than the time needed for the nucleus to come to rest (say 10^{-11}sec).

13.6.2 COULOMB EXCITATION. The lifetime measurements described in the preceding sections cover the region from the 'isomeric' lives of 10^{-6} sec down to about 10^{-15} sec, which corresponds to a radiative width of 0·6 eV. It is, however, not always convenient to produce the recoil velocities necessary for measurement of the shorter lives. Fortunately, phenomena which are determined by the radiative width become easier to observe as the mean life diminishes and may be used to measure transition probabilities when direct lifetime measurements are impracticable. The most generally applicable method is that of Coulomb excitation.

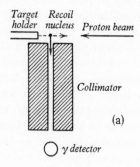

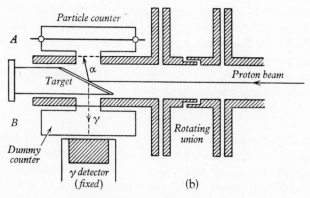

Fig. 13.8. Lifetimes by recoil techniques.
a) Recoil-distance method.
b) Recoil-Doppler method (Devons *et al.*, *Proc. phys. Soc. Lond.*, A **68**, 18, 1955).

A charged particle passing near to a nucleus (Fig. 5.3a), with an energy considerably less than the height of the mutual potential barrier so that nuclear effects may be disregarded, follows a classical trajectory prescribed by the Coulomb law of force zZe^2/r^2. The deflection of the particle (Rutherford scattering) is associated with an electric field at the nucleus which varies with time. Quantum mechanically this field may be represented as a process of emission and absorption of equivalent photons whose momentum changes create the Coulomb force between the two particles; the photon spectrum in this representation of the field is continuous so that photons of exactly the right energy to excite levels of the nucleus are always available. The cross-section for this process (Coloumb excitation) depends on the trajectory of the incident particle, and also on the width of the nuclear level concerned, which determines the absorption of energy from the electromagnetic field. Wide levels are easily excited and measurement of the cross-section for Coulomb excitation (by determining the yield of radiation from the excited level) is equivalent to a determination of lifetime.

One of the first demonstrations of Coulomb excitation was given by Huus and Zupančič who observed the yield of 136 keV radiation when tantalum was bombarded by protons of energy between 1·0 and 2·2 MeV. The radiation was detected in a sodium iodide crystal and the energy spectrum and yield curve are shown in Fig. 13.9, together with a theoretical prediction for the latter. Care was taken to discriminate against X-radiation and proton bremsstrahlung.

The cross-section for the production of radiation by Coulomb excitation using protons may be written

$$\sigma_L = f(E, Z, \Delta E)B_{eg}(L) \qquad (13.15)$$

where E is the energy of the incident particle, Ze the charge of the bombarded nucleus, ΔE ($= E_\gamma$ in Fig. 13.1) the energy of the transition concerned and f is a calculable function. The yield curves for different multipole transitions $E1$, $M1$, $E2 \ldots$ differ and may be used to yield information on nuclear spins and parities. The reduced transition probabilities $B(L)$ are obtained by direct application of 13.15. In some cases direct comparison with measurements made by other methods is possible and agreement is satisfactory.

Coulomb excitation has been observed throughout the periodic system and with many types of bombarding particle, including heavy ions such as ^{14}N and ^{40}A which are particularly effective because of their high charge and mass. A particularly important application of Coulomb excitation is in the study of rotational levels of the collective type excited by electric quadrupole ($E2$) transitions and in fact, practically all Coulomb excitation processes are of $E2$ type (cf. Fig. 12.8). In cases when $|\Delta I| = 1$ the subsequent radiative transition may be a mixture of $M1$ and $E2$ components and analysis of the mixture may be

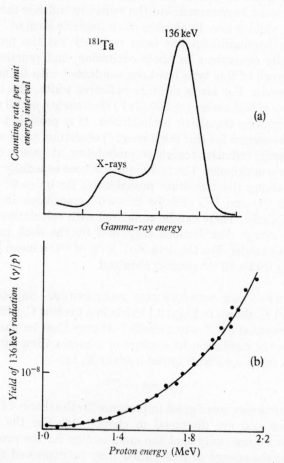

Fig. 13.9. Coulomb excitation of 136 keV level in ^{181}Ta.
a) Spectrum of radiation from target taken in scintillation spectrometer. An absorber is used to reduce the yield of X-rays.
b) Yield of 136 keV radiation as a function of proton energy, compared with theory for $E2$ excitation (full curve) (Huus and Zupančič, *Det. Kgl. Dansk. Vidensk. Selskab*, **28**, 1, 1953).

made by the methods normally applied to radioactive decay schemes.

Coulomb excitation of nuclear levels using *electrons* is in principle possible but is experimentally difficult to observe as an emission process because of the high yield of bremsstrahlung quanta. If the level is of the long-lived isomeric type, delayed activity may be observed, but the radiative width is then small and the yield is low. Excitation of an isomeric level of ^{115}In by electron bombardment has been reported but the process is essentially equivalent to photo-excitation, and practically all recent work of this type has been conducted with bremsstrahlung sources. For levels of large radiative width, the *inelastic scattering of high energy* ($\approx 200\ MeV$) *electrons* is a useful method of determining transition probabilities. It is possible to relate the cross-section for this (high energy) excitation process to the (low energy) radiative transition probability, at least in the case of electric multipoles. The technique has been especially useful* for obtaining the transition probabilities for $0^+ \to 0^+$ transitions in ^{12}C and ^{16}O and for $2^+ \to 0^+$ transitions in several even-A nuclei. These can be compared with calculations based on the charge distributions suggested by the shell model or collective model. For the 4·43 MeV level of ^{12}C a mean lifetime of $0·53 \pm 0·11 \times 10^{-13}$ sec was obtained.

13.6.3 NUCLEAR RESONANCE PROCESSES. Suppose that the level E_e shown in Fig. 13.1 exists in a nucleus C, which may be represented as C* when excited. It may then be possible to produce the excitation by capture of a bombarding particle or photon (a) in a suitable initial nucleus X, i.e.

$$X + a \to C^* \qquad (13.16)$$

These processes are of great importance for the theory of nuclear reactions and are discussed in chapter 15. For the present purpose we note only that the cross-section for the production of C* as the energy of a is varied may be expressed for well-defined states by the resonance formula

$$\sigma_a = \pi\lambda^2 g\ \frac{\Gamma_a\Gamma}{(E - E_0)^2 + \Gamma^2/4} \qquad (13.17)$$

---

* J. H. Fregeau, *Phys. Rev.*, **104**, 225, 1956.

where Γ is the total width of the level E_e and Γ_a is the partial width of the level for re-emission of a. The energy E is the excitation energy of the compound nucleus created by absorption of the incident particle (sect. 15.2.1) and E_0 ($= E_\gamma$) is the resonance energy, at which there is exact excitation of the level. The quantity λ is the reduced channel wavelength (Sect. 14.2.1) and g is a statistical factor.

If now the emission of γ-radiation from C^* is observed, the cross-section for this mode of decay is

$$\sigma_{a\gamma} = \sigma_a \frac{\Gamma_\gamma}{\Gamma} = \pi\lambda^2 g \frac{\Gamma_a \Gamma_\gamma}{(E - E_0)^2 + \Gamma^2/4} \tag{13.18}$$

Under suitable conditions this formula can be used to deduce Γ_γ from experimental cross-sections; it is of the general form of the cross-section 13.15, in which the radiative transition probability (here $\Gamma_\gamma/\hbar$) is multiplied by a factor representing the mechanism of excitation.

The statistical factor is

$$g = \frac{2I_e + 1}{(2s + 1)(2I_g + 1)} \tag{13.19}$$

where s is the intrinsic spin of the incident particle. For radiation we take $2s + 1 = 2$, corresponding to two independent directions of the polarization vector.

a) *Proton capture.* For light elements and proton energies of 1–3 MeV the proton capture (p, γ) reaction shows sharp resonances. From 13.18 the cross-section at resonance ($E = E_0$) is

$$\sigma_0 = 4\pi\lambda^2 g \frac{\Gamma_p \Gamma_\gamma}{\Gamma^2} \tag{13.20}$$

and if γ-emission and proton re-emission are the only decay modes of the excited level, $\Gamma = \Gamma_p + \Gamma_\gamma$. Usually Γ_p (≈ 10 keV) is very much greater than Γ_γ (≈ 1 eV) and then

$$\sigma_0 = 4\pi\lambda^2 g \frac{\Gamma_\gamma}{\Gamma} \tag{13.21a}$$

By observing the variation of σ with energy the total width Γ can be obtained, and then σ_0 gives $g\Gamma_\gamma$ for the virtual level excited.

b) *Neutron capture.* For elements of medium weight and slow neutrons sharp capture resonances are also found. They are normally observed as dips in transmission curves for particular solid samples as a function of neutron energy. In this case $\Gamma = \Gamma_n + \Gamma_\gamma$ and Γ_n ($\approx 10^{-3}$ eV) is much less than Γ_γ so that the resonant cross-section is

$$\sigma_0 = 4\pi \lambda^2 g \frac{\Gamma_n}{\Gamma} \qquad (13.21b)$$

The radiative width Γ_γ must thus be determined directly from the width Γ ($\approx \Gamma_\gamma \approx 0{\cdot}1$ eV) of the transmission curve. Unfortunately, these widths are so small that they may be seriously affected by a *Doppler effect*. This arises because an incident thermal neutron finds the atoms of the absorber moving with random thermal velocities and the effective absorption cross-section must be obtained by averaging over a Maxwell distribution of relative velocities. The observed width of the transmission curve and the cross-section at resonance then both involve, in addition to Γ, the Doppler width

$$\Delta = p_n \sqrt{\frac{2kT}{M}} = 2\sqrt{m_n E_n \frac{kT}{M}} \qquad (13.22)$$

where $p_n = \sqrt{2m_n E_n}$ is the momentum of the incident neutron, M is the mass of the absorbing atom, and T is the absolute temperature. For the resonance level in ^{239}U at a neutron energy of 6·7 eV, $\Delta = 0{\cdot}06$ eV for $T = 100°$C; this is comparable with radiation widths and must be allowed for in calculation of Γ_γ for virtual levels excited by neutrons. In proton capture reactions Γ is usually $\gg \Delta$ and such corrections are unimportant.

c) *Resonant scattering and absorption of γ-radiation.* A case of particular interest arises when nuclear levels are excited by radiation. From 13.17 the cross-section for absorption at resonance is

$$\sigma_\gamma = 4\pi \lambda^2 g \frac{\Gamma_\gamma}{\Gamma} \qquad (13.23)$$

which for radiation of energy 500 keV and $\Gamma_\gamma = \Gamma$ is of the order of 10^4 barns. The total electronic cross-section for attenuation of radiation of this energy in a light element such as oxygen or carbon is of the order of 10^2 barns. It might therefore be expected that nuclear attenuation could be easily observed by increasing the energy of the incident radiation until resonance absorption appeared. Unfortunately monochromatic sources of radiation of variable energy are not yet available (with certain special exceptions, see below) and if a bremsstrahlung spectrum is used for the experiment it is necessary to average the nuclear cross-section over the energy interval ΔE accepted at one setting of the detector. If 13.17 is averaged in this way the effective cross-section becomes

$$\bar{\sigma}_\gamma = 2\pi^2 \lambda^2 g \frac{\Gamma_\gamma}{\Delta E} \qquad (13.24)$$

and since the factor $\Gamma_\gamma/\Delta E$ may be 10^{-4} or less the nuclear effect becomes small compared with electronic absorption. If large angle scattering for a specimen is observed rather than absorption the situation is more favourable since the non-resonant (electronic) differential scattering cross-sections are peaked in the forward direction. It has thus been possible to observe nuclear lines in the spectrum of bremsstrahlung at about 145° from light elements such as boron* and carbon, and to deduce the width of the levels concerned (≈ 0.5 eV).

This method is unlikely to succeed for much narrower states and for these it is necessary to use resonance radiation, as in optics, i.e. to excite a level by means of the radiation emitted in the decay of similar levels in an active source. An experimental arrangement for the detection of resonant absorption and of the subsequent re-emission of the resonance line is shown in Fig. 13.10. In this case the cross-section must be averaged over the line shape and instead of 13.24 we obtain for the absorption cross-section

$$\bar{\sigma}_\gamma = 2\pi \lambda^2 g \frac{\Gamma_\gamma}{\Gamma} \qquad (13.25)$$

For *bound levels*, with which this method is mainly concerned, the only process which increases Γ above Γ_γ is internal conversion, and introducing the conversion coefficient α we obtain

$$\bar{\sigma}_\gamma = 2\pi \lambda^2 g \frac{1}{1+\alpha} = \pi \lambda^2 \frac{2I_e+1}{2I_g+1} \frac{1}{1+\alpha} \qquad (13.26)$$

---

* L. Cohen, R. A. Tobin, and J. McElhinney, *Phys. Rev.*, **114**, 590, 1959.

This is still a large cross-section ($\approx \lambda^2$) but measurement of it would be of little interest since it determines nothing new. In practice, however, the situation is drastically altered in a useful way by the existence of recoil and Doppler effects. In the

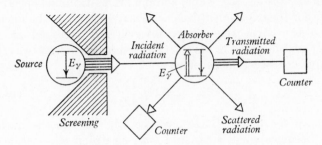

Fig. 13.10. Scattering and absorption experiment.

emission of the resonance radiation of energy E_γ ($= E_0$) from a stationary source atom of mass M, a momentum $p_\gamma = E_\gamma/c$ must be imparted to the emitting body, and the emitted radiation therefore only has energy

$$E_s \approx E_\gamma - \frac{p_\gamma^2}{2M} = E_\gamma - \frac{1}{2}\frac{E_\gamma^2}{Mc^2} \qquad (13.27a)$$

Similarly in the absorption process, the energy required for resonance is

$$E_a \approx E_\gamma + \frac{1}{2}\frac{E_\gamma^2}{Mc^2} \qquad (13.27b)$$

The emission and absorption lines are therefore shifted in energy by the recoil effect by an amount

$$2R = \frac{E_\gamma^2}{Mc^2} \qquad (13.28)$$

In addition, both source and absorber atoms are taking part in thermal motion and the lines are broadened by the Doppler effect. The Doppler width is now

$$\Delta = p_\gamma\sqrt{\frac{2kT}{M}} = \frac{E_\gamma}{c}\sqrt{\frac{2kT}{M}} \qquad (13.29)$$

The order of magnitude of these effects is shown for three cases of interest in Table **13.1**. It can be seen that the recoil

TABLE 13.1 Recoil and Doppler effects for electromagnetic radiation

RADIATING SYSTEM	WAVE-LENGTH (cm)	LINE ENERGY E_γ	Γ eV	2Δ (300°K) eV	$2R$ eV
Sodium atom	$5 \cdot 89 \times 10^{-5}$	$2 \cdot 11$ eV	$4 \cdot 5 \times 10^{-8}$	$6 \cdot 6 \times 10^{-6}$	$2 \cdot 1 \times 10^{-10}$
^{198}Hg nucleus	3×10^{-10}	412 keV	$2 \cdot 1 \times 10^{-5}$	$0 \cdot 4$	$0 \cdot 9$
^{57}Fe nucleus	$8 \cdot 6 \times 10^{-9}$	$14 \cdot 4$ keV	$4 \cdot 6 \times 10^{-9}$	$0 \cdot 02$	$0 \cdot 004$

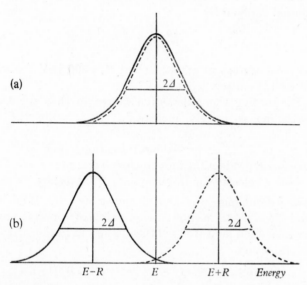

Fig. 13.11. Effect of recoil on atomic and nuclear resonance. The full line represents the intensity distribution in the incident radiation and the dotted line gives the absorption cross-section of the absorber as a function of the homogeneous incident energy.

a) Atomic resonance, $R \ll \Delta$.

b) Nuclear resonance, $R > \Delta$.

effect is negligible in *atomic* transitions and resonance absorption of Doppler broadened lines takes place as shown in Fig. 13.11a. For a *nuclear* transition with free recoil on the other hand $2R$ is always $\gg \Gamma$ for low-lying bound levels, and is often $> 2\Delta$. Nuclear resonance is therefore a weak effect unless recoil losses are restored or eliminated; the situation is as shown in 13.11b. The introduction of recoil and thermal terms into 13.26

creates a dependence of the resonant cross-sections on Γ_γ itself and permits measurement of this quantity if a sufficient effect can be achieved.

Recoil energy loss can be *restored*, and resonance between Doppler-broadened lines obtained, by the following means (Ref. 13.6):

i) By mounting a radioactive source on the tip of a high-speed rotor and using the Doppler effect to increase the frequency of the emitted radiation. From 13.28 the speed required is given by

$$E_\gamma \frac{v}{c} = \frac{E_\gamma^2}{Mc^2} \qquad (13.30)$$

and for a nucleus of mass 200 and $E_\gamma = 500$ keV the value $v = 8 \cdot 2 \times 10^4$ cm sec^{-1} is found.

ii) By heating the radioactive source so that the Doppler broadening is largely increased. Temperatures of up to 1200°C have been used.

iii) By utilizing a preceding transition, such as β-decay, γ-decay or production in a nuclear reaction to provide the necessary velocity for Doppler shift of frequency.

Nuclear γ-resonance was first demonstrated by Moon[*] using method (i). Fig. 13.12a shows the principle of apparatus used by Davey and Moon for a study of the 412 keV radiation originating in the transition

$$^{198}\text{Au} \rightarrow {}^{198}\text{Hg*} + \beta^-; \quad {}^{198}\text{Hg*} \rightarrow {}^{198}\text{Hg} + \gamma \quad (13.31)$$

The source was mounted on the tip of a high-speed rotor driven electromagnetically and resonance was sought in the back-scattered radiation from a sample of mercury as the rotor speed varied. In order to distinguish the resonant effect from non-resonant scattering comparison with the scattering from lead was made at each rotor speed. Fig 13.12b shows the observed ratio as a function of speed, and clearly exhibits the increase of yield expected as the emission peak of Fig. 13.11b moves towards the absorption line with increasing rotor speed. From the observed cross-section for the resonant scattering effect, with appropriate account taken of the thermal broadening,

---

[*] P. B. Moon, *Proc. phys. Soc., Lond.*, **64**, 76, 1951.

which is responsible for the line shape shown in Fig. 13.11, a total width of $(2\cdot1 \pm 0\cdot4) \times 10^{-5}$ eV for the 412 keV level of ^{198}Hg was found in agreement with, but more accurate than, observations by the delayed-coincidence technique.

Like Coulomb excitation, nuclear resonance shows largest effects in cases of large width, i.e. of small lifetime. The method

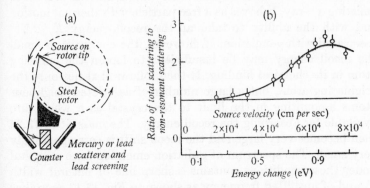

Fig. 13.12. Demonstration of nuclear resonant scattering with free recoil for the 412 keV transition in ^{198}Hg (Moon, *Proc. phys. Soc. Lond.*, **64**, 76, 1951; Davey and Moon, *Proc. phys. Soc. Lond.*, **66**, 956, 1953)
a) Apparatus.
b) Ratio of scattering observed with mercury to scattering observed with lead as a function of rotor tip speed.

is rather more limited than Coulomb excitation since gram quantities of the scatterer at least are required and the available velocities or preceding transitions may not always be adequate to supply the necessary recoil energy. The theory is however simple and direct and the detailed predictions such as the existence of a maximum scattering cross-section for the velocity $v = E_\gamma / Mc$ have been checked. The double transition $I_g \rightarrow I_e \rightarrow I_g$ is essentially the same as a cascade transition between levels of the same spins and the angular correlation of the incident and scattered radiation and polarization of the latter can therefore be predicted (Sect. 17.4.2).

The simple theory of the rotor experiment only applies if the recoil energy imparted to the radiating nucleus by any preceding transition has been dissipated. A β-particle of energy 1 MeV leaving a nucleus of mass 200 produces a recoil velocity of about 2×10^5 cm sec^{-1} (energy of about 5 eV) and with inter-atomic spacings of 10^{-8} cm it is not always certain that the nucleus is at rest, apart from thermal motion, before the γ-ray is emitted.

d) *The Mössbauer effect* (Ref. 13.7). Recoil energy loss in a resonant scattering experiment can be *eliminated* in certain special cases. It is normally assumed that a nucleus in a solid, emitting a γ-ray, behaves as a free particle with thermal motion and with the ability to take up the recoil energy $E_\gamma^2/2Mc^2$ associated with γ-emission. If, however, the energy E_γ is small the recoil energy may be insufficient to loosen the emitting atom in its chemical binding. It then follows that not only the originating atom, but a large number of associated neighbour atoms amounting in the limit to the crystal as a whole, are available for absorbing the recoil energy. The mass M in 13.28 then becomes very large and the recoil shift is correspondingly very small. The spectrum of radiation emerging from a crystal under these conditions contains a sharp line of natural width Γ_γ and of unshifted frequency as shown in Fig. 13.13 as well as the normal thermally broadened spectrum corresponding to free recoil. The same effect takes place on absorption, and if the sharp lines contain an appreciable fraction of the total spectral distribution, there is potentially available an extremely well-defined resonance phenomenon. In 1958 Mössbauer[*] using radiation from ^{191}Ir, demonstrated this narrow resonance in absorption by cooling the source and absorber; this decreases the thermal motion and increases the fraction of emissions and absorptions in the sharp line. Mössbauer was also able to obtain a direct measurement of the line width Γ_γ by *slow* motion of the source; his results are shown in Fig. 13.14, in which the velocity scale should be contrasted with that shown in Fig. 13.12b for recoil-shifted lines.

The theory of the Mössbauer effect has been extensively investigated and it has been pointed out that the phenomenon of the absorption of *momentum* by a solid lattice without the absorption of *energy* is well known in Bragg reflection of X-rays from lattice planes. The Debye-Waller formula which gives the probability of this coherent X-ray process in comparison with

---

[*] R. L. Mössbauer, *Zeits. für Physik*, **151**, 124, 1958.

incoherent scattering may be applied in the Mössbauer effect to give the fraction of emissions or absorptions occurring in the narrow line. Similar considerations were shown by Lamb, as early as 1939, to apply to the scattering of slow neutrons by crystals. The strongest Mössbauer effect known occurs in ^{57}Fe; the attenuation of recoilless 14·4 keV γ-radiation from this

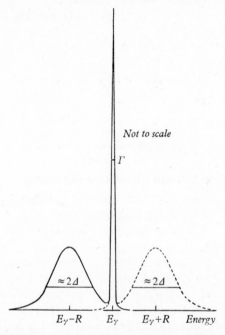

Fig. 13.13. Recoilless emission and absorption of γ-rays (not to scale). The full line represents the emission spectrum, and the dotted line the absorption cross-section; each contains a narrow line of natural width at the resonant energy and a Doppler distribution.

nucleus in an absorber of ^{57}Fe is primarily a nuclear effect in contrast with the usual predominance of non-resonant scattering processes.

The Mössbauer effect has little to offer as a method for the determination of transition probabilities but it provides a method for measuring small frequency changes with a sensitivity of better than Γ_γ/E_γ ($\approx 3 \times 10^{-13}$ for ^{57}Fe). It has therefore been used in the resolution of the hyperfine structure of a number of nuclear levels and in the determination of nuclear moments (ch. 4), but its main applications are in solid state physics.

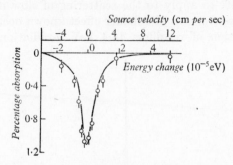

Fig. 13.14. Determination of natural line width in a resonant absorption experiment by movement of source, under conditions of recoilless emission and absorption.

13.7   Comparison between experiment and theory

The methods described in this chapter have made available a large amount of data on transition probabilities, sometimes expressed directly in this form, sometimes given as lifetimes or radiative widths. In comparing these results with theoretical prediction it is necessary in the first place to group the transitions according to multipolarity. The observed radiative width is then expressed in terms of the single particle, or Weisskopf width given by 13.1 and 13.2 for the particular multipolarity concerned. This procedure gives essentially the reduced transition probability as a fraction of the single particle value. The ratio

$$|M|^2 = \frac{\Gamma_\gamma \text{ (observed)}}{\Gamma_\gamma \text{ (Weisskopf)}}$$

then gives information on nuclear models and selection rules. The following conclusions emerge from extensive surveys: (Ref. 13.8)

a) For practically all transitions, except those of the $E2$ type, $|M|^2$ is less than one, so that observed transitions are slow compared with the single particle processes.

b) $E1$ transitions in the light nuclei have $|M|^2 \approx 0.03$. If a transition is found with a value of $|M|^2$, in relation to the

Weisskopf dipole width, which is > 0.02 it may almost certainly be identified as $E1$.

In the light nuclei with equal numbers of neutrons and protons (self-conjugate nuclei) a special selection rule for *isobaric spin* T reduces the probabilities for $E1$ emission. The strict rule is $\Delta T = 0$ for $E1$ transitions in nuclei with $N = Z$ $(T = 0)$ but the rule is frequently weakened by mixing of states and the retardation is typically a factor of about 10–50 beyond the average value of the transition probability.

c) $M1$ transitions in the light nuclei have $|M|^2 \approx 0.15$. There is also some retardation due to isobaric spin rules in self-conjugate nuclei but this is less marked than for $E1$ transitions.

d) $E1$ and $M1$ widths in medium weight and heavy nuclei have been surveyed by means of the (n, γ) capture reaction and are also in general less than the single particle value.

e) $E2$ transitions in both light and heavy nuclei include many examples with $|M|^2 \approx 10$ to 100 times the single particle value.

f) The isomeric transitions, which are found in nuclei just below the magic numbers and are usually of $E3$ or $M4$ type, show relatively little spread of $|M|^2$ within each class.

g) There is no apparent difference in strength between transitions associated with a single odd neutron or a single odd proton.

The interpretation of the observed radiative widths in terms of nuclear models is similar to the description given of static moments (ch. 12) and particle reduced widths (ch. 15). The single particle strength is considered to be distributed among a number of possible transitions, so that any specific transition has a considerably reduced strength. Specific calculations, dependent on coupling schemes, have been based on the individual particle model for light nuclei near closed shells. As the number of loose particles increases, this type of calculation becomes difficult in detail, but still suggests that the single-particle transition probability should be multiplied by a factor (< 1) depending on the number of available particles. Further away from closed shells the individual particle merges into the collective model as has already been discussed and an explanation of the large

16*

observed $E2$ moments is provided in terms of coherent motion of nucleons.

References

13.1 J. B. Blatt and V. F. Weisskopf, *Theoretical Nuclear Physics*, p. 595, Wiley, 1952.

13.2 A. H. Wapstra, G. J. Nijgh and R. van Lieshout, *Nuclear Spectroscopy Tables*, North Holland Publ. Co., 1959.

13.3 M. E. Rose, *Internal Conversion Coefficients*, North Holland Publ. Co., 1958.
'Internal Conversion', in *Nuclear Spectroscopy*, Part B, ed. F. Ajzenberg-Selove, Academic Press, 1960.

13.4 M. Deutsch, 'Gamma Rays', in *Experimental Nuclear Physics*, Vol. III, ed. Segrè, Wiley, 1959.

13.5 S. Devons, 'The Measurement of Very Short Lifetimes', *Nuclear Spectroscopy*, Part A, ed. F. Ajzenberg-Selove, Academic Press, 1960.

13.6 F. R. Metzger, 'Resonance Fluorescence in Nuclei', *Progr. nucl. Phys.*, **7**, 1959.

13.7 A. J. F. Boyle and H. E. Hall, 'The Mössbauer Effect', *Rep. prog. Phys.*, **25**, 441, 1962.

13.8 D. H. Wilkinson, 'Analysis of Gamma Decay Data', *Nuclear Spectroscopy*, Part B, ed. F. Ajzenberg-Selove, Academic Press, 1960.

13.9 G. A. Bartholomew, 'Neutron Capture γ-Rays', in *Nuclear Spectroscopy*, Part A, ed. F. Ajzenberg-Selove, Academic Press, 1960.

14. GENERAL FEATURES OF NUCLEAR REACTIONS

By 1939 all the main types of nuclear reaction induced by particles with an energy up to about 10 MeV had been discovered. Post-war development of accelerators made higher energies available and processes involving multiple emission of particles were then more frequently observed, but no phenomena of an essentially novel character were revealed until meson-producing reactions were achieved in the laboratory in 1948 with energies of the order of 100 MeV per nucleon. Some years later (1955) the production of the antiproton in proton–proton collisions, with a threshold energy of 5·6 GeV for target protons at rest, was a dramatic success for accelerator and detector technology. The post-war era is, however, also remarkable for the enormous increase in the amount of available information on reactions of familiar type, an increase which has led to confirmation, to extension and above all to a better understanding, of theories of reactions which were formulated earlier on rather meagre data.

The more important discoveries in the field of nuclear reactions are described in the following section, **14.1**. From the information presented by these early experiments, the theory of such processes began to take shape in the work of Bethe, Bohr, Breit, Peierls, Placzek, Weisskopf and Wigner. It was soon recognized that the observable features might be determined equally by the operation of 'external' factors such as the incident energy and barrier penetrability for this energy, and of 'internal' factors connected with nuclear structure. The evaluation of these internal factors from the data is based on the wave-mechanical theory of collision processes (Sect. **14.2**).

As a result of the development of theory and of the extension of experiment, several specific types of nuclear reaction mechanism can now be distinguished, each with some relevance to the nuclear models discussed in chapter 9 and chapter 12. The more important types, which will be discussed in chapter

491

15, are the compound nucleus theory of Bohr, the direct inter-action mechanism, and the generalization of such processes into the optical model for nuclear reactions. Electromagnetic transitions have already been treated (ch. 13); radioactive decay, which provided the first extensive body of material for analysis, has many features in common with nuclear reactions in general and is discussed in chapter 16.

14.1 The 'historical' reactions

14.1.1 THE DISINTEGRATION OF NITROGEN BY α-PAR-TICLES. By 1919 many of the phenomena associated with the scattering of α-particles by light nuclei had been thoroughly investigated, mainly by Rutherford and his pupils at the University of Manchester. Among the unexplained 'anomalous' effects was the production of scintillations on a zinc sulphide screen placed near an α-particle source in air, but at a distance from it greater than the range of the α-particles. It was at first felt that these scintillations were due to projected H-atoms (or protons, as we now call them) from hydrogen present in the source assembly since the elastic collision of α-particles with hydrogen had already been observed and was known to give rise to just such a phenomenon. In order to study these particles Rutherford* used the apparatus shown in Fig. 14.1a and compared the number and the range of the particles observed on the screen when the RaC–C' source assembly was evacuated with the corresponding values found when the box was filled with air. The absorption curves are shown in Fig. 14.1b and it will be noted that the introduction of air causes an *increase* in the rate of scintillation, although the range of the particles is unaltered. An extensive series of checks led to the conclusion that the extra particles were due to the introduction of *nitrogen* into the source chamber and the appearance of the light flashes, taken together with rough measurements of magnetic deflection, suggested that the particles produced were protons. Recoil nitrogen atoms would have had insufficient range to reach the screen. Rutherford concluded '. . . that the nitrogen atom is disintegrated under the intense forces developed in a close

---

* Sir E. Rutherford, *Phil. Mag.*, **37**, 581, 1919.

collision with a swift α-particle and that the hydrogen atom which is liberated formed a constituent part of the nitrogen nucleus'; both conclusions have been abundantly verified. The process observed is now written

$$^{14}N + \alpha \rightarrow {}^{17}O + p - 1\cdot19 \text{ MeV} \qquad (14.1)$$

and striking evidence for this interpretation was obtained by

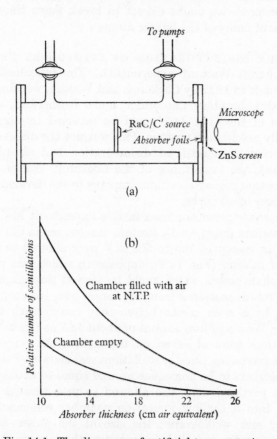

Fig. 14.1. The discovery of artificial transmutation.
a) Apparatus used by Rutherford to demonstrate the production of fast protons in the bombardment of air by α-particles from RaC'. The protons originating in the air-filled chamber passed through a thin window and through absorbing foils to the zinc sulphide screen.
b) Absorption curves obtained by variation of foil thickness (Rutherford, *Phil. Mag.*, **37**, 543 and 581, 1919).

Blackett* using a Wilson cloud chamber. Plate 10 shows one of the pictures obtained in these experiments; it was found that disintegrations of the type 14.1 were occurring at a rate of about 1 for every 5×10^5 α-tracks.

This was the discovery of artificial transmutation. The final sentence of Rutherford's paper was prophetic: '...if α-particles —or similar projectiles—of still greater energy were available for experiment, we might expect to break down the nucleus structure of many of the lighter atoms'.

14.1.2 THE DISINTEGRATION OF LITHIUM BY PROTONS (the Cockcroft–Walton† experiment). The fundamental discovery made in 1932 by Cockcroft and Walton, working in the Cavendish Laboratory, Cambridge, under Rutherford, was that reactions of the type 14.1 could be reversed by the use of artificially accelerated protons. This was not the discovery of a new process since artificial disintegration had already been established; the importance of the Cockcroft–Walton experiment was that it gave enormous impetus to the development of accelerators of all types.

The cascade generator used in this experiment has already been described (Sect. 8.1.1). Protons accelerated in the vacuum tube to an energy of 100 to 500 keV were allowed to strike a target of lithium (Fig. 14.2), opposite to which was placed a zinc sulphide screen which could be viewed through a microscope. Protons scattered from the target were intercepted and stopped by a mica screen before they could reach the zinc sulphide. With a proton current of about 1μA at 125 keV bright scintillations were observed on the screen; the range of the particles producing these scintillations was shown by the use of mica absorbers to be homogeneous and equal to about 8 cm of air. The particles were also allowed to pass through a mica window into a shallow ionization chamber connected to an amplifier and oscillograph; the size of the pulses from the particles near the end of their range was the same as that from the α-particles of polonium.

---

* P. M. S. Blackett, *Proc. roy. Soc.*, A, **107**, 349, 1924; P. M. S. Blackett and D. S. Lees, *Proc. roy. Soc.*, A, **136**, 325, 1932.

† J. D. Cockcroft and E. T. S. Walton, *Proc. roy. Soc.*, A, **137**, 229, 1932.

From these and other observations Cockcroft and Walton concluded that the nuclear reaction

$$^7\text{Li} + p \rightarrow {}^4\text{He} + {}^4\text{He} + Q \qquad (14.2)$$

had been induced. The masses of the nuclei concerned were known in 1932 with rather low precision, but the energy release Q expected in accordance with the Einstein mass–energy relation $\Delta E = \Delta M . c^2$ seemed to agree well with that deduced

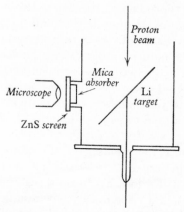

Fig. 14.2. Disintegration of elements by high velocity protons (Cockcroft and Walton, *Proc. roy. Soc.*, A, **137**, 229, 1932).

from the observed range of the α-particles. The proposed mechanism was confirmed by simultaneous detection of the two α-particles both by scintillation screens and in the cloud chamber (Dee and Walton,* Plate 11).

The variation of the yield of the α-particles from the lithium reaction as a function of proton energy (excitation function) was found by Cockcroft and Walton to have roughly the exponential shape predicted by the Gamow theory of barrier penetration (Sect. **14.2**). This theory, which had been published in 1928 and had already been applied to the problem of radioactive decay, encouraged the development of the fairly modest accelerator, since it appeared that the energies necessary to *surmount* barriers would not be required for penetration of an

---

* P. I. Dee and E. T. S. Walton, *Proc. roy. Soc.*, A, **141**, 733, 1933.

incident particle into a nucleus. The excitation function for the $^7Li(p, \alpha)^4He$ reaction was the first of a great many measurements of this type as a result of which the theory of barrier penetration has been exhaustively checked.

14.1.3 THE DISCOVERY OF THE NEUTRON.

In the years immediately following the discovery of artificial transmutation, nearly all the light elements up to potassium were found by Rutherford and Chadwick to emit protons under bombardment by α-particles. It is typical of the breadth of Rutherford's vision that he was not content to assume that only protons could be emitted in, or as a result of, these transmutations; he asked students to look for induced radioactivity (and only failed to detect it because of inadequacy of experimental technique) and in 1920 he wrote 'Under some conditions, however, it may be possible for an electron to combine much more closely with the H nucleus forming a kind of neutral doublet.... The existence of such atoms seems almost necessary to explain the building up of the nuclei of heavy elements; ...'. He referred continually to this idea over the period 1920–30 and initiated experiments to detect such a particle in a hydrogen discharge; its possible existence was in his mind when in 1930 new results on the radiations emitted in the α-particle bombardment of light nuclei began to appear.

The first new result was the demonstration by Bothe and Becker of the production of what appeared to be electromagnetic radiation in the bombardment of elements such as Li, Be, B, Mg, Al with α-particles. The radiation, which was particularly intense in the case of a beryllium target, was detected by means of its ionizing effect in a point counter. It was suggested that for some of the target elements at least the radiation might be associated with excited states of residual nuclei produced in (α, p) reactions. Further work by Bothe, by Webster and by Mme Curie-Joliot showed that the beryllium radiation possessed a penetrating power considerably greater than that of any known γ-radiation* ($\mu_m = 0.02$ cm^2 gm^{-1} for lead, cf. Fig. 5.18b). Several other puzzling properties of this

---

* The phenomenon of pair production, and the consequent minimum in the X-ray absorption coefficient, was not known in 1930.

radiation emerged in the early experiments, including the facts that the attenuation coefficients measured with a point counter and an ionization chamber were different and that the radiation was of different hardness in different directions with respect to the incident α-particles. The most striking discovery of all however was made by Mme Curie-Joliot and M. Joliot who, thinking that the new radiation might have some affinity with cosmic radiation, sought for possible secondary effects and found that the radiation from beryllium was able to eject high speed *protons* from hydrogenous material. The protons had a range of about 26 cm of air and the only possible explanation for their production, if the incident radiation were electromagnetic, seemed to be the Compton effect. The quantum energy necessary was 35–50 MeV.

The ejection of protons as a result of a Compton process was not an attractive hypothesis. The cross-section for the process seemed clearly inconsistent with that expected from the Klein–Nishina formula (Sect. 5.4.4) and the energy of the radiation seemed too large to account for as a result of the α-beryllium interaction. Accordingly, Chadwick* undertook further experiments and showed, using an ionization chamber and amplifier, that the radiation from beryllium was able to produce recoil atoms of many light elements as well as of hydrogen. This was very difficult to explain on the quantum hypothesis but was quite consistent with the supposition that the radiation was a stream of neutral particles (neutrons) of mass equal to that of the proton, which were able to project other atoms by the process of elastic collision. This proposal was able immediately to clarify all the properties of the new radiation.

The apparatus of Chadwick was extremely simple; the ionization chamber shown in Fig. 14.3a was placed near a polonium–beryllium source assembly. When the source was placed near the ionization chamber the pulse rate shown by the oscillograph increased from 0·1 per minute to about 4 per minute; this rate was further considerably increased when a sheet of paraffin wax was placed in the path of the radiation. The former increase was interpreted as due to the production of recoil nitrogen atoms in the air of the ionization chamber; the latter increase

---

*J. Chadwick, *Proc. roy. Soc.*, A, **136**, 692, 1932.

as due to the ejection of recoil protons from the paraffin wax. The recoil protons were shown to have a range of about 40 cm of air (Fig. 14.3b) by the use of aluminium absorbing foils. Other elements placed near the ionization chamber and other

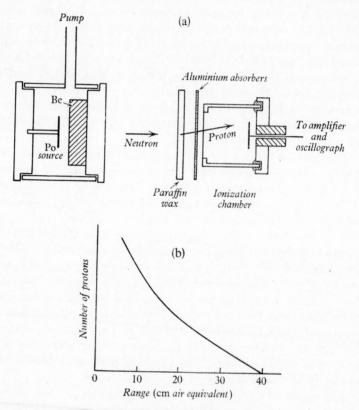

Fig. 14.3. Discovery of the neutron.
a) Apparatus, in which neutrons were produced by the (α, n) reaction in a block of beryllium and then ejected protons from a sheet of paraffin wax.
b) Number–range curve for recoil protons (Chadwick, *Proc. roy. Soc.*, A, **136**, 692, 1932).

gas fillings also furnished recoil particles. The range and the initial velocity (4.7×10^8 cm sec^{-1}) of the recoil particles in nitrogen was found from expansion chamber pictures taken by

Feather.* Comparison of these figures with the initial velocity of the hydrogen recoils ($3 \cdot 3 \times 10^9$ cm sec^{-1}) showed that γ-rays of different quantum energy in each case would be required if the Compton hypothesis were accepted. If, however, a heavy particle is assumed (with no net charge so that the great penetration is explained) the two observed recoil velocities u are consistent providing that the mass M and velocity v of the primary particle satisfies the equation (Sect. 5.1.1)

$$u = \frac{2M}{M + M_s} v \qquad (14.3)$$

where M_s is the mass of the struck atom. For hydrogen and nitrogen

$$\frac{u_H}{u_N} = \frac{3 \cdot 3 \times 10^9}{4 \cdot 7 \times 10^8} = \frac{M + M_N}{M + M_H} \qquad (14.4)$$

and solving this equation ($M_N = 14$, $M_H = 1$)

$$M = 1 \cdot 15 \text{ atomic mass units}$$

with an error of some 10%.

The nuclear reaction proposed for the production of the neutrons in a beryllium target was

$$^9\text{Be} + \alpha \rightarrow {}^{12}\text{C} + n \qquad (14.5a)$$

and since the maximum velocity of the neutron was known from the recoil experiments, this reaction could in principle have been used to give a more accurate value of the neutron mass. In 1932, however, the mass of ^{9}Be was not known, and use had to be made of the comparable neutron-producing reaction in boron

$$^{11}\text{B} + \alpha \rightarrow {}^{14}\text{N} + n \qquad (14.5b)$$

From the observed maximum neutron energy and from the known masses, Chadwick found that $1 \cdot 005 < M_n < 1 \cdot 008$, a result very close to the present day value of $1 \cdot 00898$ a.m.u. This calculation completed an experiment which by the brilliance of its conception as much as by the force of its conclusion won immediate and widespread acceptance.

The early work of Chadwick included observations on the

---

* N. Feather, *Proc. roy. Soc.*, A, **136**, 709, 1932.

attenuation of neutrons by nuclear collisions which suggested reasonable values for nuclear radii (Sect. 11.3.3). In the expansion chamber experiments already mentioned Feather not only obtained evidence for the elastic collision

$$^{14}N + n \rightarrow {}^{14}N + n \tag{14.6}$$

but also for the nuclear transmutation (Plate 12)

$$^{14}N + n \rightarrow {}^{11}B + \alpha - 0 \cdot 16 \text{ MeV} \tag{14.7}$$

and for other inelastic reactions which are now well-known. Such processes are the main cause of the attenuation of neutron beams in passing through matter; direct ionization by neutron-electron interaction was shown by Dee,[*] also using the expansion chamber, to be less than 1 ion pair in 3 metres of air.

It may be remarked that the overwhelming success of the neutron hypothesis did not divert Chadwick's attention from other processes possible in the α-beryllium interaction. There was good evidence from expansion chamber pictures of the presence of γ-radiation in addition to neutrons and he proposed that this could originate both as a result of direct capture

$$^{9}Be + \alpha \rightarrow {}^{13}C^* \rightarrow {}^{13}C + \gamma + 10 \cdot 6 \text{ MeV} \tag{14.8}$$

and as a result of the formation of excited states of residual nuclei

$$\begin{aligned} ^{9}Be + \alpha &\rightarrow {}^{12}C^* + n \\ ^{12}C^* &\rightarrow {}^{12}C + \gamma \end{aligned} \tag{14.9}$$

The latter process, for the (α, p) rather than the (α, n) reaction, had already been envisaged by Bothe and Becker. That the foundations of so many fields of investigation in nuclear physics should have been laid in one short series of experiments remains one of the triumphs of human achievement.

14.1.4 TRANSMUTATIONS OF HEAVY HYDROGEN (DEUTERIUM)

a) *The (d–d) reaction.* Heavy hydrogen was discovered by Urey, Brickwedde and Murphy in 1932 and by 1933 the first transmutations produced by accelerated beams of ^{2}H nuclei

---

[*] P. I. Dee, *Proc. roy. Soc.*, A, **136**, 727, 1932.

(deuterons) had been reported.* One of the most important reactions discovered at this time was the transmutation of deuterium itself by deuterons, which was studied by Oliphant, Harteck and Rutherford.† In these experiments, energies up to about 200 keV were used and inorganic compounds containing deuterium, such as ND_4Cl and D_3PO_4, formed the

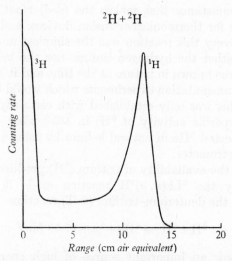

Fig. 14.4. The d–d reaction. The curve gives the differential number-range distribution for charged particles emitted in the bombardment of deuterium by deuterons of energy 200 keV (Oliphant *et al.*, *Proc. roy. Soc.*, A, **144**, 692, 1934).

targets. The radiations emitted were detected in an ionization chamber and copious production of groups of charged particles and of neutrons was established. The reactions

$$^2H + {}^2H \rightarrow {}^3H + {}^1H + 4{\cdot}03 \text{ MeV} \tag{14.10}$$

and

$$^2H + {}^2H \rightarrow {}^3He + {}^1n + 3{\cdot}27 \text{ MeV} \tag{14.11}$$

were suggested to account for these phenomena. Fig. 14.4

---

* E. O. Lawrence, M. S. Livingston and G. N. Lewis, *Phys. Rev.*, **44**, 55, 1933.

† M. L. E. Oliphant, P. Harteck and Lord Rutherford, *Proc. roy. Soc.*, A, **144**, 692, 1934.

shows a differential number–range curve for reaction 14.10; the emission of the two hydrogen isotopes in nearly opposite directions was confirmed in expansion chamber photographs taken by Dee. The (d–d) reaction was of particular interest because no large effects had been observed in the bombardment of deuterium by either protons or α-particles, and because the reaction yield was so large even at low bombarding energies. It is this circumstance that makes the (d–d) reaction of prime importance for thermonuclear fusion devices, and at the time of its discovery this reaction was the simplest nuclear process known. Neither the hydrogen isotope nor the helium isotope of mass 3 was known in nature at the time and it was not clear from the transmutation experiments which would be the stable nucleus. This was only established with certainty (because of the weak specific activity of ^{3}H) in 1939 when Alvarez and Cornog detected ^{3}He in natural helium by using a cyclotron as a mass spectrometer.

In 1948, the availability of tritium (^{3}H) produced in nuclear reactors by the ^{6}Li $(n, \alpha)^3$H reaction made it possible to investigate the deuterium–tritium (d–T) reaction

$$^2H + {}^3H \to {}^4He + {}^1n + 17.58 \text{ MeV}$$

which is now an important source of high energy neutrons (Sect. **8.6**).

b) *The photodisintegration of deuterium.* By 1935, the nuclei of deuterium and beryllium had been disintegrated by exposure to the field of suitably energetic γ-radiation, in analogy with the well-understood phenomenon of the ionization of atoms by light. In their discovery of the photo-effect in deuterium, Chadwick and Goldhaber* used the γ-rays of ThC″, of energy 2.62 MeV, which seemed enough to break up the lightly bound deuterium nucleus even allowing for the uncertainty in the probable mass value for this particle. An ionization chamber of dimensions $4 \times 6 \times 8$ cm was filled at atmospheric pressure with hydrogen enriched to 95% in deuterium and was connected to an amplifier and oscillograph. Radiothorium sources of γ-ray strength equivalent to 9 mg of radium were placed at 12–30 cm

---

* J. Chadwick and M. Goldhaber, *Nature*, **134**, 237, 1934.

from the chamber with lead absorbers to remove soft radiation. Pulses due to photo-protons from the reaction

$$^2H + \gamma \rightarrow {}^1H + {}^1n - 2 \cdot 23 \text{ MeV} \qquad (14.12)$$

were observed; these were not found when the chamber was filled with ordinary hydrogen. From the size of the pulses the binding energy of the deuteron was estimated to be 2·1 MeV (as compared with the now accepted value of 2·23 MeV). Using the best available masses for ^1H and ^2H, the neutron mass was found to be between 1·0084 and 1·0090 and to be clearly greater than that of the proton, so that the neutron must be unstable.

The neutrons from the photodisintegration were detected by slowing them down in paraffin wax and allowing the thermal neutrons either to activate silver or to disintegrate lithium or boron in a specially coated ionization chamber. With a thorium source of 8 mg equivalent activity the pulse rate in a lithium chamber increased from 40 to 2000 per hour.

The probability of the nuclear photo-effect in deuterium was calculated by Bethe and Peierls, and was shown to be in satisfactory agreement with the experimental cross-section of 5×10^{-28} cm^2 for 2·62 MeV γ-rays. Their calculation gives also the probability of the inverse process, the radiative capture of neutrons by protons; this is of considerable importance for the theory of the two-body system (ch. 18). The general agreement between theory and experiment for the deuterium photo-effect was particularly important since it confirmed the expectation that low-energy electromagnetic interactions with nuclei involved only the charge (and magnetic moment) of the component particles.

14.1.5 INDUCED ACTIVITY. One of the most thoroughly established characteristics of the phenomenon of natural radioactivity was that it appeared impossible to produce, modify or destroy an activity except by the normal processes of radioactive growth or decay. Despite this, Rutherford had always suspected that nuclear bombardment might induce activity, and had in fact sought for delayed emission of heavy particles following (α, p) or (α, n) reactions (Sect. 14.1.1). There is little doubt that induced activity would have been discovered much earlier than 1934 if Geiger–Müller counters had been more generally available, since the experiment of Curie and Joliot[*] which revealed this effect was essentially simple. These workers were studying the emission of positrons and electrons from light elements under α-particle bombardment, with the supposition that these might originate in pair internal conversion (Sect. **13.3**) when they noticed that the emission of positrons from an irradiated foil continued for some time after removal of the α-particle source. In the case of aluminium bombarded by α-particles from polonium, a positron activity decaying according to the normal radioactive law with a period of 3 min 15 sec was observed; cloud chamber photographs established the sign of the emitted particles, and absorption measurements the energy. The production process proposed was

$$\left.\begin{array}{l} {}^{27}\text{Al} + \alpha \rightarrow {}^{30}\text{P} + n - 2\cdot69 \text{ MeV} \\ {}^{30}\text{P} \rightarrow {}^{30}\text{Si} + \beta^{+} + \nu \end{array}\right\} \qquad (14.13)$$

In later experiments the aluminium was dissolved in acid and the induced activity was found to appear in the gaseous phase. This was to be expected if the active atoms were phosphorus (which forms phosphine, PH_3) but could not be explained if the active atoms were aluminium, since this element yields no sufficiently volatile compound under these conditions. This was the first application of radiochemical methods to the identification of induced activities.

Curie and Joliot suggested that activity might be induced by other agents, such as protons or deuterons. This was speedily verified; the active nitrogen isotope ^{13}N was produced by Curie and Joliot using α-particles,

$$ {}^{10}\text{B} + \alpha \rightarrow {}^{13}\text{N} + n + 1\cdot06 \text{ MeV} \qquad (14.14) $$

by Crane, Lauritsen, Henderson, Livingston and Lawrence using deuterons,

$$ {}^{12}\text{C} + d \rightarrow {}^{13}\text{N} + n - 0\cdot28 \text{ MeV} \qquad (14.15) $$

and by Cockcroft, Gilbert and Walton using protons,

$$ {}^{12}\text{C} + p \rightarrow {}^{13}\text{N} + \gamma + 1\cdot94 \text{ MeV} \qquad (14.16) $$

---

[*] I. Curie and F. Joliot, *Comptes Rendus*, **198**, 254, 1934.

These reactions lead to positron emitters because the primary process increases the proton to neutron ratio of the target nucleus. Shortly after the experiments of Curie and Joliot, Fermi* demonstrated the production of negatron emitters by the neutron capture process. In the case of aluminium the reaction

$$\left.\begin{array}{c} {}^{27}\text{Al} + n \rightarrow {}^{24}\text{Na} + \alpha - 3\cdot14 \text{ MeV} \\ {}^{24}\text{Na} \rightarrow {}^{24}\text{Mg} + \beta^- + \bar{\nu} \end{array}\right\} \qquad (14.17)$$

was established radiochemically using the neutrons from a radon-beryllium source of strength 800 mC. Fermi also pointed out that neutron reactions were not limited by energy loss of the incident particle in matter, or by Coulomb barrier effects, as in the case of charged particles. Induced activity was therefore expected, and found, for elements throughout the periodic system, including uranium. The possibility, first apparent in this work, of producing elements of atomic number greater than 92 led ultimately to the discovery of nuclear fission.

The process for inducing activity in heavy elements appeared to be the capture reaction, e.g.

$$\left.\begin{array}{c} {}^{107}\text{Ag} + n \rightarrow {}^{108}\text{Ag} + \gamma + 7\cdot23 \text{ MeV} \\ {}^{108}\text{Ag} \rightarrow {}^{108}\text{Cd} + \beta^- + \bar{\nu} \end{array}\right\} \qquad (14.18)$$

since the active isotope could not usually be separated chemically from the target material, although the $(n, 2n)$ reaction could not at first be excluded. One of the most important discoveries made in an extensive set of experiments by Amaldi, d'Agostino, Fermi, Pontecorvo, Rasetti and Segrè† was that neutron-induced activities could be increased largely by surrounding the source and target foil by hydrogenous material such as paraffin wax. This has the effect of slowing down the neutrons so that they spend longer near the target nuclei and have a greater chance of being captured ($1/v$-law of neutron absorption). The neutron slowing-down process is of the highest importance in the design of chain reacting systems.

---

* E. Fermi, *Ricerca Sci.*, **1**, 283, 1934; *Nature*, **133**, 757, 1934.

† E. Fermi, E. Amaldi, B. Pontecorvo, F. Rasetti and E. Segrè, *Ricerca Sci.*, **2**, 280, 1934; E. Amaldi, O. d'Agostino, E. Fermi, B. Pontecorvo, F. Rasetti and E. Segrè, *Proc. roy. Soc.*, A, **149**, 522, 1935.

14.1.6 FISSION AND THE TRANSURANIC ELEMENTS. The activities produced in the capture of slow neutrons by uranium presented an extremely complex picture during the years 1934–1938*. It was expected that they would be characteristic of uranium itself and of the transuranic elements now known as neptunium and plutonium which would be formed by successive β-decays following the capture of a neutron in ^{238}U

$$\left.\begin{aligned} ^{238}_{92}\text{U} + n &\rightarrow \, ^{239}_{92}\text{U} + \gamma \\ ^{239}_{92}\text{U} &\rightarrow \, ^{239}_{93}\text{Np} + \beta^- + \bar{\nu} \\ ^{239}_{93}\text{Np} &\rightarrow \, ^{239}_{94}\text{Pu} + \beta^- + \bar{\nu} \end{aligned}\right\} \qquad (14.19)$$

These processes are now known to take place, and the production of the 23-minute uranium isotope ^{239}U was recognized in the early experiments. It was thought that the other activities would be those of transuranic elements and radiochemical separations based on the expected behaviour of these new atoms were applied to separate the activities. These experiments must in fact have yielded minute quantities of neptunium and plutonium but the neutron sources used before 1939 were not sufficiently strong to make the identifications certain. Moreover it was quite clear that the main body of neutron-induced activity in uranium did not exhibit the expected chemical behaviour. Meitner, Hahn and Strassmann selected certain particular periods for detailed radiochemical study and concluded at first that several isotopes of radium must be formed, perhaps by two successive α-particle emissions from uranium. No specific evidence for these α-particle emissions was found, despite many attempts, and Hahn and Strassmann continued their experiments with the object of establishing the atomic number of the supposed radium isotope with greater certainty. In their first investigations, the activity had been extracted by use of a barium carrier, since this element is expected to behave radiochemically in the same way as radium. (The outer electron configurations are $5s^2 \, 5p^6 \, 6s^2$ for barium and $6s^2 \, 6p^6 \, 7s^2$ for radium.) The next step was to remove the radium itself from the barium salts by fractional recrystallization but at this point the surprising fact emerged that this separation could not be made. It was possible to recover known isotopes of

---

* E. Fermi, *Nature*, **133**, 898, 1934.

radium which had been deliberately added as tracers but the neutron-induced activity of period 3·5 hr remained obstinately in the barium fraction, contrary to all expectation. It is a remarkable tribute to the power of the scientific method that Hahn and Strassmann should at this point have placed implicit trust in their results; the following words in the concluding paragraphs of their paper* have become a classic reference of scientific history '... als Chemiker müssten wir eigentlich sagen, bei den neuen Körpern handelt es sich nicht um Radium, sondern um Barium; denn andere Elemente als Radium oder Barium kommen nicht in Frage.... Als der Physik in gewisser Weise nahestehende "Kernchemiker" können wir uns zu diesem, allen bisherigen Erfahrungen der Kernphysik widersprechenden, Sprung noch nicht entschliessen'.

The conclusion of Hahn and Strassmann that alkaline earth metals were produced in the irradiation of uranium by neutrons was consistent with an earlier observation by Curie and Savitch that some of the activities were concentrated by extractions of anthanum, which has an outer electronic structure $(5s^2\ 5p^6\text{-}5d^1\ 6s^2)$ similar to that of actinium $(6s^2\ 6p^6\ 6d^1\ 7s^2)$. It appeared incontrovertible that these bodies were connected by a genetic chain which should be written

$$\text{Ba} \xrightarrow{\beta^-} \text{La} \xrightarrow{\beta^-} \text{Ce} \tag{14.20}$$

rather than

$$\text{Ra} \xrightarrow{\beta^-} \text{Ac} \xrightarrow{\beta^-} \text{Th} \tag{14.21}$$

and it was not long before an explanation of this chemically based conclusion was forthcoming from the physicists. In 1938 Meitner and Frisch,† accepting the conclusions of Hahn and Strassmann, proposed that the uranium nucleus, on absorption of a slow neutron, could assume a shape sufficiently deformed to promote its rapid division into two approximately equal masses; the name *fission* was suggested for this process. The energy released in such a transformation could be estimated simply from the semi-empirical mass formula (Sect. **10.3**) and

---

* O. Hahn and F. Strassmann, *Die Naturwissenschaften*, **27**, 11, 1939.
† L. Meitner and O. R. Frisch, *Nature*, **143**, 239, 1939; O. R. Frisch, *Nature*, **143**, 276, 1939.

the appearance of two heavy *fragments*, with kinetic energies of
the order of 75 MeV, was predicted for each process. Ionization
pulses corresponding to this energy were observed in a uranium
lined chamber irradiated by neutrons. News of the fission
hypothesis was brought by Niels Bohr early in 1939 to a
meeting of the American Physical Society, and in the outburst
of experimental activity which immediately ensued, the main
characteristics of nuclear fission were established in many
laboratories throughout the world. These experiments, mainly

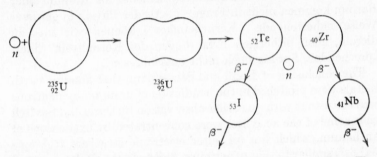

Fig. 14.5. Fission of the uranium-235 nucleus by a slow neutron. The
excited compound nucleus develops a deformation, from which a transition to the energetically favoured state of two fragments occurs.

brief, simple and clear, bore much the same relation to the
hypothesis of fission as did the work of Geiger and Marsden
nearly thirty years before to that of the nucleus; they established the following facts, some of which are illustrated in Fig.
14.5 and further discussed in Appendix 6:

a) The fission of uranium leads to a wide variety of nuclear
   fragments, which are produced in pairs such as the
   following

$$\left.\begin{array}{r} {}_{92}U + n \rightarrow {}_{52}Te + {}_{40}Zr \\ \text{or} \rightarrow {}_{56}Ba + {}_{36}Kr \end{array}\right\} \qquad (14.22)$$

b) The fission fragments recoil in opposite directions and
   have a range of about 3 cm of air (Plate 13) which is
   reasonable for particles of energy ≈ 75 MeV. Since this
   range is less than that of the normal radioactive α-particles
   from uranium, early attempts to observe 'long-range'
   particles from uranium under neutron irradiation were

clearly misdirected; had the experiments been designed to reveal increased *ionization* (Sect. 5.3.7) fission would probably have been discovered by a physicist.

c) The fission fragments are unstable against β-emission as they have excess neutrons in comparison with their charge. This is clear from the $N-Z$ diagram, Fig. 10.4. Successive β-particles therefore appear in a fission chain, e.g. $^{140}_{54}\text{Xe} \xrightarrow{\beta^-} {}^{140}_{55}\text{Cs} \xrightarrow{\beta^-} {}^{140}_{56}\text{Ba} \xrightarrow{\beta^-} {}^{140}_{57}\text{La} \xrightarrow{\beta^-} {}^{140}_{58}\text{Ce}$ (stable) leading to a stable nucleus.

d) A few fast neutrons are produced simultaneously with the fission fragments shown in eq. 14.22. This circumstance led immediately to the conception of the possibility of a chain reaction.

These and other properties of the fission process were co-ordinated early in 1939 in a paper by Bohr and Wheeler,* which gave a detailed theory of the process in terms of the liquid drop model. The outstanding point made in this paper (which was rapidly confirmed experimentally), was that the slow neutron fission process took place in the rare isotope ^{235}U of uranium.

The dramatic impact of the discovery of fission, despite what must be admitted to be a relatively small effect on the development of nuclear theory, diverted attention from the search for positive identification of transuranic elements. Success in this work, however, rapidly followed when the nature of the complicating fission process was understood; present knowledge of elements 93 to 103 is mainly due to a brilliant combination of physical and chemical techniques developed in the Radiation Laboratory and Department of Chemistry of the University of California at Berkeley. The following elements have been characterized:

$Z = 93$, Neptunium	$Z = 99$, Einsteinium
$Z = 94$, Plutonium	$Z = 100$, Fermium
$Z = 95$, Americium	$Z = 101$, Mendelevium
$Z = 96$, Curium	$Z = 102$
$Z = 97$, Berkelium	$Z = 103$, (Lawrencium suggested)
$Z = 98$, Californium	

---

* N. Bohr and J. A. Wheeler, *Phys. Rev.*, **56**, 426, 1939.

The production processes for these elements involve increase of charge either by successive neutron capture followed by β^--decay, or by direct addition through α-particle or heavy ion bombardments.

14.2   Wave-mechanical collision theory

14.2.1 FORMAL DEFINITIONS. A simple type of induced nuclear reaction, which covers a great many cases encountered in practice, including most of the reactions discussed in Sect. **14.1**, may be represented by the equation already frequently used in this book

$$X + a \rightarrow Y + b + Q \tag{14.23}$$

In this, X represents the target nucleus, a the bombarding particle or photon, Y the product nucleus, b an emitted particle or photon and Q denotes the kinetic energy released in the process (Sect. 5.1.1). The most useful broad classification of nuclear reactions in general distinguishes between

a) *elastic scattering* $(Q = 0)$ represented by

$$X + a \rightarrow X + a \tag{14.24}$$

in which the emergent particle is the same as the incident particle, and

b) *non-elastic or inelastic processes* $(Q \neq 0)$ represented by equations of the type

$$\left.\begin{aligned} X + a &\rightarrow Y + b + Q \\ &\rightarrow Y_1 + b_1 + Q_1 \\ &\rightarrow Y_2 + b_2 + Q_2 \end{aligned}\right\} \tag{14.25}$$

in which the kinetic energy of the products differs from that of the initial system. In *inelastic scattering*, b is the same type of particle as a, and the initial nucleus is left in an excited state. This process is written

$$X + a \rightarrow X^* + a' + Q \tag{14.25a}$$

The alternative processes $Y + b$, $Y_1 + b_1, \ldots$ in 14.25 are known as *reaction channels* and the system $X + a$ defines the *incident channel*. The energy release Q is calculable from the masses of X, a, Y, and b is given by

$$\left. \begin{aligned} Q &= [(M_X + M_a) - (M_Y + M_b)] \text{ a.m.u.} \\ &= [(M_X + M_a) - (M_Y + M_b)] \times 931 \text{ MeV} \end{aligned} \right\} \quad (14.26)$$

The observed energy of the product particles Y and b depends also on the energy E_a of the incident particle and the kinetic energy of the system $Y + b$ is then

$$E_a + Q \quad (14.27)$$

In the case of *exothermic reactions* Q is positive and the reaction may in principle proceed for zero bombarding energy. For *endothermic reactions*, Q is negative and there is a threshold bombarding energy below which the reaction is not observed; this is not $E_a = -Q$ because of the necessity to conserve linear momentum, which means that only the energy in the centre-of-mass system

$$\varepsilon_a = E_a \times \frac{M_X}{M_X + M_a} \quad (14.28)$$

is available for producing the reaction. The threshold energy in the laboratory system is thus

$$E_T = -\frac{M_X + M_a}{M_X} \times Q \quad (14.29)$$

The centre-of-mass energy ε_a is the *incident channel energy*; with this energy is associated a *channel wavelength* λ_a, corresponding to a particle of the reduced mass $M_a M_X / M_a + M_X$ possessing the channel energy.* The energy of particle b observed at a given angle θ_L with the direction of incidence of a may be calculated by a simple extension of the formulae given in Sect. 5.1.1. In the most accurate work on nuclear reactions, and in all experiments involving β-particles and high-energy particles, a relativistic treatment must be given.

As in the case of Rutherford scattering (Sect. 5.1.4) the general laws of collision do not predict the probability of a nuclear reaction taking place. For such predictions, more

---

* The suffix a of the channel wavelength will be omitted when this leads to no confusion.

detailed knowledge of the interaction mechanism is necessary and in general the classical approach found satisfactory to describe Rutherford scattering over a considerable range of energies is inadequate. This is because of the failure of the criterion 5.26 for classical orbits in the long-range Coulomb field as the velocity v increases; a wave mechanical treatment then becomes necessary. Classical calculations may again be used at high energies if only short-range potentials are important and if the reduced de Broglie wavelength of the incident particle is much less than the range of the forces, since the trajectory of the particle is then well-defined with respect to the size of the scattering centre.

The cross-section for a particular process, such as that represented by 14.23, will be written σ_{ab}. The *total cross-section* (Sect. 5.1.3) for the interaction of a with a specified target is then

$$\sigma_t = \sigma_a = \sigma_{aa} + \sigma_{ab} + \sigma_{ab_1} + \cdots \tag{14.30}$$
$$= \sigma_{el} + \sigma_{inel}$$

where σ_{el} ($= \sigma_{aa}$) is the *elastic cross-section* and σ_{inel} ($\sum_b \sigma_{ab}$) is the complete *non-elastic or inelastic cross-section*. This latter quantity is often written σ_r or σ_{abs} and referred to as the *reaction or absorption cross-section*. Such cross-sections may also be expressed as the integral of a differential cross-section as defined in Sect. 5.1.3.

The wave mechanical theory of collisions sets out to calculate these cross-sections in terms of assumed properties of an interaction region defined by the incident channel and bounded at a particular radius R. Several equivalent treatments have been developed and of these probably the most useful is the method of partial waves in which the effect of particles a with a definite angular momentum $l\hbar$ with respect to the target X is considered separately. A particular cross-section is then expressed as

$$\sigma_{ab} = \sum_0^{l_{max}} \sigma_{ab}^l \tag{14.31}$$

where $l_{max}\hbar$ is the maximum angular momentum contributing to the reaction. Since this is often specified uniquely by selection rules, the partial cross-sections σ_{ab}^l acquire a special significance.

14.2.2 THE METHOD OF PARTIAL WAVES.

a) *Semi-classical approach.* The partial reaction cross-sections σ_r^l are limited in value by geometrical factors. This may be seen crudely from Fig. 14.6 which represents the interaction of a steady incident stream of projectiles with a fixed target nucleus at O (a) according to the particle picture, and (b) according to the wave picture. For simplicity the incident

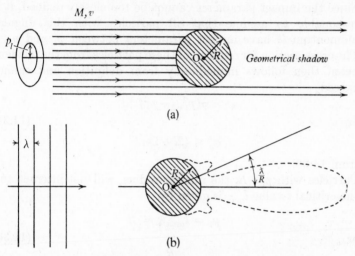

(a)

(b)

Fig. 14.6. Absorption cross-section ('black' nucleus).

a) Classical picture in which the cross-section πR^2 arises naturally as a target area.

b) Wave mechanical picture, in which an absorption cross-section πR^2 is also found for $\lambda \ll R$, but in order to create the shadow behind the target nucleus, elastic scattering occurs with a further cross-section of πR^2. The dotted line represents the angular variation of intensity of this diffraction scattering. The total cross-section is $2\pi R^2$.

particles are supposed to be uncharged and effects connected with their intrinsic spin are neglected. The wave and particle pictures are not really distinct and it must be assumed, in considering Fig. 14.6, that the incident particles have a wavelength $\lambda = h/Mv$ where Mv is the incident linear momentum. A particle with an impact parameter p_l (Sect. 5.1.4) then has an angular momentum

$$Mvp_l \qquad \qquad (14.32)$$

about the centre of the target nucleus. If the incident particle (or wave) and the target nucleus are to be regarded as one quantized system the angular momentum about O must be an integral multiple l of $\hbar$ and we have therefore

$$Mvp_l = l\hbar$$

or   (14.33)

$$p_l = l\lambda$$

Since the impact parameter cannot be too closely defined, it is reasonable to assume that all particles with this angular momentum $l\hbar$ have impact parameters between p_l and p_{l+1}. The cross-section for removal of these particles from the incident beam then follows immediately from definition and cannot exceed

$$\pi(p_{l+1}^2 - p_l^2)$$

or   (14.34)

$$\sigma_r^l \leqslant (2l+1)\pi\lambda^2$$

from 14.33.

Particles with $p_l > R$, the nuclear radius, will not interact and the critical l-value l_{max} is given by

$$p_l = l_{max}\lambda = R$$

or   (14.35)

$$l_{max} = \frac{R}{\lambda} = kR$$

where $k = 2\pi/\lambda = 1/\lambda$ is the wave number of the incident particles.

The particle picture, Fig. 14.6a, suggests a well-defined shadow and a total absorption cross-section πR^2. This is consistent with the wave picture if a large number of partial waves is effective, i.e. if $l_{max} \gg 1$, for then

$$\sigma_r = \sum_l \sigma_r^l \leqslant \pi\lambda^2 \sum_0^{R/\lambda} (2l+1)$$ (14.36)

$$\leqslant \pi(R+\lambda)^2$$

but the wave picture requires some elastic scattering in addition, as will be discussed later. For a nucleus such as ^{27}Al, 14.36 will be a good approximation for $l \approx 10$ or $E_a \approx 25$ MeV for protons.

b) *Wave-mechanical treatment of the scattering of uncharged, spinless particles.* A particle approaching a target nucleus at O in a direction parallel to the axis of z with velocity v is represented (Fig. 14.6b) by the plane wave

$$\psi_{\text{inc}} = e^{ik(z-vt)} \tag{14.37}$$

The wave number k refers to the centre-of-mass system, i.e. to a particle of the reduced mass possessing the channel energy (14.28). The wave amplitude is set equal to unity, so that there is one particle per unit volume and the incident beam is then v particles per cm^2 per sec. The position of the particle with respect to the xy axes cannot be specified in this representation and the angular momentum $l\hbar$ with respect to the nucleus can have many values. It is therefore convenient to replace the plane wave by an equivalent series of spherical waves each of which represents a particle with a definite angular momentum about the nucleus and with no component of this angular momentum in the direction of incidence. This can be done using the asymptotic form of a standard mathematical transformation of the wave function 14.37.

First of all we postulate a continuous sequence of interactions with the assumed incident beam. The problem then becomes one of the steady state and the time factor in 14.37 may be eliminated. The incident wave is then expressed

$$\psi_{\text{inc}} = e^{ikz} = e^{ikr\cos\theta}$$

$$\approx \frac{1}{kr} \sum_0^\infty (2l+1)i^l P_l(\cos\theta) \sin\left(kr - \frac{l\pi}{2}\right) \tag{14.38}$$

$$= \frac{1}{kr} \sum_0^\infty (2l+1)i^l P_l(\cos\theta) \frac{e^{i(kr-l\pi/2)} - e^{-i(kr-l\pi/2)}}{2i} \tag{14.39}$$

The latter form has the physical meaning that the plane wave can be considered as a series of spherical waves $e^{-i(kr-l\pi/2)}$ converging on O, together with a coherent superposition of waves $e^{i(kr-l\pi/2)}$ diverging from O. The interaction potential may affect the outgoing waves in phase or in amplitude and phase; in the former case we have *elastic scattering* with a certain angular distribution and in the latter there are *inelastic processes* in addition. The steady state wave function when the interaction takes place may therefore be written

$$\psi = \frac{1}{kr} \sum_{0}^{\infty} (2l+1) i^l P_l(\cos\theta) \frac{\eta_l e^{i(kr - l\pi/2)} - e^{-i(kr - l\pi/2)}}{2i} \qquad (14.40)$$

where η_l is a complex constant representing the effect of the scattering centre. The real part of η_l gives the change in amplitude and the imaginary part the change in phase. We may also regard this wave as arising from the superposition of a *scattered wave* ψ_{sc} on the incident wave, i.e.

$$\psi = \psi_{\mathrm{inc}} + \psi_{\mathrm{sc}} \qquad (14.41)$$

A suitable form for the outgoing scattered wave, which is itself a superposition of partial waves, is

$$\psi_{\mathrm{sc}} = \frac{f(\theta) e^{ikr}}{r} \qquad (14.42)$$

and this defines an elastic *scattering amplitude* $f(\theta)$. From 5.10 the differential cross-section for elastic scattering can be obtained at once using the definition 5.9; the number of particles crossing unit surface in the incident plane wave per sec is v and from 14.42 the number crossing unit area per sec at a large distance r in the scattered beam is

$$v|\psi_{\mathrm{sc}}|^2 = \frac{v|f(\theta)|^2}{r^2} = v|f(\theta)|^2 \mathrm{d}\Omega$$

so that

$$d\sigma_{\mathrm{el}} = |f(\theta)|^2 \mathrm{d}\Omega = \sigma_{\mathrm{el}}(\theta)\mathrm{d}\Omega \qquad (14.43)$$

where $\mathrm{d}\Omega$ is the element of solid angle. The scattering amplitude may be connected with the quantity η_l representing the effect of the target nucleus by writing ψ, ψ_{inc} and ψ_{sc} in 14.41 explicitly. This gives, using the identity $i^l = e^{i(l\pi/2)}$

$$f(\theta) = \sum_{0}^{\infty} f_l(\theta) = \frac{1}{2ik} \sum_{0}^{\infty} (\eta_l - 1)(2l+1) P_l(\cos\theta) \qquad (14.44)$$

If $\mathrm{d}\sigma_{\mathrm{el}}$ (eq. 14.43) is integrated over the angular range 0 to π, using this value of $f(\theta)$, it will be found that cross terms vanish and eq. 14.31, with $b = a$, follows.

We now consider the different types of interaction that may occur. For *elastic scattering* only there must be no loss of incident particles and therefore in 14.40

$$|\eta_l|^2 = 1$$

so that

$$\eta_l = e^{2i\delta_l} \qquad (14.45)$$

where δ_l is a real quantity. This gives

$$f(\theta) = \frac{1}{2ik} \sum_0^\infty (2l+1)(e^{2i\delta_l} - 1)P_l(\cos \theta) \qquad (14.46)$$

and δ_l has the physical significance of a *phase shift* in the asymptotic form of the partial wave l. This can be seen by substituting $\eta_l = e^{2i\delta_l}$ in 14.40 and converting back to the sinusoidal form. The last factor of the expression for ψ becomes

$$e^{i\delta_l} \sin \left(kr - \frac{l\pi}{2} + \delta_l \right) \qquad (14.47)$$

instead of $\sin (kr - l\pi/2)$.

If there are *inelastic processes* then $|\eta_l|^2 < 1$ so that if η_l is expressed as in 14.45

$$\delta_l = \alpha_l + i\beta_l \qquad (14.48)$$

with β_l a positive quantity.

Cross-sections for interaction in the partial wave l can be written down directly by computing the corresponding flux. For *elastic scattering*, from 14.43 and 14.44

$$d\sigma_{\text{el}}^l = \frac{1}{4k^2} |1 - \eta_l|^2 (2l+1)^2 [P_l(\cos \theta)]^2 d\Omega \qquad (14.49)$$

and by integration we find,

$$\sigma_{\text{el}}^l = \frac{\pi}{k^2} (2l+1)|1 - \eta_l|^2 = 4\pi \lambda^2 (2l+1)|e^{i\delta_l} \sin \delta_l|^2$$

$$= 4\pi \lambda^2 (2l+1) \sin^2 \delta_l \qquad (14.50)$$

using $\eta_l = e^{2i\delta_l}$ and the normalisation of the Legendre function given in Appendix 2.

The *inelastic cross-section* is obtained by computing the *net* flow of particles associated with the wave ψ. This gives, using 14.40

$$\sigma_{\text{inel}}^l = \frac{\pi}{k^2} (2l+1)(1-|\eta_l|^2) \tag{14.51}$$

The *total cross-section* is the sum of σ_{el}^l and σ_{inel}^l

$$\sigma_{\text{t}}^l = \frac{\pi}{k^2} (2l+1)2(1 - Re.\eta_l) \tag{14.52}$$

From the physical nature of the problem ($|\eta_l| \leqslant 1$) we may deduce the following useful geometrical limitations on cross-sections

$$\left. \begin{aligned} \sigma_{\text{el}}^l &\leqslant 4\pi \lambda^2 (2l+1) \\ \sigma_{\text{inel}}^l &\leqslant \pi \lambda^2 (2l+1) \\ \sigma_{\text{t}}^l &\leqslant 4\pi \lambda^2 (2l+1) \end{aligned} \right\} \tag{14.53}$$

The elastic cross-section reaches its maximum value $4\pi \lambda^2 (2l+1)$ when $\eta_l = -1$ and the inelastic cross-section then vanishes. This means, according to 14.40, that the outgoing wave has the same intensity as the incoming wave but is shifted in phase by 180°. The inelastic cross-section reaches its maximum value $\pi \lambda^2 (2l+1)$, in agreement with 14.34, when $\eta_l = 0$, corresponding to complete absorption of the partial wave; the elastic cross-section then has the same value and the total cross-section is $2\pi \lambda^2 (2l+1)$. It is also evident from 14.50 and 14.51 that although elastic scattering may take place without absorption ($|\eta_l|^2 = 1$) the converse is not true. An absorption process in which particles of orbital momentum $l\hbar$ are removed creates an elastic scattering, known as *shadow scattering*, with an angular distribution characteristic of l.

The angular distribution of elastic scattering, in the present case in which Coulomb forces are neglected, is given immediately by 14.49. From the formulae for $P_l(\cos \theta)$ given in Appendix 2 it can be seen that if the maximum l-value entering into the scattering is L, then the angular distribution contains powers of $\cos \theta$ up to $\cos^{2L} \theta$ only. The angular distributions of inelastic scattering and reactions are not given individually by the present considerations.

c) *The black disc; diffraction scattering* ($\lambda \ll R$). If the scattering centre is a perfect absorber for all particles with a classical impact parameter up to R (Fig. 14.6a) we have

$$
\begin{aligned}
\eta_l &= 0 \quad \text{for} \quad l \leqslant R/\lambda \\
\eta_l &= 1 \quad \text{for} \quad l > R/\lambda
\end{aligned} \tag{14.54}
$$

We then find, as in the semi-classical approach,

$$
\sigma_{\text{inel}} \leqslant \sum_0^{R/\lambda} \pi\lambda^2(2l+1) = \pi(R+\lambda)^2 \tag{14.55}
$$

but in addition we also have in the same way

$$
\sigma_{\text{el}} \leqslant \sum_0^{R/\lambda} \pi\lambda^2(2l+1) = \pi(R+\lambda)^2 \tag{14.56}
$$

and consequently

$$
\sigma_t \leqslant 2\pi(R+\lambda)^2 \tag{14.57}
$$

a result which is not predicted classically. The elastic cross-section is due to shadow scattering in all the waves up to l. The angular distribution of this scattering (Fig. 14.6b) can be found by summing 14.44 for the limited series of partial waves defined by 14.54. This series is seen to be in antiphase with the incident wave and thus creates the 'geometrical' shadow. The calculated angular distribution at large distances has the form, already quoted in Sect. **11.3**,

$$
d\sigma_{\text{el}} = \frac{R^4}{\lambda^2}\left\{\frac{J_1\left(\dfrac{2R}{\lambda}\sin\dfrac{\theta}{2}\right)}{\dfrac{2R}{\lambda}\sin\dfrac{\theta}{2}}\right\}^2 d\Omega \tag{14.58}
$$

as in optical diffraction and this particular type of shadow scattering is known as *diffraction scattering*. It is forward-peaked and falls to a minimum at an angle $\theta = \lambda/R$, but it deviates particles from the beam and therefore contributes to the total cross-section.

d) *The phase shift; hard sphere scattering* $(\lambda \gg R)$. The properties of the scattering centre are contained in its radius R, which determines the number of partial waves mainly concerned in an interaction and in the asymptotic phase shifts δ_l. In the simple case in which $\lambda \gg R$, $l = 0$ only is possible and the elastic scattering amplitude is

$$
f_0(\theta) = \lambda e^{i\delta_0}\sin\delta_0 \tag{14.59}
$$

This is s-wave scattering and is *isotropic*, with a differential cross-section

$$d\sigma_{el}^0 = \lambda^2 \sin^2 \delta_0 d\Omega \qquad (14.60)$$

If the scattering centre is an impenetrable sphere, then the wave amplitude must vanish at the surface $r = R$ and for the case of s-waves 14.40 gives

$$\eta_0 = e^{-2ikR} \qquad (14.61)$$

so that

$$\delta_0 = -kR = -R/\lambda \qquad (14.62)$$

and the s-wave cross-section is

$$\sigma_{el}^0 = 4\pi \frac{d\sigma_{el}^0}{d\Omega} \approx 4\pi R^2 \quad \text{if} \quad \lambda \gg R \qquad (14.63)$$

This is the scattering cross-section expected for slow neutrons at energies between nuclear resonances (ch. 15) but in slow neutron physics (Appendix 8) it is customary to use a quantity a, defined so that

$$a = -f_0(\theta) \qquad (14.64)$$

and known as the *scattering length*, instead of R.

As the incident energy increases more phase shifts are required to account for the angular distribution and cross-section. These phase shifts may be predicted from particular models of the scattering centre, e.g. a square-well potential. It can be shown generally (Ref. 14.2) that for an *attractive potential* δ_l *is positive* and for a *repulsive potential* (e.g. the hard sphere) δ_l *is negative*.

e) *Scattering of identical particles.* In a scattering process in which the incident and struck particles are the same (e.g. α-He scattering, Sect. 5.3.1) the particles scattered through angle θ_L to the left, say, in the laboratory system are accompanied by identical particles recoiling from incident particles scattered through an angle $\pi/2 - \theta_L$ to the right. In the centre-of-mass system the corresponding angles are θ ($= 2\theta_L$) and $\pi - \theta$. If each of these scattered beams is described by a wave function of the type 14.42, then the total scattered intensity at angle θ might be given by the sum of the individual intensities

$$|f(\theta)|^2 + |f(\pi - \theta)|^2 \qquad (14.65a)$$

This classical expectation however disregards the requirements of quantum statistics (Sect. **3.6**) according to which the wave-function for the pair of particles must be either symmetrical or antisymmetrical under interchange of particles. This means that 14.42 must be replaced by

$$\psi_{sc} = [f(\theta) \pm f(\pi - \theta)]\frac{e^{ikr}}{r}$$

and the scattered intensity at angle θ is given by

$$|f(\theta) \pm f(\pi - \theta)|^2 \tag{14.65b}$$

which corresponds, as is reasonable, to an addition of amplitudes rather than of intensities.

In the case of α-He scattering, the spins are zero and the total wave function must be symmetrical, i.e. the positive sign must be taken. The scattered intensity at the centre-of-mass angle $\theta = \pi - \theta = 90°$ ($\theta_L = 45°$) is then just twice the classical result, as found by experiment (Sect. 5.3.1). In the case of the scattering of identical particles with spin, both symmetrical and antisymmetrical wave functions are required and the results are somewhat more complicated. They are described in Ref. 14.6.

14.2.3 BARRIER PENETRATION.

The formulae developed in Sect. 14.2.2 take no account of possible distortions of the incident plane wave on its way to the scattering nucleus or of reflection of the incident waves at the nuclear surface (except in the case of the hard sphere). For charged incident particles, the nucleus is surrounded by a potential barrier as shown in Fig. 14.7, and the incident particles must traverse this barrier before they can initiate a nuclear reaction. For neutrons there is no Coulomb barrier, but the finite potential step at the nuclear surface $r = R$ causes reflection.

The process of barrier penetration was described qualitatively in Sect. **11.1**. We now wish to make these considerations more quantitative and to write the limiting inelastic cross-section 14.53 in the form

$$\sigma_{inel}^l \leqslant \pi \lambda^2 (2l + 1) T_l \tag{14.66}$$

where T_l is the *barrier transmission coefficient* for particles of

17*

orbital angular momentum $l\hbar$. This quantity is the ratio of the number of particles entering the nucleus per sec ($= v|\psi|^2$ for a plane wave) to the number of particles incident on the barrier

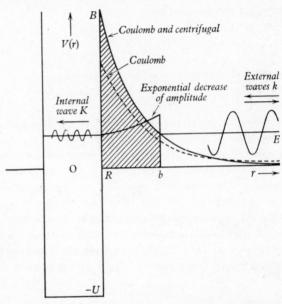

Fig. 14.7. Calculation of transmission coefficient for a potential barrier. The barrier penetration factor is the ratio of the particle densities at the nuclear surface and at $r = \infty$. The particle energy at infinity is E, and a factor $\approx 4k/K$ arises because of the change of wave number at the nuclear surface.

per sec. It will be convenient to think of T_l as composed of two factors (Fig. 14.7):

a) a *barrier penetration factor* P_l giving the probability of reaching the nuclear surface, and

b) a *potential discontinuity factor*, familiar in all types of wave problem, due to the change of wave-number from k in free space to K ($\gg k$) within the nucleus.

The potential discontinuity factor for s-wave neutrons is easily shown to be

$$\frac{4kK}{(k+K)^2} \approx \frac{4k}{K} \tag{14.67}$$

in intensity and we therefore write in general

$$T_l \approx \frac{4k}{K} P_l \qquad (14.68)$$

The barrier penetration factor P_l must be obtained by solving the Schrödinger equation for the incident particles in the potential field and finding the ratio between the beam intensity at a large distance and at the nuclear radius $r = R$. The general wave equation appropriate to this problem has already been given (3.12, with e^2/r replaced by zZe^2/r for a particle of charge ze approaching a nucleus of charge Ze). We are concerned in scattering problems with positive energy solutions of this equation and we note that the potential effective outside the range of nuclear forces is

$$V(r) = \frac{zZe^2}{r} + \frac{\hbar^2 l(l+1)}{2Mr^2} \qquad (14.69)$$

where M is the mass of the incident particle. The second term is due to the centrifugal effect, which tends to keep particles of high angular momentum away from the nucleus.

For *neutrons with* $l = 0$, $P_0 = 1$ so that $T_0 = 4k/K$. For *charged particles*, the solutions of the Schrödinger equation are complicated and although there are several methods (one of which will be outlined in Section **16.2**) for obtaining penetration factors it is best to use numerical tabulations. For $l = 0$ and high barriers ($R \to 0$) the dependence of P_0 on energy is shown by the expression (Ref. 14.3, p. 332)

$$P_0 = \frac{2\pi\eta}{e^{2\pi\eta} - 1} \qquad (14.70)$$

where $\eta = zZe^2/\hbar v$ and v is the velocity of the incident particle.

Formula 14.70 should only be used when $\eta \gg 1$ and then it becomes

$$P_0 \approx 2\pi\eta e^{-2\pi\eta} \propto \frac{1}{v} e^{-2\pi zZe^2/\hbar v} \qquad (14.71)$$

This factor, first obtained by Gamow and by Gurney and Condon (although in somewhat different form) determines the yield of nuclear reactions at low energies. Thus from 14.66,

14.68 and 14.71 we expect the cross-section for a reaction such as the ^{7}Li (p, α) process (Sect. 14.1.2) to be of the form

$$\sigma^0_{\text{inel}} \approx \pi \lambdabar^2 \cdot \frac{4k}{K} \cdot \frac{1}{v}\, e^{-2\pi z Z e^2 / \hbar v} \qquad (14.72)$$

$$\propto \frac{1}{v^2}\, e^{-2\pi z Z e^2 / \hbar v}$$

in which the exponential (Gamow) factor is by far the more important. A similar formula determines the lifetime for α-decay of radioactive nuclei (Sect. **16.2**).

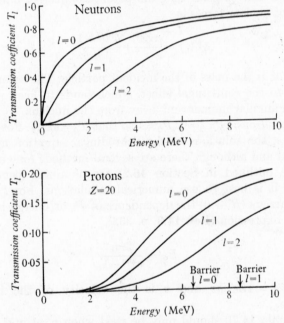

Fig. 14.8. Transmission coefficients for potential barriers.
a) Incident neutrons, $R = 5 \times 10^{-13}$ cm.
b) Incident protons, $R = 4 \cdot 5 \times 10^{-13}$ cm and $Z = 20$.

Expressions for T_l for both charged particles and neutrons with $l \geqslant 0$ are given in Ref. 14.3 and are shown in Fig. 14.8 for a particular case; the suppression of proton-induced reactions owing to the barrier is obvious. It will be noted that the transmission coefficient is still less than unity at a proton energy equal to the barrier height. In this region it may be shown (Ref. 14.3) that a good approximation for the reaction cross-section is

$$\sigma_{\text{inel}} = \pi(R + \lambda)^2 \left[1 - \frac{zZe^2}{(R + \lambda)\varepsilon} \right] \qquad (14.73)$$

where ε is the channel energy for the incident particle.

The formulae given in this section take no account of nuclear structure, i.e. it is supposed that there is no return of the incident wave from the inside of the nucleus after barrier penetration. This is the assumption of the continuum theory of nuclear reactions (Section **15.3**) but it is not true in the region of nuclear resonances (Sections **15.2, 15.5**).

References

14.1   R. T. Beyer, *Foundations of Nuclear Physics*, Dover Publ., 1949.
14.2   R. D. Evans, *The Atomic Nucleus*, Appendix C, McGraw-Hill, 1955.
14.3   J. B. Blatt and V. F. Weisskopf, *Theoretical Nuclear Physics*, p. 358, Wiley, 1952.
14.4   L. R. B. Elton, *Introductory Nuclear Theory*, chapter 6, Pitman, 1959.
14.5   D. Bohm, *Quantum Theory*, chapter 21, Constable, 1951.
14.6   L. I. Schiff, *Quantum Mechanics*, McGraw-Hill, 1949.
14.7   O. R. Frisch, 'Atomic Energy—how it all began', *Brit. jnl. appl. Phys.*, **5**, 81, 1954.

15. NUCLEAR REACTIONS (DETAILED MECHANISMS)

The wave mechanical theory outlined in chapter 14 is not a theory of nuclear reactions; it provides only a framework for a formal description and sets certain limits on cross-sections. In this chapter we consider a number of specific models for nuclear reactions which permit calculation of the asymptotic phase shifts of the formal theory. We shall approach these models from the experimental point of view, beginning with the compound nucleus model of Niels Bohr, which has little connection with structure models of the individual particle type, continuing through the direct interaction mechanism in which individual motion of nucleons is more important, and concluding with a brief introduction to the 'optical' model which attempts to fuse together the two main types of approach. Some mention is made of inelastic processes at high energies since these illustrate an application of some of the principles discussed earlier in the chapter.

All formulae presented in this chapter must be assumed to refer, when relevant, to the centre-of-mass system.

15.1 The origin of the compound nucleus hypothesis

The main nuclear phenomena known in 1935 suggested that reaction cross-sections for high-energy particles were of the order of nuclear dimensions, in agreement with the high energy limit πR^2 predicted by wave theory (ch. 14). The cross-sections for the capture of neutrons by nuclei were shown by Amaldi *et al.* (Section 14.1.5) to increase beyond the nuclear area when the neutrons were slowed down by passage through hydrogenous material. This is also consistent with the results of wave theory since the low energy limit of the reaction cross-section is $\pi \lambda^2$ and $\lambda \approx 10^{-8}$ cm for slow neutrons.

The first model which attempted to explain the variation of

neutron cross-sections with energy was essentially the single-particle shell model, in which the incident neutron was supposed to move briefly in the potential well provided by the target nucleus. In this model the probability of scattering was always large, while the probability of capture was generally small but increased proportionately with the time spent by the incident particle near the nucleus, i.e. as $1/v$. For thermal neutrons the scattering and absorption cross-sections were expected to be about equal. It was also predicted that resonance anomalies would be seen both in absorption and scattering but these would be associated with the virtual single-particle levels and would be spaced in energy by perhaps 10 MeV. They would also be ≈ 1 MeV wide because of the short time ($\approx 10^{-21}$ sec) spent by the neutron in the potential well. Variations of capture cross-section with energy in the thermal range were not likely to be affected by these resonances (Fig. 15.1a).

This picture is in sharp disagreement with observation at several points. In the first place, many nuclei were found to have large absorption cross-sections for slow neutrons but to show very small scattering. Then the work of Moon and Tillman and of Amaldi and Fermi, using reactions of the type (cf. 14.18)

$$^{107}\text{Ag} + n \rightarrow {}^{108}\text{Ag} + \gamma + 7\cdot23 \text{ MeV}$$

$$^{108}\text{Ag} \rightarrow {}^{108}\text{Cd} + \beta^- + \bar{\nu} \tag{15.1}$$

established that although slow neutron capture cross-sections varied as expected with the temperature of the surroundings, they also varied in an unexpected way when the incident neutrons passed through different types of absorber. The neutrons causing activation of silver were strongly absorbed by silver itself but much less strongly by other materials. This selective absorption is inconsistent with the prediction of a monotonic decrease of cross-section with increasing neutron velocity for all nuclei and gave the first indication that there are strong resonances in slow neutron capture cross-sections and that they are sharp and closely spaced. Later and more accurate work using neutron velocity selectors (Sect. **7.3**) has confirmed this conclusion and has shown that the level widths concerned are of the order of a few tenths of an electron volt and the level spacing perhaps a few electron volts (Fig. 15.1b, and Fig. 15.5). The total cross-sections at resonance are mainly due to the capture process.

In order to explain these observations Niels Bohr* in 1936 introduced the concept of the compound nucleus which is a many-body system of strongly interacting particles formed by

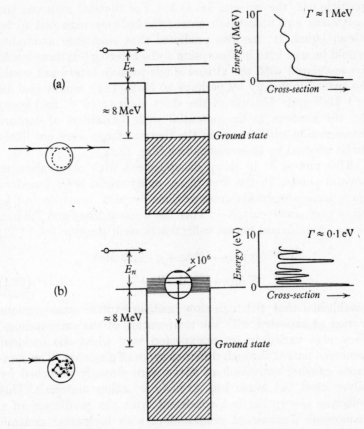

Fig. 15.1. Interaction of a neutron with a nucleus. The levels shown represent the states of excitation of the system (neutron + nucleus); a neutron of zero energy E_n produces an excitation of about 8 MeV.

a) Potential well model.

b) Compound nucleus model. Note the different energy scale of the cross-section curve.

---

* N. Bohr, *Nature*, **137**, 344, 1936.

the amalgamation of an incident particle a with a target nucleus

$$X + a \rightarrow C^* \qquad (15.2)$$

In such a system, which has analogies with a liquid drop, the incident particle a has a short mean free path and shares its energy with the other particles of the system C^* so that it cannot be re-emitted until, as a result of further exchanges, sufficient energy is again concentrated on this or a similar particle. If the incident particle is a slow neutron this may be a very long time, sufficient to permit the emission of radiation. The capture process is then complete and the compound nucleus C is formed in its ground state either by emission of a single photon,

$$C^* \rightarrow C + \gamma \qquad (15.3)$$

or by the emission of a sequence of quanta in cascade. This explains the predominance of the capture reaction and the suppression of elastic scattering; the sharp, closely spaced resonances are also naturally accounted for as the characteristic modes of the many-body system.

The progress of many types of nuclear reaction can be described, in terms of a compound nucleus, as a *two-stage process*

$$X + a \rightarrow C^* \rightarrow Y + b \qquad (15.4)$$

in contrast with the *single-stage process*

$$X + a \rightarrow Y + b \qquad (15.5)$$

envisaged by the potential well model and leading to the same products.

We shall write reactions in the form 15.4 when it is desired to draw attention to the compound nucleus, and in the form 15.5 when it is only necessary to indicate the initial and final system (cf. Sect. 14.2.1).

The second stage of the nuclear reaction according to Bohr's suggestion is to be considered as independent of the first (*independence hypothesis*). In other words, the break-up of the compound nucleus C^* into different reaction channels (Sect. 14.2.1) $Y + b$, $Y_1 + b_1$, etc. should be determined only by the properties of the compound nucleus and not by its mode of formation. If this is true (and it is not always so) the cross-section for the process $X(a, b)Y$ may be written

$$\sigma_{ab} = \sigma_a \frac{\Gamma_b}{\Gamma} \tag{15.6}$$

where σ_a is the cross-section for the formation of a compound nucleus by particle a and Γ_b is proportional to the probability of breakup into channel b. The total 'width' Γ is equal to the sum of all partial widths Γ_b. The validity of the independence hypothesis depends on the relation between the level width Γ and the spacing D of energy levels of the compound nucleus. It has already been pointed out (Sect. **9.4**) that the nuclear level spectrum may be divided into ranges for which $\Gamma \ll D$ (resonance region) and $\Gamma \gg D$ (continuum).

15.2 Discrete levels of the compound nucleus $(\Gamma \ll D)$

15.2.1 CROSS-SECTION FORMULA FOR SPINLESS PAR-TICLES. In the resonance region of the nuclear spectrum levels are discrete and the independence assumption is reasonable. Each level is characterized, as far as nuclear reactions are concerned, by the parameters listed in Sect. **9.4**, i.e. excitation energy E_0 above the ground state, angular momentum with quantum number I_e, parity ($\pm$) and partial widths for decay. We wish to find the cross-section for excitation of a well-defined nuclear level of this type by a particle or photon of energy E_a. As shown in Fig. 15.2 the excitation in the compound nucleus is

$$E = \varepsilon_a + S_a$$

where ε_a is the channel energy (eq. 14.28) and S_a is the separation energy for the particle a in the compound nucleus.

The excitation of a nuclear level by an incident particle is analogous to the excitation of the oscillations of an electrical circuit by an electromagnetic wave. We therefore expect the nuclear cross-section to vary with incident energy in the same way that the energy in a forced oscillation varies with incident frequency. The classical resonant circuit absorbs energy because of resistive losses; in the nuclear case, damping arises because of the possibility of decay, either via the incident channel, or through other open channels. Because of this possibility the nuclear state has a finite width Γ as already discussed in connection with the semi-classical theory of radiation (Sect. 3.9.1). The wave function of a decaying state of mean energy E_0 may be written

$$\psi_t = \psi_0 e^{-iE_0 t/\hbar} e^{-\Gamma t/2\hbar} \tag{15.7}$$

which corresponds to an exponential decrease of intensity of excitation $|\psi_t|^2$ with a time constant $\tau = \hbar/\Gamma$. This wave function

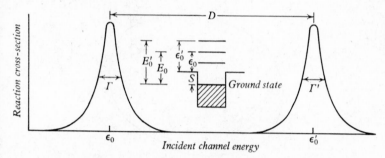

Fig. 15.2. Reaction cross-section as a function of incident channel energy ε in the resonance region of nuclear spectra.

is not that of a stationary state but may be built up from a superposition of stationary states of slightly different energy as a Fourier integral:

$$\psi_t = \int_{-\infty}^{\infty} A(E) e^{-iEt/\hbar} \, dE \tag{15.8}$$

where $A(E)$ is the amplitude of the state of energy E. From 15.7 and 15.8 we obtain, making a Fourier transform,

$$|A(E)|^2 = \frac{|\psi_0|^2}{4\pi^2} \frac{1}{(E-E_0)^2 + \Gamma^2/4} \tag{15.9}$$

and this gives the level shape (Fig. 15.2). It is exactly as for pure radiative decay except that particle emission is now included by using the total width Γ instead of the radiative width Γ_γ. The cross-section for excitation of the level by collision of particle a with nucleus X is therefore expected to have the form

$$\sigma_a = \frac{C}{(E-E_0)^2 + \Gamma^2/4} \tag{15.10}$$

where C is a constant.

To find C we use a simple statistical argument. Suppose (Fig. 15.3) that compound nucleus formation and decay take place in a box of volume Ω containing one nucleus X and one particle a. The number of states of motion of the particle, with momentum between p and $p + \mathrm{d}p$ is

$$\frac{4\pi p^2 \mathrm{d}p}{h^3} \cdot \Omega \qquad (15.11)$$

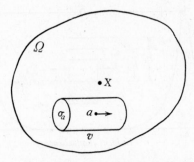

Fig. 15.3. Relation between formation and decay of a compound nucleus in a single channel.

if the states are quantized. The probability of formation of the compound level per unit time is the probability that the nucleus X is contained within the small volume $\sigma_a v$ swept out by the effective collision area per second multiplied by the number of possible states of motion, i.e.

$$\frac{\sigma_a v}{\Omega} \cdot \frac{4\pi p^2 \mathrm{d}p}{h^3} \cdot \Omega \qquad (15.12)$$

integrated over the energy spectrum. This gives the probability,

$$\frac{4\pi}{h^3} \int_{-\infty}^{\infty} v\sigma_a p^2 \mathrm{d}p = \frac{4\pi}{h^3} \int_{-\infty}^{\infty} \sigma_a p^2 \mathrm{d}\varepsilon_a = \frac{4\pi}{h} \int_{-\infty}^{\infty} \frac{\sigma_a}{\lambda^2} \mathrm{d}\varepsilon_a \quad (15.13)$$

We now assume that the variation of the channel wavelength λ of the particle over the level width Γ may be neglected and the probability of formation then becomes, using 15.10,

$$\frac{4\pi}{h\lambda^2} \frac{2\pi C}{\Gamma} = \frac{C}{\hbar\pi\lambda^2\Gamma} \qquad (15.14)$$

In a system containing a large number of particles and nuclei a, X in equilibrium this rate of formation would be balanced by the decay of the excited state back into the system $X + a$. This process has by definition the probability

$$\frac{\Gamma_a}{\hbar} \qquad (15.15)$$

per unit time where Γ_a is the partial width of the compound level for emission of a. From 15.14 and 15.15

$$C = \pi \lambda^2 \Gamma \Gamma_a \qquad (15.16)$$

and the cross-section for the formation of the level becomes

$$\sigma_a(E) = \pi \lambda^2 \frac{\Gamma_a \Gamma}{(E - E_0)^2 + \Gamma^2/4} \qquad (15.17)$$

This needs a slight modification if the level is formed by particles with orbital angular momentum $l > 0$. The spin of the level is then $I_e = l$ since intrinsic spins are assumed zero, and the level therefore has statistical weight $(2l + 1)$. Each of the substates can decay with equal probability and Γ_a should therefore be replaced by $g\Gamma_a$, where $g = 2l + 1$ for spinless particles. The cross-section formula is then

$$\sigma_a(E) = \pi \lambda^2 g \frac{\Gamma_a \Gamma}{(E - E_0)^2 + \Gamma^2/4} \qquad (15.18)$$

For the process $X(a, b)Y$ we then obtain, from 15.6

$$\sigma_{ab}(E) = \pi \lambda^2 g \frac{\Gamma_a \Gamma_b}{(E - E_0)^2 + \Gamma^2/4} \qquad (15.19)$$

This is the celebrated single-level, or *Breit-Wigner* formula for reaction cross-section. It is easily seen to be consistent with the limits derived in Sect. 14.2.2.

Thus for *elastic scattering* through the compound state, with no other process possible, $\Gamma_a = \Gamma_b = \Gamma$ and at resonance $(E = E_0)$

$$\sigma_{el} = \sigma_{aa} = 4\pi \lambda^2 (2l + 1) \qquad (15.20)$$

Also for the total *inelastic cross-section* we write $\Gamma_b = \Gamma - \Gamma_a$ and then at resonance

$$\sigma_{inel} = \pi \lambda^2 (2l + 1) \frac{\Gamma_a(\Gamma - \Gamma_a)}{\Gamma^2/4}$$

$$\leqslant \pi \lambda^2 (2l + 1) \qquad (15.21)$$

The *excitation function*, or variation of σ_{ab} with energy, is successfully described by 15.19 for many nuclear reactions. Important examples are the radiative capture of protons, and the capture and scattering of slow neutrons. These processes have been examined in Sect. 13.6.3 from the point of view of the determination of radiative widths Γ_γ, but here we are concerned mainly with their relevance to the compound nucleus theory. For *proton capture* a typical excitation func-

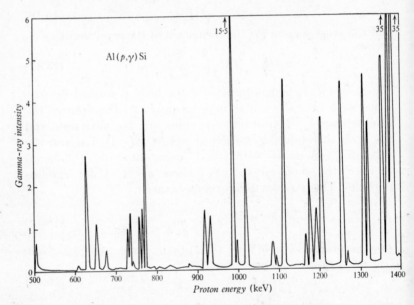

Fig. 15.4. Resonant yield of γ-radiation in the reaction $^{27}\text{Al}(p,\gamma)\text{Si}^{28}$. The peaks indicate virtual levels at an excitation of about 12 MeV in the nucleus ^{28}Si (Brostrom *et al.*, *Phys. Rev.*, **71**, 661, 1947).

tion is shown in Fig. 15.4, taken from the work of Brostrom, Huus and Tangen on the $^{27}\text{Al}\ (p,\gamma)\ ^{28}\text{Si}$ reaction. The sharp peaks in γ-ray yield as the energy of the proton beam is varied are due to levels in the compound nucleus ^{28}Si, which emits cascades of radiation in returning to the ground state

$$^{28}\text{Si}^* \rightarrow {}^{28}\text{Si} + \gamma \qquad (15.22)$$

The widths shown in Fig. 15.4 are instrumental but by use of precision analysers true widths Γ of the order of 1 keV or less can be obtained from proton excitation curves.

The total cross-section for *slow neutron interaction* in a heavy element is shown in Fig. 15.5, and the narrow, closely spaced levels of the Bohr theory are clearly evident. The widths in this

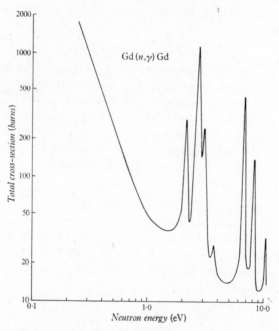

Fig. 15.5. Total cross-section for interaction of slow neutrons with gadolinium (Hughes and Schwartz, *Neutron Cross Sections*, BNL 325).

case are, apart from Doppler broadening, mainly due to (n, γ) capture since slow neutron widths are small ($\approx 10^{-3}$ eV). These widths are however, directly proportional to velocity* ($\Gamma_n \propto v$) and this fact can be used to predict the relative variation of scattering and absorption cross-section in an energy range such as that below 2 eV in Fig. 15.5. For such energies

---

* The width Γ_n is proportional to the density of states of motion of a free particle, i.e. $\Gamma_n \propto \dfrac{4\pi p^2}{h^3} \dfrac{\mathrm{d}p}{\mathrm{d}E} \propto v$. Strictly, the energy dependence of the widths Γ should be included in 15.19.

the denominator in 15.19 may be assumed constant and then

$$\sigma_{n\gamma} \propto \lambda^2 \Gamma_n \Gamma_\gamma \propto v\lambda^2 \propto \frac{1}{v} \qquad (15.23)$$

since the radiative widths Γ_γ for the 8 MeV capture radiation will vary little over the range involved. This result is the familiar $1/v$ law for neutron capture. For scattering on the other hand

$$\sigma_{nn} \propto \lambda^2 \Gamma_n^2 \propto \text{constant} \qquad (15.24)$$

In the vicinity of a resonance both cross-sections are much increased. As the neutron energy increases, the relative contribution of elastic scattering to the total cross-section also increases, and in the 100–1000 keV range, resonances in total cross-section are mainly due to scattering. The shape of the scattering resonances depends in detail on the presence of the interference effect discussed in the next section.

15.2.2 ELASTIC SCATTERING. The cross-section for elastic scattering of spinless particles at an energy near a nuclear resonance is obtained by setting $\Gamma_a = \Gamma_b$ in 15.19. If re-emission of the incident particle is by far the most probable means of removing excitation energy, then $\Gamma_a = \Gamma_b = \Gamma$ and the cross-section becomes

$$\sigma_{aa}(E) = \pi\lambda^2 g \frac{\Gamma^2}{(E - E_0)^2 + \Gamma^2/4} \qquad (15.25)$$

This formula can be obtained from the expression 14.50 by the substitution $\eta_l = e^{2i\delta_l}$ with

$$\tan \delta_l = \frac{\Gamma}{2(E_0 - E)} \qquad (15.26)$$

This has an immediate interpretation in analogy with the theory of forced vibration. The final wave is shifted in phase by an angle δ_l which varies from approximately $0°$ (if $E_0 \gg \Gamma$) through $90°$ (at resonance) to $180°$ (for $E \gg E_0$) as the incident energy varies.

Expression 15.25 represents only the compound nucleus part of the elastic scattering, i.e. that part which is associated with the adjacent level E_0. Experimentally it is observed that there is usually a background of elastic scattering for energies between resonances and that in the neighbourhood of a resonance there is an interference between this background scattering and the resonant scattering. The theoretical interpretation of the background, or average, scattering is best based on the optical model (Sect. **15.5**) which is constructed in such a way as to provide an average scattering phase angle; the corresponding physical effect is known as *potential* or *shape-elastic scattering*. It is customary in single level treatments of nuclear scattering to represent the potential scattering for the partial wave l by a phase angle ϕ_l and to write

$$\delta_l = \beta_l - \phi_l$$

where (15.27)

$$\tan \beta_l = \frac{\Gamma}{2(E_0 - E)}$$

gives the resonant phase angle. The elastic cross-section 14.50 becomes

$$\sigma_{\mathrm{el}}^l = \sigma_{aa}^l = 4\pi \lambda^2 (2l+1) \left| \frac{e^{2i(\beta_l - \phi_l)} - 1}{2i} \right|^2$$

$$= 4\pi \lambda^2 (2l+1) \left| \frac{\tfrac{1}{2}\Gamma}{E_0 - E - (i\Gamma/2)} - e^{i\phi_l} \sin \phi_l \right|^2 \quad (15.28)$$

and between resonances this tends for s-wave neutrons to the value $4\pi \lambda^2 \sin^2 \phi_0$. This is just the cross-section expected (Sect. 14.2.2) for the scattering from an impenetrable sphere of radius $R \approx \lambda \phi_0$ and the background effect is therefore sometimes known as hard sphere scattering. Although a hard sphere radius is convenient for formal analysis and may be given a specific form, such as $R = r_0 A^{1/3}$, it should not be identified with any physical dimension.

A formula such as 15.28 has been used to analyse the *elastic scattering of neutrons* by nuclei. For *charged particles* Coulomb scattering must be included and the formulae become more elaborate (Ref. 15.4). The precision of proton and α-particle scattering experiments using beams accelerated in electrostatic generators is very high, and the scattering process may be studied in detail. Thus in the case of the scattering of protons by aluminium interference between the nuclear and Coulomb

scattering may be clearly seen. Fig. 15.6a gives the yield of
scattered protons near the 985 keV resonance of the compound
nucleus ^{28}Si, and Fig. 15.6b shows the associated yield of the
(p, γ) reaction. The reaction cross-section 15.19 contains no
interference term. Analysis of these curves yields total and
partial level widths, and also information on the angular
momentum of the level (Ref. 15.3).

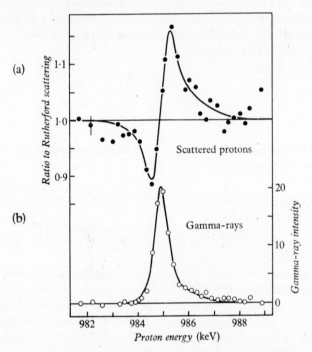

Fig. 15.6. Scattering and absorption of protons at 985 keV resonance in
the $^{27}\text{Al} + p$ interaction.
a) Yield of scattered protons at $135°$.
b) Yield of $^{27}\text{Al}(p,\gamma)\text{Si}^{28}$ reaction (Bender *et al.*, *Phys. Rev.*, **76**, 273,
1949).

If Coulomb forces may be neglected, then 15.28 shows that
the scattering cross-section far from resonances reduces to the
nuclear potential scattering. In the hard sphere approximation
(Sect. 14.2.2) the cross-section is then $4\pi R^2$ for the $l = 0$ interaction, where R is the nuclear radius. Near the resonance level
the cross-section increases to a value of approximately $4\pi \lambda^2$.

15.2.3 INTRODUCTION OF SPIN. Suppose now that the nuclei a, X have spin quantum numbers s, I, and that I_e is the spin of the single excited state of C effective in the reaction. Then the incident orbital momentum vector l must satisfy the equation

$$s + I + l = I_e \qquad (15.29)$$

The problem is simplified if the spins s, I of the initial system are combined into a number of equivalent *channel spins j* such that

and
$$\left.\begin{array}{c} s + I = j \\[2mm] s + I \geqslant j \geqslant |s - I| \end{array}\right\} \qquad (15.30)$$

This equation gives either $(2s + 1)$ or $(2I + 1)$ distinct values of j according as $s <$ or $> I$. It may easily be seen that the total number of magnetic substates is the same, namely $(2s + 1) \times (2I + 1)$ for each description of the initial colliding system, i.e. for two spins s and I or for the appropriate number of channel spins j. In an unpolarized system all these magnetic substates are equally populated, and for zero incident orbital angular momentum the probability of forming a given channel spin j from the combining spins s, I is

$$\frac{2j + 1}{(2s + 1)(2I + 1)} \qquad (15.31)$$

To form the compound state of spin I_e from a given channel spin and orbital momentum l requires an l value given by

and
$$\left.\begin{array}{c} j + l = I_e \\[2mm] j + I_e \geqslant l \geqslant |j - I_e| \end{array}\right\} \qquad (15.32)$$

with the limitation that only even or only odd values of l are permitted because of conservation of parity. The probability of forming I_e from l, j is, for unpolarized systems,

$$\frac{2I_e + 1}{(2l + 1)(2j + 1)} \qquad (15.33)$$

The two factors 15.31 and 15.33 therefore multiply the cross-section for the case of particles with spin and we obtain from 15.19

$$\sigma_{ab}^l = \pi \lambda^2 \frac{2I_e + 1}{(2s+1)(2I+1)} \frac{\Gamma_a \Gamma_b}{(E - E_0)^2 + \Gamma^2/4} \tag{15.34}$$

$$= \pi \lambda^2 g \frac{\Gamma_a \Gamma_b}{(E - E_0)^2 + \Gamma^2/4}$$

where $$g = \frac{2I_e + 1}{(2s+1)(2I+1)} \tag{15.35}$$

The maximum cross-section for elastic scattering is now

$$\sigma_{aa}^l = 4\pi \lambda^2 g \tag{15.36}$$

and only reaches this value when no reactions are possible. The maximum inelastic cross-section is

$$\sigma_{ab}^l = \pi \lambda^2 g \tag{15.37}$$

These relations are useful in finding values for the spin of compound states from observed cross-sections.

It is possible to envisage experiments in which particular channel spins could be investigated separately. In general, therefore, contributions to a reaction yield from the various possible channel spins are *incoherent* and may be added as intensities. This is in contrast with contributions from different l-values, which are coherent, since they cannot be separated without destroying the character of the incident plane wave.

15.2.4 CONSERVATION THEOREMS. In any nuclear reaction I is a good quantum number since total angular momentum must be conserved. In special cases, total orbital and spin momenta, L and S are separately conserved. If nuclear forces are charge independent, the total isobaric spin T is also a good quantum number, and this is always true for the third component m_T of this quantity, which just measures charge. Parity seems to be conserved in nuclear reactions although in β-decay processes it is not. The conservation of the quantities I, T and parity thus imposes selection rules on nuclear reactions; from observations of angular distributions and transition probabilities it may be possible to deduce values for these quantum numbers.

15.2.5 REDUCED WIDTHS; STRENGTH FUNCTION. The partial widths Γ_a, Γ_b used in preceding sections were introduced as parameters of the single-level formula. They may however be calculated if a particular model of nuclear structure is assumed. Suppose for instance that we postulate a very crude model in which one of the nuclear particles approaches the nuclear surface ν times per second with an energy sufficient for it to be emitted. The mean life would then be $\tau_0 = 1/\nu$. This is increased because of the necessity for barrier penetration and the actual mean life is

$$\tau = \frac{\tau_0}{T_0}$$

where T_0 is the transmission coefficient, taken in this simple case for $l = 0$. The partial width for particle decay is then

$$\Gamma = \frac{\hbar}{\tau} = \frac{\hbar T_0}{\tau_0} \tag{15.38}$$

The mean life without barrier τ_0 may be related to the level spacing D of the nucleus at high excitation by the argument that if the nucleus is an oscillating system of frequency ν then a set of energy levels of uniform spacing $D = h\nu = h/\tau_0$ might be expected. The Bohr liquid drop model, with its many closely spaced levels, is an approximation to such a system. Substituting in 15.38 we then have

$$\Gamma = \frac{D T_0}{2\pi} \tag{15.39}$$

and using the expression 14.68 for T_0 we obtain

$$\frac{\Gamma}{D} = \frac{2k}{\pi K} P_0 = \frac{2k}{\pi K} \quad \text{for neutrons} \tag{15.39a}$$

in which K is the wave number of the particle in the nuclear potential well and k ($\ll K$) its wave number when emitted. It is usual to define a *reduced width* γ^2 for s-wave neutrons by the equation

$$\Gamma = 2k\gamma^2 \tag{15.40}$$

and for neutrons with $l > 0$ or charged particles by

$$\Gamma_l = 2k P_l \gamma^2 \tag{15.40a}$$

where P_l is the barrier penetration factor used in Sect. 14.2.3. From (15.39a) and (15.40) we obtain an expression from which all factors external to the nucleus have disappeared

$$\frac{\gamma^2}{D} = \frac{1}{\pi K} \approx 10^{-13} \text{ cm} \qquad (15.41)$$

This is known as the *strength function* and is independent of energy for the particular case assumed of a regular, uniformly spaced series of levels. In other cases, the strength function may be found to be energy dependent and it then specifies the type of level structure or nuclear motion concerned.

Reduced widths are normally quoted as fractions of the single-particle reduced width for a square well; this may be shown to be $\hbar^2/MR$ MeV $\times$ cm where M is the nucleon mass and R the radius of the well.* Reduced widths predicted by the individual particle model are usually much less than this because the nuclear motion is usually more complicated than that of a single particle. Special cases are known however (e.g. in nuclear photodisintegration) in which reduced widths may be enhanced. In the limit of a highly co-ordinated nuclear motion, very large values of reduced widths may be found and nuclear levels are appropriately described by the collective model. In all cases this width is to be interpreted as the probability of a nucleus dissociating into a certain pair of particles at the nuclear surface. The single particle reduced width plays the same part in the interpretation of particle emission and absorption as does the 'Weisskopf' unit in the interpretation of radiative transitions.

15.3   Overlapping levels of the compound nucleus $(\Gamma \gg D)$

15.3.1 THE STATISTICAL ASSUMPTION. Equation 15.41 suggests that the strength function γ^2/D for a nuclear model in which levels are uniformly spaced is constant. As the excitation energy increases the *total* width of levels also increases because more channels become available and each channel may be more easily entered. Since the yield of a nuclear reaction follows the

---

* In Ref. 15.4 and much subsequent literature 15.40 includes a radius of the order of the nuclear radius R. Reduced widths are then measured in MeV and the single-particle reduced width is $\hbar^2/MR^2$.

total width, sharp resonances are no longer observable when $\Gamma \gg D$ and contributions from many overlapping levels must be assumed at any given energy. In this *continuum region* it is no longer obvious that the assumptions of the Bohr theory of nuclear reactions will hold. If, for instance, only a few levels contribute to the total wave function of a nucleus at a certain energy then this nucleus may well 'remember' the way in which it was formed and the independence assumption will be invalid. If, however, the number of contributing wave functions becomes large, i.e. in the limit of strong overlapping, there are so many random contributions to a given process that the second stage of a reaction may again appear independent of the first. The cross-section for a nuclear reaction may then once more be written in the form 15.6 but this is now dependent on the *statistical assumption* of random motion in the compound state. Calculations based on this assumption are often described as part of the *statistical theory of nuclear reactions*.

The independence of the processes of formation and decay for nuclei formed with excitations in the continuum region has been demonstrated directly. Fig. 15.7 shows the results of Ghoshal for the yield of ^{62}Zn and ^{63}Zn formed by the reactions

$$\left.\begin{array}{l} {}^{60}\text{Ni} + \alpha \rightarrow {}^{64}\text{Zn} \searrow {}^{62}\text{Zn} + 2n \\ \qquad\qquad\qquad \searrow {}^{63}\text{Zn} + \ n \\ {}^{63}\text{Cu} + p \rightarrow {}^{64}\text{Zn} \searrow {}^{62}\text{Zn} + 2n \\ \qquad\qquad\qquad \searrow {}^{63}\text{Zn} + \ n \end{array}\right\} \qquad (15.42)$$

and assessed by the resulting activity. It is clear that the different formation processes, if plotted on a scale of equal excitation energy for the compound nucleus ^{64}Zn, lead to nearly the same ratio of disintegration products.

In continuum theory it is assumed that at high energies when transmission coefficients are unity the cross-sections for scattering and absorption are given by the black nucleus values 14.55, 14.56, and 14.57.

15.3.2 PARTIAL WIDTHS FOR DECAY; EXCITATION FUNCTIONS.

Fig. 15.8 represents the final stage of the compound nucleus reaction X(a, b)Y. The compound nucleus is excited to an energy in the continuum and emits particle b to form the final nucleus Y in an excited state which is also supposed to be in a region of high-level density. Nucleus Y emits a photon in returning to its ground state, or, if the excitation is high enough, another particle to form a new nucleus.

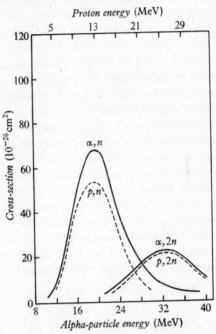

Fig. 15.7. Independence assumption for the continuum region of nuclear spectra. The full lines show the yield of ^{63}Zn and ^{62}Zn formed in α-particle bombardment of ^{60}Ni and the dotted lines the yield of these isotopes from the proton bombardment of ^{63}Cu. The energy scales are adjusted so that the excitation of the compound nucleus is the same for the two targets at the indicated bombarding energies (Ghoshal, *Phys. Rev.*, **80**, 939, 1950).

The cross-section for formation of the compound nucleus is the cross-section for inelastic processes in the Bohr strong interaction theory and we assume that it has its maximum value (14.66)

$$\sigma_a = \pi \lambda_a^2 (2l+1) T_l \qquad (15.43)$$

We may use this formula, and relation 15.39, to find the probability of decay. Thus, neglecting intrinsic spins,

$$\Gamma_b = \frac{D_c T_l}{2\pi}$$

where D_c is the level spacing in the nucleus C. Substituting for T_l and applying 15.43 to particle b

$$(2l+1)\Gamma_b = \frac{D_c}{2\pi^2 \lambda_b^2} \sigma_b \qquad (15.44)$$

where σ_b is the cross-section* for the formation of C by bombardment of Y (strictly in an excited state) with particle b

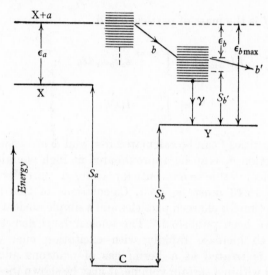

Fig. 15.8. Emission of particle b from a compound nucleus with excitation of levels of the continuum in nucleus Y. If the excitation of Y is greater than the separation energy of a particle b', this particle can be emitted.

In the following calculations, which do not refer to specific states with known quantum numbers, the factor $(2l+1)$ will be omitted.

The probability of emission of b with *any* energy from the excited state of C is obtained by integrating 15.44 over the levels of Y available between the ground state and the maximum excitation $\varepsilon_{b\,\max}$ permitted in the reaction. This gives

$$\Gamma_b = \frac{D_c}{2\pi^2} \int_0^{\varepsilon_{b\,\max}} \frac{\sigma_b}{\lambda_b^2} \, \omega_Y d\varepsilon_b \qquad (15.45)$$

---

* This formula may also be obtained by averaging the single level formula 15.18 over an energy interval containing many levels.

18+N.P.

where the kinetic energy of particle b has been set equal to the channel energy ε_b (i.e. recoil of the heavy nucleus is neglected) and $\omega_Y = 1/D_Y$ is the level density in nucleus Y at the excitation energy $E_Y = \varepsilon_{b\,\max} - \varepsilon_b$. This formula may be rewritten

$$\Gamma_b = \frac{D_c M}{\pi^2 \hbar^2} f_b(\varepsilon_{b\,\max}) \tag{15.46}$$

where M is the mass of particle b and

$$f_b(\varepsilon_{b\,\max}) = \int_0^{\varepsilon_{b\,\max}} \varepsilon_b \sigma_b \omega_Y d\varepsilon_b$$

$$= \int_0^{\varepsilon_{b\,\max}} I(\varepsilon) d\varepsilon \tag{15.47}$$

The quantities f can be calculated if σ_b and ω are assumed. The cross-section σ_b may be approximated at high energies by the geometrical value πR^2, but for charged particles the full formula 15.43 must be used. Calculations of this formation cross-section for charged particles and a simple nuclear potential well have been published.* The nuclear level densities ω are known to increase rapidly with excitation energy. If the nucleus is treated as a Fermi gas of neutrons and protons confined within a certain volume, it may be shown (Sect. 15.3.4) that at an excitation energy E

$$\omega(E) = \text{constant} \times e^{2\sqrt{(aE)}} \tag{15.48}$$

where a is a constant for a given nucleus at least (although it has different values for Z, N even–even, odd–odd and even–odd). With this assumption, and with a value for a chosen from surveys of nuclear levels, the widths Γ_b can be calculated and the relative yields of different possible reactions predicted using 15.6.

A case of special interest arises when the nucleus Y is left, after the emission of particle b, in a state from which the emission of a further particle b' is energetically possible. A *secondary*

---

* M. M. Shapiro, *Phys. Rev.*, **90**, 171, 1953.

reaction then takes place; in the case of neutrons it can easily be seen, from Eqs. 15.6 and 15.46 and Fig. 15.8 that

$$\sigma_{a2n} = \sigma_{an} \frac{\displaystyle\int_0^{\varepsilon_{b\,max} - S_n} I(\varepsilon)d\varepsilon}{\displaystyle\int_{\varepsilon_{b\,max} - S_n}^{\varepsilon_{b\,max}} I(\varepsilon)d\varepsilon} \qquad (15.49)$$

since only those first neutron emissions which lead to an excitation of Y greater than the neutron separation energy S_n are followed by a second neutron. This equation can also be evaluated in terms of an assumed density function and the observed cross-section for a secondary process expressed in terms of the parameter a.

The competition between alternative emission processes when multiple emission of particles is possible has been shown in many experiments, including those of Ghoshal already mentioned (Sect. 15.3.1). The (α, n) $(\alpha, 2n)$ and $(\alpha, 3n)$ reactions leading to radioactive products are especially suitable for this type of demonstration and Fig. 15.9a shows the relative yields expected. As soon as a new process becomes energetically possible the yield of previously occurring processes diminishes if all the processes concerned derive from a compound nucleus. The total yield of all types of reaction should aggregate to give the cross-section for compound nucleus formation σ_a. The general forms of excitation functions for proton and neutron induced reactions according to the statistical theory are shown in Fig. 15.9; the proton type of curve is well known for (p, n) reactions[*]; the neutron type of curve is distinguished by its monotonic behaviour which is essentially a consequence of the low probability of re-emission of the incident particle from the compound nucleus. It will be seen later that this is only a first approximation to the truth.

The level density formula 15.48 may also be checked by measurement of neutron capture cross-sections with an inhomogeneous energy of about 1 MeV, in elements of $A > 20$ for which an average over many levels may be expected. From

---

[*] A convenient experimental arrangement for studying (p, n) excitation functions is a stack of foils of the target element through which a cyclotron beam may be passed.

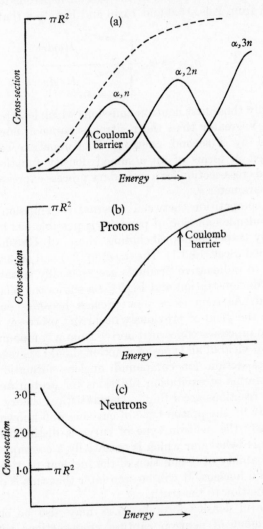

Fig. 15.9. Cross-sections in the continuum theory (schematic).
a) Competition in (α, xn) reactions. The dotted curve represents the theoretical cross-section for formation of the compound nucleus.
b) Reaction cross-section for protons. The rise is due to increasing barrier transmission.
c) Reaction cross-section for neutrons, showing transition from low energy value $\approx \pi \lambda^2$ to the high energy value $\approx \pi R^2$.

15.44 the cross-section for formation of the compound nucleus by the incident neutrons is

$$\sigma_n = 2\pi^2 \lambdabar_n^2 \frac{\Gamma_n}{D_c} \qquad (15.50)$$

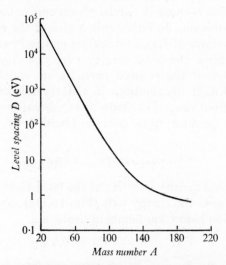

Fig. 15.10. Level spacing as a function of mass number determined from neutron capture cross-section (Hughes *et al.*, *Phys. Rev.*, **91**, 1423, 1953).

where Γ_n is the neutron width, which will be approximately equal to the total width Γ for 1 MeV neutrons. The cross-section for γ-ray emission is then

$$\sigma_{n\gamma} = \sigma_n \frac{\Gamma_\gamma}{\Gamma} = 2\pi^2 \lambdabar_n^2 \frac{\Gamma_\gamma}{D_c} \qquad (15.51)$$

With known values of Γ_γ of the order of 0·1 eV, Hughes, Garth and Levin obtained the results shown in Fig. 15.10. The variation of D_c ($= 1/\omega_c$) with A shows the dependence of the constants in the level density formula on mass number.

15.3.3 EVAPORATION SPECTRA. The energy spectrum of neutrons emitted from an excited nucleus C, in the continuum region, is given by $I(\varepsilon)d\varepsilon$, Eq. 15.47, and is of the form sketched in Fig. 15.11a for discrete levels of the nucleus Y and for a reasonable level density function. The excitation of low-lying levels is the stronger because of the factor ε. In practice it will usually be impossible to distinguish such levels individually (except near the ground state) because of experimental resolution and the spectrum then appears as in Fig. 15.11b; the peak develops because ω increases as ε decreases. If the emitted particle is charged, barrier effects may enter to suppress low energy emission. In either case a plot of the experimental results in the form of $I(\varepsilon)/\varepsilon\sigma(\varepsilon)$ against emitted particle energy ε should exhibit the level density $\omega(\varepsilon_{b\,\max}-\varepsilon)=\omega(E_Y)$. The energy spectra of the emitted particles are usually obtained from pulse height distributions in CsI crystals or solid state counters or from range distributions in nuclear emulsions. The spectrum of protons from gold bombarded by 40 MeV α-particles,

$$^{197}\text{Au}+\alpha \rightarrow\, ^{201}\text{Tl} \rightarrow\, ^{200}\text{Hg}+p \qquad (15.52a)$$

indicates a level density in ^{200}Hg of the form 15.48, i.e. a curve concave towards the energy axis (Fig. 15.11c). Similar results are obtained in heavy ion bombardments, e.g.

$$^{27}\text{Al}+\,^{14}\text{N} \rightarrow\, ^{41}\text{Ca} \rightarrow\, ^{37}\text{A}+\alpha \qquad (15.52b)$$

Proton spectra from $(n,\,p)$ reactions and from inelastic scattering of protons on the other hand often show just the opposite effect, with the appearance of too many protons of both high and low energies; and with a pure exponential increase of level density in between. The excess protons of low energy in $(n,\,p)$ reactions arise from the $(n,\,np)$ reaction in which, owing to particular circumstances of binding energy, the residual nucleus formed after emission of a first neutron can decay by proton emission but not by a second neutron. The additional protons of high energy are usually noticed at forward angles and are due to non-compound nucleus processes (Sect. **15.4**). Fig. 15.12a shows the separation of a typical proton spectrum into these components. Energy spectra intended to determine level densities should therefore be taken at backward angles and preferably with complex incident particles. The chance of backward projection of single nucleons without compound nucleus formation is then likely to be small because of the high forward momentum.

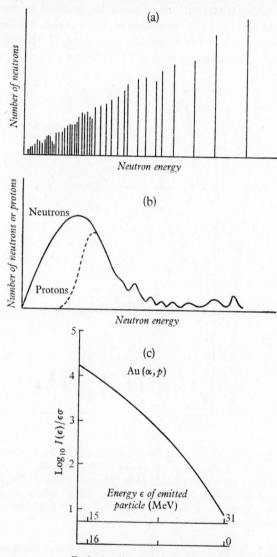

Fig. 15.11. Evaporation spectra (continuum theory).
a) Ideal resolution (Ref. 15.4).
b) Finite resolution (Ref. 15.4).
c) Protons from (α, p) reaction; logarithmic plot to show level density of residual nucleus (Eisberg *et al.*, *Phys. Rev.*, **100**, 1309, 1955).

The angular distributions of particles emitted by compound nuclei excited to the continuum have been studied both theoretically and experimentally. In general the mixing of many states leads to *symmetry* of emission about an angle of

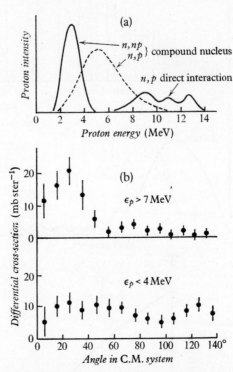

Fig. 15.12. Protons emitted in reactions of 14 MeV neutrons with medium weight nuclei such as Fe, Ni.
a) Component processes (Allan, *Proc. phys. Soc. Lond.*, **70**, 195, 1957).
b) Angular distributions of high energy (direct interaction) and low energy (compound nucleus) groups from ^{60}Ni$(n,p)^{60}$Co (March and Morton, *Phil. Mag.*, **3**, 577, 1958).

$90°$, although *isotropy* is only expected if the level density of the residual nucleus is proportional to $2I + 1$ for levels of spin I. These distributions are found for particles emitted with a low energy, but the higher energy particles exhibit the forward-peaked angular distributions characteristic of non-compound nucleus process (Fig. 15.12b).

15.3.4 NUCLEAR TEMPERATURE. The energy distribution of emitted particles shown in Fig. 15.11b has a general resemblance to the distribution of energy among the molecules of a gas in thermal equilibrium. This suggests that an excited heavy nucleus emitting particles from states in the continuum region might be considered as a thermodynamic system with a certain 'temperature'. The emission of particles from a nucleus would correspond to the evaporation of molecules from a heated liquid drop, but would differ from it because the emission of each nuclear particle causes the removal of a large amount of energy. In the development of these ideas (Ref. 15.4) the level density and entropy of the system are connected by the formula of statistical thermodynamics.

$$S(E) = \log \omega(E) \tag{15.53}$$

Applying this to the residual nucleus Y, whose excitation energy (Fig. 15.8) is $E_Y = (\varepsilon_{b\,max} - \varepsilon)$, we may write, for $\varepsilon \ll \varepsilon_{b\,max}$

$$S(\varepsilon_{b\,max} - \varepsilon) \approx S(\varepsilon_{b\,max}) - \varepsilon \left(\frac{\partial S}{\partial E}\right)_{\varepsilon_{b\,max}}$$

$$= S(\varepsilon_{b\,max}) - \frac{\varepsilon}{T} \tag{15.54}$$

where

$$\frac{1}{T} = \frac{\partial S}{\partial E} \tag{15.55}$$

This is the usual definition of a temperature (except for the omission of Boltzmann's constant k) and T, measured in energy units may be regarded as the temperature of the residual nucleus at its maximum excitation in the reaction. To the extent that the expansion 15.54 is valid, the energy spectrum of emitted particles may be written

$$I(\varepsilon)d\varepsilon = \sigma_b \varepsilon \exp\left[S(\varepsilon_{b\,max}) - \frac{\varepsilon}{T}\right]d\varepsilon$$

$$= \text{constant } \varepsilon\sigma_b e^{-\varepsilon/T} d\varepsilon \tag{15.56}$$

If σ_b varies only slowly with energy then this is exactly the Maxwellian distribution. The most probable energy for the emitted particle is T MeV and the average energy removed in each emission is $2T$ MeV $(= \int \varepsilon^2 e^{-\varepsilon/T} d\varepsilon / \int \varepsilon e^{-\varepsilon/T} d\varepsilon)$.

18*

Eq. 15.56 has been much used in analysis of the energy distribution of particles emitted in reactions of the type (p, p') (p, n) (α, n) and (n, p) but direct determination of relative level density, as indicated in Sect. 15.3.3 seems preferable. The two methods may be connected if the energy of excitation of a nucleus can be expressed in terms of its temperature. This can be done for a Fermi gas of nucleons by using the known result of statistical mechanics for this type of system,

$$E \propto T^2 = aT^2, \text{ say} \tag{15.57}$$

The entropy is then

$$S = \int \frac{dE}{T} = 2aT + \text{const.}$$

$$= 2\sqrt{(aE)} + \text{const.} \tag{15.58}$$

and from 15.53 this is equivalent to the expression already used

$$\omega(E) = \text{constant} \times e^{2\sqrt{(aE)}} = Ce^{2\sqrt{(aE)}} \tag{15.59}$$

Values of a and C obtained by analysis of many experimental results, including spectra, excitation functions, (n, γ) cross-sections, and ratios of cross-sections for competitive processes are given in Ref. 15.4. Both a and C depend on mass number; for a large range of nuclei $a \approx A/10\cdot5$ MeV^{-1} and the nuclear equation of state is then

$$E = \frac{AT^2}{10\cdot5} \text{ MeV} \tag{15.60}$$

This expression, and the energy spectrum, 15.56, provide a convenient means of discussing the decay by evaporation of compound nuclei formed in many nuclear processes. The nuclear temperature may be obtained from the spectral distribution by forming the quantity

$$\frac{1}{T} = -\frac{\partial}{\partial \varepsilon} \log \frac{I(\varepsilon)}{\varepsilon \sigma_b} \tag{15.61}$$

Experimental values of T obtained from the slope of logarithmic plots of $I/\varepsilon\sigma_b$, commonly lie between 1 and 2 MeV.

15.4 Direct interaction processes

15.4.1 INSUFFICIENCY OF THE COMPOUND NUCLEUS MECHANISM. The experimental illustrations given in Sects. 15.2 and 15.3 leave little doubt that the hypothesis of compound nucleus formation gives an excellent account of many diverse types of nuclear reaction. Single-level phenomena are perhaps best described, but the competitive processes and evaporation spectra of the continuum region are also well predicted. The features of nuclear reactions *not* easily described in this theory have gradually emerged as the study of nuclear reactions induced by particles of energy 2–20 MeV have proceeded. Perhaps the best known non-compound nucleus effect is deuteron stripping (Sect. 15.4.3) but it is now realized that a substantial number of reactions proceed in the same way, with especial emphasis on the properties of the nuclear surface. The general features of these processes, which are known as *direct interactions* are:

i) Emission of excess particles of high energy in comparison with the number expected according to the statistical evaporation theory. These particles often show resolvable structure due to levels of the final nucleus (Fig. 15.12a). An associated effect is the observation of high cross-sections for (n, p) and (n, α) reactions in heavy target nuclei, from which the emission of charged particles should be severely hindered by the Coulomb barrier.

ii) Forward peaking of the higher energy particles of the spectrum, in contrast with the symmetric angular distributions expected of evaporation particles (Fig. 15.12b).

iii) Gradual and usually monotonic dependence of yield on bombarding energy. In the continuum region this is of course expected (Fig. 15.9), but in the region of discrete levels a slowly varying 'background yield' may often be ascribed to a direct process.

These differences between direct and compound nuclear processes arise because the former are single-stage processes (15.5) in which the incident momentum of a tends to be transferred directly to b, while the latter are two-stage processes (15.4) in which the momentum is conveyed in the first instance to the compound nucleus C.

Despite the undoubted existence of direct processes the compound nucleus theory still accounts for a large part of the observable yield for many reactions. For the (n, p) reaction in nuclei of mass number $A \approx 50$ the direct interaction cross-sections of up to 100 mb are usually considerably less than those for the compound nucleus process.*

15.4.2 THEORY OF DIRECT INTERACTION PROCESSES IN GENERAL.

The Bohr theory of a compound nucleus reaction assumes that, in the resonance region of excitation at least, the mean free path of an incident nucleon in the compound nucleus is small. Although this may be true for energies near resonance, it is not necessarily true in the first interaction of the incident particle with the target nucleus, particularly for energies of the order of 10 MeV. The theories of direct interaction assume that in a scattering or reaction process the first event is a collision between the incident particle and a nucleon near the surface of the target nucleus. If a mean free path of the order of nuclear dimensions is assumed, the struck nucleon may emerge from the nucleus without the formation of a compound nucleus and the direct process, e.g. a (n, p) reaction, is complete.

In quantitative developments of this hypothesis, it is usually assumed that the direct interaction is confined to a surface layer of the target nucleus. Interactions within the nuclear core are not impossible, but there is a high probability of reflection of the resulting particles at the boundary and consequent enhancement of compound nucleus formation. For surface processes there is a fairly definite radius of interaction and, following Butler, Austern and Pearson† it is possible to give a simple semi-classical picture of the mechanism of these reactions. Let $\mathbf{k}_i$ and $\mathbf{k}_f$ (Fig. 15.13a) be the wave vectors for an incident and an emergent particle, both of which (for

---

* D. L. Allan, *Nuclear Physics*, 24, 274, 1961.
† S. T. Butler, *Phys. Rev.*, 106, 272, 1957; S. T. Butler, N. Austern and C. Pearson, *Phys. Rev.*, 112, 1227, 1958.

simplicity) traverse the surface of a nucleus of radius R without refraction. The direct interaction takes place at the point P, distant $\mathbf{r}$ from the centre of the nucleus. Then the change of

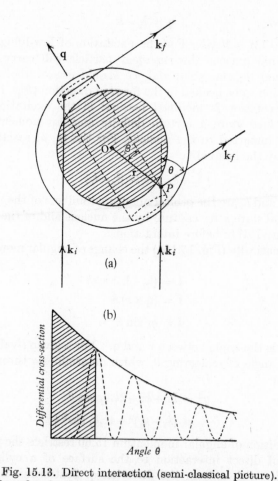

Fig. 15.13. Direct interaction (semi-classical picture).

a) Collision of an incident particle with a surface particle P. Conservation of angular momentum restricts the interaction to the surface of a certain cylinder; nuclear absorption confines it to large radii.

b) Angular distribution for a direct reaction. The full line is the classical expectation and the shaded area is excluded by the necessity for angular momentum conservation. The oscillations in the actual pattern arise from interference between the two rays shown in (a) (Butler, *Phys. Rev.*, **106**, 272, 1957).

linear momentum of the nucleus, i.e. the recoil momentum of the target is

$$(\mathbf{k}_i - \mathbf{k}_f)\hbar = \mathbf{q}\hbar \qquad (15.62)$$

where

$$\mathbf{q} = \mathbf{k}_i - \mathbf{k}_f \qquad (15.63)$$

(since $k_i = 1/\lambda_i = Mv_i/\hbar$). For the excitation of low-lying states of the final nucleus the emergent particle will carry a high momentum ($\mathbf{k}_i \approx \mathbf{k}_f$, $\mathbf{q} \approx 0$) and we should expect the angular distribution to be peaked in the forward direction (Fig. 15.13b). This expectation is modified because in the excitation of a discrete final state a certain definite angular momentum $l\hbar$ must be imparted to the nucleus. For the (n, p) reaction l is limited by the inequality*

$$l_n + l_p \geqslant l \geqslant |l_n - l_p| \qquad (15.64)$$

where l_n and l_p are the orbital quantum numbers of the neutron in its final state after capture by the nucleus and of the proton in its initial state before interaction.

Kinematically (Fig. 15.13a) the change of angular momentum is

$$\mathbf{l} = (\mathbf{k}_i - \mathbf{k}_f) \times \mathbf{r}\hbar \qquad (15.65)$$

or

$$\mathbf{l} = (\mathbf{q} \times \mathbf{r})\hbar$$

so that

$$l = qr \sin \beta \qquad (15.66)$$

where β is the angle between $\mathbf{r}$ and $\mathbf{q}$. For a given l-value, and a given angle of scattering θ, which determines q through the equation

$$q^2 = k_i^2 + k_f^2 - 2k_i k_f \cos \theta$$
$$= (k_i - k_f)^2 + 4k_i k_f \sin^2 \tfrac{1}{2}\theta \qquad (15.67)$$

the condition of angular momentum 15.66 restricts the possible points of direct interaction to the surface of a cylinder of radius l/q with axis in the direction $\mathbf{q}$. Scatterings from the nuclear interior are not likely to lead to direct interactions because of internal reflection, and the effective scattering elements are therefore the two spherical caps at the ends of the cylinder. Interference from the waves originating at these

---

* Change of intrinsic spin direction is neglected.

two areas leads to the maxima and minima in the angular distribution.

In the case that $l/q > R$ (15.66) shows that there will be no direct interaction. This may happen, for a given l, for small values of q, i.e. for the forward direction. The larger the l-value concerned, the greater the angle at which the first scattering peak is observed in the angular distribution; for $l = 0$ a forward peak may be seen. The angular distribution expected for a direct reaction, associated with the nuclear surface, is therefore as shown in Fig. 15.13b. The forward peak associated with the high forward momentum of particles connected with low-lying residual states is forbidden (except for $l = 0$) by the condition of angular momentum. The first peak in the angular distribution occurs at the angle for which

$$qR = l \qquad (15.68)$$

These conclusions are confirmed by quantum mechanical calculation which predicts an angular distribution given by

$$d\sigma \propto [j_l(qR)]^2 d\Omega \qquad (15.69)$$

The spherical Bessel function j_l has its first maximum for the value of the argument given by 15.68.

Many reactions have now been analysed in this way, following Butler's suggestion that the surface interaction mechanism might be of much wider application than had originally appeared. Fig. 15.14 gives an example of one process, typical of many (n, p), (p, p'), (α, α') reactions at fairly high incident energies. The main deduction from the analysis has usually been the angular momentum change in the reaction, but if this is clear from other evidence, as in the excitation of well-known states in inelastic scattering, a radius of interaction may be obtained from the angular position of the zero of the oscillations.

15.4.3 STRIPPING AND PICKUP REACTIONS. The theory of direct interactions outlined in the preceding section grew from an earlier study of the deuteron stripping reaction stimulated by R. E. Peierls and undertaken by S. T. Butler.* When

---

* S. T. Butler, *Proc. roy. Soc.*, A, **208**, 559, 1951.

accurate studies of the angular distributions of protons emitted in (d, p) reactions for deuterons of energy about 10 MeV became available in 1949–50, the appearance of strong forward peaks was noted. Thus in the reaction

$$^{16}\text{O} + d \to {}^{17}\text{O} + p + 1.92 \text{ MeV} \tag{15.70}$$

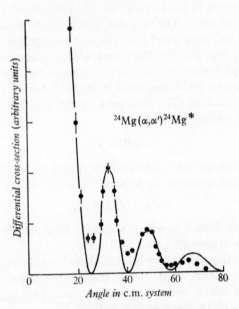

Fig. 15.14. Comparison of direct interaction theory with experiment for the inelastic scattering of 31 MeV α-particles by ^{24}Mg (1·37 MeV level) (Butler, *Phys. Rev.*, **106**, 272, 1957).

the differential cross-section (Fig. 15.15a) rises by a factor of 5 or more between 90° and the angle of the forward peak in the centre-of-mass system. This behaviour cannot easily be understood on the basis of a compound nucleus mechanism, because very high order Legendre polynomials would be required to account for the peak, and these would not appear if the interaction took place within the nuclear radius at energies of the order of 10 MeV. If, however, the release of protons takes place well away from the centre of the nucleus these particles can more easily have a high orbital angular momentum and it is then possible to understand the forward peak. The fact that the deuteron is a loosely bound structure in which the two particles spend most of their time at a mutual distance greater than the range of the forces between them makes such a process possible.

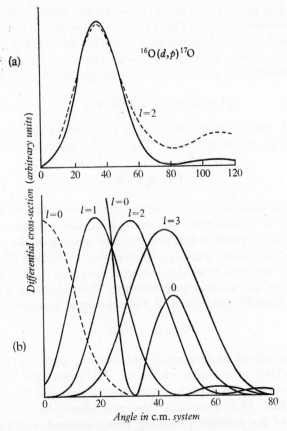

Fig. 15.15. Deuteron stripping reaction.
a) Comparison of experimental (dotted) and theoretical (full) proton angular distributions for ^{16}O bombarded by 8 MeV deuterons.
b) Theoretical angular distributions for different l-values in the stripping reaction. Two scales are used for the $l = 0$ curve (Butler, *Proc. roy. Soc. A*, **208**, 559, 1951).

In the approach of a deuteron to a nucleus one of the particles (in the case of reaction 15.70 the neutron) may collide with a nucleon in the nuclear surface while the other particle (the proton) is released at a distance from the nucleus of the order of the deuteron diameter. The proton continues with approximately its original forward momentum and with little or no interaction with either the original or residual nucleus. The process has an obvious resemblance to the direct interaction mechanism illustrated in Fig. 15.13; thus referring to this figure, and considering a (d, p) reaction occurring by a direct process in the rim of the nucleus, the linear momentum carried into the nucleus by the absorbed neutron is $q\hbar$ where

$$q^2 = (k_d - k_p)^2 + 4k_p k_d \sin^2 \tfrac{1}{2}\theta \tag{15.71}$$

and k_d, k_p are the wave numbers of the incident deuteron and emergent proton respectively. The angular momentum change is

$$\mathbf{l} = (\mathbf{q} \times \mathbf{r})\hbar \tag{15.72}$$

where $|\mathbf{r}| \approx R$ is the radius of interaction. The neutrons will be absorbed at points over the nuclear surface between which interference is possible and maxima and minima in the proton angular distribution will arise as discussed in Section 15.4.2.

Special features arise in deuteron stripping which are of importance for nuclear spectroscopy. Thus although process 15.70 is formally equivalent to the capture of a neutron:

$$^{16}O + n \rightarrow {}^{17}O^* \tag{15.73}$$

along the axis of nuclear recoil, this neutron may, in the case of excitation of residual states of ^{17}O below the neutron binding energy, be captured with *negative energy*. It may be shown (Ref. 15.5) that this does not affect the theoretical analysis of the reaction providing that a reduced width (Sect. 15.2.5) is attributed to these bound states. The stripping process then offers a means of determining these widths. The main interest of the reaction has however been in determination of l-values from the angular distributions, particularly for comparison with predictions of the single-particle shell model (Sect. **11.5**). These distributions are of the type shown in Fig. 15.15b with a pattern of peaks that is strongly characteristic of the angular momentum carried in by the absorbed particle. This gives immediately and directly the *parity change* between the initial and final nuclear states, and sets limits on the *spin* I_f of the final state because of the obvious selection rule

$$I_i + l + \tfrac{1}{2} \geqslant I_f \geqslant |I_i \pm l \pm \tfrac{1}{2}|_{\min} \qquad (15.74)$$

where I_i is the spin of the initial nucleus and the number $\tfrac{1}{2}$ is the spin of the absorbed nucleon. The theoretical angular distribution has been presented in several equivalent forms, each of which includes a factor G^2 specifying the contribution of the internal motion of the deuteron to the momentum changes, the reduced width γ^2 which determines the ease with which the nucleon can be absorbed, and an angular distribution function approximating to the squared spherical Bessel function. Thus for a single l-value

$$\sigma(\theta) \approx G^2 \gamma^2 [j_l(qR)]^2 \qquad (15.75)$$

Determination of l-value is usually a matter of comparison of angular distributions for a discrete group of particles with curves calculated for a reasonable radius R, although difficulties of interpretation arise when the final state may be formed by two l-values (e.g. 0 and 2, or 1 and 3, since the parity change must be the same). The radius is usually taken to be

$$R = (1 \cdot 22 A^{1/3} + 1 \cdot 17) \times 10^{-13} \text{ cm}$$

Determination of γ^2 requires observation of an absolute cross-section at, for instance, the peak of a stripping curve and unless the spin of the final state is known, only the quantity $(2I_f + 1)\gamma^2$ is obtained.

The earliest versions of stripping theory, which were immediately successful, were based on plane wave approximations for the incident deuteron and emergent particle, and also neglected nuclear interactions between these particles and the nuclear core. The success of the theory despite these drastic assumptions is due to the fact that the stripping interaction essentially takes place at a large distance from the nucleus, so that perturbing factors are minimized. When these factors are included, new phenomena, such as polarization of the outgoing particles are predicted. This has been checked experimentally. The existence of heavy distortions due to Coulomb effects at low energies renders the deuteron stripping reaction less useful for nuclear spectroscopy in the region $E_d < 5$ MeV than at higher energies; for $E_d >$ 20 MeV the problem of resolution of discrete groups becomes troublesome. At low energies, nearly isotropic backgrounds in angular distributions have often been found; these are usually attributed to the alternative compound nucleus mechanism, e.g. to the process

$$^{16}O + d \rightarrow {}^{18}F \rightarrow {}^{17}O + p \tag{15.76}$$

in the case of reaction 15.70. The compound nucleus and stripping mechanisms will generally be incoherent because of the short times ($\approx 10^{-21}$ sec) involved in direct processes.

The stripping reaction with absorption of a proton, e.g.

$$^{9}Be + d \rightarrow {}^{10}B + n \tag{15.77}$$

may be discussed in the same way as the (d, p) reaction and has been extensively studied. Both processes may be reversed and then become the pickup reactions

$$\left.\begin{aligned} ^{17}O + p &\rightarrow {}^{16}O + d \\ ^{10}B + n &\rightarrow {}^{9}Be + d \end{aligned}\right\} \tag{15.78}$$

in which a nucleon is removed from the target nucleus. The deuteron spectrum in this case gives information on the single particle levels *below* the highest occupied state of the nuclear potential well just as the proton or neutron spectrum gives similar information on levels just above this state.

Historically, deuteron stripping was first observed in the bombardment of nuclei by 190 MeV deuterons. At these energies many residual states are excited and angular momentum conservation provides no useful results. The angle and energy distribution of the stripped particles were calculated by Serber from the internal momentum function for the particles of the deuteron (Ref. 15.5).

15.5 The optical model for nuclear reactions

The Bohr theory of the compound nucleus, and the direct interaction mechanism, are together able to account for a wide range of nuclear reaction phenomena, but there is a fundamental difference in approach between these two theories. The Bohr theory assumes essentially that as soon as an incident particle reaches the surface of a nucleus a compound nucleus is formed, and that the subsequent decay is independent of the mode of formation. Moreover the probability of re-emission of the incident particle, although finite (so that narrow resonances at low energies result) is nevertheless small, so that the incident wave is heavily damped in the compound nucleus. In the particle picture this corresponds to a short mean free path in the compound nucleus. On the other hand the direct interaction mechanism seems to require a long mean free path for the incident particle, comparable with nuclear dimensions, so that it may readily escape from the nucleus. The possibility of such motion is also suggested strongly by the success of the nuclear shell model in describing the static properties of nuclei; some type of permanence of single particle orbital motion, apparently inconsistent with the Bohr theory, must be possible. The theory of nuclear reactions is therefore faced with the problem already encountered in theories of nuclear structure (ch. 12), namely, how to ensure that models of an underlying individual particle type can yet show features of a more collective nature.

The optical model, which treats a nuclear reaction in analogy with the propagation of light through a partially absorbing medium,* has proved useful in reconciling these apparently conflicting aspects of nuclear behaviour. A general formulation of such a model in terms of a complex scattering potential was proposed in 1940 by Bethe, but extensive development of the theory followed much later, after measurements of neutron cross-sections at both high and low energies had shown obvious conflict with the predictions of the Bohr theory. In the continuum region the total cross-section for neutrons (Sect. 15.3.1) should be given by the black nucleus formula

$$\sigma_t = 2\pi(R + \lambda)^2 \qquad (15.79)$$

This predicts only a smooth dependence of σ_t on incident energy E (through λ) and on target mass number A (through R), and the nuclear radius at high energies as $\lambda \to 0$ should be given by

$$R = \sqrt{\frac{\sigma_t}{2\pi}} \qquad (15.80)$$

Nuclei were expected to become 'blacker' as the incident energy increased because of the increasing number of possible

---

* The model was at one time known as the 'cloudy crystal ball model'.

reaction processes. In contrast with this expectation the experiments of Cook, McMillan, Peterson and Sewell* in 1949 with 90 MeV neutrons from the 184-in. synchrocyclotron, showed that nuclei appeared consistently *smaller* to 90 MeV particles than to lower energy (≈ 25 MeV) projectiles. This behaviour had already been predicted by Serber,† who pointed out that at high energies incident particles would tend to interact with individual target nucleons rather than with the nucleus as a whole and that the probability of compound nucleus formation would accordingly be reduced. There would on the other hand be an enhanced probability for the bombarding particle to emerge without engaging in any interaction at all, and the target nuclei would therefore appear partially transparent, i.e. to have a smaller radius than expected. This idea was developed quantitatively by Fernbach, Serber and Taylor‡ into the high energy version of the optical model.

Low energy data also suggested an interaction which could be represented by a simple potential well. The scattering of slow neutrons by nuclei at energies not adjacent to resonance levels is expected in the compound nucleus theory to yield the 'hard sphere' cross-section of $4\pi a^2$ where $a \approx R$, the nuclear radius. The variation of cross-section with mass number should therefore follow that of R^2; i.e. should be proportional to $A^{2/3}$ and the scattering length should vary as $A^{1/3}$. When the available data for a wide range of elements were assembled by Ford and Bohm,§ (Fig. 15.16a), it became clear that discontinuities occurred at certain mass numbers and these were interpreted as due to resonance of the internal wave function in a nuclear potential well whose dimension depended on A. The spacing of these resonances in A corresponds to *single-particle* levels, not to the fine structure levels of the Bohr theory. Later, extensive studies of neutron total cross-sections in the energy range 1–3 MeV by workers at the University of Wisconsin and elsewhere, first collected together by Barschall‖ revealed these single particle

---

* L. J. Cook, E. M. McMillan, J. M. Peterson and D. C. Sewell, *Phys. Rev.*, **75**, 7, 1949.

† R. Serber, *Phys. Rev.*, **72**, 1008, 1947.

‡ S. Fernbach, R. Serber and T. B. Taylor, *Phys. Rev.*, **75**, 1352.

§ K. W. Ford and D. Bohm, *Phys. Rev.*, **79**, 745, 1950.

‖ H. H. Barschall, *Phys. Rev.*, **86**, 431, 1952.

resonances very clearly. Fig. 15.17 shows the results of this work; broad peaks are found for a given element as the neutron energy varies, and these peaks occur at different energies as A varies. This behaviour is again similar to that expected in the interaction of a particle with a potential well and is in disagreement with the monotonic energy dependence of averaged cross-sections indicated by 15.79. Furthermore the averaged

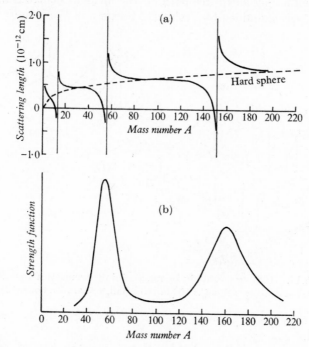

Fig. 15.16

a) Slow neutron scattering length as a function of mass number. The dotted curve is the expectation for hard sphere scattering. The experimental points are not shown, but roughly follow the full curves, which are predictions for the scattering by a square well potential (Ford and Bohm, *Phys. Rev.*, **79**, 745, 1950).

b) Low energy neutron strength function, deduced from total cross-section measurements.

ratio of neutron reduced width to spacing for the individual fine structure levels was not independent of mass number as suggested by 15.41 but showed peaks which agreed in position with the anomalies in scattering length (Ref. 15.8 and Fig. 15.16b) The two curves in this figure show respectively the dispersive and absorptive effect of a well which is able to capture particles as an alternative to scattering them. The behaviour shown is quite unexpected if the incident neutron is strongly absorbed by the target nucleus, as assumed in the Bohr theory. The interpretation of the observations in terms of a long mean free path for the incident neutrons in the target was examined by Feshbach, Porter and Weisskopf* who

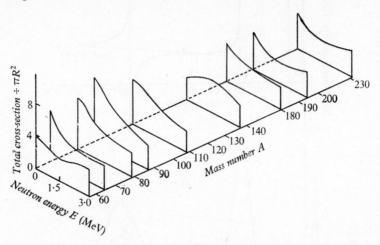

Fig. 15.17. Total cross-section of nuclei for neutrons as a function of energy E and mass number A (from Barschall, *Phys. Rev.* **86**, 431, 1952).

were thus led to develop the low energy form of the optical model.

In uniting these two lines of evidence the optical model supposes that a nuclear reaction should be treated as two-body problem, in which an incident particle sees the target nucleus as a limited region of complex potential

$$V(r) + iW(r) \quad (i = \sqrt{-1}) \tag{15.81}$$

The potentials $V(r)$ and $W(r)$ are energy dependent and at low (effectively negative) energies, V is the potential required by the nuclear shell model. Elastic scattering produced by the

---

* H. Feshbach, C. E. Porter and V. F. Weisskopf, *Phys. Rev.*, **96**, 448, 1954.

potential V is evidently of the single particle type and can account for the broad resonances seen in the results of Barschall and of Ford and Bohm. The imaginary part W of the potential attenuates the incident wave and is directly associated with the mean free path of the incident particle in the target nucleus; it is chosen to yield the mean free path required by the experiments at all energies. In the low energy region, W is often taken

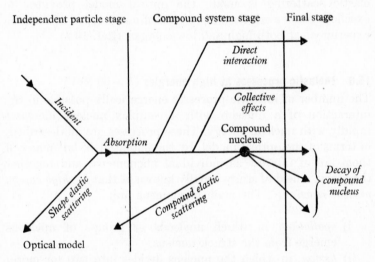

Fig. 15.18. Nuclear reaction scheme, according to Weisskopf (*Rev. mod. Phys.*, **29**, 174, 1957).

to describe compound nucleus formation but it may also account for direct interaction processes. The long mean free path associated with low values of W is at variance with the strong interaction theory of Bohr, but it may be understood because the Pauli principle will inhibit collisions which lead to occupied momentum states.

The course of a nuclear reaction according to these ideas may be represented as in Fig. 15.18. There is a preliminary or *single particle* stage, in which the interaction of the incident wave with the potential V leads to *shape-elastic* or *potential scattering*. Part of the wave is also absorbed (potential W) to form a *compound system* of which the Bohr compound nucleus is only one of several possible manifestations and in which direct interaction and collective excitations appear as possible competitors. The final stage of the reaction includes decay of the compound nucleus in the manner already discussed (Sect. **15.3**). It will be noted that this yields a certain amount of *compound elastic scattering* which is so far not distinguishable experimentally from the shape-elastic scattering, and which is not predictable in detail by the optical model. If compound elastic scattering is small, the optical model provides an excellent framework for a discussion of many types of reaction experiment at both high and low energies (Ref. 15.8).

15.6 Inelastic processes at high energies $(E > 50 \text{ MeV})$

The number of inelastic processes energetically possible in the interaction of a nucleon with a complex nucleus increases rapidly with nucleon energy. These processes are all described, in terms of the optical model, by the potential W but many of them are of interest as individual phenomena, and together they form a field of study usually known as that of '*high energy nuclear reactions*'. The main phenomena are:

i) *spallation*, in which nucleons or groups of nucleons emerge from the struck nucleus,

ii) *fission*, in which the nucleus divides into two (or more) nearly equal masses, and

iii) *fragmentation*, in which 'cracks' develop in the nucleus, and several large fragments (e.g. light nuclei) emerge.

These processes each lead to a characteristic distribution of products in a reaction, and the relative importance of the various processes depends on energy. Fig. 15.19 illustrates this for the case of the proton bombardment of bismuth ($Z = 83$, $A = 209$). At $E_p = 40$ MeV a few elements with mass numbers near 209 are produced; at $E_p = 480$ MeV two clearly defined groupings of mass are evident, the higher mass numbers corresponding to spallation products and the lower group to fission fragments; at $E_p = 3000$ MeV the spallation and fission groups broaden and merge together and an increase in low mass number yields, probably due to fragmentation, is observed.

Our present understanding of high energy reactions is based on Serber's hypothesis that there is:

i) *a knock-on or cascade phase* in which the incident nucleon collides with nucleons of the target nucleus rather than with the nucleus as a whole. This process is rapid and leaves a residual nucleus with a considerable energy of excitation. This is removed in

ii) *the evaporation phase* (including fission), in which normal decay of an excited nucleus, as discussed in Sect. 15.3.2 takes place. The distribution of excitation energy in a number of residual nuclei is determined by details of the preceding knock-on phase.

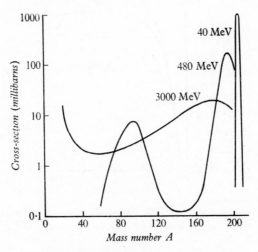

Fig. 15.19. Mass yield curve for the proton bombardment of bismuth $A = 209$ (Ref. 15.9).

The initial cascade phase may be thought of as a succession of two body collisions in a nucleus with a certain internal momentum distribution, as a result of which several high energy particles emerge roughly in the forward direction (Plate 14). At energies above 400 MeV these particles are mainly π-mesons and form the cascade showers familiar in nuclear emulsion studies of cosmic radiation as 'grey tracks'. At lower energies forward-going protons are seen (conveniently in a hydrocarbon bubble chamber, or nuclear emulsion) and their angle of emission may be used to check the law of internal momentum distribution. The progress of the cascade cannot be calculated in detail, but the so called 'Monte-Carlo' method may be used to suggest for a given initial condition a sequence of uncorrelated events, terminated by the escape of the primary nucleon, and leading to the deposition of a certain energy in the residual nucleus.

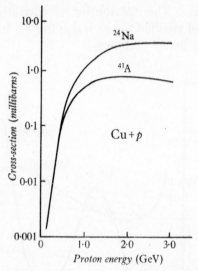

Fig. 15.20. Excitation functions for production of radioactive nuclei from copper irradiated by protons (Ref. 15.9).

In the evaporation phase particles are emitted isotropically, with an energy of the order of the nuclear temperature, which may be estimated from the nuclear equation of state. These particles if charged form the 'black tracks' of nuclear stars; some of these may be seen in Plate 14.

Spallation products are those remaining as stable or β-active nuclides after the emission of a small number of particles in the knock-on and evaporation phase of the nuclear reaction. In both cases their formation implies that most of the energy of the incident particle has been removed by the emergent shower particles. The yield of a particular spallation product should therefore rise sharply from the production threshold, but should be relatively independent of incident energy after this rise. This is the behaviour shown by the spallation products ^{24}Na and ^{41}A from the proton bombardment of copper (Fig. 15.20); it differs essentially from the normal excitation function for a compound nucleus reaction. The distribution in mass number of the spallation products from $Cu + p$ agrees with the Monte Carlo calculations. A correlation has been observed between spallation products, determined radio-chemically, and the distribution of evaporation particles, observed for Ag and Br nuclei directly in the photographic emulsion.

References

15.1   D. J. Hughes and R. B. Schwartz, *Neutron Cross Sections*, Brookhaven National Laboratory Report BNL 325.

15.2   L. I. Schiff, *Quantum Mechanics* (ch. V), McGraw-Hill, 1949.

15.3   H. T. Richards, 'Charged Particle Reactions', in *Nuclear Spectroscopy*, Part A, ed. F. Ajzenberg-Selove, Academic Press, 1960.

15.4   J. B. Blatt and V. F. Weisskopf, *Theoretical Nuclear Physics*, Wiley, 1952.

15.5   R. Huby, 'Stripping Reactions', *Progr. nucl. Phys.*, **3**, 177, 1953.

15.6   H. E. Gove, 'Resonance Reactions, Experimental', in *Nuclear Reactions*, ed. Endt-Demeur, North Holland, 1959.

15.7   K. J. LeCouteur, 'The Statistical Model', in *Nuclear Reactions*, ed. Endt-Demeur, North Holland, 1959.

15.8   A. E. Glassgold, 'Optical Model for Nuclear Scattering', *Progr. nucl. Phys.*, **7**, 123, 1959; K. K. Seth, 'Nuclear Radii by Low Energy Neutron Scattering', *Rev. mod. Phys.*, **30**, 442, 1958.

15.9   J. M. Miller and J. Hudis, 'High Energy Nuclear Reactions', *Annual Review of Nuclear Science*, **9**, 159, 1959.

16. RADIOACTIVE DECAY

The main phenomena of natural radioactive decay were established long ago and have been described in chapter 2. Since 1935 many new α- and β-emitting bodies have been prepared, the former only among the heavy elements and the rare earths, but the latter throughout the periodic system. The factors determining the lifetime of these two types of unstable nuclei appear to be general and there is no important distinction between the naturally occurring and the artificially prepared species in this respect.

In Sect. **10.4** it was pointed out that all naturally occurring nuclei with $A > 150$ are unstable against α-emission, since the energy required to remove 4 nucleons from a nucleus can then be supplied by the combination of those 4 nucleons into a tightly bound α-particle. The fact that *α-emission* is a relatively rare phenomenon compared with *α-instability* is due to the exponential dependence of emission probability on decay energy (Sect. **16.2**). The α-emission observed in the rare earths is due to an increase of available energy resulting from closure of the $N = 82$ neutron shell. Coulomb effects also influence β-emission probabilities but there is no sharp dependence on transition energy and the main consequence is an inhibition of positron decay in heavy nuclei in favour of electron capture. Nuclei with N/Z near the β-stability limits (Fig. 10.7) often exhibit alternative decay modes, e.g. β^- or β^+ (^{40}K), β^- or α (ThC), E.C. or α(^{211}At); for more extreme values of N/Z the β-processes are much more probable than emission of other particles.

In chapters 9 and 10 α- and β-decay were used as general evidence in favour of the single-particle shell model, and as examples of the application of the principles of nuclear stability. In this chapter we survey the data in rather more detail, with particular attention to the decay mechanism; α-decay will be seen to be essentially a nuclear reaction in reverse, but β-decay presents entirely new and (until recently) unexpected features.

16.1 Experimental information on α-decay

Observations of α-decay energies have been made since the discovery of radioactivity using methods of continually increasing precision, many of which have already been described in chapter 7. The earliest measurements with ionization chambers and point counters established the lifetime for α-emission and the genetic relationships between the α-activity of given lifetime and that of its parent or daughter element (ch. 2). Range measurements with shallow ionization chambers (Bragg, 1906) demonstrated the approximate homogeneity in energy of the main α-activity from a given element. A correlation between the lifetime and energy of the α-particle emission was noticed by Geiger and Nuttall as early as 1911; more recent work has greatly enlarged the scope of this law. The resolution of α-particle energy measurements was much improved by the introduction of the differential ionization chamber and of the magnetic spectrometer and many groups originally thought to be homogeneous have now been resolved into components.

The experimental data comprise (a) *energy-mass number* relationships, giving information on nuclear stability, (b) *energy-lifetime relationships*, giving information on decay mechanisms, and (c) *α-particle spectra*, giving information on nuclear states. Two types of spectra have been distinguished, namely those exhibiting *fine structure* and those containing *long-range* α-particles.

In discussing α-decay we must distinguish between the energy E_α of the emitted particle and the total decay energy. The latter is greater than E_α by the energy of nuclear recoil, and must be used when calculating mass changes.

16.1.1 DEPENDENCE OF α-DECAY ENERGY ON MASS NUMBER. The regularities of the ground-state α-decay energies in the heavy element region are illustrated in Fig. 16.1. This is based on data from artificially produced isotopes, including transuranics (Sect. 14.1.6) as well as from the naturally occurring series. A sequence of α-particle emissions (Fig. 2.8) finally leads to a β-unstable nucleus by alteration of the ratio N/Z and one or two β-emissions then occur before α-transformations are resumed. The series thus contains a number of isotopes of certain elements. In Fig. 16.1 emphasis has been placed on the energy in relation to a given element, rather than to a particular series, by drawing appropriate lines; the

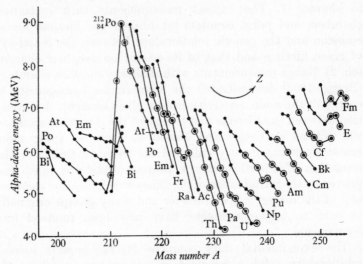

Fig. 16.1. Energy release in the α-decay of the heavy elements, showing effect of neutron shell closure at $N = 126$. The nuclides ringed are β-stable (adapted from Ref. 16.1).

variation of decay energy with A (or N) for a given Z is then apparent. For each mass number, the mass parabolas (Sect. 10.4) show that one or more isotopes are β-stable and these isotopes are especially indicated in the figure. It is evident that the α-decay energy of the β-stable elements decreases as Z increases towards U ($Z = 92$), in contrast with the prediction of the semi-empirical mass formula, but for $Z > 92$ this trend is reversed. Other notable features in Fig. 16.1 are that

   i) E_α increases with Z for constant A,
  ii) E_α decreases as A increases for constant Z,
 iii) If A is decreased until $N(= A - Z)$ falls below 128 the variation of E_α with A reverses abruptly over a limited region.

iv) A similar anomaly may be traced at $Z = 84$ since the decay energies of bismuth isotopes ($Z = 83$) are lower than expected and lead ($Z = 82$) and thallium ($Z = 81$) show no α-activity at all.

The variation of α-energy of β-stable elements with A, and effects (iii) and (iv) above are due to the closure of a neutron shell at $N = 126$ and a proton shell at $Z = 82$. A maximum in

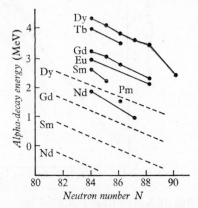

Fig. 16.2. Energy release in the α-decay of the rare earths showing effect of neutron shell closure at $N = 82$. The dotted lines show the energies expected from the semi-empirical mass formula (Ref. 16.1).

α-decay energy occurs when two loosely bound nucleons just above a closed shell are removed by the α-emission; thus $^{212}_{84}\text{Po}$ (ThC′, $N = 128$) and $^{213}_{85}\text{At}$ ($N = 128$) should have exceptionally high decay energies.* The effect of the 126-neutron shell for the polonium isotopes is also shown in Fig. 10.3.

The effect of the 82-neutron shell in the rare earth region is shown in Fig. 16.2. With the exception of ^{147}Sm the species shown are all artificially produced. The decay energies exceed those predicted by the semi-empirical mass formula for $N = 84$ and above and no α-activity is observed for $N < 84$.

The systematic behaviour of α-decay energies shown in Fig. 16.1, coupled with similar regularity in the energy dependence

---

* This is verified for ThC′, but ^{213}At remains to be confirmed. The high decay energy means a short half-life.

19 + N.P.

of half-lives (Sect. 16.1.2) has been of great use in the prediction of the properties, including the masses, of artificially produced transuranic elements.

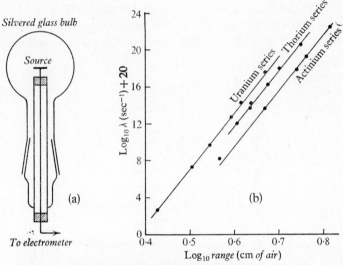

Fig. 16.3. The Geiger–Nuttall law.

a) Apparatus, showing source of α-particles in a vessel which can be evacuated. A potential of 700 V is applied to the inner silvered surface of the glass bulb. The ionization current falls off at the pressure at which the α-particle range becomes greater than the radius of the bulb (Geiger and Nuttall, *Phil. Mag.*, **22**, 613, 1911).

b) Logarithmic plot of decay constant against range for α-emitting nuclei known in 1921 (Ref. 16.1).

16.1.2 ENERGY-LIFETIME RELATIONSHIPS. The earliest energy-lifetime relationship was the celebrated law given by Geiger and Nuttall*. Using the apparatus shown in Fig. 16.3a, these workers determined the mean range of the α-rays from a number of naturally occurring elements and plotted their results logarithmically against the measured decay constant. The results available in 1921 (Fig. 16.3b) fell on three straight lines of equal slope, one for each of the naturally occurring

---

* H. Geiger and J. M. Nuttall, *Phil. Mag.*, **22**, 613, 1911; H. Geiger, *Zeits. Physik*, **8**, 45, 1921.

radioactive families, and demonstrated that for each of these families

$$\log \lambda = a + b \log R \qquad (16.1)$$

Since the range of an α-particle of a few MeV energy is connected with its velocity by the Geiger rule, 5.62b,

$$R \propto v^3 \qquad (16.2)$$

the Geiger-Nuttall rule may be written

$$\log \lambda = a + b' \log v \qquad (16.3)$$

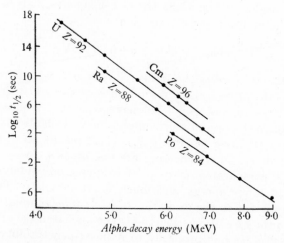

Fig. 16.4. Energy-lifetime relation for even–even α-emitting nuclei of indicated Z. The energy scale is linear in $E_\alpha^{-\frac{1}{2}}$ (Ref. 16.1).

It is now known that this rule is valid only for a rather limited number of even Z–even N nuclides.

Recent results are usually presented as diagrams such as Fig. 16.4, which relates the measured half-period and energy directly for nuclides of a given type.

The lifetimes used are obtained from observed decay constants corrected for alternative decay modes such as β-emission or electron capture by determination of branching ratios. Regular behaviour in plots of this type is most marked in the decay of the ground states of even–even nuclei. If curves for odd Z elements are drawn between those for the even Z

elements on this diagram, they too may be used as standards with which experimental results can be compared. In this way 'hindrance factors' for particle decays can be defined; it is for theories of nuclear structure to explain these factors. Thus in ^{235}U the partial decay constant for the ground-to-ground transition is about 1000 times smaller than that for an even Z–even N transition of the same energy.

16.1.3 FINE STRUCTURE OF α-PARTICLE SPECTRA.

Fine structure in α-ray spectra was demonstrated in the high resolution experiments of Rosenblum (1929) and of Rutherford and his students. Fig. 16.5a shows a magnetic analysis of the α-particles emitted in the transition

$$\text{ThC} \to \text{ThC}'' + \alpha + 6 \cdot 20 \text{ MeV} \qquad (16.4)$$

and Table 16.1a gives the measured energies and intensities of the discrete groups. Low resolution experiments with simple ionization chambers would not have separated groups α_0 and α_1, although the resolution required is now available with semi-conductor counters (cf. Fig. 6.3b). These results are typical of many α-decays in which there are one or two closely spaced groups of comparable intensity and a few more widely spaced groups of lower energy and much lower intensity. This fine structure is due to the excitation of *levels of the residual nucleus* (ThC$''$ in the case of reaction 16.4). The low intensity of groups α_2, α_3 and α_4 is due primarily to reduced penetrability of the potential barrier of ThC$''$ for the α-particles of lower energy, although nuclear structure effects are also important in affecting these intensities.

The excited residual nucleus ThC$''$ may lose its energy by γ-ray emission. The role of the γ-radiation as the electro-magnetic spectrum of a nucleus has already been mentioned (Sect. 2.6.2 and Fig. 2.12). The γ-rays from many radioactive transitions were examined by Ellis (1922) using a magnetic spectrometer and relations of the form

$$h\nu_3 = h\nu_1 + h\nu_2 \qquad (16.5)$$

were found among the γ-ray transition energies deduced from conversion spectra, as would be expected from Fig. 16.5b. A satisfactory correlation between the level schemes indicated by the γ-ray observations and by the later α-particle measurements has been established. The exact association between charged particle groups and the subsequent de-excitation spectra is now

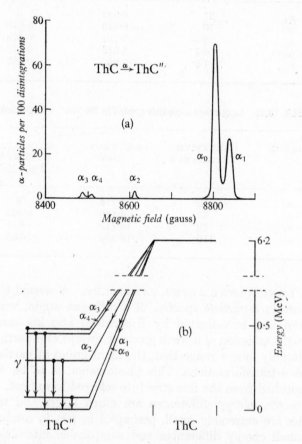

Fig. 16.5. Fine structure of α-particle spectra.
a) Magnetic analysis of groups from ThC $\xrightarrow{\alpha}$ ThC'' transition.
b) Level scheme, showing γ-ray transitions in final nucleus (Ref. 16.2).

familiar throughout the whole range of nuclear spectroscopy and is extensively used in the investigation of nuclear reactions and level schemes.

TABLE 16.1a   Fine structure of α-particle emission in the ThC $\rightarrow$ ThC″ transition

GROUP	RELATIVE ABUNDANCE	α-ENERGY MeV	EXCITATION ENERGY IN ThC″ MeV
α_1	27	6·082	0
α_0	70	6·043	0·040
α_2	1·8	5·761	0·328
α_4	0·1	5·619	0·472
α_3	1·0	5·600	0·492

TABLE 16.1b   Long-range α-particle groups in the ThC′ $\rightarrow$ ThD transition

GROUP	RELATIVE ABUNDANCE	α-ENERGY MeV	EXCITATION ENERGY IN ThC′ MeV
α_0	10^6	8·776	0
α_2	35	9·489	0·725
α_3	20	10·417	1·671
α_1	170	10·536	1·793

16.1.4 LONG-RANGE ALPHA PARTICLES.   A second type of
structure in α-particle spectra, of a different origin, was also
observed and investigated by Rutherford and his students.
This is the emission of a weak group or groups of α-particles of
considerably longer range than the main group of particles in
certain α-transformations. This phenomenon is to be clearly
distinguished from the fine structure referred to in Sect. 16.1.3
because the energy differences are much larger and the intensities are extremely small, perhaps 1 in 10^5, in comparison
with small energy differences and comparable intensities for
the main fine-structure groups. The long-range α-particles are
associated with disintegrations of an *excited state of the initial
nucleus*, as illustrated in Fig. 16.6 for the ThC $\rightarrow$ ThC′ $\rightarrow$ ThD
transformation. A β-particle process can populate highly
excited states of its product nucleus, because, in contrast with
α-emission, the probability of β-decay is not an extremely sharp
function of energy. The β-decay of ThC therefore leaves ThC′

not only in its ground state but also in three excited states at 0·725, 1·671 and 1·793 MeV (with partial β-spectra corresponding to each of these transitions). The ground state of ThC′ decays by α-emission to ThD emitting a single group of particles, and the excited states of ThC′ may radiate to the ground state in the normal way. The excited states are also unstable to α-emission and since the energy release is large the barrier

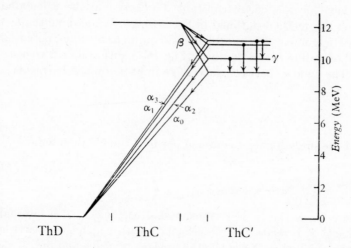

Fig. 16.6. Long-range α-particles in the ThC $\xrightarrow{\beta}$ ThC′ $\xrightarrow{\alpha}$ ThD transition (Ref. 16.2).

penetration factor is so far reduced that α-decay can compete with radiative emission. In about 2 cases in 10^4 a long-range α-particle is observed instead of a γ-ray or internal conversion electron; the actual intensities for ThC $\to$ ThC′ $\to$ ThD are shown in Table 16.1b.

The observation of long range α-particles has an important historical significance in connection with the estimation of radioactive decay constants (Sect. 13.6.1).

The γ-ray spectra from the parent nucleus (ThC′ in the case discussed here) have also been shown to agree with the levels predicted from the energies of the long-range particles. For one group of long-range α-particles from RaC′ no associated γ-radiation could be found, although the corresponding conversion lines were already well known from the work of Ellis and the α-particle evidence suggested that the transition in RaC' (of energy 1·414 MeV) should be strong. The phenomenon was interpreted by Fowler as a *total internal conversion* of the radiative transition, due to a spin change of $0 \rightarrow 0$ (Sect. **13.4**).

16.2   Theory of α-decay*

The partial width Γ_α for α-decay of an energetically unstable nucleus (or the decay constant $\lambda = \Gamma_\alpha/\hbar$) may be calculated using the method outlined in Sect. 15.2.5. We assume that an α-particle moves backwards and forwards in a simple potential well of radius R and depth U (Fig. 16.7) with uniform velocity v_α. The time τ_α between successive impacts on the barrier is

$$\tau_\alpha = \frac{2R}{v_\alpha} \tag{16.6}$$

and the probability of emission per unit time is therefore

$$\frac{1}{\tau_\alpha} T_0 = \frac{\Gamma_\alpha}{\hbar} \tag{16.7}$$

where T_0 is the barrier transmission coefficient. The internal velocity v_α is related to the velocity v with which the α-particle is observed when it has left the nucleus by the equation

$$\tfrac{1}{2}m_\alpha v_\alpha^2 = \tfrac{1}{2}m_\alpha v^2 + U = E_\alpha + U \tag{16.8}$$

where m_α is the mass of the α-particle and E_α its kinetic energy at a large distance from the nucleus. Nuclear recoil is neglected in this calculation.

The barrier transmission coefficient may be calculated as indicated in Sect. 14.2.3; the only difference in the present case is that the wave amplitude is large inside and small outside the nucleus, in contrast with the case of particle absorption. If we express T_0 as the product of a potential discontinuity factor at $R=r$ and a barrier penetration coefficient we have approximately

$$T_0 = \frac{4k'}{K} P_0 \tag{16.9a}$$

---

* G. Gamow, *Zeits. Physik*, **51**, 204, 1933.

where k' is the (imaginary) wave number of the α-particle just outside the nuclear boundary at $r=R$ and K is the wave number within the potential well. If these wave numbers are expressed in terms of potentials we obtain

$$T_0 = 4\sqrt{\frac{B-E_\alpha}{U+E_\alpha}}\, P_0 \tag{16.9b}$$

where $B = zZe^2/R$ is the barrier height.*

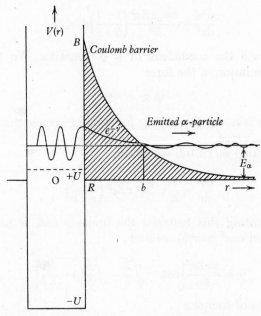

Fig. 16.7. Theory of α-decay. The wave representing the α-particle has a large amplitude within the nucleus and is attenuated exponentially in the region of negative kinetic energy ($R \leqslant r \leqslant b$). The emitted particle has total energy E_α, equal to the potential energy zZe^2/b at the point $r=b$. The internal nuclear potential is drawn at a level $-U$; for a heavy nucleus it is more realistic to take a positive value of internal potential, but the decay probability is not a sensitive function of this quantity.

* In Ref. 16.1 the internal potential U is taken positive, to represent the effect of the Coulomb force at small distances (cf. Fig. 11.1d). With this assumption the potential discontinuity factor becomes $4\sqrt{(E_\alpha - U)/(B-E_\alpha)}$ and the sign of U in 16.8 must be changed.

19*

The barrier penetration coefficient P_0 represents the decay of *intensity* of the α-particle wave over the region of negative kinetic energies between $r = R$ and $r = b$, the point at which the α-particle leaves the Coulomb barrier. For s-wave emission, the wave *amplitude* is a solution of the Schrödinger equation

$$\frac{d^2\psi}{dr^2} + \frac{2m_\alpha}{\hbar^2}\left(E_\alpha - \frac{zZe^2}{r}\right)\psi = 0 \qquad (16.10a)$$

and since $E_\alpha = \frac{1}{2}m_\alpha v^2 = zZe^2/b$ this may also be written

$$\frac{d^2\psi}{dr^2} + \frac{2m_\alpha zZe^2}{\hbar^2}\left(\frac{1}{b} - \frac{1}{r}\right)\psi = 0 \qquad (16.10b)$$

For $R \leqslant r \leqslant b$ the coefficient of ψ is negative. We therefore assume a solution of the form

$$\psi \approx e^{-\gamma(r)}$$

where $\gamma(r)$ is a slowly varying function of r such that $d^2\gamma/dr^2$ may be neglected.

Substituting in 16.10b we obtain

$$\frac{d\gamma}{dr} = \frac{1}{\hbar}\sqrt{2m_\alpha zZe^2}\left(\frac{1}{r} - \frac{1}{b}\right)^{\frac{1}{2}}$$

and integrating this between the limits b and R (using the substitution $\cos^2 x = r/b$) we find

$$\gamma = \frac{2zZe^2}{\hbar v}\left[\cos^{-1}\sqrt{\frac{R}{b}} - \sqrt{\frac{R}{b}\left(1 - \frac{R}{b}\right)}\right] \qquad (16.11a)$$

or, in terms of energies

$$\gamma = \frac{2zZe^2}{\hbar v}\left[\cos^{-1}\sqrt{\frac{E_\alpha}{B}} - \sqrt{\frac{E_\alpha}{B}\left(1 - \frac{E_\alpha}{B}\right)}\right] \qquad (16.11b)$$

In the present approximation the barrier penetration factor for intensity is

$$P_0 = e^{-2\gamma}$$

and for the decay constant we obtain

$$\lambda = \frac{v_\alpha}{2R}T_0 = \frac{2v_\alpha}{R}\sqrt{\frac{B - E_\alpha}{U + E_\alpha}}\,e^{-2\gamma} \qquad (16.12)$$

The main dependence of the decay constant on α-particle energy arises from the exponential factor $e^{-2\gamma}$ in 16.12 and it is a good approximation to write

$$\log \lambda = \text{const.} - 2\gamma \qquad (16.13)$$

This is not the same as the empirical Geiger-Nuttall rule 16.3 but it exhibits the same sharp dependence of emission probability on energy. Observed decay constants are not very sensitive, in this model, to the internal potential U but depend mainly on the ratio E_α/B. For the heavy nuclei an increase of 1 MeV in E_α increases λ by a factor of about 10^5 while a 10% increase in R (decrease in B) multiplies λ by 150.

In the limit of high barriers, $R \to 0$ and $B \to \infty$ effectively, and then

$$\gamma \to \frac{2zZe^2}{\hbar v} \cdot \frac{\pi}{2} \qquad (16.14)$$

The factor determining α-emission is then

$$P_0 = e^{-2\gamma} \approx e^{-2\pi zZe^2/\hbar v}$$

the well-known *Gamow factor* already mentioned in Sect. 14.2.3.

The theory given so far is one-dimensional. If the α-particle carries angular momentum $l\hbar$, the centrifugal barrier appearing in 14.69 must be introduced into the penetrability calculation. The effect of this extra barrier on the emission probability is small in comparison with the effect of E_α or R; for a typical heavy nucleus, at the nuclear radius,

$$\frac{\text{Centrifugal barrier}}{\text{Coulomb barrier}} \approx 0 \cdot 002 l(l+1)$$

in contrast with the situation for light nuclei, where centrifugal barriers are often larger than charge barriers. Formula 16.12 may be applied to determine the 'decay constant without barrier' $v_\alpha/2R$ and the nuclear radius from the experimental data. If this is done values of the order of 10^{21} sec^{-1} and $1 \cdot 5 A^{1/3} \times 10^{-13}$ cm are obtained. The radius values used in the theoretical formula, which are based on a sharp potential discontinuity, are not equal to the true nuclear radius and must be corrected for the finite extent of the α-particle.

A more important use of the theoretical formula for α-decay is in the co-ordination of experimental data of the type displayed on energy-lifetime plots (Fig. 16.4), with the object of determining shell structure effects and hindrance factors. The main points which emerge from this type of comparison are:

i) *For even-even nuclei* ($I = 0$ to $I = 0$ with no parity change) transitions between ground states are well described by 16.12 and may be taken to represent normal α-decay. From 16.13 and 16.14 a relation of the form

$$\log t_{\frac{1}{2}} = a + \frac{b}{E_\alpha^{\frac{1}{2}}}$$

might be expected between half-life and decay energy and, as shown in Fig. 16.4, the isotopes of each element define a line on a plot of this type.

ii) *For odd–odd nuclei* regularities in α-transition rates are less obvious than with even–even nuclei, but no transition is more probable than the 'normal' transition of even–even nuclei.

The notable success of the single-body theory of α-decay in accounting in a single formula for a range of lifetimes differing by a factor of 10^{25} should not divert attention from the fact that some of the assumptions of the theory are questionable. The plausibility of the assumption of preformed particles was questioned by Bethe who suggested that the width without barrier of ≈ 1 MeV corresponding to the repetition time $\tau_\alpha \approx 10^{-21}$ sec should be replaced by a width of about 1 eV, which would be reasonable for neutron emission. This is essentially a many-body theory, and it leads to larger nuclear radii since the decreased width without barrier must be compensated by increased barrier transmission to give the same agreement with experiment. The increase in radius of about 40% resulting from this theory is not acceptable in view of recent determination of nuclear size by electron scattering (Sect. **11.2**) and the many-body theory does not in fact offer any picture of the formation of an α-particle from neutrons and protons.

Another weakness of the simple theory of α-decay is its inability to account for the intensity of transitions to excited states of residual nuclei. Progress is now being made in calculations of the penetrability for a spheroidal potential well; one of the consequences of such calculations is that α-particles should be emitted preferentially where the barrier is thinnest. This may be tested by observing the angular distribution of α-particles from oriented nuclei and such experiments are being tried.

16.3   Experimental information on β-decay

Until 1957, when non-conservation of parity was discovered, study of the β-decay process was mainly a confirmation and interpretation of the characteristics of electron emission that had been established in the early days of radioactivity (ch. 2). We shall refer to the experiments of this period as the 'classical' experiments of β-decay although in fact there is little classical about the phenomenon. It has been responsible for the introduction of the radically new concept of the neutrino, and the objective demonstration of the existence of this particle may in a sense be said to complete the 'classical' period.

The emission of positive or negative electrons from nuclei, and the alternative process of electron capture, determine the stability limits for nuclei throughout the periodic system as shown in Sect. **10.4**. The process changes the atomic number by ± 1, e.g. in the decay of radioactive sodium

$$^{22}_{11}\text{Na} \rightarrow {}^{22}_{10}\text{Ne} + \beta^+ + \nu \qquad (16.15)$$

stable neon is formed and the chemical identity both of the active nucleus and of its product have in some cases been verified. The electrons or positrons that arise in a typical β-decay such as 16.15, have a *continuous spectrum* of energies up to a definite limit determined by the mass change (Fig. 2.4) but one β-particle only is emitted per nuclear disintegration. The homogeneous lines observed in many such spectra are due to internal conversion of γ-rays and are not directly connected with the β-decay process. When however, a β-transition leads to an excited state of its product nucleus, internal conversion lines may be used to identify the product, since they give accurate values of the X-ray energies of this body (Sect. **13.2**). The electrons emitted in β-decay have the same $|e/m|$ as the ordinary atomic electrons and it has been established (Goldhaber) that the negative β-particles cannot form a new K-shell in a neutral atom. The β-particles are therefore identical with atomic electrons.

The techniques of β-spectroscopy have been outlined in chapters 6 and 7; they provide information on nuclear energy changes of an accuracy comparable with or better than that obtained from heavy particle reactions. The data comprise:

a) a survey of the *production and location of β-active species* in the N-Z diagram, establishing the limits of nuclear stability,

b) *energy–lifetime relationships*, giving a general classification of decay data and offering information on nuclear structure, in particular on spin and parity changes,

c) *detailed studies of spectrum shape*, and *correlations* between electrons and subsequent γ-radiation, giving information on nuclear decay schemes, or correlations between electrons and neutrinos, giving information on the decay mechanism, and

d) *'modern'* experiments (Sect. **16.7**).

We shall omit discussion of correlation experiments and deal only briefly with the 'modern' work.

16.3.1 PRODUCTION OF β-ACTIVE NUCLEI. Many β-active bodies are found in the naturally occurring radioactive series. These are mainly negatron emitters because the nuclei concerned have an excess of neutrons. The lighter members of the thorium series provide well-known examples of naturally occurring β-emitters and of their relation to the associated α-decay (Fig. 2.8).

Both positron and negatron emitters are readily produced in nuclear reactions; (p, n) reactions such as

$$^{48}_{22}\text{Ti} + p \rightarrow ^{48}_{23}\text{V} + n + Q_1 \qquad (16.16)$$

are usually endothermic (negative Q-value) and the product nucleus is generally positron or electron-capture active

$$^{48}\text{V} \rightarrow ^{48}\text{Ti} + \beta^+ + \nu + Q_2$$

or (16.17)

$$^{48}\text{V} + e_K^- \rightarrow ^{48}\text{Ti} + \nu + Q_3$$

The radioactive decay reverses the neutron to proton change induced by the nuclear reaction and the observed positron energy may be calculated exactly from the energy threshold for the production of neutrons observed in reaction 16.16.

The (n, p) reaction produces negatron emitters, e.g.

$$^{32}_{16}S + n \rightarrow {}^{32}_{15}P + p + Q_1 \tag{16.18}$$

which revert to the stable isobar with the emission of an electron

$$^{32}P \rightarrow {}^{32}S + \beta^- + \bar{\nu} + Q_2 \tag{16.19}$$

and again the energy release in the forward and backward processes are found to agree.

Many other reactions produce unstable products, notably the (d, p), (d, n), (p, γ) and (n, γ) processes in which an extra nucleon is added. In practice the most prolific source of negatron emitters for industrial and other purposes is the complex of fission products obtained from nuclear reactors (cf. 14.22).

Addition products formed by heavy ion bombardments are, by contrast, neutron deficient and are either positron emitters or electron-capture bodies.

16.3.2 LIFETIMES OF β-EMITTERS. The first attempt to classify β-emitting bodies was made by Sargent* who plotted the decay constant logarithmically against the maximum kinetic energy in the β-spectrum for a number of naturally occurring nuclei (Table **2.1**). The Sargent diagram (Fig. 16.8) shows clearly a grouping of points about two lines which are now interpreted as 'allowed' and 'forbidden' lines, corresponding to different changes of nuclear spin as discussed in Sect. 16.5.2.

The discovery of artificial radioactivity has provided many hundreds of examples of β-active nuclei and the Sargent diagram may now be widely extended. Since, however, according to 16.48 the decay constant may be written

$$\lambda\left(= \frac{0 \cdot 693}{t_{1/2}} \right) \propto f(Z, W_0) \tag{16.20}$$

where W_0 is the maximum total energy of the β-spectrum in units of mc^2, a plot of $\log \lambda$ against $\log (W_0 - 1)mc^2$ will obviously only give a straight line over a limited range of values

---

* B. W. Sargent, *Proc. roy. Soc.*, A, **139**, 659, 1933.

of Z and W_0, for which $f(Z, W_0)$ may be considered nearly independent of Z and proportional to some power of $(W_0 - 1)$ $\times mc^2$, the kinetic energy. Recent classifications are based on the *comparative half-life* $f(Z, W_0) \times t_{\frac{1}{2}}$ (or ft) for which use must be made of tabulated values or nomograms of the function $f(Z, W_0)$ (Ref. 16.5); the half-life used must be obtained from the partial decay constant for the particular decay if there are competitive processes. The result of this classification for odd-mass nuclei is shown in Fig. 16.9.

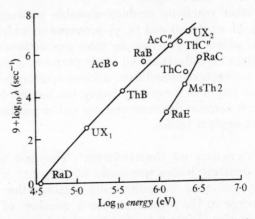

Fig. 16.8. Sargent diagram, showing relation between disintegration constant λ and β-decay (kinetic) energy for heavy radioactive nuclei (Sargent, *Proc. roy. Soc.*, A, **139**, 659, 1933).

Well-defined groups in histograms such as this suggest that in such a group the nuclear factors in the decay probability are reasonably independent of Z and W_0. Such groups are seen

i) *for* $log\ ft \approx 3$–4. These are the especially probable transitions and are known as 'super-allowed' or favoured. Mirror nuclei and certain nuclei of mass $4n + 2$ fall into this class and it seems likely that the nuclear wave function remains practically unaltered as a result of the neutron $\leftrightarrow$ proton transition.

ii) *for* $log\ ft \approx 4$–5. These transitions are allowed in the sense of the selection rules (Sect. 16.5.2), but are un-favoured by comparison with the superallowed group because of some change in nuclear wave function.

iii) *for log ft* ≈ 6–10. This group includes the forbidden transitions (Sect. 16.5.2).

The connection between the *ft* groups and the selection rules for spin and parity changes can often be made with fair certainty from the predictions afforded by the single-particle shell model. Conversely β-decay data have supplied an important test of the predictions of the model for the spins of unstable nuclei (Ref. 16.6).

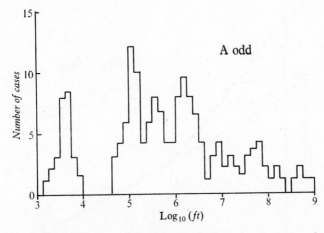

Fig. 16.9. Comparative half-life for β-transitions between ground states of odd-mass nuclei (Ref. 16.4).

16.3.3 THE SHAPE OF β-SPECTRA. The theory of β-decay (Sect. **16.5**) predicts that the probability of emission of an electron with momentum between p and $p + dp$ is

$$P(p)dp \propto p^2 F(Z, p)(W_0 - W)^2 dp \qquad (16.21)$$

where $F(Z, p)$ is a tabulated Coulomb correction factor known as the Fermi function. The energies W are measured in units of mc^2 and include the rest mass of the electron; p is measured in units of mc. A magnetic spectrometer set at momentum p will record an intensity proportional to $pP(p)$ since the slit width of the instrument is directly proportional to the momentum. If the momentum is varied over the spectrum then $P(p)$ can be obtained as a function of p and from 16.21 a graph of the function

$$\sqrt{\frac{P(p)}{p^2 F(Z, p)}} \qquad (16.22)$$

against total energy W should be a straight line. This *Fermi plot* (also known as a *Fermi-Kurie* plot, particularly when simplified forms of $F(Z, p)$ are used) extrapolates, so long as

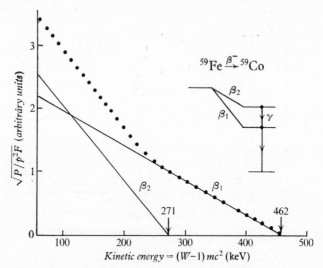

Fig. 16.10. Fermi plots of partial β-spectra of ^{59}Fe. There is also a third weak β-spectrum, not shown, leading to the ground state of ^{59}Co (Metzger, *Phys. Rev.*, **88**, 1360, 1952).

16.21 is valid, to the end point W_0 of the β-spectrum. This is the standard analysis for determination of end points; values of $F(Z, p)$ are given in Ref. 16.5 and p is related to W by the relativistic equation

$$W^2 = 1 + p^2 \qquad (16.23)$$

Deviation of the Fermi plot from a straight line indicates either a forbidden transition, in which case the use of an appropriate correction factor produces a linear plot, or a complex spectrum involving transitions to more than one state of the residual nucleus, e.g.

$$^{59}\text{Fe} \rightarrow {}^{59}\text{Co} + \beta_1^- + \bar{\nu} + Q_1$$
$$\rightarrow {}^{59}\text{Co*} + \beta_2^- + \bar{\nu} + Q_2 \qquad (16.24)$$

for which the Fermi plot is shown in Fig. 16.10. In this case partial β-spectra with end points of 271 keV and 462 keV are found, and there is an associated γ-transition of energy $\beta_1 - \beta_2 = 191$ keV in the residual nucleus.

The measurement of the lifetime of the neutron against β decay and the determination of the resulting β-spectrum (Robson†) are notable both for the technical elegance of the experiment and for the theoretical importance of the results. A slow neutron beam of $1 \cdot 5 \times 10^{10}$ neutrons sec^{-1} from a reactor passed through a vacuum vessel (Fig. 16.11a) in which decay protons from the process

$$n \rightarrow p + \beta^- + \bar{\nu} + 780 \text{ keV} \qquad (16.25)$$

were produced. The protons have initially a distribution of energies up to about 1 keV and they were accelerated by a voltage of 13 kV before detection by an electron multiplier. A lens-type magnetic spectrometer was used to focus protons of the expected energy from the decay region on to the first electrode of the multiplier. Electrons from the neutron decay were detected, also after magnetic analysis, by an anthracene scintillation crystal, and coincidences between electron and proton signals were obtained by inserting a delay in the electron channel to allow for the time of flight of the slow protons. By careful determination of the volume from which protons were collected, the disintegration rate for a given neutron beam was found and the half-life of the neutron was calculated to be‡

$$t_{\frac{1}{2}} = 12 \cdot 8 \pm 2 \cdot 5 \text{ min.}$$

The momentum spectrum of the decay electrons was obtained in coincidence with the recoil protons and the Fermi plot (setting $F(1, p) = 1$) is shown in Fig. 16.11b. The extrapolated kinetic energy endpoint is 782 ± 13 keV.

---

† J. M. Robson, *Phys. Rev.*, **83**, 349, 1951.
‡ A recent Russian value is $t_{\frac{1}{2}} = 11 \cdot 7 \pm 0 \cdot 3$ min.

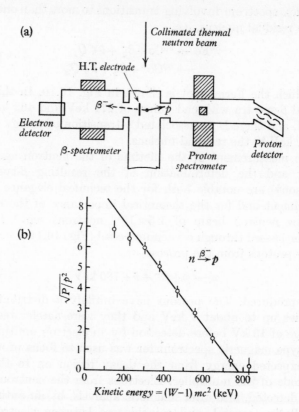

Fig. 16.11. Beta-decay of the neutron.

a) Apparatus for detection of recoil proton and decay electron from thermal neutrons decaying during the passage of a beam through a known volume.

b) Fermi-Kurie plot of the electron momentum spectrum, against kinetic energy (Robson, *Phys. Rev.*, **83**, 349, 1951).

16.4 Neutrinos and antineutrinos

The continuous nature of the β-spectrum presented the first major problem for the theory of β-decay. The energy release in a nuclear transition is a definite quantity, given by the mass difference between the nuclei (A, Z) and $(A, Z \pm 1)$ and this energy release accords well with the end point of the β-spectrum. This was first verified by considering the energies in the two branches of the ThC decay (Sect. 2.4.3); as shown below these agree if the upper limit of the β-spectrum is used.

$$Q_\beta = 2\cdot25 \qquad \text{ThC} \qquad Q_\alpha = 6\cdot21$$

$$\beta \diagup \qquad \diagdown \alpha$$

$$\text{ThC}' \qquad \text{ThC}''$$

$$Q_\alpha = 8\cdot95 \qquad \alpha \diagdown \qquad \diagup \beta+\gamma \qquad Q_\beta = 2\cdot37$$

$$\text{ThD} \qquad Q_\gamma = 2\cdot62$$

$$\text{Total} \quad \underline{11\cdot20} \text{ MeV} \qquad\qquad \underline{11\cdot20} \text{ MeV}$$

Only one electron is emitted per β-disintegration, as may be seen by comparing successive α- and β-decays and the final nucleus cannot be left in a continuous series of residual states, since low-lying states are discrete and well-separated. The possibility that another absorbable type of radiation accompanied the decay electrons was eliminated in careful calorimetric experiments on RaE by Ellis and Wooster. They established that the energy of the absorbable radiation emitted agreed closely with the *mean* energy of the continuous spectrum rather than with the upper limit.* The unattractive possibility of the non-conservation of energy was seriously considered at this point.

A further difficulty arose when the neutron-proton model of nuclear structure became accepted. This predicts that the spins of odd-mass nuclei are always half-integral. The decay electron itself has half-integral spin, and β-decay changes only the charge and not the mass number of a nucleus. The conservation of angular momentum, as well as of energy, was therefore also questioned.

The way out of these difficulties was found by Pauli who suggested that a new light particle should be emitted in every β-transition. The simplest of all β-processes, the radioactive decay of the neutron, would then be represented by 16.25, and the converse process (which does not occur with free protons of course but is possible within a nucleus where energy is available) by:

$$p \to n + \beta^+ + \nu - 1800 \text{ keV} \tag{16.26}$$

---

* Although the ThC branching is of historical interest, it may be noted that many cases of partial β-spectra and subsequent γ-radiation (e.g. process 16.24) now lead more convincingly to this conclusion.

It is now customary following Fermi to describe the particle denoted by ν as a *neutrino* and the particle $\bar{\nu}$ as an *antineutrino* and to consider these as particle and antiparticle in the sense of the Dirac theory of the electron. We have indicated the emission of one or other of these particles in the equations for β-processes throughout this book.

The properties required of the neutrino are that it shall have:

a) *zero charge,*

b) *zero or nearly zero rest mass,* according to experiments on the shape of β-spectra near the upper limit (Sect. 16.5.2),

c) *half-integral angular momentum* (component $\frac{1}{2}\hbar$) in order to conserve this quantity,

d) *extremely small interaction with matter,* and hence essentially zero *magnetic moment* because of the failure of intensive experiments to show even the feeblest ionization caused by the passage of neutrinos through matter, and

e) a definite *helicity,* in order to account for the 'modern' experiments on β-decay. Helicity is a two-valued quantity (± 1) which implies that the intrinsic spin momentum of a particle is either parallel or antiparallel to its direction of motion.

The neutrino differs from a light quantum in respects (c), (d) and (e), in the fact that it is not associated with an electromagnetic field, and because of the probable existence of a distinct antiparticle.

Although the phenomenon of β-decay is itself the most compelling evidence for the existence of neutrinos, many attempts have been made to demonstrate the particle directly. The most convincing evidence for the fact that *linear momentum* may be carried away in β-decay, by a particle other than the electron and recoil nucleus, is to be found in beautiful photographs published by Szalay and Csikai. They introduced ^{6}He atoms into an expansion chamber and observed the process

$$_2^6\text{He} \rightarrow {}_3^6\text{Li} + \beta^- + \bar{\nu} \tag{16.27}$$

Plate (15) shows that there is a large angle between the tracks of the electron and the recoil lithium nucleus as would be expected, owing to the finite neutrino momentum associated with all but the maximum energy electrons.

Another attractive possibility is to cause the neutrino to induce a β-process in the reverse direction. Nuclear reactors contain enormous quantities of β-decaying fission products and furnish an intense source of antineutrinos. In each β-decay, e.g. the decay of ^{131}I, a nuclear process of the type 16.19 occurs with the emission of the particle $\bar{\nu}$. If now these particles are used to bombard a suitable target, they might be expected to give rise to an observable yield of a radioactive product. The reaction tried* was

$$^{37}_{17}Cl + \bar{\nu} \rightarrow {}^{37}_{18}A + \beta^- \qquad (16.28)$$

and a search was made for ^{37}A decaying by the electron-capture process

$$^{37}_{18}A + e^- \rightarrow {}^{37}_{17}Cl + \nu \qquad (16.29)$$

An extremely low, essentially zero, cross-section for the reaction was found. This, however, does not necessarily mean that the neutrino does not exist, but only that the neutrino ν and the antineutrino $\bar{\nu}$ are different particles, like the positive and negative electron apart from charge. The true converse of reaction 16.29 is

$$^{37}Cl + \nu \rightarrow {}^{37}A + \beta^- \qquad (16.30)$$

rather than the process shown in 16.28.

Evidence that the neutrino and antineutrino are distinct particles is also afforded by experimental evidence on double β-decay (Sect. **10.4**) between even-mass isobars. There are many examples of pairs of even–even nuclei which could decay in this way energetically, e.g.

$$^{124}Sn \rightarrow {}^{124}Te + 2\beta^- + 2\bar{\nu} \qquad (16.31)$$

but the lifetime calculated for such a process is $\approx 10^{21}$ yrs. If, however, the neutrino and antineutrino are the same particle, then the reaction can be written

$$^{124}Sn \rightarrow {}^{124}Sb + \beta^- + \bar{\nu} \qquad (16.31a)$$

$$\bar{\nu} + {}^{124}Sb \rightarrow {}^{124}Te + \beta^- \qquad (16.31b)$$

in which the neutrino emitted in the first stage is absorbed in the second stage. In this scheme the two electrons together have

---

* R. Davis, *Phys. Rev.*, **97**, 766, 1955.

a constant energy and the lifetime is much shorter, $\approx 10^{17}$ years. Positive evidence for double β-decay is scanty but favours the longer lifetime; negative evidence is fairly plentiful and rules out the shorter lifetime. It therefore appears that 16.31b is not a possible reaction and that it requires absorption of a ν particle rather than $\bar{\nu}$.

A successful demonstration of an inverse β-process was made by Reines and Cowan* using a spectacular apparatus in which antineutrinos from a powerful reactor entered a liquid scintillator of volume $1\cdot4 \times 10^3$ litres. The reaction sought was the inverse of the neutron decay 16.25, i.e.

$$\bar{\nu} + \beta^- + p \to n - 780 \text{ keV} \qquad (16.32)$$

using the protons of the liquid scintillator as target. Reaction 16.32 is equivalent, in terms of a Dirac theory for the electron and neutrino, to reaction 16.26 and also to the process

$$\bar{\nu} + p \to n + \beta^+ - 1800 \text{ keV} \qquad (16.33)$$

in which antineutrino absorption by a proton should release a neutron and a positron simultaneously if the antineutrino energy is above the threshold. In the experiment (Fig. 16.12) a 'prompt' signal was produced by the passage of the fast positron through the scintillator. The associated neutron (16.33) was slowed down by elastic nuclear collisions in the scintillator and was finally captured in a cadmium nucleus present in the scintillator in a suitable compound. The (n, γ) capture process produced a photon spectrum of total energy about 9 MeV per capture, which was detected by the liquid scintillator, with a delay time of up to 30 μsec, corresponding to the slowing down process. The neutron and positron pulses were detected in delayed coincidence and the difference between the counting rate with the reactor on and off was taken to represent true antineutrino absorption events.

From the 'reactor associated' counting rate of 36 ± 4 events per hour the cross-section for the inverse β-decay was found to be

$$(11 \pm 2\cdot6) \times 10^{-44} \text{ cm}^2 \qquad (16.34)$$

---

* F. Reines and C. L. Cowan, *Phys. Rev.*, **113**, 273, 1959.

The measurement of an effect with this extraordinarily small cross-section is a remarkable technical achievement. The result is consistent with theoretical expectation and the experimental verification of the Pauli neutrino hypothesis at last seems complete.

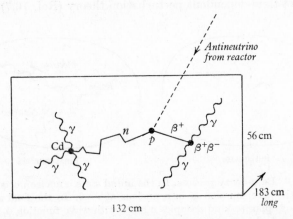

Fig. 16.12. Free antineutrino absorption cross-section. The diagram shows the principle of the liquid scintillator antineutrino detector in which a prompt pulse from the decay positron is followed by a delayed γ-pulse from capture of the associated neutron by a cadmium nucleus (Reines and Cowan, *Phys. Rev.*, **113**, 273, 1959).

16.5 The Fermi theory of β-decay

16.5.1 FORMULATION. Long before any direct attempt to verify the neutrino hypothesis had been made, Fermi[*] had embodied it in his theory of the β-process, which is the starting point for all theoretical studies of the subject and also the basis of the semi-empirical classification of experimental data (Sect. **16.3**). The Fermi theory does not explain the actual *rate* of β-decay, but it enables 'external' energy dependent factors to be removed from the experimental data. In this respect the theory plays much the same part in lepton physics as does the theory of reduced widths in the physics of nuclear reactions or the concept of reduced transition probabilities in the study of electromagnetic radiation.

The basic assumption of Fermi's treatment is that the light

---

[*] E. Fermi, *Zeits. Physik*, **88**, 161, 1934.

particles, the electron and neutrino, are created by the transformation of a neutron into a proton in a nucleus, or vice versa, in much the same way that a photon arises in an electromagnetic transition between energy levels of an atom or nucleus. The β-transition probability is obtained by applying the formulae of time-dependent perturbation theory (Ref. 16.7) to an

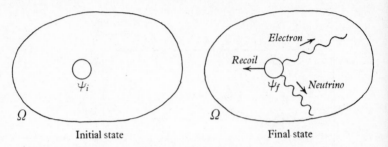

Fig. 16.13. Beta-decay process. In the initial state a nucleon occupies a state with wave function ψ_i in a nucleus at $r = 0$. In the final state a nucleon of opposite kind occupies a state with wave function ψ_f in the nucleus and electron and neutrino waves emerge. These waves are quantized within an arbitrary volume Ω.

initial system consisting of a single nucleon inside a volume Ω (Fig. 16.13). The final system is a different nucleon, an electron and a neutrino within the same volume; the nucleons in both initial and final systems may occupy states with wave functions ψ_i, ψ_f within a nucleus. The probability per unit time of the transition is

$$\frac{2\pi}{\hbar} |H_{if}|^2 \rho(E) \tag{16.35}$$

where H_{if} is the (unknown) potential or interaction relating the initial and final states, and 'causing' the transition, and $\rho(E)$ is the number of momentum states in the final system per unit energy range. Owing to the energy of recoil the neutrino momentum is not completely determined when the electron momentum is given and the total number of momentum states per unit energy range is therefore given by

$$\frac{4\pi p_e^2 \mathrm{d}p_e}{h^3} \times \frac{4\pi p_\nu^2 \mathrm{d}p_\nu}{h^3} \times \frac{\Omega^2}{\mathrm{d}E_e} \tag{16.36}$$

where the momenta p_e and p_v are related to the corresponding total electron and neutrino energy by the equations

$$E_e{}^2 = p_e{}^2c^2 + m^2c^4; \quad E_v = cp_v \quad \text{(assuming zero rest mass)} \quad (16.37)$$

and $E_v + E_e = E_0$ the energy corresponding to the upper limit of the β-spectrum, together with that corresponding to one electron mass. The probability of emission of an electron of momentum p_e per unit time is then, from (16.35), (16.36) and (16.37).

$$P(p_e)\mathrm{d}p_e = \frac{2\pi}{\hbar} |H_{if}|^2 \frac{p_e{}^2\mathrm{d}p_e p_v{}^2\mathrm{d}p_v}{4\pi^4\hbar^6} \frac{\Omega^2}{\mathrm{d}E_e}$$

$$= \frac{|\Omega H_{if}|^2}{2\pi^3\hbar^7} \frac{p_e{}^2(E_0 - E_e)^2}{c^3} \mathrm{d}p_e \quad (16.38)$$

Apart from numerical factors, this formula contains:

a) *the statistical factor* $p_e{}^2(E_0 - E_e)^2\mathrm{d}p_e$ which basically determines the shape of the β-spectrum. The distribution falls to zero for both high and low electron momenta; it would have been symmetrical if the electron and neutrino had been assumed of equal mass but for the known masses there are more electrons of low energy,

b) *the factor* $|\Omega H_{if}|^2$ which relates the electron and neutrino emission to the associated nuclear transformation. The precise analytical form of the interaction cannot yet be predicted theoretically although its form is limited by relativistic laws. For the present we shall assume that this factor contains electron, neutrino and nuclear wave functions which are normalized in the volume Ω and that we may write

$$|\Omega H_{if}|^2 = g^2|M|^2$$

where g is an arbitrary constant to be chosen to give the right strength for the β-decay and M contains details of the interaction so far unspecified. The general formula 16.38 then becomes

$$P(p_e)\mathrm{d}p_e = \frac{g^2|M|^2}{2\pi^3\hbar^7c^3} p_e{}^2(E_0 - E_e)^2\mathrm{d}p_e \quad (16.39)$$

Frequently this is expressed differently by writing

$$p_e = p.mc \quad \text{and} \quad E_e = W.mc^2$$

so that

$$P(p)\mathrm{d}p = \frac{m^5 g^2}{2\pi^3 \hbar^7} |M|^2 c^4 p^2 (W_0 - W)^2 \mathrm{d}p$$

$$= \frac{G^2}{2\pi^3} |M|^2 p^2 (W_0 - W)^2 \mathrm{d}p \qquad (16.40)$$

or, in terms of energies rather than momenta

$$P(W)\mathrm{d}W = \frac{G^2}{2\pi^3} |M|^2 p W (W_0 - W)^2 \mathrm{d}W \qquad (16.41)$$

where $\qquad G^2 = \dfrac{m^5 c^4}{\hbar^7} g^2$

16.5.2 SPECTRUM SHAPE, DECAY RATE AND SELECTION RULES FOR β-DECAY. No account has been taken so far of the nuclear charge of the transforming nucleus and when this is allowed for, the spectrum shape given by 16.40 or 16.41 differs according as positrons or electrons are emitted. Low-energy electrons are 'held back' and low energy positrons are 'pushed forward' so that the momentum distributions are as illustrated in Fig. 16.14a, and the energy distributions are as shown in Fig. 16.14b. Analytically we write instead of 16.40

$$P(p)\mathrm{d}p = \frac{G^2}{2\pi^3} |M|^2 F(Z, p) p^2 (W_0 - W)^2 \mathrm{d}p \qquad (16.42)$$

where $F(Z, p)$ is the *Fermi function* which corrects for finite nuclear charge. This is the formula on which the *Fermi-Kurie plots* of experimental data are based. The factor $F(Z, p)$ is essentially a barrier penetration factor and the non-relativistic approximation 14.70, with $\eta = Ze^2/\hbar v$ for positrons and $= -Ze^2/\hbar v$ for electrons may be used. In the case of a nucleus such as ^{64}Cu which undergoes dual decay the ratio of positrons to electrons of a given momentum is, using 16.42,

$$\frac{P_+(p)}{P_-(p)} = \frac{|M_+|^2}{|M_-|^2} \frac{F_+(Z, p)}{F_-(Z, p)} \frac{(W_0 - W)^2_+}{(W_0 - W)^2_-} \qquad (16.43)$$

The variation of this ratio with p is thus mainly determined by the Coulomb factors, and this has been checked experimentally.

The energy distribution of the electrons emitted in β-decay gives important evidence on the mass of the associated anti-neutrino. If the mass of this particle is zero the distribution 16.40 follows and this approaches the upper limit W_0 as $(W_0 - W)^2$, i.e. with a horizontal tangent (Fig. 16.15). On the

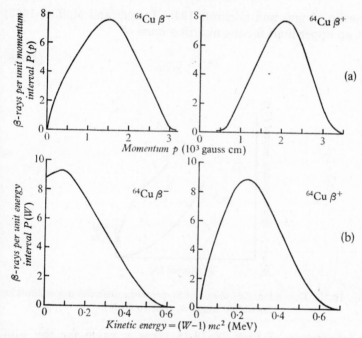

Fig. 16.14. Shape of β-spectra, illustrated by the case of ^{64}Cu, which shows dual decay
a) Momentum spectrum for electrons and positrons.
b) Energy spectrum for electrons and positrons. The β^- spectrum **has** a finite intensity at zero kinetic energy (Ref. 16.2).

other hand if the neutrino mass is finite, then near the upper limit the electron energy, electron momentum and neutrino energy ($\approx m_v c^2$) are all slowly varying and the neutrino may be treated nonrelativistically. The density of states 16.36 is then proportional to

$$p_e{}^2 \, \mathrm{d}p_e p_v \qquad (16.44)$$

since $\mathrm{d}E_e = - \mathrm{d}E_v \propto p_v \, \mathrm{d}p_v$
The electron momentum distribution $P(p)$ in this case becomes

proportional to the neutrino momentum p_ν, *i.e.* to $\sqrt{(W_0 - W)}$ and this distribution has a vertical tangent (Fig. 16.15). Accurate proportional counter and magnetic spectrometer studies of the tritium disintegration

$$^3\mathrm{H} \rightarrow {}^3\mathrm{He} + \beta^- + \bar{\nu} \tag{16.45}$$

(Curran, Angus and Cockroft 1948; Langer and Moffatt 1952) set an upper limit for the neutrino mass of

$$m_\nu < \frac{m}{2000} \tag{16.46}$$

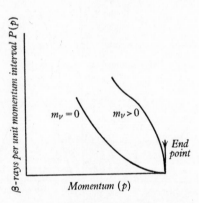

Fig. 16.15. Dependence of shape of β-spectrum near the upper limit on neutrino mass m_ν (not to scale).

Integration of formula 16.42 gives a value for the total probability per unit time of decay of the β-unstable nucleus. This is the decay constant and we write it, assuming the energy variation of $|M|^2$ to be small,

$$\lambda = \frac{\log_e 2}{t_{1/2}} = \frac{1}{\tau} = \int_0^{p_0} P(p)\mathrm{d}p$$

$$= \frac{G^2}{2\pi^3} |M|^2 f(Z, p_0) \tag{16.47}$$

or, if the Coulomb functions are given in terms of energy

$$\lambda = \frac{G^2}{2\pi^3} |M|^2 f(Z, W_0) \tag{16.48}$$

where $t_{1/2}$ is the half-life, τ the mean life for the decay and $f(Z, W_0)$ is an integral of the Fermi function over the spectrum and differs for positron emission, negatron emission and electron-capture. Abbreviating this integral to the symbol f we write

$$ft_{1/2} = \frac{2\pi^3}{G^2} \frac{\log_e 2}{|M|^2} \text{ sec} \tag{16.49}$$

where the quantity $ft_{1/2}$, usually written ft, is the comparative half-life used in the systematization of experimental data (Sect. 16.3.2).

The quantity $|M|^2$ depends theoretically on nuclear wave functions, taken together in a way which in turn depends on how the electron and neutrino are emitted. If these two particles emerge with their spins $\frac{1}{2}\hbar$ opposed we speak of *Fermi-type transitions*; if the spins of the light particles are parallel, giving a total spin angular momentum of $1\hbar$, we have *Gamow-Teller type transitions*.

Allowed transitions are those in which the light particles are emitted as an *s*-wave, and do not remove orbital momentum. The parity of the transforming nucleus consequently does not change. From the conservation of angular momentum we obtain the following *selection rules* for allowed β-transitions of a nucleus of spin I,

Fermi allowed $\Delta I = 0$, no parity change,

Gamow-Teller allowed $\Delta I = 0, \pm 1$, no parity change, and in the latter case the transition $I = 0$ to $I = 0$ must be excluded since spin momentum must be carried away. Pure Fermi allowed transitions take place between such states, e.g.,

$$^{14}\text{O} \rightarrow {}^{14}\text{N}^* + \beta^+ + \nu \tag{16.50}$$

while pure Gamow-Teller allowed decays are found when there is a spin change of 1, e.g.,

$$^{6}\text{He} \rightarrow {}^{6}\text{Li} + \beta^- + \bar{\nu} \tag{16.51}$$

The examples 16.50 and 16.51 are in fact also *superallowed* according to the experimental ft values. This is because in these cases the initial and final nucleons occupy the same state of orbital motion and M has its maximum value. This is not in general so, as shown by the spread of ft values for the allowed group of transitions (Sect. 16.3.2).

For the allowed transitions in light nuclei at least we may write

$$|M|^2 = |C_{\text{F}}|^2 |M_{\text{F}}|^2 + |C_{\text{GT}}|^2 |M_{\text{GT}}|^2 \qquad (16.52)$$

where $|C_{\text{F}}|^2 + |C_{\text{GT}}|^2 = 1$ and M_{F} and M_{GT} are integrals over nuclear wave functions for the Fermi and Gamow-Teller interactions. Equation 16.49 may then be expressed in the form

$$ft = \frac{B}{(1-x)|M_{\text{F}}|^2 + x|M_{\text{GT}}|^2} \qquad (16.53)$$

where $x = |C_{\text{GT}}|^2$. The constants in this formula can be obtained from experimental results on nuclei such as ^1n, ^3H, ^6He and ^{14}O for which the quantities M_{F} and M_{GT} are known because of the simple nuclear structure. It is found that B, the fundamental time of β-decay theory, is 2787 ± 70 sec and $x = 0.56$. From the value of B the coupling constant g is calculated to be 1.4×10^{-49} erg cm^3.

If in a β-decay process the nuclear parity changes, as it would for a nucleon transition between an s-state and a p-state the light particles cannot be emitted as an s-wave. They originate effectively at a distance λ from the nuclear centre, where λ is the electron or neutrino wavelength, and the probability of emission is reduced by a factor of the order $(R/\lambda)^2$ in comparison with s-wave emission, where R is the nuclear radius. This is exactly analogous to the emission of high multipoles in radiation theory. The factor $(R/\lambda)^2$ is typically about $1/100$ for an average nucleus, and transitions of this type are known as *first forbidden*. When such weak processes are considered it is really unsatisfactory to use anything less than a fully relativistic treatment of the problem, and the selection rules become much more complicated. For the non-relativistic case, however, the nuclear angular momentum and parity changes are summarized in the following table:

TABLE 16.2 Selection rules for β-decay (non-relativistic)

TYPES OF TRANSITION	FERMI RULES		GAMOW-TELLER RULES	
	SPIN CH.	PARITY CH.	SPIN CH.	PARITY CH.
Allowed	0	No	$0, \pm 1^*$	No
1st forbidden	$0, \pm 1^*$	Yes	$0, \pm 1, \pm 2^*$	Yes

* $0 \rightarrow 0$ transitions forbidden.

Forbidden transitions in general lead to β-spectra of 'non-allowed' shape and energy-dependent correction factors, predicted from a more detailed theory, must be introduced into 16.42.

16.6   Electron-capture decay

It has already been pointed out (Sect. **10.4**) that whenever positron decay can occur the capture of a K or L electron is an alternative process. This was first observed by Alvarez.[*] Electron-capture is energetically favoured over positron emission by an amount $2mc^2$, because no positron rest mass has to be created, and the rest mass of the captured electron is added to the energy release. This energy is removed by a neutrino, e.g. the decay of ^{7}Be is written

$$^7_4\text{Be} + e^-_K \rightarrow {}^7_3\text{Li} + \nu + 0\cdot86 \text{ MeV} \qquad (16.54)$$

The neutrino energy is slightly less than that predicted by the mass change because the absorption of the K electron of ^{7}Be by the nucleus leaves the product ^{7}Li atom neutral but with a K-shell vacancy. In the subsequent atomic rearrangement energy equivalent to the energy of the K-edge is radiated as X-rays or removed by Auger electron emission.

Equation 16.54 shows that electron capture is a two-body process, so that the neutrino would be expected to have a unique energy, in contrast with the distribution found in β-decay. This alters the formula corresponding to 16.48 for the decay constant since only the neutrino phase-space factor is required. The electron factor is replaced by a term representing the density of bound electrons at the nucleus and the decay constant for an allowed transition is expressed in the form

$$\lambda_K = \frac{G^2}{2\pi^3} |M|^2 f_K \qquad (16.55)$$

where

$$f_K \approx 2\pi(\alpha Z')^3 (W_0 + 1)^2 \qquad (16.56)$$

in which α is the fine structure constant ($=1/137$), W_0 is the *total* energy available for positron decay and Z' is the atomic

---

[*] L. W. Alvarez, *Phys. Rev.*, **52**, 134, 1937; **54**, 486, 1938.

20+N.P.

number of the decaying nucleus. The energy of the shell from which the electron is taken is omitted in this approximate formula. In the decay of heavy neutron-deficient nuclei, electron-capture is strongly preferred, not only because of the favourable energy release but also because a positron would have to penetrate a high potential barrier and the K-electron density in such nuclei is relatively large. In some cases when K-electron capture is energetically impossible, L-electron capture may still be possible because less energy is necessary to ionize the L shell than to ionize the K shell of the product atom. The L-capture is always possible when K-capture takes place, and competition between the two has been observed (^{37}A). The ratio of decay constants for allowed electron-capture and positron emission is seen from (16.48) and (16.55) to be

$$\frac{\lambda_+}{\lambda_K} \approx \frac{f(Z, W_0)}{2\pi(\alpha Z')^3(W_0 + 1)^2} \qquad (16.57)$$

which is independent of the nuclear factor $|M|^2$ so that the ratio is determined essentially by Coulomb effects. The observation of this ratio, which is known for a number of nuclei, is therefore a good test for β-decay theory.

Electron-capture is usually observed by detection of the X-radiation from the product nucleus. The special part played in this capture process by the electron density permits the decay constant to be influenced by chemical methods; it has for instance been found that for the process 16.54 the decay constants of ^{7}Be in the forms Be and BeO differ by about 1 part in 10^4. A similar effect is found in low energy internal conversion (Sect. **13.2**).

The energy release in an electron-capture such as 16.29 or 16.54 can be found by observing the energy of the recoil nucleus, which is typically a few eV, by means of a retarding potential. The energy can also be obtained by a time-of-flight method, using the K X-ray transition as a signal of zero time, and employing an electron multiplier as a detector of the slow recoil ion. It is also possible to obtain the disintegration energy by observing the energy distribution of a weak continuous radiation (inner bremsstrahlung) which always accompanies electron-capture. This is a radiative effect associated with the change of nuclear charge, and is involved in all β-decay processes.

16.7   Parity non-conservation and β-decay

Towards the end of 1956 an experiment was conducted* which had until then been thought unnecessary because there appeared to be no doubt about the result that would be obtained. Fig. 16.16a shows the experimental arrangement; a source of ^{60}Co, a well-known β-emitter with the decay scheme shown in Fig. 16.16b was incorporated in a crystal of cerium magnesium nitrate, which possesses a strong internal magnetic field. The crystal was cooled by adiabatic demagnetization to $0.01°$K and the ^{60}Co nuclei were then polarized (ch. 17) by applying a subsidiary magnetic field to the crystal. The polarization was checked and estimated by observing the anisotropy of gamma ray emission by means of counters A and B (Fig. 16.16a, c). The anthracene scintillation counter was then used to study the intensity of β-emission as a function of the direction of alignment (i.e. the direction of polarizing field), and the result shown in Fig. 16.16d was obtained. The asymmetry of β-emission and the anisotropy of γ-emission both disappeared as the crystal warmed up because of equalization of population of magnetic sub-states.

The demonstration of β-asymmetry in this experiment provided dramatic confirmation of the suggestion of Lee and Yang (Ref. 16.8) that parity might not be conserved in certain types of process, known as weak interactions, of which β-decay is one. A similar confirmation for another such process, the $\pi \rightarrow \mu \rightarrow e$ mesonic decay, was almost simultaneously forthcoming. To see why this experiment demonstrates parity non-conservation, we invoke the principle (ch. 17) that an asymmetric angular distribution always involves interference between amplitudes of opposite symmetry. The β-asymmetry therefore means that the transition between the ground state of ^{60}Co and the second excited state of ^{60}Ni (both of definite parity) can take place by emission of an electron-antineutrino pair in both odd and even parity states and that the two corresponding amplitudes

---

* C. S. Wu, E. Ambler, R. W. Hayward, D. D. Hoppes and R. P. Hudson, *Phys. Rev.*, **105**, 1413, 1957.

interfere, leading to an angular distribution of electron emission
of the form

$$a + b \cos \theta \tag{16.58}$$

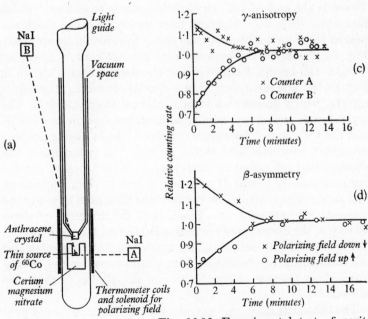

Fig. 16.16. Experimental test of parity
conservation in β-decay.

a) Apparatus.

b) Decay scheme of ^{60}Co (Gamow-Teller decay).

c) Gamma-ray anisotropy obtained from counters A and B at different times as the crystal warms up. The difference between the curves measures the net polarization of the nuclei.

d) Beta-ray asymmetry shown by counting rate in the anthracene crystal for two directions of polarizing field (Wu *et al.*, *Phys. Rev.*, **105**, 1413, 1957).

with respect to the nuclear axis. An alternative statement is
that the measurement of the direction of emission of the β
particle in relation to the direction of the nuclear angular
momentum vector defines the sense of a screw, and that one

screw sense is preferred in β-decay to the other. In the particular case of ^{60}Co, and generally for emitters of negative electrons, the electrons prefer to come out in the direction opposite to the

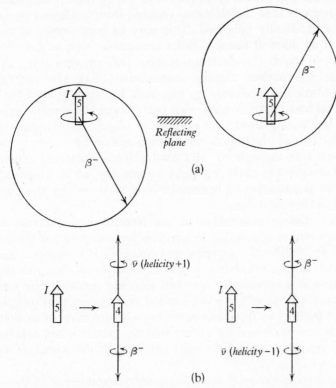

Fig. 16.17 Interpretation of ^{60}Co decay (allowed Gamow-Teller).
a) Reflection of the nuclear spin I (an axial vector) and the electron momentum (a polar vector) in a horizontal plane. The polar diagram is schematic only.
b) Explanation of the asymmetry in terms of a two-component neutrino theory. In order to change the nuclear spin by $\hbar$ the spins of the light particles must point along the nuclear axis.
If the helicity of the antineutrino is prescribed only one of the two decay mechanisms shown is possible and the β-emission is asymmetric with respect to the axis of nuclear spin.

nuclear spin (Fig. 16.17a). That this circumstance violates parity conservation is easily understood in terms of the reflection principle (Sect. **3.4**). Nuclear spin is an axial vector but the linear momentum of an electron is a polar vector, and the reflection of such a system in a mirror leads to a different system (Fig. 16.17a).

Another observable consequence of parity non-conservation in β-decay is that the electrons emitted from unaligned nuclei are longitudinally polarized. This may be seen simply in the case of an allowed Gamow-Teller transition (such as the ^{60}Co decay) in which the electron-neutrino pair emerges along the axis of the nuclear angular momentum. Since this angular momentum has to change by one unit, the spins ($\frac{1}{2}\hbar$) of both electron and neutrino must also point along the nuclear axis. This has been proved in a number of elegant experiments in which the polarization is determined either by rotating the electron spin through 90° and conducting a scattering experiment designed to show left-right asymmetry, or by observing circular polarization of bremsstrahlung produced by the electrons as they slow down.

The intimate association of the electron and neutrino in β-decay makes it possible to account for the observed phenomena by attributing a parity non-conserving property to the neutrino and antineutrino. In the *two-component theory* of the neutrino it is specifically assumed that the neutrino has zero rest mass and that it is a left-handed particle, i.e. that its spin vector points in a direction opposite to its direction of motion. This is also expressed by saying that the neutrino has helicity -1*: the antineutrino is a right-handed particle, with helicity $+1$.

The interpretation of the β-asymmetry experiment of Wu *et al.* in terms of the two-component theory of the neutrino is illustrated in Fig. 16.17b. Many similar experiments have now been performed and the general effect of the discovery of parity non-conservation has been greatly to clarify our understanding of the β-decay process in particular and of weak interactions in general.

References

16.1   G. C. Hanna, 'Alpha-Radioactivity', in *Experimental Nuclear Physics*, Vol. III, ed. E. Segrè, Wiley, 1959.

16.2   R. D. Evans, *The Atomic Nucleus*, McGraw-Hill, 1955.

* This assumption has been directly verified in a beautiful experiment by Goldhaber, Grodzins and Sunyar, *Phys. Rev.*, **109**, 1015, 1958.

16.3 M. Deutsch and O. Kofoed-Hansen, 'Beta-Rays', in *Experimental Nuclear Physics*, Vol. III, ed. E. Segrè, Wiley, 1959.

16.4 E. Feenberg and G. Trigg, 'Comparative Half-Lives', *Rev. mod. Phys.*, **22**, 399, 1950.

16.5 A. H. Wapstra and G. J. Nijgh, *Nuclear Spectroscopy Tables*, North Holland Publ. Co., 1959.

16.6 M. G. Mayer, S. A. Moszkowski and L. W. Nordheim, 'Nuclear Shell Structure and Beta-Decay', *Rev. mod. Phys.*, **23**, 315, 1951.

16.7 L. I. Schiff, *Quantum Mechanics*, chapter VIII, McGraw-Hill, 1949.

16.8 O. R. Frisch and T. H. R. Skyrme, 'Parity Non-Conservation in Weak Interactions', *Prog. nucl. Phys.*, **6**, 267, 1957.

16.9 P. M. S. Blackett, 'Non-conservation of Parity', *The American Scientist*, **47**, 509, 1959; see also The Rutherford Memorial Lecture, *Proc. roy. Soc.*, A, **251**, 293, 1959; P. Morrison, *Scientific American*, Vol. 196, April 1957.

16.10 B. W. Ridley, 'The Neutrino', *Prog. nucl. Phys.*, **5**, 188, 1956.

16.11 P. B. Moon, *Artificial Radioactivity*, Camb. Univ. Press, 1949.

16.12 C. S. Wu, 'The Neutrino', in *Theoretical Physics in the Twentieth Century* (Pauli Memorial Volume), ed. M. Fierz and V. F. Weisskopf, Interscience, 1960.

16.13 Nuclear Data Cards, National Academy of Sciences, Washington.

17. NUCLEAR ORIENTATION AND ANGULAR CORRELATION EXPERIMENTS

Nuclear spin affects the behaviour of nuclei in many phenomena and has already been introduced at several points in this book. In the present chapter we consider in rather more detail (a) the angular distribution of radiations arising from nuclei with pre-determined spin directions, and (b) the production of systems of spin-oriented nuclei. The techniques described often permit the determination of the spin and magnetic moment of excited states, and thus supplement the methods described in chapter 4 for determination of these properties for the ground state. It will be seen that many of the methods discussed in chapter 4 in fact lead to systems of oriented nuclei.

17.1 Definitions: polarization, orientation, alignment

The particles or quanta emitted from a radioactive source placed in a field free region are distributed isotropically in space. If the active nuclei have spin $\mathbf{I}$ (and magnetic moment $\boldsymbol{\mu}_I$), as defined in Sect. **4.1**, isotropic emission will result if the directions of the vectors $\mathbf{I}$, $\boldsymbol{\mu}_I$ are randomly distributed, although the angular distribution of the radiation from a particular nucleus is not isotropic with respect to its spin axis (Sect. **3.9**). Quantum mechanically, isotropic radiation means that if a certain axis Oz is defined by a vanishingly small magnetic field (cf. Sect. **4.1**) then for the whole assembly of nuclei there are equal numbers with components of angular momentum I $(I-1)\ldots-(I-1)$, $-I$ units of $\hbar$ along Oz. Thus for a single nucleus the probability $W(m)$ of the occurrence of any particular value $m\hbar$ of the resolved angular momentum* is independent of m and the system is *unoriented* (Fig. 17.1a). A given value of m defines one of the $(2I+1)$ *magnetic substates*, or independent spin states

---

* We shall omit the suffix I when it is not necessary to distinguish between nuclear and atomic or electronic spins.

of the nucleus of spin I with respect to the axis Oz. If the magnetic field is zero, the magnetic substates all have the same energy and there is degeneracy with respect to m.

If $W(m)$ does depend on m then a system of nuclei is *oriented* (Fig. 17.1b, c). If more spins point in one direction $(+Oz)$ than in the opposite direction $(-Oz)$, $W(+m)$ is not equal to $W(-m)$ and

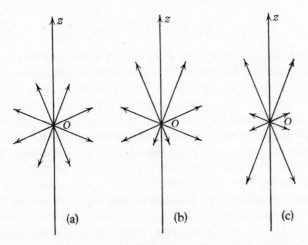

Fig. 17.1. Nuclear magnetic substates. Oz is an axis of quantization and the arrows represent allowed directions of orientation of a nuclear spin. The lengths of the arrows show the number of nuclei in an assembly with the particular orientation.
a) Unoriented assembly.
b) Oriented assembly (polarized).
c) Oriented assembly (aligned).
The distributions are assumed to have axial symmetry about Oz.

the system of nuclei is *polarized* (Fig. 17.1b). If $W(m)$ depends only on m^2 so that $W(m) = W(-m)$ the system is *aligned* (Fig. 17.1c); it has equal numbers of nuclei pointing in opposite directions and is therefore unpolarized but is nevertheless oriented with respect to Oz since the populations of the spin states are not equal. The polarization P of a system may be defined as

$$P = \frac{1}{I} \sum m W(m) \tag{17.1}$$

and is then a number giving the excess of spins pointing in one
20*

direction. In the particularly simple case of a system of nuclei with spin $\frac{1}{2}$, of which N_1 are pointing 'up' $(m = +\frac{1}{2})$ and N_2 are pointing down $(m = -\frac{1}{2})$, we have

$$W(\tfrac{1}{2}) = \frac{N_1}{N_1+N_2}, \qquad W(-\tfrac{1}{2}) = \frac{N_2}{N_1+N_2}$$

and

$$P = \frac{2}{N_1+N_2}\,(\tfrac{1}{2}N_1 - \tfrac{1}{2}N_2) = \frac{N_1-N_2}{N_1+N_2} \qquad (17.2)$$

In general, Eq. (17.1) defines P to have a value between 1 and -1. Alignment as distinct from polarization is only meaningful for nuclei of spin greater than $\frac{1}{2}$. Orientation can arise in systems of nuclei of atoms bound in a solid lattice, in collision-free beams (as discussed in ch. 4), or in gases at low pressure. Although magnetic fields may be instrumental in the production of orientation, they are not essential to its existence. The detection of orientation depends on the nature of the system; oriented assemblies will usually show some anisotropy in subsequent emission of radiations but oriented beams are usually best studied in scattering or magnetic deflection experiments. In nearly all orientation phenomena the interaction between nuclear spin systems and their atomic environment is of great importance, both for the production and maintenance of their orientation.

17.2 Oriented nuclear systems

We consider first the most usual method of detecting nuclear orientation, and then the methods by which it has been produced.

17.2.1 ANGULAR DISTRIBUTION OF RADIATION FROM ORIENTED NUCLEI. The semi-classical theory of radiation indicates that the radiation of multipolarity (L,M) emitted in a transition between nuclear states of spin $(I_i m_i)$ and $(I_f m_f)$ has a definite angular distribution $F_L^M(\theta)$ with respect to the axis of quantization. The quantum numbers are related by the selection rules

$$\left.\begin{array}{c} I_i + I_f \geqslant L \geqslant |I_i - I_f| \\ m_i - m_f = M \end{array}\right\} \qquad (17.3)$$

where $|M| \leqslant L$. The selection rule for M limits the number of components observable in the transition $I_i \to I_f$ (Fig. 17.2). In optical transitions the spin states may be separated out clearly by application of a magnetic field, as in the Zeeman effect, and the different component transitions may be observed individually. In the nuclear case the separations obtainable are only about 10^{-8} eV and are only observable in special circumstances,

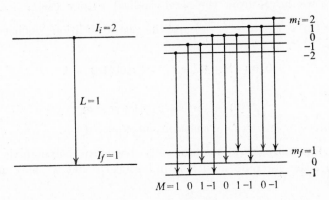

Fig. 17.2. Components of a radiative transition of multipolarity 1 between states of spin $I_i = 2$, $I_f = 1$.

such as those offered by the Mössbauer effect (Sect. 13.6.3). Usually all the line components are unresolvable experimentally, and the angular distribution observed must be obtained by adding the angular distributions of the components incoherently.

The probability of the vectors $\mathbf{I}_i$, $\mathbf{I}_f$ combining to give a vector $\mathbf{L}$, with particular magnetic quantum numbers, is given by a transformation amplitude or vector addition coefficient,[*] which may be written $(I_i I_f m_i m_f | LM)$. The angular distribution arising from a given substate m_i of the initial level can then be written

$$W(\theta) = \sum_M (I_i I_f m_i m_f | LM)^2 F_L^M(\theta) \qquad (17.4)$$

---

[*] Often known as a Wigner coefficient or Clebsch-Gordan coefficient. These coefficients are tabulated in Ref. 17.1.

and if the initial substates have a weight $W(m_i)$, which depends on m_i, the total angular distribution is

$$W(\theta) = \sum_{M,m_i} W(m_i)(I_i I_f m_i m_f | LM)^2 F_L^M(\theta) \qquad (17.5)$$

This must reduce to a constant if $W(m_i)$ is independent of m_i, i.e. if the initial levels are equally populated (random orientation). Thus, for example, if $I_i = 1$, $I_f = 0$, $L = 1$ (dipole radiation) we have, from the semi-classical theory (Sect. 3.9.2), $F_1^0 \propto \sin^2 \theta$, $F_1^{\pm 1} \propto \dfrac{1 + \cos^2 \theta}{2}$ and the vector addition coefficients are

$$(010 \pm 1 | 1 \pm 1) = 1 \qquad (0100|10) = 1$$

so that

$$W(\theta) = \sin^2 \theta + 2 \cdot \tfrac{1}{2}(1 + \cos^2 \theta)$$
$$= \text{constant, as expected.}$$

The functions $F_L^M(\theta)$ contain only Legendre polynomials of even order for pure multipole radiation so that we may also write

$$W(\theta) = a_0 + a_2 \cos^2 \theta + a_4 \cos^4 \theta + \ldots + a_{2L} \cos^{2L} \theta \qquad (17.6)$$

which again expresses the result already noted in Sect. **3.9** that no term in $\cos \theta$ of power higher than $2L$ appears. The distribution is symmetric with respect to the plane $z = 0$, a consequence of the validity of parity as a quantum number for electromagnetic transitions.

Observation of anisotropic distributions of radiation is thus clear evidence for nuclear orientation, and may provide information on I_i, I_f and L.

17.2.2 ORIENTATION OF NUCLEI IN SOLIDS AT LOW TEMPERATURE.

a) *Principle.* The principle of all methods of obtaining nuclear orientation using low temperatures is to produce in a solid a sequence of energy levels for each of which the nuclei have different m_I values with respect to an axis of quantization. Unequal distribution of nuclei between these levels (i.e. orientation) arises in thermal equilibrium if the temperature is low enough, and also in non-equilibrium states at rather higher temperatures as a result of induced electromagnetic transitions. The sequence of energy levels may be produced either by an externally applied magnetic field or by internal fields existing in the solid. The low temperatures ($\approx 0 \cdot 01\,°K$) required are usually obtained by adiabatic demagnetization using a suitable crystal in which the nuclei to be oriented are incorporated.

b) *Direct orientation.* It has been already noted (Sect. 4.2.1) that a system of nuclei with spin exhibits weak paramagnetism because of the excess population of the lower energy levels in a magnetic field owing to the operation of the Boltzmann distribution factor. In a given field H_0 a nuclear *polarization*

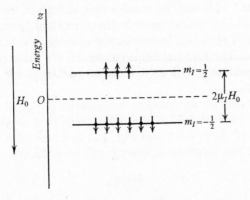

Fig. 17.3. Separation of magnetic substates for a nucleus of spin $I = \frac{1}{2}$ and magnetic moment μ_I in a magnetic field H_0.

therefore exists in thermal equilibrium and it is directly proportional to the nuclear paramagnetic susceptibility. For a free nucleus of spin $\frac{1}{2}$ and moment μ_I there are just two levels (Fig. 17.3) separated by an energy $\mu_I H_0/I = 2\mu_I H_0$ and an appreciable difference between the population of these levels arises at a temperature T such that

$$\mu_I H_0 \approx kT \qquad (17.7)$$

For μ_I equal to a nuclear magneton

$$\frac{H_0}{T} = 2 \cdot 8 \times 10^7 \text{ gauss } °K^{-1} \qquad (17.8)$$

so that extremely low temperatures, or high fields, or both are necessary. A nuclear polarization of about 2% has been obtained by this method for ^{115}In at 0·05 °K.

c) *Orientation by hfs methods.* Gorter and Rose suggested independently in 1948 that the large internal magnetic fields ($H_i \approx 10^5 - 10^6$ gauss) existing in paramagnetic ions might be used in place of the large external field H_0 in 17.8 to produce nuclear orientation. If for instance the internal field is due to a single electron spin then at low temperatures this spin can be oriented by an external field of only a few hundred gauss because of the large electronic magnetic moment. The nuclear spin will follow the electron spin because of the hyperfine coupling and a nuclear polarization will exist in thermal equilibrium.* This may be much larger at a given low temperature than is obtainable by the direct method because of the magnitude of H_i which increases the spacing between levels of different m_I. The internal fields concerned are those responsible for the hyperfine splittings in electron paramagnetic resonance (Sect. 4.3.2).

For purposes of illustration we consider a simple system in which the internal field is due effectively to a single electron spin $S = \frac{1}{2}$ (cf. Sect. 4.3.2 and Fig. 4.3) and acts on a nucleus of spin $I = \frac{1}{2}$. The interaction energy will be written†

$$Am_I m_S \qquad (17.9)$$

where in this case $m_I = \pm \frac{1}{2}$, $m_S = \pm \frac{1}{2}$ and Oz is the axis of quantization defined by an external field. The energy levels of this system as a function of external field H_0 are shown in Fig. 17.4. At fields of a few hundred gauss the vectors **I** and **S** are decoupled and the spin directions are shown in the figure. In states a, b, the electron spin is 'up', and in states c, d, it is 'down', and the energy separation between (ab) and (cd) is approximately $2\mu_0 H_0$ where μ_0 is the Bohr magneton. The energy separation between a and b, or between c and d, is $\frac{1}{2}A$ (putting $m_S = \frac{1}{2}$, $m_I = \pm \frac{1}{2}$ in 17.9). At very small fields $F = I \pm S$

---

* Non-stationary methods of producing nuclear orientation are described in Ref. 17.4. See also Sect. 17.3.1.

† This is exactly as in eq. 4.11 except that it is customary to use A instead of a when the internal field may be due to more than one electron.

is a good quantum number and a hyperfine pattern of states $a'b'c'd'$ of the type discussed in chapter 4 arises.

In the Gorter–Rose method of alignment the sample is brought to a temperature T ($\approx 0{\cdot}01\,°K$) such that $kT \approx \frac{1}{2}A$ in a residual field H_0 (Fig. 17.4). A nuclear *polarization* then exists because of preferential population of state d. In the *hfs* orientation methods proposed by Pound and by Bleaney single

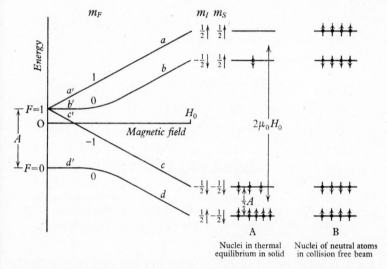

Fig. 17.4. Hyperfine structure of the ground state of an atom with $I = \frac{1}{2}$, $S = \frac{1}{2}$ in a magnetic field H_0. The figure is suitable for discussion of the hydrogen atom, or a paramagnetic ion with $S = \frac{1}{2}$. To the right of the diagram are shown the levels and nuclear spin directions at high fields (> 100 gauss, say). The spin symbols (A) represent the population of the levels in equilibrium at a temperature such that $kT \approx \frac{1}{2}A$. At B are shown the populations for a beam of neutral atoms.

crystals in which anisotropic electric fields exist are used. The crystalline field provides an axis of quantization and causes splitting of the nuclear ground state so that no external field is required. Nuclear orientation results either from interaction between the electric field gradient and the nuclear quadrupole moment (Pound) or from an indirect interaction between the electronic and nuclear moments via the crystalline electric field (Bleaney). Since there is no external magnetic field, the energy in a particular state is unaltered by reversing both the nuclear and electronic spin and states with equal and opposite values of m_I have the same energy (Fig. 17.5). These methods therefore only apply for $I > \frac{1}{2}$ and then give nuclear *alignment* rather than polarization in thermal equilibrium at temperatures of the order of $0 \cdot 01°$K (Fig. 17.5). Since the angular distribution of γ-rays from nuclear states involves only even powers of

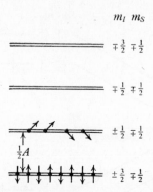

Fig. 17.5. Magnetic substates for $I = \frac{3}{2}$, $S = \frac{1}{2}$ in a crystalline field. A series of doublets of spacing $\frac{1}{2}A$ arises and at low temperatures nuclear alignment is obtained, as shown by the spin symbols.

$\cos \theta$, aligned nuclei give the same pattern as nuclei with the corresponding polarization, but asymmetries, such as those observed in the parity experiments (Sect. **16.7**), cannot be detected in this way.

The Bleaney method of orientation has been more frequently used than the others, but the general techniques are similar in each method. A number of radioactive atoms, corresponding to an activity of about 20 μC, are incorporated in a magnetically dilute paramagnetic single crystal, with suitable internal fields. This is brought to a low temperature of $\approx 0 \cdot 01°$K by ordinary adiabatic demagnetization. If alignment only is required, demagnetization proceeds to zero field, but for polarization a residual field is necessary and the initial field in the demagnetization apparatus must be correspondingly higher if the same final temperature is to be reached. The angular distribution of γ-radiation with respect to the crystalline axis (or direction of applied field in the Rose–Gorter method) is observed, and expressed as an *anisotropy* ε where

$$\varepsilon = \frac{W(\frac{1}{2}\pi) - W(0)}{W(\frac{1}{2}\pi)} \qquad (17.10)$$

and $W(\theta)$ is the intensity of radiation at an angle θ with the axis. The anisotropy is obtained at a number of temperatures as the crystal warms up; temperatures are measured by determination of the magnetic susceptibility of the specimen

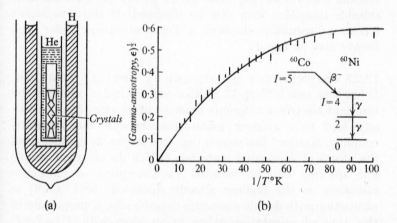

(a)   (b)

Fig. 17.6. Alignment of ^{60}Co nuclei.

a) Cryostat containing crystals of a Tutton salt (copper rubidium sulphate) surrounded by jackets of liquid helium and liquid hydrogen. The active cobalt nuclei are included in the crystal.

b) Gamma-ray anisotropy for the ^{60}Co decay plotted (as $\varepsilon^{\frac{1}{2}}$) against the inverse of the temperature. In this particular decay each of the two gamma rays is expected to have the same angular distribution. The curve corresponds to $I=5$, $\mu_I = 3.5 \pm 0.5$ nuclear magnetons for ^{60}Co (Bleaney *et al.*, *Proc. roy. Soc.*, A, **221**, 170, 1954).

($\chi \propto 1/T$). Fig. 17.6 shows the cryostat used by Daniels *et al.** in the first successful nuclear orientation experiment, and the results for ^{60}Co nuclei aligned in this way. The angular distribution of γ-radiation depends in a calculable way on the nature of the β-transition and on the spins of the states concerned

* J. M. Daniels, M. A. Grace and F. N. H. Robinson, *Nature*, **168**, 780, 1951; B. M. Bleaney, J. M. Daniels, M. A. Grace, H. Halban, N. Kurti, F. N. H. Robinson and F. E. Simon, *Proc. roy. Soc.*, A., **221**, 170, 1954.

in the γ-transitions. It also depends on the degree of alignment, i.e. the distribution of initial states with respect to m_I^2 and at a given temperature this is determined by the interaction constant A which involves the nuclear moment μ_I of the initial state and the internal fields. If the internal field can be calculated, μ_I can be found; alternatively comparison can be made with results obtained with another isotope of known moment.

Nuclear alignment experiments give information for single radiative transitions which is otherwise only obtainable for cascade transitions; the ratio of $E2$ to $M1$ components in a suitable transition may also be obtained. If the γ-radiation follows a β-transition the ratio of Fermi to Gamow-Teller type decays may be found.

17.2.3 ORIENTATION OF NUCLEI BY OPTICAL PUMPING.

It has been seen in Sect. 17.2.2 that any method of orienting the resultant electronic magnetic moment of an atom can potentially lead to a nuclear orientation through the hyperfine coupling. Kastler* has shown that free atoms, as distinct from the atoms of condensed materials (which do not emit simple line spectra), can be oriented by absorption of resonance radiation, in the manner already discussed (Sect. 4.4.6) in connection with double resonance experiments. A simple case of this type of orientation arises in an atom with $F (= I + J)$ equal to $\frac{3}{2}$ in an excited state and $\frac{1}{2}$ in the ground state as shown in Fig. 17.7a, which also indicates the hyperfine components of the optical transition between the levels. If an unexcited atom of this type absorbs its resonance radiation, the population of the magnetic substates of the excited state may be controlled by selecting a particular polarization of the incident light. The direction of incidence defines an axis of quantization, and if it is arranged that only right circularly polarized radiation (σ) is absorbed then only the substates with $m_F = \frac{1}{2}$ and $\frac{3}{2}$ in the excited state are populated. The state $m_F = \frac{1}{2}$ can decay however by emission of both σ-radiation and π (plane polarized) radiation in accordance with the selection rule $\Delta m_F = \pm 1$ or 0 and this means that as a result of the combined absorption and re-emission (Fig. 17.7b) atoms are continually being transferred

---

* A. Kastler, *Proc. phys. Soc., Lond.*, **67**, 853, 1954.

from the ground level with $m_F = -\frac{1}{2}$ to the state with $m_F = +\frac{1}{2}$. A system of atoms can thus be oriented even at room temperature, and since with hyperfine coupling the nuclear spin will follow the electronic spin, a nuclear orientation also exists, as in the Gorter–Rose method.

In practice, this method requires the use of a vapour at a pressure of the order of 10^{-4} mm of mercury, or of a collision-free beam in order to minimize disorientation by collisions. The

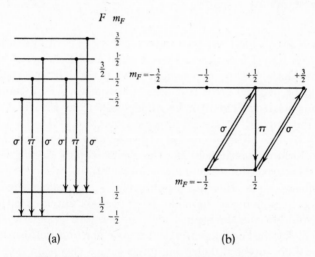

Fig. 17.7. Orientation by optical pumping.

a) Hyperfine structure of an optical transition between atomic states with $F = \frac{3}{2}$ and $\frac{1}{2}$.

b) Transference of atoms from the state $m_F = -\frac{1}{2}$ to the state $m_F = +\frac{1}{2}$ by absorption of circularly polarized resonance light and re-emission of circular plus plane polarized light.

effect of small transverse magnetic fields may be serious, but can be minimized if a small axial field, in the direction of the incident light, is employed. If the pumping light is interrupted the oriented atoms will relax on the walls of a containing vessel in a time of about $\frac{1}{10}$ sec. If the density of oriented atoms can be increased without destroying the orientation, this method may be able to provide polarized targets for nuclear experiments. Work so far has been mainly with mercury and alkali atoms.

17.3 Oriented particle beams

From the point of view of scattering and transmutation experiments, the production of oriented beams of bombarding particles is as interesting as alignment of target nuclei. We therefore consider briefly the means that have been proposed or used for providing sources of polarized nucleons, and the methods that are available for detecting polarization in particle beams. Since the nucleon spin is $\frac{1}{2}$, only polarization, as distinct from alignment, need be considered; for deuterons ($I = 1$) extra parameters are required.

17.3.1 MAGNETIC SEPARATION OF SPIN STATES. It was proposed by Clausnitzer, Fleischmann and Schopper* that a Stern–Gerlach type experiment with neutral hydrogen atoms could be used to provide a beam of atoms in which the nuclei were polarized. This can be understood from Fig. 17.4 which can be applied to the hydrogen atom ($I = \frac{1}{2}$, $J = S = \frac{1}{2}$). If a collision-free beam of neutral hydrogen atoms is passed through a uniform magnetic field H_0, the electron spins are aligned and the beam contains the four components a, b, c, d, in equal intensity, since thermal equilibrium is not established. The electronic magnetic moment is oppositely directed in states (ab) and (cd) and the beams (ab) can therefore be separated from (cd) by letting the magnetic field H_0 become non-uniform so that oppositely directed deflecting forces arise. The beam (ab) in the field H_0 has no net nuclear polarization but if this beam passes into a region of very low field, F becomes a good quantum number again because of the hyperfine coupling. Beam b' ($F = 1, m_F = 0$) becomes a mixture of the uncoupled states b and d and has no net polarization but beam a' is a pure state ($F = 1$, $m_F = 1$) and is fully polarized. The nuclear polarization of beams ($a'b'$) is therefore 50%.

In the practical development of the first scheme for injection of polarized ions into a linear accelerator,† an inhomogeneous field with sextupole symmetry is used for intensity reasons. A

---

* G. Clausnitzer, R. Fleischmann and H. Schopper, *Z. Phys.*, **144**, 336, 1956.

† G. H. Stafford, J. M. Dickson, D. C. Salter and M. K. Craddock, *Nucl. instrum. and Methods*, **15**, 146, 1962.

beam of atoms from a radiofrequency ion source (Sect. 8.1.3) enters this magnet axially and particles with an electronic moment corresponding to the states (ab) (Fig. 17.4) are focused, while those corresponding to the states (cd) are deflected away. On leaving the sextupole field, the polarized atoms enter a chamber over which a small field is maintained to provide the quantization axis, and in which an intense beam of electrons causes ionization of the incident atoms. The polarized protons

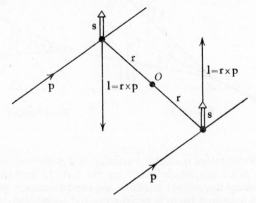

Fig. 17.8. Asymmetry of interaction of polarized nucleons with a nucleus, centre O.

then enter the accelerator; an intensity of about 10^{-5} µA with 30% polarization, at an energy of 30 MeV, has been achieved in the first trials of such a system.

An increased polarization is possible if radiofrequency transitions between states b and d can be induced in the field H_0 and if ionization takes place subsequently in this field.

17.3.2 POLARIZATION BY ELASTIC SCATTERING. It is known from the success of the single-particle shell model (Sect. **9.3**) that the energy of a nucleon in a bound state depends on the relative orientation of its orbital and spin momenta. The same spin–orbit effect may be expected in unbound states, i.e. in the scattering of nucleons by complex nuclei. This introduces an asymmetry into the scattering of polarized nuclei, as may be seen from Fig. 17.8. Nuclei of given spin (s) orientation passing to right or to left of a nuclear centre O generate orbital vectors **l** of opposite sign. If the scattering depends on the sign of the scalar **s·l** the contributions to the scattering at a given angle from the two sides of the nucleus will be unequal. Interference between this one-sided scattering and any background scattering which may be present leads to an asymmetric angular distribution.* Particles with spin 'up' are then preferentially

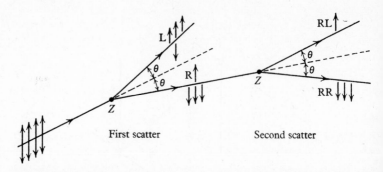

First scatter   Second scatter

Fig. 17.9. Polarization in elastic scattering of unpolarized nucleons by a nucleus Z. After one elastic scattering the left (L) and the right (R) scattered beams have equal intensity but complementary polarization. If the right scattered beam is again scattered elastically the left (RL) and right (RR) beams have different intensity.

scattered to the left or right and it may easily be seen (Fig. 17.9) that the elastic scattering of an unpolarized beam leads to scattered beams of equal intensity at a given angle of scattering but of opposite polarization. The existence of the polarization may be demonstrated by a second scattering, after which an asymmetry between the left and right scattered beams will be observed.

The first demonstration of the production of polarized beams was given by Heusinkveld and Freier† who studied the double scattering of 3·5 MeV protons by helium. The spin–orbit asymmetry arises in this case because the compound nucleus ^{5}Li has a ground state and first excited state which form a

---

* See the discussion of the high energy case given by Fermi, *Nuovo Cim. Suppl.*, Ser. 10, Vol. 2, 1955, p. 92.

† M. Heusinkveld and G. Freier, *Phys. Rev.*, **85**, 80, 1951.

p-doublet with spins $\frac{3}{2}$ and $\frac{1}{2}$ respectively ($j = l \pm s$). If the energy of a proton incident upon a helium nucleus is such that one of these states is preferentially formed, interaction is stronger for one $\mathbf{s} \cdot \mathbf{l}$ orientation than for the other, and a polarized beam results. The interference here is between the resonant $p_{3/2}$ or $p_{1/2}$ wave and the non-resonant s-wave background. The polarization was checked by a second scattering in helium, and was found to agree with that predicted from the angular distributions of elastic scattering, which can be analysed to give phase shifts for the s- and p-waves. The helium scattering can give proton polarizations of 100% at certain angles and energies, and has been much used as a polarization analyser.

In the elastic scattering of protons of energy 10–20 MeV by heavier nuclei polarization arises because the potentials effective for left-sided and right-sided scattering are different owing to the different sign of the spin–orbit term $\mathbf{s} \cdot \mathbf{l}$. Polarization of slow neutrons by passage through magnetized iron (as used in the determination of the magnetic moment of the neutron, Sect. 4.4.5) also arises because of an interference effect, in this case between nuclear scattering and scattering from aligned atomic electrons.

17.4   Angular distribution and correlation experiments

17.4.1 INTRODUCTION. The observation of angular distributions and polarizations of nuclear radiations adds important information to that obtainable from total cross-sections or excitation functions. This information relates to

a) the spin, parity, and occasionally magnetic moment of nuclear levels, and

b) the reaction mechanism.

We shall consider mainly two types of experiment from which this information is obtained; namely the *angular correlation experiment* (Sect. 17.4.2) in which two quanta appear in rapid succession in a nuclear decay scheme, and the *angular distribution, or differential cross-section experiment* (Sect. 17.4.3) in which a nuclear reaction takes place. This division of phenomena is not comprehensive; many processes can be described in either way, and many more complicated processes, such as triple correlations, have been studied. A common feature however is that either the emission of a quantum, or the incidence of a bombarding particle, defines a direction, or axis of quantization, and the distribution of intensity of emission of the second radiation round this axis can then be observed. If the second radiation is a particle the angular distribution is determined by the orbital angular momenta which it is permitted by selection rules to remove; if it is a photon, particular angular distribution patterns arise for each permitted multipole. In single-stage reactions of the type

$$X + a \rightarrow Y + b \qquad (17.11)$$

the connection between the initial and final state is direct and the angular distributions can be predicted directly from the conservation of angular momentum; we shall not consider these reactions. In two-stage reactions involving a compound nucleus

$$X + a \rightarrow C^* \rightarrow Y + b \qquad (17.12)$$

the properties of the nucleus C^* determine the angular distribution of b since the magnetic substates of the levels of C will not usually be uniformly populated. The angular distribution calculation then becomes a particular case of nuclear orientation theory.

The permitted orbital angular momenta and radiation patterns which form the basic elements of angular distribution calculations are connected with the intrinsic spins of the nuclei concerned through the conservation laws. Within these limits angular momenta may couple together in different ways (e.g. L–S, or j–j coupling) and it may be possible to learn something of the coupling scheme from the observed angular distributions. For simplicity only two-stage reactions involving well-separated single levels of the compound nucleus will be considered. Relativistic problems such as β-decay, in which spin and orbital motion should not be separated, will not be dealt with.

17.4.2 ANGULAR CORRELATION OF SUCCESSIVE RADIA-TIONS. Many excited nuclei decay by emitting a cascade of two or more gamma rays. This is especially noticeable when the state excited (I_2, Fig. 17.10a) has a spin which differs by several units of $\hbar$ from that of the ground state and levels of intermediate spin (I_1, Fig. 17.10a) lie between I_2 and the ground state I_0. In such cases a succession of radiations of low multipolarity is more probable than a more energetic 'cross-over' transition of high multipolarity. In the particular case of a

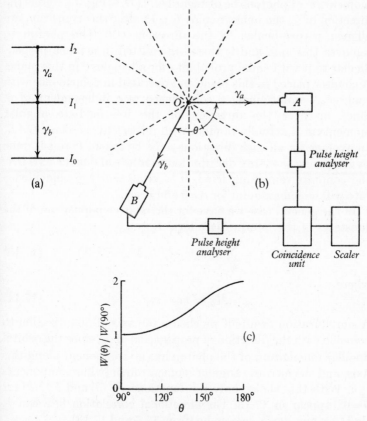

Fig. 17.10. Angular correlation of successive radiations from a radioactive nucleus at O.

a) Decay scheme.

b) Experimental arrangement of counters and coincidence unit.

c) Angular correlation $W(\theta) = 1 + \cos^2 \theta$.

radiation γ_a followed by γ_b the observation of γ_a in a particular direction picks out a set of nuclei in states I_1 with an anisotropic distribution of spin directions. If this distribution of spins persists until γ_b is emitted and if γ_b is observed in coincidence with γ_a then an angular distribution of the form 17.6 is obtained.

That such a correlation exists may be seen in a simple case in a way indicated by Moon.* Let γ_a and γ_b both be electric dipole transitions and let $I_2 = I_0 = 0$, $I_1 = 1$ and let the intrinsic angular momentum of photons be disregarded. If OA (Fig. 17.10b) is the direction of γ_a the nuclear spins $I_1 = 1\hbar$ after this transition are aligned perpendicular to the direction OA. The photon γ_b removes this spin and is therefore emitted in a plane perpendicular to it with equal probability for all angles θ in this plane. A counter placed in this plane and operated in coincidence with counter A would show a coincidence rate independent of θ. Since however the direction of the intermediate angular momentum is actually random with respect to the plane OAB, an average for all such directions must be taken. If this is done by imagining the γ-ray distribution to rotate about the axis OA, the counters remaining fixed, it is clear that the coincidence rate will be a maximum for $\theta = 0$ and $\theta = \pi$.

In the general case we have for the relative population of the substates of the intermediate level I_1

$$W(m_1) = \sum_{m_2} (I_1 I_2 m_1 m_2 | L_a M_a)^2 F_{L_a}^{M_a}(\theta) \qquad (17.13)$$

where

$$M_a = m_2 - m_1 \qquad (17.14)$$

A simplification results if we choose the axis of quantization to coincide with the direction of propagation of γ_a, since the orbital angular momentum of the photon has no component along this axis, and the intrinsic angular momentum only has components $\pm\hbar$. With this choice only the functions $F_{L_a}^1(\theta)$ and $F_{L_a}^{-1}(\theta)$ for $\theta = 0°$ appear in 17.13. The directional correlation between γ_a and γ_b is now easily seen to be (from 17.5 and 17.13),

$$W(\theta) = \sum_{m_0 m_1 m_2} (I_1 I_2 m_1 m_2 | L_a \pm 1)^2 F_{L_a}^{\pm 1}(0)$$
$$\times (I_0 I_1 m_0 m_1 | L_b M_b)^2 F_{L_b}^{M_b}(\theta) \qquad (17.15)$$

In the particular example quoted with $I_2 = I_0 = 0$, $I_1 = 1$ the transitions permitted when γ_a is observed at angle $\theta = 0°$ are

---

* P. B. Moon, *Artificial Radioactivity*, Cambridge University Press, 1949, p. 98.

$(I,m) = (0,0) \rightleftarrows (1, \pm 1)$. The Clebsch–Gordan coefficients are unity (as always when one of the combining vectors is zero) and from 17.15 the angular correlation is given by

$$W(\theta) = F_1^{\pm 1}(0)[F_1^1(\theta) + F_1^{-1}(\theta)]$$
$$\propto (1 + \cos^2 \theta)$$

in agreement with prediction from the simple model.

Similar calculations may be made for more complicated cascades but the numerical evaluation of the correlation function becomes very tedious because of the large number of summations over magnetic quantum numbers which are necessary. Fortunately it is possible to avoid this through algebraic methods developed by Racah and it is now customary to write the general angular correlation function in the form

$$W(\theta) = \sum A_\nu P_\nu(\cos \theta) \qquad (17.16)$$

where

$$\nu = 0, 2, 4 \ldots$$

and

$$A_\nu = F_\nu(L_a I_2 I_1) F_\nu(L_b I_1 I_0) \qquad (17.17)$$

The functions F_ν are tabulated for the simpler cases by Biedenharn and Rose* and depend on the multipolarity of the successive transitions and on the spins (but not parities) of the levels.

A typical experimental arrangement for the observation of angular correlations in cascade transitions is shown in Fig. 17.10b. The counters A, B are usually sodium iodide crystals attached to photomultipliers and the output pulses are selected according to size in the pulse analysers so that unwanted radiations may be excluded. The required pulses are combined in the coincidence unit and the number of coincidences $W(\theta)$ is determined as a function of the angle between the counter axes. The anisotropy

$$\varepsilon = \frac{W(\tfrac{1}{2}\pi) - W(0)}{W(\tfrac{1}{2}\pi)} = \frac{W(90°) - W(180°)}{W(90°)}$$

can be compared with that predicted by 17.16, or a complete curve for $W(\theta)$ (Fig. 17.10c) may be obtained.

---

* L. C. Biedenharn and M. E. Rose, *Rev. mod. Phys.*, **25**, 729, 1953, Table I.

Circuits of the type shown in Fig. 17.10b will work with a resolving time as high as 10^{-6} sec but with strong sources the number of accidental coincidences, for which correction must be made, will be comparable with the number of true coincidences. Faster operation is possible with the sodium iodide counters, because their output pulses are large and can be differentiated strongly to produce short signals, but energy discrimination is then bad. This may be overcome by taking *two* signals from each photomultiplier, one a fast signal for the coincidence circuit and another a slow signal for energy analysis.

Directional correlation experiments of this type have contributed to the analysis of many decay schemes. The information obtained is only directly comparable with theory when the lifetime of the intermediate state is small compared with the times required for the nuclear moments (magnetic dipole or electric quadrupole) to alter their orientation in internal fields. The attenuation of angular correlation functions in cases $(\tau > 10^{-8}$ sec) where this is not so may be used to study the electric fields existing in solids and liquids, and care is necessary in these cases in the choice of source material if an unperturbed angular correlation is desired. If an externally applied magnetic field is used the gyromagnetic ratio for the intermediate state may be measured and its magnetic moment determined if the spin is known. This has been done for the 0.243 MeV $(d_{5/2})$ state of ^{111}Cd $(\tau = 10^{-7}$ sec) with fields up to 7000 gauss and a value $\mu_I(d_{5/2}) = -(0\cdot7 \pm 0\cdot1)$ nuclear magnetons has been obtained.

The angular correlation function involves only the spins of the nuclear levels concerned and not their parities. The parities of electric and magnetic radiation of the same multipolarity are however opposite, i.e. their electric vectors are in perpendicular planes with respect to the radiating moment and if counter B is replaced by a polarization-sensitive detector and the polarization at a given angle (other than $0°$ or $180°$) determined, the parity change may be established.

It will be observed that the formulae developed in this section apply equally well if the first transition is an absorption rather than an emission process. The angular distribution of nuclear resonant scattering (Sect. 13.7.3) about the direction of the incident radiation is therefore given by 17.16 for the spin sequence $I_0 \to I_1 \to I_0$.

17.4.3 ANGULAR DISTRIBUTION IN A TWO STAGE RE-
ACTION.* Formulae for the total cross-section for a two stage
reaction X(ab)Y passing through a discrete level in the compound nucleus C, have been given in chapter 11. The description of the incident system in terms of channel spins
has also been explained. To calculate the angular distribution
of the radiation b we consider separately the specification of the
initial system X + a, and the formation and decay of the compound nucleus C.

a) *The initial system* is a plane wave of particles a approaching the nucleus X in the direction Oz. This may be represented
by the usual series of coherent partial waves

$$e^{ikz} \rightarrow \frac{1}{kr} \sum_0^\infty (2l+1)i^l \sin\left(kr - \frac{l\pi}{2}\right) P_l(\cos\theta) \qquad (17.18)$$

The component l_z of the orbital momentum corresponding to
the partial wave l is zero since Oz is the direction of incidence.
The spins I_x and I_a of the two nuclei combine to give either
$(2I_x + 1)$ or $(2I_a + 1)$ channel spins j, and these are independent
parameters, which may contribute in different measure to the
reaction. We therefore specify in the first instance a given
channel spin j.

b) *In the formation of the compound state* the channel spin
combines with an orbital momentum l to yield the angular
momentum of the level of C, i.e.

$$\mathbf{j} + \mathbf{l} = \mathbf{J} \qquad (17.19)$$

and since Oz is the direction of incidence

$$j_z = J_z \qquad (17.20)$$

The l-values permitted are limited firstly by the vector addition,
i.e.

$$j + J \geqslant l \geqslant |j - J| \qquad (17.21)$$

and secondly by the conservation of parity which requires that
only even, or only odd values of l shall be effective if pure
nuclear states are concerned. The probability of combining two

---

*The author would like to acknowledge his indebtedness to lectures
by A. P. French on this subject.

given vectors **j** and **l** together to yield **J**, subject to the condition 17.20 is given by the square of a Clebsch–Gordan coefficient which may be written in this case

$$(lj0j_z|JJ_z) \tag{17.22}$$

This is a purely geometrical factor connecting angular momenta; it gives no information on the intrinsic nuclear probability of the formation of the level J from a wave representing a particle of angular momentum l and energy E. This nuclear probability has already been discussed (ch. 15); it involves a penetrability factor, a reduced width and a resonance (Breit–Wigner) denominator. These factors, although important for determining reaction yield, do not affect the angular distribution and may be grouped together into an amplitude

$$f(E, l, J) \tag{17.23}$$

which is independent of j_z. The probability amplitude for the formation of C* in the state J from the specified initial state is then the product of expressions 17.22 and 17.23.

The probability of the formation of a given substate J_z of the state J is now obtained by summing these amplitudes *coherently* for the permitted l-values (which are phase-related owing to their appearance in the incident wave) and *incoherently*, with arbitrary weight t_j; for the different channel spins. This gives

$$W(E, J, J_z) = \sum_j t_j \Big| \sum_l f(E, l, J)(lj0j_z|JJ_z) \Big|^2 \tag{17.24}$$

which represents the state of orientation of C*. As in the case of the emission of successive quanta, the lifetime of C* must be $\ll$ about 10^{-8} sec in order that precession of the nuclear moment in internal fields should not destroy the correlation pattern.

c) *Decay of the compound state* may take place either by particle emission or quantum emission. In the former case the procedure just outlined is reversed, so that the compound state (J, J_z) decays into final states with channel spin j', orbital momentum l' and angular distribution $P_{l'}(\cos \theta)$. Summation over J_z, weighted by $W(E, J, J_z)$ and over the parameters for the final state leads to a predicted total angular distribution. For quantum emission, the Legendre polynomials are replaced by the basic radiation patterns $F(\theta)$ (Sect. 3.9.2).

d) *Examples* of this procedure are provided by many reactions, of which we select here one of the simplest, namely the emission of high energy γ-radiation in the bombardment of tritium by protons, i.e.

$$^3\text{H} + {}^1\text{H} \rightarrow {}^4\text{He}^* \rightarrow {}^4\text{He} + \gamma + 19 \cdot 8 \text{ MeV} \qquad (17.25)$$

Experimentally the angular distribution for a proton energy of $2 \cdot 5$ MeV is found to be

$$W(\theta) = A + B \sin^2 \theta$$

where $A \ll B$.

To analyse this reaction we assume that an excited ^4He nucleus is formed as an intermediate state, and we note that since $W(\theta)$ is anisotropic, waves of $l > 0$ must be involved. The spin of each initial nucleus is $\frac{1}{2}$ and channel spins $j = 0$ ($j_z = 0$) and $j = 1$ ($j_z = 0, \pm 1$) are possible, corresponding to interaction with opposite or parallel spins. If orbital momentum $l = 1$ ($l_z = 0$) is assumed, the possible compound states (of odd parity, since the initial nuclei are even parity particles) are:

for $j = 0$ $J = 1;$ $J_z = 0$

$j = 1$ $J = 0, 1, 2;$ $J_z = 0, \pm 1$

Of these $J = 0$ is ruled out because this would lead to isotropy. If then a state of $J = 1^-$ is assumed, it may be formed in two ways, and it will decay to the final state $J = 0$ of ^4He by emission of electric dipole radiation.

The angular distribution can now be seen to be proportional to

$$\sum_{j j_z} t_j (1j0j_z|1J_z)^2 (1J_z|10J_z0)^2 F_{1^z}^J(\theta) \qquad (17.26)$$

since the quantities $f(E, l, J)$ in 17.24 do not depend on j or j_z. Inserting values for j, j_z and using tabulated values for the Clebsch–Gordan coefficients, e.g.

$$(1000|10) = 1, \qquad (1101|11) = \frac{1}{\sqrt{2}}, \qquad (1100|10) = 0$$

we find

$$W(\theta) \propto t_0 F_1^0(\theta) + \frac{t_1}{4}[F_1^1(\theta) + F_1^{-1}(\theta)]$$

$$\propto 3 \sin^2 \theta t_0 + \frac{3}{4}(1 + \cos^2 \theta)t_1$$

$$\propto \sin^2 \theta + A(1 + \cos^2 \theta)$$

where

$$4A = \frac{t_1}{t_0} = \frac{\text{probability of reaction with parallel spins}}{\text{probability of reaction with opposite spins}}$$

is, according to the experimental results, very small.

The procedure just outlined and illustrated gives a physical picture of the structure of an angular correlation pattern. For all but the simplest cases, however, the process of calculation becomes tedious and the methods developed by Racah and others are used to eliminate explicit summations over magnetic quantum numbers. Expressions of the form given in 17.16, multiplied if necessary by 'particle factors', are used in practice.

17.4.4 LIMITATIONS ON COMPLEXITY OF PATTERN. There are a number of general results of angular correlation theory which are helpful in a first approach to an analysis of distributions. These are, assuming unpolarized incident particles:

a) Angular distributions are *isotropic* if $l = 0$ for the incident or emitted particle or if $J = 0$ or $\frac{1}{2}$ for the compound state, since then the magnetic substates are equally populated.

b) Anisotropic angular distributions are *symmetric* if only one compound state is involved or more states but of the same parity. They are *asymmetric* if states of opposite parity can be formed, at a given energy, from the same channel spin since there is then interference between waves with even and odd values of l.

c) If only incoming waves of orbital angular momentum l contribute appreciably to a reaction, the angular distribution of the outgoing particles in the centre of mass system is an even polynomial in $\cos \theta$ with an exponent not higher than $2l$. Multipole radiation of order L behaves in this respect as a particle of angular momentum L so that if in any reaction dipole radiation appears the angular correlation cannot be more complicated than $a + b \cos^2\theta$.

References

17.1   A. H. Wapstra, G. J. Nijgh and R. van Lieshout, *Nuclear Spectroscopy Tables*, North Holland, 1959.
17.2   R. J. Blin-Stoyle, M. A. Grace and H. Halban, 'Oriented Nuclear Systems', *Progr. nucl. Phys.*, **3**, 63, 1953.

17.3   R. J. Blin-Stoyle and M. A. Grace, 'Oriented Nuclei', *Encyclopedia of Physics*, Vol. 42, p. 555, Springer, 1957.

17.4   H. Frauenfelder, 'Angular Correlation' in *Beta- and Gamma-Ray Spectroscopy*, ed. K. Siegbahn, North Holland, 1955; 'The Measurement of Electromagnetic Moments of Nuclear States' in *Nuclear Spectroscopy, Part A*, ed. F. Ajzenberg-Selove, Academic Press, 1960.

17.5   M. J. Steenland and H. A. Tolhoek, 'Orientation of Atomic Nuclei at Low Temperature', *Progr. low temp. Phys.*, **2**, 292, 1957.

17.6   'International Symposium on Polarisation Phenomena of Nucleons', *Helv. phys. Acta*, Suppl. VI, 1961.

17.7   J. M. Daniels and J. Goldemberg, 'Nuclear Reactions with Oriented Target Nuclei and Polarized Beams', *Rep. progr. Phys.*, **25**, 1, 1962.

Part E

THE BASIC INTERACTIONS OF NUCLEAR PHYSICS

18. NUCLEAR FORCES

This book has so far been mainly concerned with the static properties of complex nuclei (Part C) and with the behaviour of such nuclei in nuclear reactions (Part D). Nuclear models are used in coordinating these phenomena since insufficient is known about nuclear forces to permit exact calculations for a many-body problem even if such calculations are technically possible. It is of course necessary that nuclear models should be consistent with what is known about forces between nucleons, and it is in any case interesting to see how far one can proceed with detailed calculations for simple systems. In this chapter a brief account will be given of present-day knowledge of nuclear forces, and of their connection with nuclear properties. In surveying this field two approaches are useful:

a) one may derive as much information as possible on inter-nucleon forces by studying the properties, and particularly the regularity of properties, of complex nuclei, and

b) one may examine the behaviour of two-nucleon systems, both in the bound state (the deuteron) and in scattering. This will involve experiments extending up to high energies at which meson production is important.

As a result of these investigations it is now possible to give an account of the main features of the force between nucleons. It would of course be intellectually more satisfactory to derive the law of nuclear force from a more fundamental theory based on the properties of mesons, in the way that the Coulomb law of force may be associated with a photon field. Unfortunately this approach has so far had only a limited success.

The properties of the force between nucleons inferred from a study of complex nuclei are not necessarily those that would be expected for a pair of nucleons in free space. It remains to be proved that the internucleon force is unaffected by the presence of other nucleons near by, or that specifically nuclear many-body forces, depending on the presence of three or more nucleons, do not exist. This possible complication will be disregarded in this chapter.

It will be assumed that the fundamental constituents of a nucleus are neutrons and protons. The reasons why electrons cannot play a part in nuclear structure have already been discussed (ch. 9).

18.1　Information on nuclear forces from study of complex nuclei

18.1.1 SATURATION PROPERTY.　Measurements of the size (ch. 11) and of the total binding energy (ch. 10) of nuclei show that to a fair approximation all nuclei with $A > 40$ have the same density and the same binding energy per nucleon; i.e. the nuclear radius may be written

$$R = r_0 A^{1/3} \qquad (18.1)$$

with $r_0 = 1 \cdot 2$ fm, and the total binding energy is

$$B_A \propto A \qquad (18.2)$$

for a nucleus of mass number A. These facts imply that the nuclear force *saturates*, i.e. that the number of nucleons with which a given nucleon interacts strongly is limited.

To see this we recall (Sect. 9.1) that the kinetic energy of a Fermi gas of A nucleons is proportional to $A^{5/3}$ and the potential energy to $\frac{1}{2}A(A-1)$ if all pairs of nucleons interact attractively. The most stable state of such a nucleus will be one in which it has collapsed to a size of the order of the range of nuclear forces, and for a heavy nucleus the binding energy B_A will then follow the potential energy and increase as A^2. It is of course known from the scattering experiments and from calculations of the binding energy of simple systems (as first emphasized by Wigner) that the nuclear force is of short range (2×10^{-13} cm, Fig. 18.1), and a collapsed nucleus will thus have too small a radius. It therefore becomes necessary to limit the number of attractive interactions within the nucleus.

One way of ensuring saturation is to assume that the potential energy of a pair of nucleons has the functional form known for the potential energy between the molecules of a liquid drop, a system which also shows saturation properties. This potential, sketched in Fig. 18.1, indicates an attractive force at extreme range, as is indicated by low energy scattering experiments, and a repulsive force at very short distances. This gives a minimum in the potential energy curve which may be associated with stable binding. The *repulsive core*, for which there is now good experimental evidence from scattering experiments at energies in the range 300–1000 MeV, prevents collapse and determines the nuclear volume.

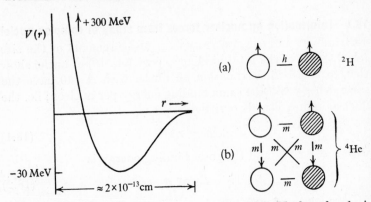

Fig. 18.1. The internucleon force (schematic). The curve shows the potential energy of two nucleons at a distance r between centres. Coulomb forces are neglected. Each nucleon has its own distribution of charge and magnetic moment.

Fig. 18.2. Nuclear bonds in the two-nucleon and four-nucleon system. The letters h, m refer to particular types of force, which are discussed in Sect. 18.3. The arrows represent spin directions.

In early discussions of the saturation property the idea of a repulsive core to the internucleon force did not appear reasonable. For an average nucleus the binding energy of a nucleon is about 8 MeV and this is made up from the difference between a kinetic energy ≈ 20 MeV arising from the confinement of the nucleon to the nuclear volume, and a potential energy of about 30 MeV. The well depth in Fig. 18.1 is thus about 30 MeV and the height of the repulsive core, which has a much shorter range, must be much greater in order to be effective. A value of about 300 MeV is required, and this appeared incommensurate with what was known about nuclear energies. Moreover, a repulsive core could not be predicted from any type of meson field theory. Two alternatives considered were:

a) the existence of *many-body forces*, and

b) the possibility of *exchange forces*.

Of these, Heisenberg chose to develop the latter hypothesis, since it could be based on theory, and since this type of force was already known in molecular problems. Although it now appears more reasonable to revert to the repulsive core explanation of saturation, there is also clear evidence that nuclear forces have important exchange characteristics. The way in which such forces might saturate will be discussed in Sect. **18.3**. It may be noted that ordinary long-range forces, due for instance to electrostatic, magnetic or gravitational fields, are far too weak to account for nuclear binding energies within the observed nuclear size.

18.1.2 SYSTEMATICS OF STABLE NUCLEI; CHARGE INDEPENDENCE. If the distribution of stable nuclei among mass numbers (ch. 10) is examined it is seen that for light nuclei $N \approx Z \approx A/2$, which suggests that there is a tendency for neutrons and protons to pair off. Furthermore the large binding energy per nucleon for ^{4}He and the special stability of nuclei with $A = 4n$ indicate that the saturated nuclear system consists of two neutrons and two protons. This is in accordance with the Pauli principle according to which each proton or neutron can interact with one particle of the same type (but with opposite spin) and with two particles of the opposite type in the same state of orbital motion. It is to be expected that maximum binding energy for this system will arise, for attractive forces, when all the particles are in S-states of relative motion. If a fifth particle is added to this system it must enter a p-state and is less strongly bound, so that the average binding energy per nucleon for $A = 5$ is less than for $A = 4$. It will be seen from Fig. 18.2 that there are 6 'bonds', 4 associated with (np) forces and 1 with (pp) and (nn) forces. In spectroscopic terminology the S-state interactions of two nucleons comprise

> a) the ^1S singlet configurations $^1(np)$, $^1(pp)$, $^1(nn)$ (18.3)

and

> b) the ^3S triplet configuration $^3(np)$ (18.4)

The evidence of the light nuclei is that the corresponding nuclear forces are attractive in each of these states. The neutron excess in heavy nuclei, which is required to balance the Coulomb repulsion of the protons, confirms that the $^1(nn)$ force is attractive, but it is insufficiently attractive to lead to a stable di-neutron.

There is also good reason to suppose that for corresponding states of motion, e.g. in the singlet spin state, the (np), (pp) and (nn) forces are approximately equal. If this is accurately so, we characterize the forces as *charge independent*: if, however, only the equality of (nn) and (pp) forces can be established, the forces are *charge symmetric*. The similar number of nuclei with even Z, odd N and with odd Z, even N suggests charge symmetry (ch. 10), as does the approximate equality of neutron and proton separation energies. A closer test of these properties is, however, provided by the ground state energies and level systems of isobaric nuclei. Charge symmetry in particular seems established by these properties for odd mirror nuclei (Sect. 11.2.4) and charge independence, to a good approximation, by the corresponding properties for the even isobars (Sect. **12.1**). Under conditions of charge independence we describe the spin singlet and triplet configurations of the two-nucleon system by the isobaric spin (Sect. **12.1**) quantum numbers $T = 1$ and $T = 0$ respectively.

In a state of $T = 1$, but not of $T = 0$, a neutron or proton may be changed to the other particle without offending the exclusion principle. The concept of isobaric spin therefore permits a useful generalization of the Pauli principle in the case of charge independent forces. It is no longer necessary to specify nucleons of a particular kind in applying this principle; permitted states of two nucleons are those which are antisymmetrical for exchange of all coordinates, i.e. isobaric spin, ordinary spin and position.

18.1.3 THE SHELL MODEL; SPIN-ORBIT EFFECT. The potentials of the single-particle shell model (ch. 9) are effective potentials for a complex system in interaction with a nucleon, but they are derivable in principle from the pure internucleon potentials. Some progress in this direction has been made by Brueckner. For the present purpose we recognize only that special features of the shell and optical model potentials probably have their origin in similar properties of the force between nucleons. Thus polarization phenomena (Sect. 17.3.2) are most easily interpreted in terms in the interaction between intrinsic spin and orbital motion which is assumed in the j-j coupling shell model. The internucleon force may be assumed to show the same property; polarization in high energy nucleon–nucleon collisions has in fact been observed.

18.2 Information on nuclear forces from the two-body problem

18.2.1 THE BINDING ENERGY OF THE DEUTERON. The deuteron has a binding energy of 2·23 MeV and no stable excited states. It has an angular momentum of unity and both a magnetic dipole moment μ_d and an electric quadrupole moment. The magnetic moment is not equal to the algebraic sum of the magnetic moments of the proton μ_p and neutron μ_n, but it is sufficiently near to preclude the possibility of relative orbital motion of the two particles. The simplest structure to assume for the ground state of the deuteron is therefore a neutron and a proton in an S-state of orbital motion with parallel spins, i.e. a $^3S_1$ state. The $^1S_0$ state of the deuteron, in which the proton and neutron have antiparallel spins, is unbound.

If an interaction potential for a neutron and a proton in this triplet state is prescribed, the binding energy of the deuteron may be calculated by solution of the Schrödinger equation, as in the corresponding problem of the hydrogen atom in atomic physics. It is simplest to assume a spherically symmetrical square-well potential function (Sect. **3.2**) representing an attractive interaction whenever the neutron and proton approach within a distance a (Fig. 18.3). The ground state of the deuteron is represented in Fig. 18.3 by a line drawn at energy $E = -\varepsilon$, the binding energy.

The solution of the wave equation proceeds as in chapter 3. If ψ is the wave function for the relative motion we have in general

$$\psi = R(r) Y_l^m(\theta, \phi) \tag{18.5}$$

but for an S-state there will be no angular dependence and

$$\psi = R(r) = \frac{u(r)}{r} \tag{18.6}$$

The wave function ψ (or u) determines the probability of finding a separation r between the neutron and proton in the deuteron.

21*

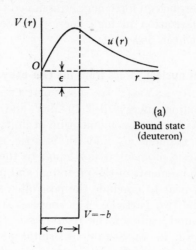

(a)
Bound state
(deuteron)

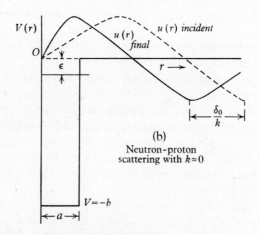

(b)
Neutron-proton
scattering with $k \approx 0$

Fig. 18.3. The two-nucleon system.

a) The deuteron. The S-state wave function $u = r\psi$ of relative motion of a neutron and proton interacting through a square well potential is shown. For $r > a$ the kinetic energy of the particles is negative and the wave function decays exponentially to zero.

b) Neutron-proton scattering at low energy. The effect of the attractive interaction on an incident neutron wave function is shown; within the range of the force the wave function approximates to that of the deuteron.

In terms of the function $u(r)$ the Schrödinger equation for a stationary state E for a nucleon of mass M moving in a potential field $V(r)$ in an S-state is

$$\frac{\mathrm{d}^2 u}{\mathrm{d}r^2} + \frac{2M}{\hbar^2}[E - V(r)]u = 0 \qquad (18.7)$$

In the deuteron the masses of the two particles are nearly equal, each to the nucleon mass M, and they move about their centre of mass. Correction for this is obtained by using the reduced mass $\frac{1}{2}M$ in place of M in 18.7. The quantity $E - V(r)$ is the kinetic energy of the two particles, which has a non-classical, negative value for $r > a$. The solution of 18.7 is carried out in two stages:

I   *Region $r > a$, $V(r) = 0$, $E = -\varepsilon$*
   Eq. 18.7 becomes

$$\frac{\mathrm{d}^2 u}{\mathrm{d}r^2} - \frac{M}{\hbar^2}\,\varepsilon u = 0 \qquad (18.8)$$

which has the solution

$$u = Ae^{-\alpha r} \quad \text{with} \quad \alpha^2 = \frac{M\varepsilon}{\hbar^2} \qquad (18.9)$$

assuming that $u(r)$ vanishes at $r = 0$ as it must if $|\psi|^2$, the particle density, is to remain finite.

II   *Region $r < a$, $V(r) = -b$, $E = -\varepsilon$*
   Eq. 18.7 becomes

$$\frac{\mathrm{d}^2 u}{\mathrm{d}r^2} + \frac{M}{\hbar^2}(b - \varepsilon)u = 0 \qquad (18.10)$$

which has the solution

$$u = B \sin Kr \quad \text{with} \quad K^2 = \frac{M}{\hbar^2}(b - \varepsilon) \qquad (18.11)$$

again assuming that $u(r)$ vanishes at the origin; K is the internal wave number. This solution is a particular case of the more general form 9.3. The two solutions 18.9 and 18.11 must be joined together at the potential boundary $r = a$. This may be done by requiring that $\dfrac{1}{u}\dfrac{du}{dr}$ (a measure of the particle density and current) shall be continuous at this point. This gives

$$\left(\frac{1}{u}\frac{du}{dr}\right)_{r=a} = K \cot Ka = -\alpha \qquad (18.12)$$

or
$$\cot^2 Ka = \frac{\alpha^2}{K^2} = \frac{\varepsilon}{b - \varepsilon}$$

If now $b \gg \varepsilon$ it follows that

$$Ka \approx \frac{\pi}{2} \qquad (18.13)$$

or, from 18.11,

$$ba^2 \approx \left(\frac{\pi}{2}\right)^2 \frac{\hbar^2}{M} \approx 1\cdot 0 \text{ MeV} \times \text{barn} \qquad (18.14)$$

The wave function $u(r)$ is shown in Fig. 18.3; the quantity $1/2\alpha = 2\cdot 15 \times 10^{-13}$ cm can be taken to represent the radius of the deuteron. It is interesting to note that there is a high probability ($\approx 50\%$) of the particles in the deuteron being separated by more than the range of nuclear forces; the 'size' of the deuteron is determined by its binding energy, not by the force range.

Eq. 18.13 and Fig. 18.3 show that in the deuteron the range of the forces is about equal to one quarter of the de Broglie wavelength of relative motion. The wave function for $r < a$ then just turns over in a distance a to meet the rising wave function for $r > a$. The relation 18.14 between the range of the forces and the depth of the potential well necessary to bind the deuteron is clearly independent of the precise form of the potential function so long as $b \gg \varepsilon$. The quantity ba^2 will remain finite, for a bound deuteron, in the zero range limit $a = 0$. For a well depth of ≈ 30 MeV the range of force required is about $1\cdot9 \times 10^{-13}$ cm. The kinetic energy for this separation is therefore about 28 MeV; this is of course essentially the energy indicated by the uncertainty principle for a nucleon confined within the distance a.

No more information about the neutron-proton force than is contained in 18.14 can be obtained from the binding energy of the deuteron. Further knowledge of the force law must be obtained from a study of the unbound system, i.e. from neutron-proton scattering experiments. These establish that the neutron–proton force is *spin-dependent*, which may also be inferred from the absence of a bound state of the deuteron in which the nucleons have antiparallel spins (^1S).

18.2.2 LOW ENERGY NEUTRON–PROTON SCATTERING.

If a slow neutron is captured by a proton, a γ-ray of energy 2·23 MeV is emitted and a deuteron is formed. The neutron is then forbidden classically to enter the region $r > a$ (Fig. 18.3) in which its wave number is imaginary. If capture does not take place, and if there is no loss of energy in excitation processes, the neutron is elastically scattered by the proton and leaves the region $r < a$ with its original laboratory energy E_n and (small) wave number. Within the region $r < a$, however, the wave number increases because of the attractive potential and is approximately equal to the internal value K calculated in Sect. 18.2.1.

The cross-section for elastic scattering may be calculated following the general method given in Sect. 14.2.2. In the present case, for $E_n = 1$ MeV the wavelength of relative motion is $5 \cdot 5 \times 10^{-12}$ cm, which is much greater than the expected range of the neutron-proton force (Sect. 18.2.1). A *zero-range approximation* may therefore be used and only s-wave scattering need be considered ($\lambda = 1/k \geqslant a$). The effect of the interaction is to introduce a phase shift δ_0 into the asymptotic s-wave, which according to 14.40 and 14.47 may be written

$$u(r) = r\psi = \frac{e^{i\delta_0}}{k} \sin(kr + \delta_0) \qquad (18.15)$$

where k is the channel wave number (Sect. 14.2.1) given by

$$k^2 = \frac{M}{\hbar^2} \tfrac{1}{2} E_n \qquad (18.16)$$

In Sect. 14.2.2, δ_0 was evaluated for an impenetrable sphere but in the present problem we have knowledge of the internal structure of the interaction region and δ_0 can be estimated in terms of the deuteron binding energy. This is done by making the internal and external wave functions join smoothly at the potential boundary $r = a$ (Fig. 18.3b).

For the internal function we have from 18.11

$$u(r) = B \sin Kr \qquad (18.17\text{a})$$

and for the external function from 18.15

$$u(r) = C \sin (kr + \delta_0) \qquad (18.17\text{b})$$

Continuity of the quantity $\dfrac{1}{u} \dfrac{du}{dr}$ at $r = a$ gives

$$-K \cot Ka = -k \cot (ka + \delta_0)$$
$$= \alpha \qquad (18.18)$$

from 18.12, so that

$$\delta_0 = \cot^{-1}\left(-\frac{\alpha}{k}\right) - ka$$

$$\approx \cot^{-1}\left(-\frac{\alpha}{k}\right) \quad \text{since } ka \ll 1 \qquad (18.19)$$

for the s-wave interaction. The cross-section for scattering is then, from 14.60 and 14.63

$$\sigma_{\text{el}}^0 = \frac{4\pi}{k^2} \sin^2 \delta_0$$

$$= \frac{4\pi}{k^2(1 + \cot^2 \delta_0)} = \frac{4\pi}{k^2 + \alpha^2} \qquad (18.20)$$

which may also be expressed, using 18.9 and 18.16 as

$$\sigma_{\text{el}}^0 = \frac{h^2}{\pi M} \frac{1}{\varepsilon + \frac{1}{2}E_n} = \frac{5 \cdot 2}{\varepsilon + \frac{1}{2}E_n} \text{ barn} \qquad (18.21)$$

This formula indicates an energy variation of the neutron cross-section of the form shown in Fig. 18.4, curve a, for energies up to 10 MeV. The experimental results, obtained by transmission experiments, are shown in curve b of this figure,[*] and are seen to lie above the curve predicted by the simple theory[†] for energies for which E_n is not very large compared with ε.

The reason for this discrepancy was first given by Wigner, who pointed out that although the $^1S_0$ state is unbound in the

---

[*] E. Melkonian, *Phys. Rev.*, **76**, 1744, 1949.

[†] The sharp increase at very low energies is due to a chemical binding effect (Appendix 8).

deuteron, its effect must be included in the scattering calculation. In a neutron-proton collision the probability of a triplet collision (parallel spins, $I = 1$) is three times that of a singlet collision (antiparallel spins, $I = 0$) because of the statistical factor $(2I + 1)$ and if the singlet state has a binding energy ε' the low-energy cross-section should be, in extension of (18.20),

$$\sigma_{el}^{0} = \frac{4\pi}{k^2} \tfrac{1}{4}\{3 \sin^2 \delta_{0t} + \sin^2 \delta_{0s}\}$$

$$= \frac{h^2}{4\pi M}\left\{\frac{3}{\varepsilon + \tfrac{1}{2}E_n} + \frac{1}{|\varepsilon'| + \tfrac{1}{2}E_n}\right\} \qquad (18.22)$$

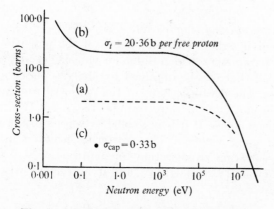

Fig. 18.4. Interaction of neutrons with protons.
a) Scattering cross-section according to theory based on triplet-state interaction only.
b) Experimental results for total cross-section. The cross-section rises at low energies because the two protons in the hydrogen molecule cannot then be treated as free (Appendix 8).
c) Capture cross-section of protons for thermal neutrons.

which gives a better account of the experimental results at low energies providing that ε' is small. The observed cross-section indicates that ε' is about 50 keV. This is clear evidence for a spin dependence of the neutron–proton force, leading to a different well-depth for the spin parallel and spin antiparallel interactions. This is in agreement with the evidence from complex nuclei with $A = 4n + 2$ for which it has been seen (Sect. 12.1) that the ^3S state of two particles outside a closed shell lies lower than the ^1S state. The neutron–proton scattering cross-section by itself does not prove that the ^1S state is *unbound* but this may be inferred from the cross-section for the capture of slow neutrons by protons (Sect. 18.2.3) and from coherent scattering phenomena (Appendix 8).

The zero-range approximation used in these calculations conceals all information on the shape of the neutron–proton potential. It is of some interest to reformulate the s-wave phase shift in such a way that the extent of the approximations is more obvious. It is shown in Refs. 18.1, 18.2, and 18.3 that

$$k \cot \delta_0 = -\frac{1}{l} + \tfrac{1}{2}r_0 k^2 - P r_0^3 k^4 \dots \qquad (18.23)$$

where l is a *scattering length** and r_0 an *effective range* of the force, embodying the width and depth of the potential well. These two parameters, which differ for the singlet and triplet states, are all that can be obtained by analysis of the s-wave experiments. The detailed shape of the potential well appears in the coefficient P of the third term in (18.23) but this term is small at low energies. If it is neglected, we speak of the *shape-independent approximation*. The scattering length l in 18.23 gives the scattering cross-section for neutrons of zero energy ($k = 0$) since from 18.20 and 18.23, and in agreement with 14.63 and 14.64,

$$\sigma_{\text{el}}^0 \to 4\pi l^2 \quad \text{as} \quad k \to 0 \qquad (18.24)$$

This length may be either positive or negative; the former corresponds to scattering in which wave functions are modified by a bound state and the latter to scattering involving an unbound (virtual) state. For the bound state of the neutron–proton system, i.e. the deuteron, the effective range formula corresponding to 18.23 is

$$\alpha = \frac{1}{l_t} + \tfrac{1}{2}\alpha^2 r_{0t} \qquad (18.25)$$

where α gives the binding energy of the deuteron through eq. 18.9 and the suffix denotes the triplet interaction. The binding

---

* We use l in this chapter in place of the customary a in order to avoid confusion with the range of forces.

energy of a singlet or triplet state is related to the corresponding scattering length by the following approximate expression

$$|\varepsilon| \approx \frac{\hbar^2}{Ml^2} \qquad (18.26)$$

using 18.25 and 18.9.

18.2.3 ELECTROMAGNETIC TRANSITIONS IN THE NEUTRON–PROTON SYSTEM.

a) *Capture of slow neutrons by protons.*

It was found by Fermi in 1935 that slow neutrons live only for about 10^{-4} sec in a large block of paraffin and that they disappear chiefly by the radiative capture process

$$^1n + {}^1H \rightarrow {}^2H + \gamma + 2 \cdot 23 \text{ MeV} \qquad (18.27)$$

The photons emitted in this capture have been detected and measurement of their energy* has provided one of the most accurate determinations of the binding energy of the deuteron. Although capture *removes* thermal neutrons, the measured cross-section of $0 \cdot 3$b is small compared with the scattering cross-section.

It has already been noted that on account of the short range of nuclear forces, a neutron and proton with a relative energy of up to about 10 MeV interact mainly in the s-state of orbital motion. For a relative orbital angular momentum with $l \geqslant 1$ the separation of the two particles exceeds the range of the nuclear force. The probability of capture will also be proportional to $1/v$, i.e. to the time that the neutron spends within the range of forces and it follows that the capture cross-section, like that for other slow neutron reactions, will increase with decreasing velocity. The two particles may interact in either the $^1S_0$ or the $^3S_1$ state (since the P-state interaction is improbable at low energies) and the final state is the $^3S_1$ ground level of the deuteron. Of the two possible magnetic dipole transitions

$$^3S \rightarrow {}^3S \quad \text{and} \quad {}^1S \rightarrow {}^3S \qquad (18.28)$$

the former may be shown (Ref. 18.1, p. 604) to be forbidden and the capture process is therefore the latter, in which the

---

* R. E. Bell and L. G. Elliott, *Phys. Rev.*, **74**, 1552, 1948.

neutron or proton undergoes a spin-flip and the $M1$ photon transports angular momentum $\hbar$. The angular distribution of the emitted photons will be isotropic because only S-states are involved.

The probability of the magnetic dipole process depends on the quantity $(\mu_p - \mu_n)$ and also on an integral over the wave functions of the singlet and triplet states. It follows from the observation of the photomagnetic capture that the magnetic moments of the neutron and proton are not equal and also that the singlet and triplet wave functions are determined by different potential wells, since otherwise the integral would vanish. This is further confirmation of the spin dependence of nuclear forces. The calculated cross-section for photomagnetic capture is sensitive to the sign of the binding energy of the singlet state. If comparison is made with the scattering cross-section we find for zero energy neutrons

$$\left.\begin{array}{ll} \dfrac{\sigma_{\text{sc}}}{\sigma_{\text{cap}}} = 118 & (^1S_0 \text{ state bound)} \\[2mm] \phantom{\dfrac{\sigma_{\text{sc}}}{\sigma_{\text{cap}}}} = 71 & (^1S_0 \text{ state virtual)} \end{array}\right\} \qquad (18.29)$$

The experimental value, Fig. 18.4, is $20 \cdot 0 / 0 \cdot 332 = 60$, confirming an unbound state.

Correction of the cross-section formula by the effective range theory leads to a value, unfortunately rather inaccurate, for the difference $r_{0t} - r_{0s}$, from which r_{0s} can be obtained using the more accurately known triplet range.

b) *Photodisintegration of the deuteron*

The process converse to radiative capture is the disintegration of the deuteron by radiation, according to the scheme

$$^2\text{H} + \gamma \rightarrow {}^1\text{H} + {}^1\text{n} - 2 \cdot 23 \text{ MeV} \qquad (18.30)$$

This reaction (Sect. 14.1.4) has been used in an accurate determination of the deuteron binding energy; the threshold energy for photoneutron or photoproton production is observed, using electron bremsstrahlung from an electrostatic generator of precisely defined energy.

The process 18.30 can be either *photomagnetic*

$$^3S \rightarrow {}^1S \quad \text{(magnetic dipole)} \qquad (18.31)$$

which is exactly inverse to the capture of slow neutrons by protons, or *photoelectric*

$$^3S \to {}^3P \quad \text{(electric dipole)} \tag{18.32}$$

in which a transition to a P-state of the continuum of energies is induced by the electric vector of the electromagnetic wave, in analogy with the photoelectric effect in the atom. In the photomagnetic disintegration there is spin-flip, but no change of orbital motion; in the photoelectric disintegration the spin is unaltered but the neutron and proton are emitted with one unit of relative orbital momentum. The angular distribution of the magnetic dipole process is isotropic but that of the electric process has a normal dipole distribution with respect to the electric vector of the γ-radiation, i.e. $\sigma(\theta) \propto \sin^2 \theta$ where θ is the angle between the direction of the proton and the line of flight of the radiation.

The cross-sections for these processes as a function of energy can be calculated easily in the zero-range approximation and are shown in Fig. 18.5. The photomagnetic cross-section rises rapidly

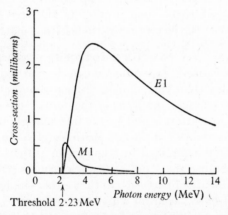

Fig. 18.5. Energy dependence of the photoelectric ($E1$) and photo-magnetic ($M1$) cross-sections for disintegration of the deuteron. The threshold is at the deuteron binding energy (Ref. 18.3).

at the threshold to a maximum because it leads to the $^1S_0$ state whose energy is near zero for the n-p system. It is related simply by arguments of detailed balancing to the cross-section for capture of slow neutrons by protons, and increases linearly at first with the velocity of the disintegration particles. The photoelectric cross-section rises more slowly at first because a P-state is not favoured for slow particles; this is why the electric dipole absorption of slow neutrons is not observed. It reaches a maximum for $h\nu \approx 2\varepsilon$, where ε is the binding energy of the deuteron.

The deuteron photodisintegration has been studied experimentally, both for cross-section and angular distribution, over a wide range of energies. Measurements with radioactive sources have given information on the photomagnetic transition near threshold, and similar work with γ-rays from nuclear reactions and with electron bremsstrahlung has extended up to 300 MeV. The photoelectric cross-section determines primarily the triplet effective range, r_{0t}, which enters as a correction to the zero range approximation, and the photomagnetic effect, as expected by analogy with its inverse process, yields the difference $r_{0t} - r_{0s}$.

The order of magnitude of the photoelectric cross-section is the area of the deuteron $\pi/4\alpha^2$ multiplied by the fine structure constant $e^2/\hbar c = 1/137$, which represents the strength of the coupling between the electromagnetic field and matter.

18.2.4 LOW-ENERGY PROTON–PROTON SCATTERING. Proton–proton scattering experiments can be carried out with greater accuracy than the comparable neutron–proton experiments at most energies. Analysis of the results is complicated by the Coulomb scattering and by the fact that allowance must be made for the identity of the two particles (cf. α-He scattering, Sect. 5.3.1). It is simplified in comparison with the neutron–proton case because the Pauli principle excludes certain states of motion for identical particles, so that either singlet or triplet states, but not both, occur for a given orbital state.

The Coulomb scattering of identical particles was calculated wave-mechanically by Mott and is discussed in Ref. 18.3. Experimental results confirm this formula for energies of the order of 300 keV or less and thus verify that interference between waves corresponding to scattering and recoil particles occurs. At higher energies extra scattering is observed at large angles ($\approx 90°$ c.m. Fig. 18.6), and this must be attributed to the nuclear force. For energies up to about 10 MeV a phase shift analysis of angular distributions (Ref. 18.3) confirms that only *s*-wave interaction is important, as is expected because of the short range of the force ($ka \ll 1$). The Pauli principle then limits the interaction to the singlet state $^1S_0$ and there is only one phase shift δ_0 instead of the two required for the neutron–proton scattering (18.22).

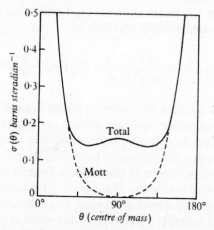

Fig. 18.6. Angular distribution for the scattering of 2·4 MeV protons by protons. Near $\theta = 90°$ (laboratory angle 45°) the scattering is mainly nuclear (Ref. 18.3).

The Mott scattering, which results from the long-range Coulomb force, involves both singlet and triplet states and all relative orbital momenta. There is consequently interference with the nuclear scattering and the final expression for the low-energy angular distribution for the centre-of-mass system may be written in the form

$$\sigma_{pp}(\theta) = \sigma_{Mott}(\theta) - A(\theta, \delta_0)\sin \delta_0 + \lambda^2 \sin^2 \delta_0 \qquad (18.33)$$

where λ is the reduced de Broglie wavelength for the relative motion ($= 2\hbar/m_p v$, where v is the incident velocity and m_p the proton mass) and $A(\theta, \delta_0)$ is a calculable coefficient. The last term is the nuclear *s*-wave scattering and the second term is due to Mott—nuclear interference. The presence of the interference term permits the sign as well as the magnitude of δ_0 to be obtained from the experimental results; it is found to be positive, corresponding to an attractive nuclear force. The interference is thus destructive for the s-wave and leads to a reduced cross-section, as already noted for the α-helium scattering (Sect. 5.3.1).

The effective range theory used to discuss the (np) interaction was developed by Jackson and Blatt to describe the variation of the $^1S_0$ phase shift for (pp) scattering with energy. The formula corresponding to 18.23 is

$$\frac{\pi \cot \delta_0}{(\exp 2\pi\eta - 1)} + h(\eta) = \frac{\hbar^2}{m_p e^2}\left(-\frac{1}{l_s} + \tfrac{1}{2}r_{0s}k^2 - Pr_{0s}{}^3k^4 \ldots \right) \quad (18.34)$$

in which $h(\eta)$ is a calculable function of the Coulomb parameter $\eta = e^2/\hbar v$. The quantity dividing $\pi \cot \delta_0$ is part of the penetration factor for the potential barrier between the two protons, and appears when a fit is required between internal and external (Coulomb) wave functions at the nuclear boundary. In the case of neutron-proton scattering the s-wave phase shift is derived directly from the observed scattering cross-section, but owing to the strong Coulomb scattering, total cross-sections for the low energy (pp) interaction cannot easily be measured. The phase shift δ_0 is therefore obtained by analysis of the angular distribution 18.33 at a number of energies; 18.34 then yields values for the singlet parameters l_s and r_{0s}. The (pp) scattering length l_s is found to be negative, corresponding to an unbound state for the two-proton system, in analogy with the singlet state of the (np) interaction.

18.2.5 COMPARISON OF LOW-ENERGY PARAMETERS. The parameters used in the effective range theory have the values in the following table according to the best experiments available in the energy range for which the s-wave interaction is predominant. The singlet scattering length for the (pp) interaction is obtained from the observed l_s ($-7 \cdot 69$ fm) by correcting for the effect of Coulomb forces. Coherent scattering determinations of the (np) scattering lengths are described in Appendix 8.

TABLE 18.1   Parameters of the 2-Nucleon System

PARA- METER	VALUE (10^{-13} cm) (np)	(pp)	METHOD OF DETERMINATION	REFER- ENCE
Triplet scattering length l_t	$+5 \cdot 38 \pm 0 \cdot 02$		Low energy (np) scattering Coherent scattering	§ 18.2.2 App. 8
Singlet scattering length l_s	$-23 \cdot 69 \pm 0 \cdot 05$	$-17 \pm 0 \cdot 6$	Low energy (np) scattering Coherent scattering Low energy (pp) scattering	§ 18.2.2 App. 8 § 18.2.4
Triplet effective range r_{ot}	$+1 \cdot 70 \pm 0 \cdot 03$		Binding energy of deuteron Photodisintegration	§ 18.2.1 § 18.2.3
Singlet effective range r_{os}	$+2 \cdot 7 \pm 0 \cdot 5$	$2 \cdot 65 \pm 0 \cdot 08$	Low energy (np) scattering Low energy (pp) scattering Capture of slow neutrons by protons	§ 18.2.2 § 18.2.4 § 18.2.3

These parameters give a good account of most of the low-energy two-body phenomena, and contain all the information that can be extracted from such experiments. The existence of different singlet and triplet interactions, as has already been emphasized, is evidence for the spin dependence of nuclear forces. This is large enough, and in the right direction, to prevent stable binding of the singlet systems $^1(np)$, $^1(pp)$, i.e. the excited deuteron and the di-proton. The singlet effective ranges are similar for these two systems and this strongly supports the hypothesis of charge independence of nuclear forces for nucleons in the s-state of relative motion. It may be inferred that the remaining singlet state $^1(nn)$, the di-neutron, is also unstable. The singlet scattering length for this interaction has been estimated from experiments on nuclear reactions in which two neutrons exist in the final state, e.g. $^2H(n, p)2n$, and a value $l_s = -22 \pm 2$ fm appears reasonable.* This is in agreement with the values shown in Table **18.1** although it is not so firmly based.

18.2.6 NON-CENTRAL FORCES. The central force assumption so far made in this chapter is unable to explain the nature

*K. Ilakovac, L. G. Kuo, M. Petravić and I. Slaus, *Phys. Rev.*, **124**, 1923, 1961.

of the electromagnetic moments of the deuteron. In a simple picture of a $^3S_1$ state of a neutron and a proton the magnetic moment should be the algebraic sum of the magnetic moments μ_p, μ_n of the two particles and the electric quadrupole moment Q should vanish since there is only a symmetric charge distribution in an S-state. In fact the deuteron moment is smaller than that of the proton, so that the neutron moment must be negative but furthermore

$$\mu_d = 0{\cdot}857411 \pm 0{\cdot}000019 \text{ n.m.}$$

whereas

$$\mu_n + \mu_p = 0{\cdot}87950 \pm 0{\cdot}00010 \text{ n.m.}$$

(18.35)

and a quadrupole moment now known to be $2{\cdot}82 \times 10^{-27}$ cm^2 was established in 1940 by the magnetic resonance method (ch. 4).

These facts can be explained, without appreciable modification of the effective range theory, by the addition of an extra term to the central potential which creates a *tensor force*. Since the effects to be explained exist at low energies this force must be finite in the zero velocity limit. The tensor force resembles a magnetic interaction between two dipoles although its origin must be quite different; it results in a lower potential energy for the neutron and proton when the line joining them is parallel to the spin direction than when it is perpendicular (Fig. 18.7). The effect of such a non-central term, which can change markedly for different relative orientations of the spin axis and the interparticle axis, is to adjust the orbital motions to favour the low potential configuration (a), Fig. 18.7. The deuteron then becomes egg-shaped, and a positive electric quadrupole moment develops. At the same time the extra orbital motion contributes a magnetic moment which must be combined with the proton and neutron moments.

In quantum mechanical language, the tensor force mixes a fraction of ^3D-state wave function in with the predominantly S-state wave function of the deuteron ground state. Since total angular momentum and parity are good quantum numbers for a stable state the only possible admixture is $^3S_1 + {}^3D_1$. Detailed calculations show that if about 4% of the ground state wave function is effectively a D-state, then the electromagnetic moments of the deuteron are correctly predicted (Ref. 18.9).

Tensor forces are not effective in the singlet state (Fig. 18.7c) because there is no resultant spin and no preferred spin axis. It might therefore be possible to ascribe the whole of the spin dependence of nuclear forces to the existence of non-central effects in the triplet state. The tensor force is not the type of non-central force postulated in the single-particle shell model, which supposes a coupling between the spin and orbital motion of a single nucleon in a potential field. This *spin–orbit force* (which also does not exist in the singlet state of two nucleons)

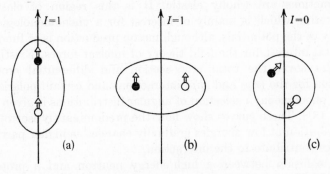

Fig. 18.7. Effect of tensor force on charge distribution in deuteron.
  a) Ground state ($I=1$) Q positive.
  b) Ground state ($I=1$) Q negative.
  c) Virtual state ($I=0$) $Q=0$.

is velocity-dependent and vanishes in the low-energy limit. It is therefore not able to explain the electromagnetic moments of the deuteron, but it is necessary, in addition to the tensor force, to account for high-energy scattering phenomena in the two-body system. A force of this type, too, existing between nucleons and complex nuclei, is used to interpret the polarization observed in elastic scattering.

18.2.7 HIGH-ENERGY EXPERIMENTS. At energies above about 20 MeV partial waves with $l \geqslant 1$ become increasingly important in nucleon scattering, and effective range theory is no longer applicable. It might be expected that at these energies information about the nuclear well shape might be obtained and that more precise tests of the hypothesis of charge independence might be forthcoming. Unfortunately the increased number of possible states of relative motion makes detailed analysis difficult, and the conclusions which have so far been drawn are of a rather general nature. It is possible that low-energy experiments of high accuracy may still provide more information on these points.

Nucleon–nucleon scattering has now been studied at a large number of energies between 20 MeV and 28 GeV. At about 300 MeV meson production becomes energetically possible, but below this energy both the neutron–proton and proton–proton interactions are wholly elastic. It is this region of elastic scattering which is mainly of interest for a phenomenological study of the potentials, although meson production is of fundamental interest for the field theory of nuclear forces. Existing results cover the total cross-section and differential cross-section for the (np) and (pp) interactions and certain polarization phenomena; a selection of angular distributions is given in Fig. 18.8. These curves show how the predominantly isotropic distribution at low energies gradually changes as higher partial waves contribute to the interaction.

A collision between a high-energy neutron and a proton might be expected usually to cause little deviation in the path of the neutron because only an energy of the order of the well depth (30 MeV) can be transferred so that a forward peak of scattered particles is reasonable. Fig. 18.8a, however, also shows a neutron peak of nearly equal strength at backward angles in the centre-of-mass system. This is strong evidence for an *exchange interaction* between the two particles as a result of which the incident neutron becomes a proton by exchange of charge with a target proton, which in turn becomes a neutron. Fig. 18.9a, b, represents scattering by ordinary and exchange processes in the centre-of-mass system; the experimental results (which show peaks at 0° and 90° in the laboratory system) suggest that ordinary and exchange forces are about of equal importance in the (np) interaction.

The (np) scattering occurs in a mixture of $T = 0$ and $T = 1$ states (Sect. 18.1.2) and cannot be compared directly with the (pp) case which is a pure $T = 1$ process. The (pp) scattering remains isotropic until an energy of about 400 MeV and the differential cross-section of $3 \cdot 6 \, d\Omega$ mb is too large to be accounted for by s-wave scattering which gives a maximum differential cross-section of $\lambda^2 d\Omega$ or about $2d\Omega$ mb. For the $T = 1$ interaction only space-spin states of overall antisymmetry such as ^1S, ^3P, ^1D, or ^3F . . . are allowed by the Pauli principle and to explain the cross-section some of the higher states must

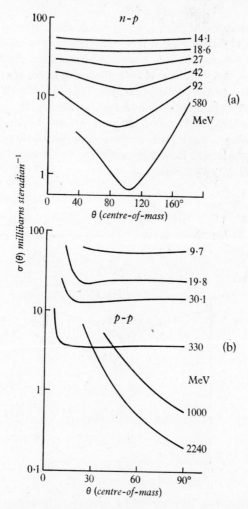

Fig. 18.8. Angular distribution for the scattering of (a) neutrons by protons, (b) protons by protons, shown for the centre-of-mass system as a function of laboratory energy of the incident particle (Ref. 18.6).

contribute, in such a way that isotropy of angular distribution is preserved. The observation of polarization in (pp) scattering at 315 MeV confirms the intervention of ^3P and ^3F states or both, since polarization cannot arise in singlet states and indicates moreover the existence of non-central forces in the nucleon–nucleon interaction which can link spin and orbital motion.

A detailed study of the proton–proton scattering at 315 MeV has been made with the object of extracting a unique set of phase shifts for the possible states of interaction. An important result is that the $^1S_0$ phase shift is negative in contrast with the positive value found at low energies. This indicates a repulsive core for the nucleon–nucleon force; other singlet phases are positive, corresponding to an attractive force beyond the core. Several attempts have been made to predict these phase shifts using potentials and it seems necessary to invoke both tensor and spin–orbit type forces.

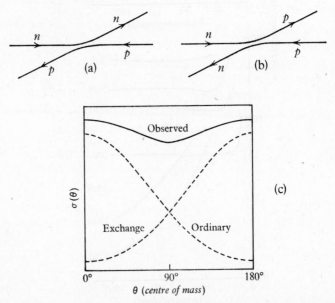

Fig. 18.9. Scattering of neutrons by protons (schematic) with (a) ordinary forces, (b) charge-exchange forces. The interpretation of an observed angular distribution as due to a mixture of ordinary and exchange interactions is shown in (c) (Ref. 18.3).

The high-energy information is thus consistent with what has been learned of nuclear forces at low energies, but adds little to it, except for the clear demonstration of a spin–orbit term in the triplet potential.

18.3　Exchange forces

The angular distribution of the scattering of high-energy neutrons by protons suggests that the nuclear force contains a component with exchange properties, as originally proposed by Heisenberg (Sect. 18.1.1). Although it is no longer necessary to insist on the degree of exchange necessary to ensure saturation, because of the discovery of the repulsive core interaction, the concept of exchange forces has proved of extreme importance for the development of theories of nuclear structure.

Exchange forces are familiar in chemistry in the theory of the homopolar bond; they are responsible for the binding of the hydrogen molecular ion (Sect. 3.8.1) in which an electron can be shared between the two protons. An exchange interaction can develop, quantum mechanically, when two interacting particles can exist in a state in which some common property can be shared. In the case of the molecular ion the property is the orbital electron and the problem can be solved exactly; for two nucleons, Heisenberg assumed first of all that the property shared would be the charge. In Sect. **18.4** we shall discuss the mechanism of this exchange in terms of absorption and re-emission of virtual π-mesons but for the present it is only necessary to regard the neutron–proton system as a superposition of two states,

$$n_1 + n_2, \qquad n_1' + n_2'$$

which differ only because a certain property has been exchanged between the two nucleons. Because of the identity of these two systems in the sense that neither particle can be uniquely specified, the total energy is reduced below what it would be without exchange, and binding results.*

In order to see how an exchange force might ensure saturation of nuclear density and binding energy we consider again briefly

---

* This is analogous to the normal mode of lower frequency in the classical problem of coupled pendulums, Sect. 3.7.1.

the binding of a heavy nucleus in which only *ordinary* short-range attractive forces operate. As indicated in Sect. 18.1.1 this nucleus collapses, the binding energy becomes too large and the radius too small, as shown in Fig. 18.10a. If only *exchange* forces operate, the interaction between a pair of

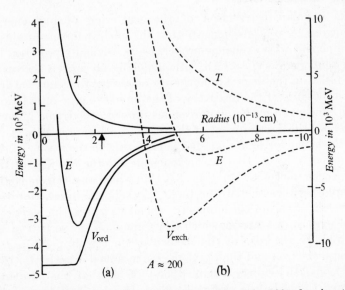

Fig. 18.10. Binding energy of a heavy nucleus ($A \approx 200$) showing the potential energy, kinetic energy and total energy as a function of radius. For ordinary forces the stable nucleus has a radius of the order of the range of nuclear forces, indicated by the arrow, and a very high binding energy. With exchange forces both the radius and the binding energy are nearer to the observed values (Ref. 18.1).

nucleons will be strong only if these nucleons occupy similar states of motion, i.e. if the nucleons have similar wave functions. Since the Pauli principle limits the number of particles in an assembly of fermions which may enter a given spatial state, the introduction of exchange forces immediately reduces the number of effective interactions in a way which does not arise for ordinary forces. This is one of the requirements for saturation.

Furthermore, when an exchange potential is used, the sign of the potential energy depends on whether the wave function of the nucleon pair concerned is symmetric or antisymmetric for the exchange. If the symmetric state is taken to produce binding (as in the deuteron) the force between antisymmetric pairs must be repulsive. Since the Pauli principle ensures that antisymmetric pairs of nucleons will always be found in a nucleus with $A > 4$, the repulsive interactions can contribute to the saturation requirement.* The result of a typical calculation of nuclear binding energy and radius for a heavy nucleus in which exchange forces operate is shown in Fig. 18.10b.

We now consider the different types of exchange force that have been proposed, remarking at the outset that they must be assumed to act between pairs of identical nucleons as well as between non-identical nucleons because of the similarity of the $^1(nn)$, $^1(pp)$ and $^1(np)$ systems which is well established (Sect. **18.1, 18.2**). Charge is not the only property that may be exchanged between the nucleons; Majorana pointed out that spin direction might also be shared. The possible types of exchange for the $^1S_0$ neutron–proton system are shown in Fig. 18.11 together with the names by which the corresponding forces are known. It will be seen that the exchange of charge and spin (Majorana force) is exactly equivalent to an exchange of position and this force is sometimes known as a *space-exchange* force. Similarly the Heisenberg charge exchange is equivalent to a joint exchange of spin and position. We may use these equivalences to express the exchange property symbolically as follows: Let

$$\psi(\mathbf{r}_1\sigma_1;\ \mathbf{r}_2\sigma_2) \tag{18.36}$$

be the wave function of the neutron and proton shown in Fig. 18.11; $\mathbf{r}$ and σ give respectively the spatial position of the nucleon and the z-component of the intrinsic spin (σ_1 spin up, σ_2 spin down). The first pair of symbols refers to the neutron and the second to the proton. In the exchanged state the wave functions are as shown in Table **18.2**.

---

* The present arguments are only qualitative. In fact both ordinary and exchange forces lead to potential energy integrals of the direct and exchange type (Sect. 3.7.1). One integral corresponds to saturating, and the other to non-saturating forces. A detailed examination of the situation is given in Ref. 18.8.

TABLE 18.2　Types of Exchange Force

NAME	PROPERTY EXCHANGED	WAVE FUNCTION	
Ordinary (Wigner) force	No exchange	$\psi(\mathbf{r}_1\sigma_1; \mathbf{r}_2\sigma_2)$	
Heisenberg force	Charge (spin and position)	$\psi(\mathbf{r}_2\sigma_2; \mathbf{r}_1\sigma_1)$	(18.37)
Majorana force	Charge and spin (position)	$\psi(\mathbf{r}_2\sigma_1; \mathbf{r}_1\sigma_2)$	
Bartlett force	Spin (charge and position)	$\psi(\mathbf{r}_1\sigma_2; \mathbf{r}_2\sigma_1)$	

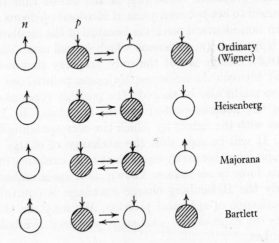

Fig. 18.11. Basic types of exchange interaction between nucleons. The properties which may be exchanged are charge (represented by shading) and spin (represented by arrows).

The potential energy integral for a pair of nucleons will be of the form (cf. 3.31 and 3.32)

$$\int \psi^* V P \psi \, d\tau \tag{18.38}$$

where V is a radial function and P an operator specific to the particular exchange force. Since ψ is either symmetric or antisymmetric when the exchange of space or spin coordinates (or both) is made

$$P\psi = \pm \psi \tag{18.39}$$

which means that $P = \pm 1$. It is usual to choose the sign of V so that P is $+1$ for the ^3S state of the neutron–proton system (i.e. the deuteron). The sign of P for singlet states and for odd orbital states can then be found by noting whether the change from 18.36 to 18.37 has led to a change of sign or not. Remembering that the space exchange $r_1 \rightarrow r_2$ is symmetric for even parity and antisymmetric for odd parity and that triplet spins are symmetric but singlet spins antisymmetric, we obtain the following results:

TABLE 18.3　Exchange Operators for the Two-Particle System

| | EVEN PARITY STATES | | ODD PARITY STATES | |
	TRIPLET $S = 1$	SINGLET $S = 0$	TRIPLET $S = 1$	SINGLET $S = 0$
Wigner	1	1	1	1
Heisenberg	1	-1	-1	1
Majorana	1	1	-1	-1
Bartlett	1	-1	1	-1

The Heisenberg and Bartlett forces are spin dependent and are adequate to describe the deuteron (Fig. 18.2a). They cannot account for the increased binding energy per nucleon in the α-particle, in which equal numbers of singlet and triplet groupings of nucleons exist and all particles are in relative S-states (Ref. 18.1, p. 202). Majorana forces however are attractive in both singlet and triplet states for even parity and six attractive bonds arise (Fig. 18.2b). The Majorana space exchange force is responsible for an important part of the general nuclear binding energy.

With four varieties of nuclear force to employ, it is possible to ensure saturation and to prevent collapse by choice of appropriate mixtures. The operator appearing in the potential energy integrals is

$$wP_\mathrm{W} + hP_\mathrm{H} + mP_\mathrm{M} + bP_\mathrm{B} \qquad (18.40)$$

with particular coefficients w, h, m, b. One set of coefficients is predicted by meson theory and although this force mixture is satisfactory in accounting for the low-energy phenomena, it fails to predict the high-energy neutron–proton scattering. This latter experiment agrees with the prediction of a force proposed by Serber, which gives no interaction in odd orbital states and therefore a symmetrical angular distribution, but elimination of the odd states spoils the saturation property of the force. The solution to this difficulty seems to lie not in modification of the exchange force mixture but in the addition of the repulsive core to the nuclear interaction. The hypothesis of exchange forces will probably need to be retained even with this assumption in order to satisfy all the conditions imposed upon the fundamental interaction.

18.4   Field theory of nuclear forces

18.4.1 SUMMARY OF KNOWLEDGE OF THE NUCLEON–NUCLEON FORCE. From the evidence presented in Sects. **18.1** and **18.2** and from the arguments outlined in Sect. **18.3** it appears that the force between nucleons has the following properties:

    i) Charge symmetry, and most probably charge independence.

    ii) Short range (≈ 2 fm).

    iii) An exchange component, although not so much as was required by the old saturation conditions.

    iv) A repulsive core of radius ≈ 0.4 fm in the ^1S state and probably also in other states of relative motion.

    v) A tensor component and probably a spin–orbit term in addition to the central forces.

The potential energy function for the central part of the force is typically as shown in Fig. 18.1.

The force necessary to account for the many relevant experimental phenomena is obviously a complicated one and it has long been felt desirable to derive its main features analytically from some simpler concept. Attempts to achieve this constitute the field theory of nuclear forces, which stems from the work of Yukawa (1935).*

18.4.2 PION EXCHANGE. In electromagnetic theory the long-range Coulomb potential $V = e/r$ is a solution of the equation

$$\nabla^2 V = 0 \qquad\qquad (18.41)$$

---

*H. Yukawa, *Proc. phys.-math. Soc.*, *Japan*, **17**, 48, 1935.

which is itself the static limit of the wave equation

$$\nabla^2 V - \frac{1}{c^2}\frac{\partial^2 V}{\partial t^2} = 0 \qquad (18.42)$$

The wave equation is derived from Maxwell's equations and describes the propagation of electromagnetic waves in free space. Any change in the potentials can only be conveyed to a distant point with a velocity c, and the relation between wavelength and frequency given by 18.42 is

$$c = \nu\lambda \qquad (18.43)$$

In quantum theory it is assumed that although light is propagated as a wave, the energy is carried as discrete quanta or photons. Since these must travel with velocity c, they must have no rest mass according to the theory of relativity and their energy and momentum are

and

$$\left.\begin{array}{l} E = h\nu \\ p = \dfrac{h}{\lambda} = \dfrac{h\nu}{c} \end{array}\right\} \qquad (18.44)$$

These relations have been verified in detail in studies of the Compton effect. In relativistic notation we relate the energy and momentum of a photon by the equation

$$E^2 - p^2 c^2 = 0 \qquad (18.45)$$

In order to obtain a force of shorter range than the Coulomb force between charges, we may, following Yukawa, modify 18.42 to the form

$$\nabla^2 U - \frac{1}{c^2}\frac{\partial^2 U}{\partial t^2} - K^2 U = 0 \qquad (18.46)$$

where K is a constant and U is a potential function. Substituting a wave-like solution into this equation we obtain for the relation between wavelength and frequency

$$-\frac{1}{\lambda^2} + \frac{\nu^2}{c^2} - \frac{K^2}{4\pi^2} = 0 \qquad (18.47)$$

and using the de Broglie expressions for the energy and momentum of a material particle (or photon) this gives

$$E^2 - p^2c^2 - M^2c^4 = 0 \qquad (18.48)$$

where

$$M = \frac{\hbar K}{c} \qquad (18.48a)$$

This is the relativistic energy-momentum relation for a particle of rest mass M. Moreover, the static case of equation 18.46 is

$$\nabla^2 U - K^2 U = 0 \qquad (18.49)$$

which gives for the corresponding potential

$$U = g \frac{e^{-Kr}}{r} \qquad (18.50)$$

where g is an arbitrary constant. With proper choice of K this can be made to represent a short-range force; to obtain the range indicated by experiment, Yukawa proposed that K should be about 10^{13} cm^{-1}, which implies the existence of a particle, according to 18.48a, of mass equal to about 300 electron masses which should interact strongly with nuclei. The theoretical prediction of the existence of this particle and the subsequent discovery of the π-meson (pion) which has the predicted mass and nuclear interaction, together form one of the major joint achievements of theoretical and experimental physics of the twentieth century.

The role of the pion as the quantum of the nuclear force field may be considered from the standpoint of the simple physical picture already given (Sect. **18.3**). The charge exchange process there described may be effected by allowing a π-meson to pass between the neutron and proton, in analogy with the passage of an electron between a hydrogen atom and a proton in the binding of the hydrogen molecular ion. This exchange is not observable for free nucleons because the process

$$p \to n + \pi^+ \qquad (18.51)$$

is classically forbidden for a proton at rest by the law of conservation of energy. According to quantum mechanics, however, the energy $\Delta E = Mc^2$ necessary may be borrowed providing that it is returned within a time given by

$$\Delta E . \Delta t = \hbar$$

and the meson exchange can therefore be considered as a virtual process. In the time Δt the meson can travel a maximum distance $c\Delta t$ and if we identify this distance with the range of the nuclear force (Fig. 18.1) we obtain

$$a = c\Delta t = \frac{c\hbar}{\Delta E} = \frac{\hbar}{Mc} = \frac{1}{K} \tag{18.52}$$

which is the value indicated by the potential 18.50.

The theory of nuclear exchange forces first proposed by Heisenberg envisaged an exchange of β-particles between nucleons

$$p \to n + \beta^{+} \tag{18.53}$$

and linked the nuclear force field in this way to the lepton field of β-decay. Beta-decay, however, is a very slow process on a nuclear time scale and is quite unable to account for the observed strength of nuclear forces. This may be seen if we characterize the interactions of nuclear physics by the squares of coupling constants expressed in a suitable dimensionless form. We obtain

a) for the electromagnetic interaction $1/137$,
b) for β-decay (weak interaction) 5×10^{-14},
c) for the field of nuclear force (strong interaction) 15.

The coupling constant for the pion–nucleon field is in fact so large that it is no longer possible to develop the meson theory in terms of a small correction to a static force. The most suitable methods of treatment of this problem are still being worked out. There seems to be general agreement, however, that the basic idea of pion exchange is correct and that the difficulties still remaining in giving a satisfactory derivation of the nuclear potential are primarily mathematical.

One of the earliest results of the application of field theory to the explanation of nuclear forces was the prediction by Kemmer of the existence of a neutral meson (π^0). The meson exchanges

$$\begin{aligned} p &\to n + \pi^{+} \\ n &\to p + \pi^{-} \end{aligned} \tag{18.54}$$

are unable to explain the force between like nucleons. For this it is supposed that the exchange particle is the π^0 meson

$$p \to p + \pi^0$$
$$n \to n + \pi^0 \qquad (18.55)$$

If all three pion exchanges are permitted, it is straightforward to couple the corresponding fields to nucleons in such a way that charge independence results (symmetric meson theory).

References

18.1   J. M. Blatt and V. F. Weisskopf, *Theoretical Nuclear Physics*, Wiley, 1952.

18.2   G. L. Squires, 'The Neutron–Proton Interaction', *Prog. nucl. Phys.*, **2**, 89, 1952.

18.3   R. D. Evans, *The Atomic Nucleus*, McGraw-Hill, 1955.

18.4   L. Hulthen and M. Sugawara, 'The Two-Nucleon Problem', *Encyclopedia of Physics*, **39**, 1, Springer 1957.

18.5   D. J. Hughes and R. B. Schwartz, *Neutron Cross Sections*, Brookhaven National Laboratory Report BNL 325, 1958.

18.6   W. O. Lock, *High Energy Nuclear Physics*, Methuen, 1960.

18.7   R. E. Marshak, 'The Nuclear Force', *Scientific American*, **202**, March, 1960.

18.8   L. Rosenfeld, *Nuclear Forces*, North Holland Publishing Co., 1948.

18.9   M. A. Preston, *Physics of the Nucleus*, Addison-Wesley, 1962.

Appendices

APPENDIX 1

THE BOHR THEORY OF A HYDROGEN-LIKE ATOM

Consider an electron (mass m, charge $-e$, velocity v) moving uniformly in a circle of radius r round a positive charge Ze which is taken to remain at rest (Fig. A 1.1a). For equilibrium

$$\frac{mv^2}{r} = \frac{Ze^2}{r^2} \qquad \text{(A 1.1)}$$

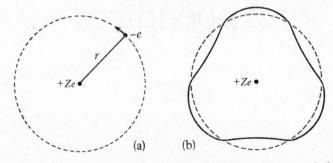

(a)   (b)

Fig. A 1.1. A hydrogen-like atom (a) in the Bohr theory and (b) according to wave mechanics.

and the kinetic and potential energies of the electron are respectively

$$T = \tfrac{1}{2}mv^2 = \frac{Ze^2}{2r} \quad \text{and} \quad V = -\frac{Ze^2}{r} \qquad \text{(A 1.2)}$$

The total energy of the system is then

$$E = T + V = -\frac{Ze^2}{2r} \qquad \text{(A 1.3)}$$

and is negative, corresponding to a bound state.

This purely classical calculation neglects the radiation loss from the electron which has an acceleration when moving uniformly in a circle, and it permits any value of r, providing that v is chosen in accordance with A 1.1. To obtain a suitable model for the hydrogen spectrum Bohr proposed that the motion must be *quantized* and made the following specific postulates:

a) the electron motion is confined to certain discrete states and there is no radiation associated with the continual motion in such an orbit,

b) the discrete orbits are chosen from the continuous range of orbits possible classically by imposing a quantum condition on the angular momentum

$$mvr = \frac{nh}{2\pi} \qquad (A\ 1.4)$$

where h is Planck's constant and n is an integer.

c) the observed lines of the hydrogen spectrum are associated with the transition of the electron between one discrete orbit (energy E_i) and another (energy E_f) and the frequency radiated is given by the quantum condition

$$h\nu = E_i - E_f \qquad (A\ 1.5)$$

From A 1.1 and A 1.4

$$r = \frac{n^2 h^2}{4\pi^2 e^2 m Z} \qquad (A\ 1.6)$$

from A 1.3 and A 1.6

$$E_n = -\frac{2\pi^2 m e^4 Z^2}{n^2 h^2} \qquad (A\ 1.7)$$

and from A 1.5 and A 1.7

$$\nu = \frac{2\pi^2 m e^4 Z^2}{h^3}\left(\frac{1}{n_f^2} - \frac{1}{n_i^2}\right)$$

or

$$\tilde{\nu} = \frac{2\pi^2 m e^4 Z^2}{h^3 c}\left(\frac{1}{n_f^2} - \frac{1}{n_i^2}\right) = R Z^2 \left(\frac{1}{n_f^2} - \frac{1}{n_i^2}\right) \qquad (A\ 1.8)$$

where R is the Rydberg number for infinite mass. This equation, with $Z=1$, is the basic expression for the line spectrum of hydrogen (cf. 3.8 and 3.9).

In the simplest picture, the Bohr orbits are circular and the corresponding energies are determined (A 1.7) by the *principal quantum number* n. For $n=1$ we have the ground state of

22*

hydrogen with an orbit radius a_0 where, by putting $Z = 1$ in A 1.6

$$a_0 = \frac{h^2}{4\pi^2 me^2} = 0.53 \times 10^{-8} \text{ cm} \qquad \text{(A 1.9)}$$

The extension of the Bohr theory to elliptic orbits is discussed in Ref. A 1.1.

The connection between the orbital and wave mechanical theories of the hydrogen atom may be established by noting that the de Broglie wavelength λ of the electron in a given stationary (i.e. non-radiating) state of motion with observable angular momentum $l\hbar$, is just such that l wavelengths fit into the corresponding Bohr orbit. This follows since for radius r

$$\frac{2\pi r}{\lambda} = \frac{2\pi rmv}{h} = \frac{mvr}{\hbar} = l \qquad \text{(A 1.10)}$$

(Fig. A 1.1b).

APPENDIX 2

SPHERICAL HARMONICS

The functions $Y_l^m(\theta, \phi)$ are of frequent occurrence in atomic and nuclear physics. They provide a convenient means of describing any deformation of an initially spherical surface and can consequently be used to represent the angular 'shape' of wave functions. In particular, certain values of θ, ϕ will define nodal planes over which $Y_l^m(\theta, \phi)$ vanishes; the probability of finding a particle described by the wave function near these planes is small. A discussion of the properties of these functions is given in Ref. A 2.1, p. 49, where it is shown that

$$Y_l^m(\theta, \phi) = \text{normalization factor} \times P_l^m(\cos \theta) \times e^{im\phi}$$

The function $P_l^m(\cos \theta)$ is an *associated Legendre function* which may be derived from the corresponding *Legendre function* (or polynomial) $P_l(\cos \theta)$ by a process involving repeated differentiation. The normalization factor provides that the squared modulus of the spherical harmonic, integrated over a sphere ($\theta \to 0$ to π, $\phi \to 0$ to 2π), shall be unity, i.e.

$$\int |Y|^2 \, d\Omega = 1 \quad \text{where } d\Omega = \sin \theta \, d\theta \, d\phi.$$

The similar normalization for the Legendre functions is

$$\int P_l^2 \, d\Omega = \frac{4\pi}{2l+1}$$

while for the associated Legendre functions

$$\int (P_l^m)^2 \, d\Omega = \frac{4\pi}{2l+1} \frac{(l+|m|)!}{(l-|m|)!}$$

Expressions for the first few of these quantities are given in the following table:

LEGENDRE FUNCTION	ASSOCIATED LEGENDRE FUNCTION	SPHERICAL HARMONIC
$P_0(\cos\theta) = 1$	$P_0^0(\cos\theta) = 1$	$Y_0^0(\theta,\phi) = \sqrt{\dfrac{1}{4\pi}}$
$P_1(\cos\theta)$ $= \cos\theta$	$P_1^0(\cos\theta)$ $= \cos\theta$	$Y_1^0(\theta,\phi)$ $= \sqrt{\dfrac{3}{4\pi}}\cos\theta$
	$P_1^{\pm 1}(\cos\theta)$ $= (1-\cos^2\theta)^{1/2}$	$Y_1^{\pm 1}(\theta,\phi)$ $= \mp\sqrt{\dfrac{3}{8\pi}}(1-\cos^2\theta)^{1/2}e^{\pm i\phi}$
$P_2(\cos\theta)$ $= \tfrac{1}{2}(3\cos^2\theta - 1)$	$P_2^0(\cos\theta)$ $= \tfrac{1}{2}(3\cos^2\theta - 1)$	$Y_2^0(\theta,\phi)$ $= \sqrt{\dfrac{5}{16\pi}}(3\cos^2\theta - 1)$
	$P_2^{\pm 1}(\cos\theta)$ $= 3\cos\theta(1-\cos^2\theta)^{1/2}$	$Y_2^{\pm 1}(\theta,\phi)$ $= \mp\sqrt{\dfrac{15}{8\pi}}\cos\theta(1-\cos^2\theta)^{1/2}e^{\pm i\phi}$
	$P_2^{\pm 2}(\cos\theta)$ $= 3(1-\cos^2\theta)$	$Y_2^{\pm 2}(\theta,\phi)$ $= \mp\sqrt{\dfrac{15}{32\pi}}(1-\cos^2\theta)e^{\pm 2i\phi}$

It will be noted that for a given l there are $2l+1$ spherical harmonics with different m-values.

The functions $Y_l^m(\theta,\phi)$ have nodal planes in the angular coordinate θ, obtained by setting $Y_l^m(\theta,\phi)=0$. There are also nodal planes in the coordinate ϕ, which are obtained by considering the zeros of the real forms

$$\tfrac{1}{2}(Y_l^m + Y_l^{-m}) \quad \text{and} \quad \tfrac{i}{2}(Y_l^m - Y_l^{-m})$$

which are equally good solutions of the second-order equation used to define Y. The total number of nodal planes in the angular coordinates is l. Thus for $l=1$ (p-state) we have wave functions with the angular dependence

$$\cos\theta$$
$$\sin\theta\cos\phi$$
$$\sin\theta\sin\phi$$

in each of which there is one nodal plane.

It follows from the definition of the spherical harmonics (Ref. A 2.1) that if the operator which in wave mechanics represents the square of the total angular momentum of a particle is applied to a wave function $Y_l^m(\theta,\phi)$, the result is $l(l+1)\hbar^2 \times Y_l^m(\theta,\phi)$.

APPENDIX 3

MULTIPOLE MOMENTS

A 3.1 Classical moments of a charge distribution

Consider a static distribution of charges confined within a volume Ω (Fig. A 3.1) surrounding the origin O. The electrostatic potential at the point P is given by

$$\phi_P = \sum_i \frac{e_i}{|\mathbf{R} - \mathbf{r}_i|} = \sum_i \frac{e_i}{\sqrt{R^2 + r_i^2 - 2Rr_i \cos\theta_i}} \qquad \text{(A 3.1)}$$

where $\mathbf{R}$, $\mathbf{r}_i$ are the position vectors, with absolute lengths R, r_i, of the points P and A (charge e_i) and θ_i is the angle between $\mathbf{R}$ and $\mathbf{r}$. For distances OP which are large compared with the linear dimension a of the charge distribution, i.e. for $R \gg r$ the denominator may be expanded in powers of r/R giving

$$\phi_P = \frac{\sum e_i}{R} + \frac{\sum e_i r_i \cos\theta_i}{R^2} + \frac{\sum e_i r_i^2 (3\cos^2\theta_i - 1)}{2R^3} + \dots$$

$$= \phi_0 + \phi_1 + \dots + \phi_L + \dots \qquad \text{(A 3.2)}$$

in which the term ϕ_L is proportional to $1/(R^{L+1})$.

These potentials may be interpreted as follows:

ϕ_0 is the potential at P due to the resultant charge $\sum e_i$

$$\phi_1 = \frac{\sum e_i r_i \cos\theta_i}{R^2} = \sum e_i \mathbf{r}_i \cdot \operatorname{grad} \frac{1}{R} \text{ is the potential at } P \text{ due to}$$

the static *dipole moment* $\mathbf{D} = \sum e_i \mathbf{r}_i$ of the charge distribution
$\qquad \qquad \qquad \qquad \qquad \qquad \qquad \qquad \qquad \qquad \qquad \text{(A 3.3)}$

ϕ_2 and subsequent terms represent contributions from quadrupole, octupole and higher moments of the system. Together, this set of moments located at the origin produces the same electrostatic field at a distant point as the charge distribution. As expressed in A 3.2 these moments are not generally useful because they involve θ_i, which is based on the arbitrary direction OP. It is possible, however, to define moments with respect to axes fixed in the charge distribution (perhaps aligned with a particular axis of symmetry) by transforming r_i and θ_i

appropriately. In Cartesian coordinates the vector dipole moment then has components

$$\mathbf{D} = \sum e_i x_i, \quad \sum e_i y_i \quad \text{and} \quad \sum e_i z_i$$

and the higher moments are symmetric tensors. The quadrupole moment for instance may be written

$$Q = \sum_i e_i \begin{vmatrix} xx, & xy, & xz \\ yx, & yy, & yz \\ zx, & zy, & zz \end{vmatrix} \qquad \text{(A 3.4)}$$

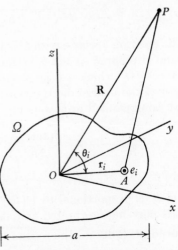

Fig. A 3.1. Static charge distribution. Charges e_i are supposed to be confined within a volume Ω of linear dimension $\approx a$.

where each term in the square array defines a partial moment, which must be included in the total quadrupole effect. The symmetries, and the relation $x_i^2 + y_i^2 + z_i^2 = r_i^2$ reduce the number of independent components from 9 to 5 (and for the Lth moment, to $2L+1$). An equivalent expression for an element of the quadrupole tensor is

$$Q_{xy} = \sum_i e_i (3x_i y_i - r_i^2 \delta_{x_i y_i}) \qquad \text{(A 3.5)}$$

where $\delta_{xy} = 0$ if $x \neq y$ and $= 1$ if $x = y$. Permutation of the coordinates gives the individual quadrupole moments. These are closely related to the five spherical functions necessary to describe the most general quadrupole deformation of a sphere (Appendix 2), as may be seen if the forms A 3.5 are converted to polar coordinates using the relations (Fig. 3.5).

$$\begin{aligned} x &= r \sin \theta \cos \phi \\ y &= r \sin \theta \sin \phi \\ z &= r \cos \theta \end{aligned} \qquad (A\ 3.6)$$

The higher moments of the charge distribution become important when the resultant charge $\sum e_i$ is zero and the dipole term also vanishes. A quadrupole moment may be generated for instance by displacing and inverting a dipole so that both $\sum_i e_i$ and $\sum_i e_i \mathbf{r}_i = 0$ but $\sum e_i r_i^2$ is finite. Typical charge distributions illustrating these points are shown in Fig. 3.16. The 2^L-pole moment, appearing in the term ϕ_L in A 3.2 is a quantity of the order $\sum e_i r_i^L$.

If the charge distribution has spherical symmetry, all moments as defined by A 3.2 vanish, If there is axial symmetry with respect to Oz the dipole moment vanishes but the quadrupole moment

$$Q_{zz} = \sum e_i (3z_i{}^2 - r_i{}^2) \qquad (A\ 3.7)$$

is finite. This leads immediately to the important case of a nucleus with axial symmetry; the intrinsic quadrupole moment with respect to this axis is

$$Q_0 = \int \rho (3z^2 - r^2)\, d\tau \qquad (A\ 3.8)$$

where $\rho\, d\tau$ is the charge within the volume element $d\tau$. It is customary in nuclear physics to remove the dimensions of charge from this expression by use of the equation

$$Q_0 = \frac{1}{e} \int \rho (3z^2 - r^2)\, d\tau \qquad (A\ 3.9)$$

The quadrupole moment is then measured in cm^2 or barns. For an oblate nucleus Q is positive and for the prolate shape Q is negative.

A 3.2   Radiation from time-varying moments

The classical calculation of the radiation from a charge distribution which varies sinusoidally with time is given in Refs.

A 3.1, A 3.2 and A 3.3. It is shown that the second term of A 3.2 corresponds to the field of electric dipole ($E1$) radiation, while the third term leads not only to electric quadrupole ($E2$), but also to magnetic dipole ($M1$) fields. All higher moments (L) yield EL and $M(L-1)$ radiation and as far as A 3.2 is concerned, these two types of radiation would be expected to arise in comparable intensity, which is much less than the intensity of radiation corresponding to moments of lower order unless these are abnormally small.

If the energy dependent factors arising in the calculation of the fields are written out explicitly we find that the *electric* fields at the point P (Fig. A 3.1) have the following dependence:

MULTIPOLARITY	ELECTRIC RADIATION	MAGNETIC RADIATION	
1	$E_1 \propto \omega k D$	$E_1 \propto \omega k \dfrac{v}{c} D$	
2	$E_2 \propto \omega k^2 Q$	$E_2 \propto \omega k^2 \dfrac{v}{c} Q$	(A 3.10)
L	$E_L \propto \omega k^L Q_L$	$E_L \propto \omega k^L \dfrac{v}{c} Q_L$	

where ω is the circular frequency of the time variation of the charge distribution, $k = 2\pi/\lambda = \omega/c$ and the Lth moment Q_L is of the order of ea^L or a^L according to definition for a radiator of dimension a. The intensities radiated are proportional to the field vectors squared.

The general relation that the field of magnetic radiation is weaker than that of electric radiation of the same multipolarity by the factor v/c (intensity weaker by the factor $(v/c)^2$) may easily be seen in the case of simple orbital motion of a single charge. In this case the magnetic moment is $\pi r^2 i = \pi r^2 \dfrac{e\omega}{2\pi}$ $= \dfrac{1}{2} \dfrac{evr}{c} \approx \dfrac{v}{c} D$. For a Bohr orbit $mvr = \hbar$ so that $\dfrac{v}{c} = \dfrac{\hbar}{mcr}$ and the magnetic dipole intensity is proportional to $\left(\dfrac{\hbar}{mcr}\right)^2 D^2$ which is independent of r the radius.

A 3.3　Moments in quantum mechanics

In quantum mechanics an observable physical quantity such as an energy, or a momentum or a length, is represented by an *operator*, which indicates the performance of a certain mathematical transformation when applied to a function of coordinates. The average of a series of measurements on the quantity whose operator is O, for the state of a quantum mechanical system whose wave function is ψ_n, is the *expectation value*

$$\bar{O}_{nn} = \int \psi_n^* O \psi_n \, \mathrm{d}\tau \qquad (A\ 3.11)$$

where $\mathrm{d}\tau$ is a volume element of configuration space. Such quantities are of course properties of the state ψ_n, e.g. the static moments of an atomic or nuclear system. Since, however, the system usually has a range of states which may be treated as quasi-stationary, we may also consider the quantities

$$\bar{O}_{nn} = \int \psi_n^* O \psi_{n'} e^{\frac{i(E_n{'} - E_n)t}{\hbar}} \, \mathrm{d}\tau \qquad (A\ 3.12)$$

in which the same operator is used to connect two states. The observable represented by the operator O is then described by the whole array or *matrix* of quantities $\bar{O}_{nn'}$ for a range of n and n' values. The individual expressions (A 3.12) are known as *matrix elements*. This formalism, which is further discussed in Ref. A 1.1, can be immediately adapted to give quantum mechanical expressions for the moments of an atomic or nuclear system.

For the *static moments* generated by the motion of a single particle in a state with wave function ψ we use the expression A 3.11. Suitable operators for the electric moments are $r^L Y_L^0(\theta, \phi)$ as may be seen from A 3.2 and the quantum mechanical formula effectively averages these quantities for the state ψ. For the electric quadrupole term for instance the single particle moment is

$$Q = \int \psi_n^* r^2 Y_2^0(\theta, \phi) \psi_n \, \mathrm{d}\tau$$

$$\propto \int \psi_n^* (3z^2 - r^2) \psi_n \, \mathrm{d}\tau \qquad (A\ 3.13)$$

and the moment is evaluated for the state of motion in which the magnetic quantum number has its maximum value (e.g. $m_I = I$). The quantity $\psi_n\psi_n^*$ gives the density distribution for this state.

For the *transition moments* (or probabilities) of radiation theory we use the same operators. The single-particle matrix elements take the place of the classical radiating moments and the radiative width for a 2^L-pole transition may be written

$$\Gamma_L \propto |\bar{O}_{nn'}|^2 \propto \sum | \int \psi_n^* O \psi_{n'} \, d\tau|^2 \qquad \text{(A 3.14)}$$

where the summation takes account of the various combinations of magnetic quantum numbers permitted by selection rules. For the single-particle electric quadrupole width we thus have

$$\Gamma_2 \propto \sum | \int \psi_n^* (3z^2 - r^2)\psi_{n'} \, d\tau|^2 \qquad \text{(A 3.15)}$$

Similar expressions may be written down for the magnetic moments. For a many particle system summations must also be made over the total number of particles, as in the classical case. The final results are the moments as determined by static measurements and by atomic and nuclear spectroscopy. The existence of the transition moments requires that the selection rules based on conservation of angular momentum and parity shall be satisfied. The static moments are also limited by these rules, as shown in Ref. A 3.4; the general conclusions are:

    a) for stationary states, all electric multipole moments with odd L and all magnetic moments with even L vanish.

    b) $M1$ moments are only observable in states with $I \geqslant \frac{1}{2}$. $E2$ moments are only observable in states with $I \geqslant 1$.

Quantum mechanical states with $I = 0$ and $I = \frac{1}{2}$ have spherically symmetrical charge distributions and electric (E) moments are not observed for such states. This does not mean that a nucleus in such a state is necessarily a spherical object, since the spherical symmetry may arise because of the averaging of an anisotropic charge distribution over spin directions. Thus if an ellipsoidal nucleus has an intrinsic quadrupole moment Q_0 (cf. 12.10) with respect to the spin axis, the indeterminacy of location of the angular momentum vector with respect to an axis fixed in space (Ref. A 3.3, p. 66) leads to a maximum observable moment

$$Q_I = \frac{2I-1}{2I+2} Q_0 \qquad (\text{A } 3.16)$$

If the nucleus rotates, as in the collective model, the axis of resultant angular momentum coincides with neither the nuclear symmetry axis nor the axis fixed in space and the maximum observable quadrupole moment is

$$Q_{I,K} = \frac{3K^2 - I(I+1)}{(I+1)(2I+3)} Q_0 \qquad (\text{A } 3.17)$$

where K is the projection of I along the nuclear symmetry axis. For the ground state $I = K$ and eq. 12.11 follows.

APPENDIX 4

SIMPLIFIED DERIVATION OF IMPACT PARAMETER-ANGLE RELATION FOR RUTHERFORD SCATTERING

Consider the deflection of an incident charged particle (M_1, ze) by a scattering centre (M_2, Ze) which will be considered to be infinitely heavy, i.e. fixed in space. Let the impact parameter (Fig. A 4.1a) be p and the initial velocity v_1.

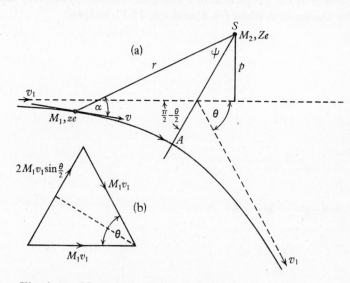

Fig. A 4.1. Momentum change in Rutherford scattering.
a) Section of path of charged particle in scattering from a fixed nucleus.
b) Vector diagram for initial and final momenta.

The effect of the collision is to deviate the incident particle through an angle θ, without changing its energy. The momentum change necessary results from the Coulomb force acting between the two charges and can be seen from Fig. A 4.1b to be

$$2M_1v_1 \sin \theta/2 \tag{A 4.1}$$

in the direction of SA. The impulse due to the Coulomb force, resolved along SA, is

$$\int_0^\infty \frac{zZe^2}{r^2} \cos\psi\,dt = \int_{-\infty}^\infty \frac{zZe^2}{r^2} \cos\psi\,\frac{ds}{v}$$

$$= zZe^2 \int_{-\left(\frac{\pi}{2}-\frac{\theta}{2}\right)}^{\frac{\pi}{2}-\frac{\theta}{2}} \frac{\cos\psi}{r^2 v}\,\frac{r\,d\psi}{\sin\alpha} \qquad (A\ 4.2)$$

where α is the angle between the radius vector and the trajectory. The law of conservation of angular momentum requires that

$$pv_1 = vr\sin\alpha \qquad (A\ 4.3)$$

so that A 4.2 becomes

$$zZe^2 \int_{-\left(\frac{\pi}{2}-\frac{\theta}{2}\right)}^{\frac{\pi}{2}-\frac{\theta}{2}} \frac{\cos\psi\,d\psi}{pv_1} = \frac{2zZe^2}{pv_1}\cos\frac{\theta}{2} \qquad (A\ 4.4)$$

Equating this to A 4.1 we obtain

$$p = \frac{zZe^2}{M_1 v_1^2}\cot\frac{\theta}{2} \qquad (A\ 4.5)$$

which is equation 5.22.

This type of calculation can be used to give the energy lost by a heavy charged particle in collision with an electron. In this case the incident particle is essentially undeflected (Eqn. 5.3 with $M_1 \gg M_2$) and the electron absorbs the momentum created in the collision. This is, in analogy with A 4.4,

$$zZe^2 \int_{-\frac{\pi}{2}}^{\frac{\pi}{2}} \frac{\cos\psi}{pv_1}\,d\psi = \frac{2zZe^2}{pv_1} \qquad (A\ 4.6)$$

and the corresponding electron energy is

$$Q = \frac{1}{2m}\left(\frac{2zZe^2}{pv_1}\right)^2 = \frac{2z^2 e^4}{mp^2 v^2} \qquad (A\ 4.7)$$

writing $Z=1$ and $v_1 = v$ for simplicity. This is the energy lost by the heavy charged particle in the collision with impact parameter p and agrees with 5.28 if $p^2 \gg b^2/4$.

APPENDIX 5

OSCILLATIONS IN ORBITAL ACCELERATORS

Consider a particle of charge e, mass m and velocity v moving in the median plane of a steady magnetic field H_z in a path of radius r. The field is symmetrical about the z-axis and varies with radius according to the formula

$$H_z = H_0 \left(\frac{r_0}{r}\right)^n \tag{A 5.1}$$

The field index n is then given by

$$n = -\frac{r}{H_z} \frac{\partial H_z}{\partial r} \tag{A 5.2}$$

The *radial equation of motion* is

$$\frac{d}{dt}(m\dot{r}) = \frac{mv^2}{r} - \frac{H_z e v}{c} \tag{A 5.3}$$

If r differs from the radius R of a stable orbit by a small radial displacement x then

$$\begin{aligned}
m\ddot{x} &= \frac{mv^2}{R+x} - \frac{ev}{c}\left(H_z + x\frac{\partial H_z}{\partial r}\right)_{r=R} \\
&\approx \frac{mv^2}{R}\left(1 - \frac{x}{R}\right) - \frac{evH_z}{c}\left(1 - \frac{nx}{R}\right) \\
&= -\frac{mv^2}{R^2} x(1-n)
\end{aligned} \tag{A 5.4}$$

since for the stable orbit $\ddot{R} = 0$ and $\dfrac{mv^2}{R} = \dfrac{H_z e v}{c}$.

It follows that

$$\ddot{x} + 4\pi^2 f^2 (1-n)x = 0 \tag{A 5.5}$$

where $f = v/2\pi R$ is the revolution frequency in the stable orbit. This equation indicates a frequency of radial oscillation

$$f_r = \sqrt{1-n}\, f \tag{A 5.6}$$

694

The radial oscillation frequency is real if $n < 1$; if $n > 1$ A 5.5 has an exponential solution and the orbit is not closed. This situation is realized in the peeler-regenerator method of particle extraction.

The *vertical equation of motion*, for axial displacement z out of the median plane may be written (Fig. 8.11)

$$\frac{\mathrm{d}}{\mathrm{d}t}(m\dot{z}) = \frac{H_r ev}{c} = \frac{ev}{c} z \frac{\partial H_r}{\partial z} \qquad (A\ 5.7)$$

where H_r is the radial component of the field at height z above the median plane.

For a static field

$$\mathrm{curl}\ \mathbf{H} = 0$$

so that

$$\frac{\partial H_r}{\partial z} = \frac{\partial H_z}{\partial r} = -\frac{n H_z}{R} \qquad (A\ 5.8)$$

This gives

$$\frac{\mathrm{d}}{\mathrm{d}t}(m\dot{z}) = -\frac{nev}{c} \frac{z}{R} H_z = -nm\left(\frac{v}{R}\right)^2 z$$

from which

$$\ddot{z} + 4\pi^2 f^2 n z = 0 \qquad (A\ 5.9)$$

and the frequency of vertical oscillation is

$$f_v = \sqrt{n}\, f \qquad (A\ 5.10)$$

This frequency is real if $n > 0$; if $n < 0$ a circulating beam diverges vertically.

The radial and vertical oscillations were first studied in connection with the stability of betatron orbits, and are known as *betatron oscillations*. They are of period comparable with the period of revolution and must be distinguished from the slower *synchrotron or phase oscillations*.

In constant gradient accelerators n lies between 0 and 1, but certain resonance values for which f_r and f_v are small multiples of each other, or of the revolution frequency f, must be avoided. At these n-values energy will be exchanged between one type of motion and another and instability will usually result. These effects are especially important in synchrotrons because of the large number of turns necessary in the acceleration process.

Resonances occur for $n = 0.25$ $(2f_v = f)$, 0.75 $(2f_r = f)$, 0.5 $(f_r = f_v)$ and 0.2 $(f_r = 2f_v)$ and the synchrotron n-value is usually chosen to lie between 0.5 and 0.75.

The connection between the motion of charged particles in an orbital accelerator and in a double focusing magnetic spectrometer (Sect. 7.2.5c) is now easily seen. For double focusing the resonance condition $f_r = f_v$ is exactly what is required since then the radial and vertical motions possess nodes (one of which may be at the source and one at the detector) at the same angular coordinate. The n-value necessary is thus 0.5 and the first node occurs at an angle $\pi \dfrac{f}{f_r} = \dfrac{\pi}{\sqrt{0.5}} = 254.6°$ from the start of the oscillation. This is the angle required for double focusing in a spectrometer in which the source and detector are placed within the magnetic field.

FISSION

The discovery of the fission of uranium by slow neutrons and the main experimental phenomena are described in Sect. 14.1.6. A complete interpretation of the salient features of fission was given, within a few months of its discovery, by Bohr and Wheeler.* Their theory, which is based on the liquid drop model of the nucleus (Sects. **9.1, 10.3**), is summarized in the following section.

A 6.1 The primary fission process

The fission reaction in ^{235}U

$$^{235}U + n \rightarrow {}^{236}U \rightarrow A + B + Q \qquad (A\ 6.1)$$

where A and B are unstable nuclei of mass number between say 70 and 170 and Q is an energy release of the order of 150 MeV appears superficially much different from more familiar types of slow neutron reaction proceeding through a compound nucleus, e.g.

$$^{14}N + n \rightarrow {}^{15}N \rightarrow {}^{14}C + {}^{1}H + Q' \qquad (A\ 6.2)$$

In fact the difference is only quantitative; the energy release Q, although much greater than Q', is calculable in the same way from the masses of the nuclei concerned and the reactions both proceed with observable yield only because there is sufficient energy available for the particles to overcome their mutual potential barrier.

The energy release Q in binary† fission was calculated by Bohr and Wheeler by an application of the semi-empirical mass formula (Sect. **10.3**). This is still a useful approach because of its generality, although the masses of many fission products can now be estimated more reliably from knowledge of their decay chains. The results of these calculations may be qualitatively predicted from Fig. 10.1. The binding energy per nucleon is

---

* N. Bohr and J. A. Wheeler, *Phys. Rev.*, **56**, 426, 1939.

† There are rare modes of fission in which three heavy particles (one usually an α-particle) are emitted.

about 7·5 MeV for $A = 240$ and 8·5 MeV for $A = 120$; division of the former nucleus into two fragments which decay finally into stable species of mass 120 could therefore release about 240 MeV in all. A more detailed calculation gives the energy release for any specified pair of fragments. Since heavy nuclei contain excess neutrons in order to balance the Coulomb repulsion of the protons (Sect. **10.4**), the fission fragments initially formed contain too many neutrons for stability and undergo successive β^--decays. This process, and occasionally neutron emission from excited nuclei formed as a result of β-decay, accounts for part of the overall energy release (Sect. **A 6.2**).

Meitner, Hahn and Strassmann found that a 23-minute β^--activity was induced in uranium by neutrons of a few volts energy and pointed out that the observed cross-section for this process would greatly exceed $\pi \lambda^2$ for the incident neutron if ^{235}U were the isotope responsible. The activity was therefore attributed to a resonant radiative capture process in ^{238}U. The complex distribution of fission product activities found with thermal neutrons was not observed for neutrons of the energy required for resonant capture in ^{238}U; Bohr and Wheeler therefore suggested that fission by thermal neutrons took place in the rare isotope ^{235}U only, present in normal uranium to an extent of 1 part in 140. Fission in uranium was also observed with neutrons of energy above 1 MeV, with a cross-section too large to permit the effect to be ascribed to ^{235}U (because of its low abundance). This process, with a threshold of about 1 MeV, was therefore assigned to ^{238}U. These conclusions were confirmed by experiments with separated isotopes and were shown to be theoretically reasonable when calculations were made of the fission threshold in terms of a classical model.

We consider the compound nucleus (A, Z) formed by the absorption of a neutron by a heavy target nucleus as a spherical drop of incompressible fluid. The atomic mass $M(A, Z)$ is supposed to be given by the semi-empirical mass formula 10.9 and is greater than the sum of the masses of two constituent fragments by an energy equivalent Q; the question is, under what circumstances will fission into the two fragments take place? The stability of the initial nucleus against fission depends critically on the relative importance of the short-range nuclear forces and the long-range Coulomb forces, whose effects are represented in the semi-empirical mass formula by the terms with the coefficients a_v, a_s, a_c. In the case of a postulated very heavy nucleus ($A \approx 300$ say) the Coulomb force is the more important and the nucleus, once formed, can fly apart as two fragments almost instantaneously. This is illustrated in curve (a) Fig. A 6.1, which shows the potential energy of the two fragments as a function of their separation. For a lighter nucleus ($A = 236$) the repulsion of the protons may be more than compensated by the short-range attractions providing that the nucleus (A, Z) has an economical shape, i.e. one in which it presents a minimum surface so that the maximum effect of the main binding term in 10.9 can be felt. For such a nucleus the potential energy graph as a function of fragment separation is as shown in curve (b) Fig. A 6.1; for small deformations from the spherical shape the initial nucleus is stable but for larger deformations the free surface is so much increased that the effect of short-range attractions is reduced and the Coulomb repulsion is no longer compensated. We thus arrive at the concept of a 'fission barrier' or 'critical energy for fission' E_f at which separation of fragments, already possible energetically with the energy release Q, becomes rapid. Before the deformation corresponding to E_f is reached, separation of fragments may still take place, but slowly, because of the necessity for penetration of the fission barrier. This process is analogous to the emission of α-particles from radioactive nuclei, and is described as *spontaneous fission*. For a still lighter nucleus ($A \approx 100$) the fission barrier is higher (Fig. A 6.1, curve (c)). In each case shown in Fig. A 6.1 the two fragments, once formed, repel each other, and at infinite separation have a kinetic energy determined by the mass change (apart from prompt emission of energy in the form of γ-rays or neutrons).

The critical energy for fission E_f, which must be supplied by the incident particle in the case of induced fission, depends on the quantity Z^2/A for the compound nucleus. This parameter enters because the surface correction to the main binding energy term is proportional to $A^{2/3}$, and the Coulomb potential energy is proportional to $Z^2/A^{1/3}$. Since the fission of ^{238}U requires a neutron of energy about 1 MeV the E_f value for ^{239}U must be at least 6 MeV, i.e. the neutron separation energy of 5·2 MeV together with the incident kinetic energy. This fact enabled

Bohr and Wheeler to estimate that a nucleus would be instantaneously fissile if

$$\frac{Z^2}{A} \geqslant 47 \cdot 8 \qquad\qquad \text{(A 6.3)}$$

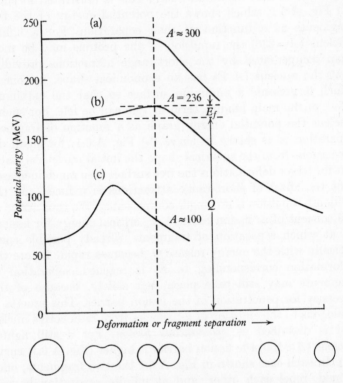

Fig. A 6.1. Critical energy and energy release in fission. The left-hand part of the curves shows the potential energy of a nucleus as a function of deformation; the right-hand part shows the potential energy as two fragments separate under their mutual Coulomb repulsion.

and to calculate the energy E_f, at which the potential energy reaches its maximum value, for nuclei with Z^2/A less than this limiting value. For ^{236}U (^{235}U $+ n$) the critical energy appeared to be 5 MeV; since this is less than the neutron separation energy (6·4 MeV) it is made available by absorption of a neutron of zero energy, and ^{235}U, in contrast with ^{238}U, is fissionable by thermal neutrons. The increased neutron separation energy in the case of ^{236}U, as compared with ^{239}U, is due to the fact that the former is an even–even nucleus, which is more tightly bound in its ground state than an adjacent nucleus of even–odd type. It is a general rule that the thermally fissile nuclei form even–even compound nuclei by absorption of a slow neutron.

It is clear from these arguments and from Fig. A 6.1 that slow neutron induced fission will be confined to only a few nuclei. If A is too small, insufficient energy is made available by neutron capture to enable the nucleus to surmount the

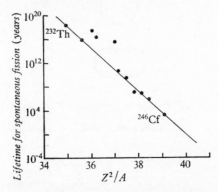

Fig. A 6.2. Spontaneous fission. The diagram shows the dependence of the half-value period of a nucleus, assumed to decay by fission only, on the parameter Z^2/A. The points represent known nuclei between ^{232}Th and ^{246}Cf (Ref. A 6.3).

fission barrier; if A is too large, spontaneous fission already takes place. The occurrence of this mode of disintegration limits the number of transuranic nuclei that may be produced; Fig. A 6.2 shows how the lifetime for spontaneous fission decreases as the limiting value of Z^2/A is approached.

The fission process as envisaged by Bohr and Wheeler may now be represented schematically as shown in Fig. A 6.3. The two excited fragments of the compound nucleus, carrying many excess neutrons in comparison with stable nuclei of their particular charge, separate in a time short compared with the radiative lifetime of the compound state (i.e. $\ll 10^{-14}$ sec). At about the instant of separation, a number of neutrons, known as prompt neutrons, are emitted as the first stage of the process of decay towards stability. The discovery of these neutrons immediately suggested the possibility of a self-sustaining chain reaction in uranium. Further energy is lost by the emission of prompt γ-radiation from excited levels in typical γ-ray lifetimes of the order of 10^{-14} sec. The fragments (Plate 13) are brought to rest in matter by the normal processes of energy loss for

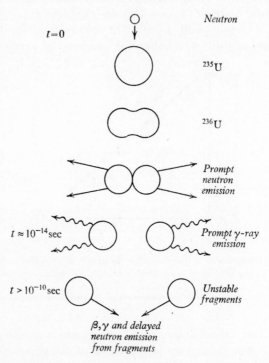

Fig. A 6.3. Schematic representation of the fission process in ^{235}U, showing emission of neutrons and γ-radiation and final decay of fission products. The time scale gives orders of magnitude only.

charged particles (Sect. 5.3.7); they are still neutron-rich and decay sequences involving β^--emission occur in the further process of reducing the neutron–proton ratio. A typical decay chain is that studied in part by Hahn and Strassmann (14.22a)

$$^{140}_{54}\text{Xe} \xrightarrow{16 \text{ sec}} {}^{140}_{55}\text{Cs} \xrightarrow{66 \text{ sec}} {}^{140}_{56}\text{Ba} \xrightarrow{2 \cdot 8 \text{ day}} {}^{140}_{57}\text{La} \xrightarrow{40 \text{ hr}} {}^{140}_{58}\text{Ce (stable)} \quad (\text{A } 6.4)$$

In some of these decay chains a β-process may leave a product nucleus so highly excited that neutron emission is a predominant alternative to β^--decay. An emission of delayed neutrons, with a half-life corresponding to that of the preceding β-emitter, then ensues. A well-known case is illustrated in Fig. A 6.4.

The importance of compound nucleus formation is implicit in the discussion just given of the fission mechanism, but it was not demonstrated objectively in the earliest experiments. It is

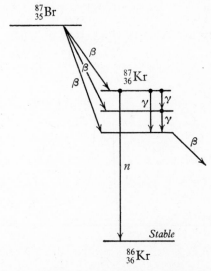

Fig. A 6.4. Delayed neutron emission from ^{87}Kr.

now known that fission does indeed show the resonances (Fig. A 6.5) expected from a compound nucleus model, which might at first sight appear surprising in view of the collective motion which is obviously about to occur at the fission threshold. Present-day theories of fission, based on the collective model, are able to preserve both features.

A 6.2 Characteristics of fissile materials*

The characteristics of the important thermally fissile nuclei ^{233}U, ^{235}U and ^{239}Pu; which are required with high accuracy by the designers of nuclear reactors, have been obtained by an

---

* The material presented in this section has been kindly supplied by Dr. J. Walker.

exhaustive series of experiments in many national laboratories. Continual intercomparison and checking of data takes place and the nuclear properties of these materials must be regarded as among the best established data of nuclear physics.

a) *Production*

^{233}U is obtained by slow neutron capture in thorium

$$^{232}\text{Th} + n \rightarrow {}^{233}\text{Th} + \gamma \xrightarrow{\beta-} {}^{233}\text{Pa} \xrightarrow{\beta-} {}^{233}\text{U} \qquad (\text{A } 6.5)$$

^{235}U is naturally available to the extent of 1 part in 140 of ordinary uranium.

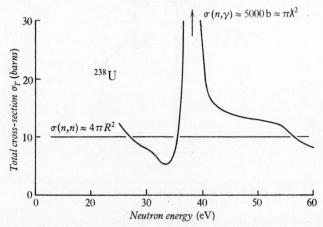

Fig. A 6.5. Total cross-section of ^{238}U for neutrons in the energy region 25–60 eV (Ref. A 6.4).

^{239}Pu is produced by capture of slow (resonance) neutrons in ^{238}U

$$^{238}\text{U} + n \rightarrow {}^{239}\text{U} + \gamma \xrightarrow{\beta-} {}^{239}\text{Np} \xrightarrow{\beta-} {}^{239}\text{Pu} \qquad (\text{A } 6.6)$$

The total cross-section for the interaction of slow neutrons with ^{238}U is shown over a certain energy range in Fig. A 6.5. At the resonance, only the neutron capture and neutron scattering are important, and the total cross-section is divided approximately equally between them.

b) *Decay schemes*

NUCLEUS	PARTICLE EMITTED	ENERGY (MeV)	HALF-VALUE PERIOD (YR)	SPONTANEOUS FISSION RATE (DISINTEGRATIONS $GM^{-1} SEC^{-1}$)
^{233}U	α, no β	4·8	$1·6 \times 10^5$	$< 2 \times 10^{-4}$
^{235}U	α, no β	4·4	7×10^8	3×10^{-4}
^{239}Pu	α, no β	5·1	$2·4 \times 10^4$	$1·0 \times 10^{-2}$

c) *Energy released in fission of* ^{235}U *(average values)*

Kinetic energy of fission fragments	165 MeV
Prompt and delayed neutrons	5
Prompt γ-radiation	7
Delayed β-particles, associated antineutrinos and γ-radiation from radioactive decay	25
	202 MeV

If allowance is made for the fact that the antineutrinos do not deposit their energy in the fission source it follows that

$$3·2 \times 10^{10} \text{ fissions sec}^{-1} \text{ develop a power of 1 watt}$$

d) *Mass and energy distribution of fission fragments*

A distribution of primary fragment masses, determined by extensive physical and chemical study of decay chains, is shown in Fig. A 6.6a. Symmetric fission is rare in the slow neutron induced phenomenon, but is much more probable in high-energy ($E > 20$ MeV) fission. In general there are heavy and light fragments in each fission process; the energy distribution between these fragments is determined by the requirement of conservation of linear momentum and is shown in Fig. A 6.6b.

e) *Energy distribution of neutrons and gamma rays*

The fission neutron spectrum extending up to about 12 MeV is approximately that to be expected if evaporation from an excited nucleus takes place. It has been shown that the angular distribution of neutrons is consistent with evaporation from a moving fragment, as indicated in Fig. A 6.3. The fast neutron yields, ν, per thermal fission processes are:

^{233}U	2·51
^{235}U	2·47
^{239}Pu	2·91

More than 99% of the neutrons are prompt.

23 + N.P.

The spectrum of γ-radiation is that to be expected as a result of transitions between the lower excited states of nuclei in the decay chains.

The delayed neutrons fall into six groups with periods in the range 0·2 to 55 sec.

f) *Cross-sections*

The total cross-section for the interaction of thermal neutrons

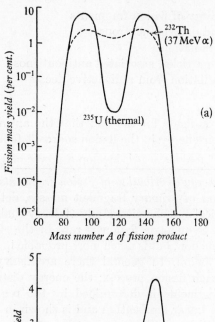

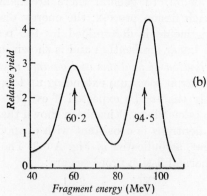

Fig. A 6.6. Fission fragments
a) Mass distribution (Ref. A 6.3).
b) Energy distribution (Ref. A 6.1).

with ^{235}U is 708 b. The processes which compete in building up this value are (for $v_n = 2200$ m sec^{-1}):

i) scattering (n, n) $\sigma(n, n) = 10\text{b}$

ii) capture (n, γ) reaction forming ^{236}U in ground state $\sigma(n, \gamma) = 108\text{b}$

iii) fission $\sigma_{\mathrm{F}} = 590\text{b}$

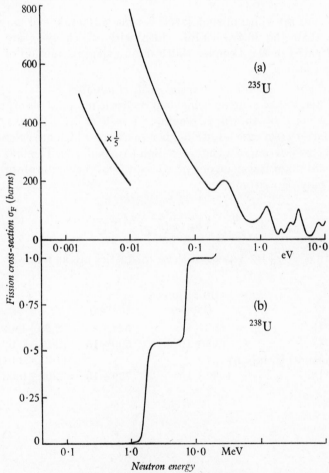

Fig. A 6.7. Fission cross-sections.

a) ^{235}U in the thermal and slow neutron energy range, showing $1/v$ law.

b) ^{238}U in the fast neutron energy range, showing threshold at about 1 MeV (Ref. A 6.4).

The variation of the fission cross-section with energy is shown in Fig. A 6.7a, and the curve for ^{238}U above the fission threshold is given in Fig. A 6.7b. The partial cross-sections for the competitive processes stand in the ratio of the corresponding widths at particular resonance levels and these are as follows for the level at 0·29 eV incident neutron energy:

$$\Gamma_n = 0 \cdot 004 \text{ mV}, \quad \Gamma_\gamma = 31 \text{ mV}, \quad \Gamma_F = 110 \text{ mV}$$

The natural width of such levels is thus ≈ 100 mV and may be less than the instrumental width with which they are investigated or the Doppler width due to thermal motion of the target atoms.

g) *Neutrons emitted per thermal neutron absorbed*

When a slow neutron is incident on fissile material absorption takes place by the (n, γ) reaction as well as by fission. Only the latter yields the additional fast neutrons which are essential to the generation of a chain reaction (Appendix 7). The factor η is the ratio of fast neutrons produced to slow neutrons absorbed and may be written

$$\eta = \nu \frac{\sigma_F}{\sigma_F + \sigma(n, \gamma)} = \frac{\nu}{1 + \alpha} \qquad (A\ 6.7)$$

where $\alpha = \dfrac{\sigma(n, \gamma)}{\sigma_F}$. Values of these quantities are as follows:

	$\sigma(n, \gamma) + \sigma_F$ (barns)	σ_F (barns)	η
^{233}U	593 ± 8	524 ± 8	$2 \cdot 29 \pm 0 \cdot 03$
^{235}U	698 ± 10	590 ± 15	$2 \cdot 08 \pm 0 \cdot 02$
(Natural Uranium)			$(1 \cdot 31 \pm 0 \cdot 01)$
^{239}Pu	1032 ± 15	729 ± 15	$2 \cdot 08 \pm 0 \cdot 03$

APPENDIX 7

THE NUCLEAR REACTOR

A 7.1 The chain reaction

The discovery of the emission of about 2·5 fast neutrons in each thermal fission of ^{235}U suggested the possibility that these neutrons could be used to produce further fissions and thus to generate a chain reaction. Such chain reactions are known in chemistry, and lead to an explosive development of chemical reactions. If such a process could be initiated between nuclear reactants the availability of enormous amounts of energy, greater than those known in chemical explosions by roughly the ratio of nuclear to chemical binding energies, could be envisaged. An uncontrolled release of such energy in a short time would constitute a nuclear explosion; controllable release of the same energy, over a longer time would provide a useful nuclear source of power. With these considerations in mind, physicists in 1939 commenced an intensive study of the conditions under which a chain reaction might become possible. The difficulty is essentially to prevent loss of the fission neutrons by processes other than further fission; such processes cannot be eliminated but their effect can be minimized by careful experimental design.

In 1939 the only fissile material available was natural uranium, in the form of uranium oxide. It is clear from Fig. A6.7 that in this material fission in ^{235}U takes place with a high probability only with thermal neutrons, and it is therefore necessary to reduce the average energy of the fission neutrons from ≈ 1 MeV to $\approx \frac{1}{40}$ eV with a minimum loss of neutron flux. Since fast neutron cross-sections are of the order of nuclear areas, the mean free path for any type of energy-reducing collision in a solid is of the order of 50 cm and a large system is therefore necessary. If this were just a large mass of natural uranium, slowing down would certainly take place, but the neutrons would in the end lose energy gradually because of the small transfer of energy per collision to the massive uranium nuclei. All would then at some stage reach an energy at which

709

they could be absorbed resonantly by ^{238}U producing the unprofitable (n, γ) reaction (cf. Fig. A 6.5). In order to avoid these narrow 'resonance traps', the neutrons must be slowed down quickly by collisions in each of which a large amount of energy is on the average lost, and this can be achieved if the uranium is dispersed in a large volume of material containing light atoms to act as 'moderator'. The moderator used must be one in which neutron capture through the (n, γ) reaction is small. The earliest experiments of this type were made by Joliot, Halban and Kowarski in France. Using various geometrical arrangements of uranium oxide and water, surrounding a neutron source, they were able to show that the neutron density in the assembly was greater than that expected on the basis of the known number of neutrons released per fission. This could only be so if a convergent chain reaction were taking place, i.e. if each thermal neutron absorbed were giving rise to k (<1) new thermal neutrons which were available to produce further fissions. In such a situation the neutron density in the assembly would be expected to rise by a factor

$$1 + k + k^2 + \ldots = \frac{1}{1-k} \qquad (A\ 7.1)$$

Such a system thus *multiplies* the primary neutron flux, by a factor which may nowadays be very large, but so long as k, the reproduction factor, is less than 1 no continual build-up of flux or divergent reaction is possible.

Joliot, Halban and Kowarski realized that their initial experiments had in fact made it credible that a divergent chain reaction could be realized if neutron leakage and absorption could be further reduced. They therefore arranged to repeat their work with a heavy water moderator, since the (n, γ) reaction in deuterium has a much smaller cross-section than the same reaction in hydrogen. The story of the completion of this experiment is one of the epics of the Second World War. The 165 litres of heavy water necessary had been brought to France from Norway just before the invasion of that country, and it was sent on to England at the time of the fall of France in June 1940. Joliot remained in France but Halban and Kowarski completed their experiment in the Cavendish Laboratory, Cambridge, in December 1940 and produced in the words of a subsequent British Government statement, 'strong evidence that in a system composed of uranium oxide or uranium metal, with heavy water as the slowing down medium, a divergent slow-neutron chain reaction would be realized if the system were of sufficient size'. It is almost certain that, but for the war, such a system would have been achieved in France in 1941; in fact the first self-sustaining nuclear chain reaction in a reactor or 'pile' of natural uranium and graphite, was realized under the direction of Enrico Fermi at Chicago in 1942. The history of that project and its outcome in both military and economic fields may be read elsewhere (Ref. A 7.1; A 7.2).

A 7.2　Neutron economy in a reacting system: critical size

We now give a somewhat more quantitative account of these phenomena, dealing first with neutron multiplication in an infinite system containing natural uranium and a moderator which will be assumed to be pure graphite, and outlining a simple estimate of the critical size at which a finite system can sustain a chain reaction.

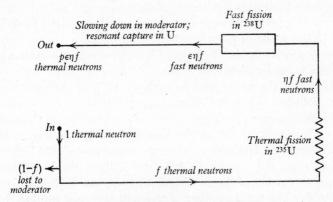

Fig. A 7.1. Sequence of processes following the birth of a neutron in a system containing moderator and uranium.

The essential condition for a diverge... chain reaction in an infinite system is that the *reproduction factor* k_∞ shall be at least unity, so that the disappearance of a slow neutron is followed by processes which lead to the reappearance of a further slow neutron. The intermediate processes are represented diagrammatically in Fig. A 7.1, which takes as its starting point the appearance of a thermal neutron at some point within the system. The probability of the absorption of this neutron in uranium (^{235}U + ^{238}U) is known as the *thermal utilization factor* f; the probability of the competing processes of absorption in moderator and in various constructional materials is $1-f$. If ν is the average number of fast neutrons produced by thermal fission of ^{235}U then the original thermal neutron will produce ηf fast neutrons where η is the quantity defined in Sect. A 6.2 (g).

The ηf fast neutrons are born in an environment of uranium, and slow down, both in uranium and in moderator by a variety of processes. Collisions of neutrons of average energy ≈ 1 MeV with abundant ^{238}U nuclei result in an inelastic scattering

$$^{238}\text{U} + n \rightarrow {}^{238}\text{U}^* + n' \qquad \text{(A 7.2)}$$

with a loss of energy of some hundreds of keV; there is also a small but not negligible chance of fast fission in ^{238}U, which is represented by the *fast fission factor* ε ($\approx 1 \cdot 02$). The fast fission factor is small because unless the uranium content in the assembly is very large, the main process of slowing down is due to elastic collisions between the neutrons and carbon atoms. About 100 collisions with carbon atoms are required to reduce the initial neutron energy to the thermal value; using known cross-sections or mean free paths it may be calculated that this process occupies about 10^{-3} sec.

Although the neutrons lose perhaps 10% of their energy in each collision this is insufficient to guarantee that the energy will not in some cases have a value corresponding to the resonance absorption peaks in the abundant ^{238}U (cf. Fig. A 6.5). We therefore introduce a *resonance escape probability* factor p, which gives the chance that a fast neutron reaches thermal energy as a result of the slowing down processes in the particular assembly. The total number of thermal neutrons produced for each thermal absorbed, i.e. the reproduction factor for the infinite system is thus

$$k_\infty = \varepsilon \eta p f \qquad \text{(A 7.3)}$$

This is known as the four-factor formula. For the power-producing reactors of the U.K.A.E.A. at Calder Hall the lattice constants are

$$\eta = 1 \cdot 31, \quad \varepsilon = 1 \cdot 02, \quad p = 0 \cdot 89, \quad f = 0 \cdot 88$$

giving a value

$$k_\infty = 1{\cdot}05 \qquad\qquad (A\ 7.4)$$

In order to design an efficient reacting system p and f should be made large. The thermal utilization can be increased by increasing the amount of uranium in the system, but this reduces the amount of carbon and hence decreases p, since the slowing down process will then be more gradual and the resonant capture more serious. If the reacting system consists of a homogeneous mixture of carbon and uranium, the values of f and p are fixed by the relative concentration. It is, however, more favourable to use 'lattices' in which the uranium is concentrated into rods or lumps. In this case, owing to the high cross-section for resonant capture, neutrons of this energy are absorbed unprofitably in only the surface layers of the uranium, and the bulk of the fissile material does not contribute to resonance losses, although it is available for the desired thermal fission processes, which are less attenuated in the surface of the lump. All practical reactors using natural uranium and graphite are therefore based on a lattice; a typical arrangement is shown in Fig. A 7.2. The calculation of the factors f and p for a lattice is a matter of some complication and must be checked by direct experimental observation using non-reacting assemblies of similar construction but of small size.

It is not difficult to obtain a reproduction factor k_∞ greater than unity if pure materials are used. It becomes in fact very easy if uranium enriched in ^{235}U is employed. This, however, may not be economically feasible for large power-producing installations. For systems of finite size, the actual value of k_∞ is of extreme importance since for each thermal neutron absorbed only $k_\infty - 1$ neutrons can be permitted to escape from the system and the smaller the system the greater the likelihood of escape. A finite reactor with a given lattice therefore has a critical size below which the chain reaction will not diverge; this can be seen for a simple case as follows.

Consider a spherical system (Fig. A 7.3) and suppose that a distance M, known as the *migration length*, is taken to represent crudely the path length of a neutron between birth as a fast neutron and absorption as a thermal. Only neutrons which originate within the shell of thickness M will have an appreciable

23*

chance of escaping from the system, and to obtain orders of magnitude we assume that all such neutrons do escape. The ratio of this number to the number of neutrons which do not escape is approximately

$$\frac{\text{volume of shell}}{\text{volume of sphere}} \times \frac{\text{neutron density in shell}}{\text{neutron density in sphere}}$$

$$\approx \frac{3M}{R} \times \frac{M}{R} = \frac{3M^2}{R^2}$$

since we may assume that the neutron density distribution is as shown in the lower part of Fig. A 7.3.

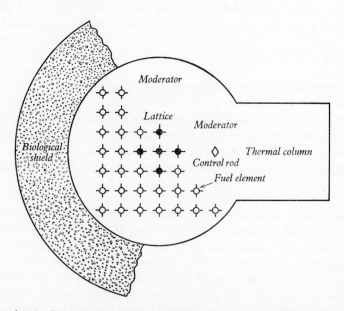

Fig. A 7.2. Cross-section of a reactor lattice (not to scale). Fuel elements (e.g. U) are embedded in a moderating medium (e.g. C) and the whole is surrounded by a massive concrete radiation shield. In most reactors a graphite neutron reflector (not shown) is installed between the lattice volume and the concrete shield in order to minimize the neutron losses. The thermal column (of moderator) is a region in which the ratio of thermal to fast neutrons increases with increasing distance from the lattice.

The fraction of neutrons lost by leakage is thus $1 - 3M^2/R^2$ and the effective reproduction constant is consequently

$$k_{\text{eff}} = k_\infty \left(1 - \frac{3M^2}{R^2}\right) \qquad\qquad (A\ 7.5)$$

The critical radius R_c at which k_{eff} becomes equal to 1 is therefore given by

$$R_c^2 = \frac{3M^2 k_\infty}{(k_\infty - 1)} \approx \frac{3M^2}{(k_\infty - 1)} \qquad\qquad (A\ 7.6)$$

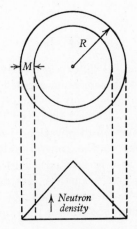

Fig. A 7.3. Calculation of critical size for a simple system (Ref. A 7.3)

For $k_\infty = 1{\cdot}05$ and $M = 50$ cm (for graphite) $R_c = 385$ cm. Obviously a reactor in which k_∞ is larger will be correspondingly smaller. A reactor employing *fast* fission as the basic process will also be smaller because of the smaller migration length M.

A 7.3   Construction and operation of a reactor; reactor types

A critical assembly in which high levels of neutron density are to be reached must be provided with adequate biological screening. In most reactors this takes the form of a thick concrete box enclosing the reactor, including the arrangements for the insertion of samples for irradiation, instruments and the control rods. These are usually massive bars of cadmium, which has a high cross-section for the absorption of thermal neutrons by the (n, γ) reaction. In the control of a reactor the cadmium rods are withdrawn until the reproduction constant k rises above unity. The reactor neutron density ρ then increases in accordance with the equation

$$\frac{d\rho}{dt} = \frac{\rho(k-1)}{t_0} \qquad (A\ 7.7)$$

where t_0 is the neutron lifetime from birth to absorption, $\approx 1\cdot 4 \times 10^{-3}$ sec. The density thus rises exponentially with a time constant T, where

$$T = \frac{t_0}{(k-1)} \qquad (A\ 7.8)$$

so that even a very small (1%) excess reactivity leads to a time constant of as little as $\frac{1}{10}$ sec. Such a rapid rise of pile power would be difficult to manage but fortunately the existence of the delayed neutrons, with periods of up to 55 sec, greatly increases the effective multiplication time, and permits mechanical adjustment to the control rods to be made. In bringing a reactor up to a prescribed level the control rods are thus first adjusted to give a small excess reactivity and then inserted to bring $k-1$ to zero when the required neutron density has been reached; the reactor then operates at constant power.

In an *uncontrolled* reacting system, or bomb, an enriched material (^{235}U or ^{289}Pu) is suddenly given a large excess reactivity by bringing together two masses to form a volume which is considerably greater than the critical size. The reaction proceeds by fast fission with a neutron mean free path of perhaps a few cm only and the generation time is only about 4×10^{-9} sec. From Eq. A 7.8 the neutron density increases with a time constant of about 4×10^{-8} sec for a 10% excess reactivity and the number of fission processes, each releasing about 200 MeV, will increase by a factor of about 10^{11} in 1 μsec. This is the condition obtained in the explosion of a fission bomb.

It is not proposed here to give a list of the many types of production and research reactor which have been developed.

We may, however, note the following versions, which have become important:

  i) The natural-uranium graphite lattice, used in the U.K. A.E.A. power production programme.

 ii) The natural uranium-heavy water lattice which can be smaller than (i) because of the lower absorption, and consequently yields a higher flux density. Such reactors are mainly found in national research establishments.

iii) The enriched uranium–ordinary water lattice which leads to the extremely simple type of construction known as the swimming pool. Reactors of this type are certain to become familiar in universities in the future.

 iv) The enriched uranium–heavy water lattice, also mainly found in national research establishments, which is especially designed for the production of high neutron densities at low powers.

These reactors differ considerably in the measures adopted to remove the heat and if necessary to convert it into electrical power. The average power levels and central thermal neutron fluxes* for a number of reactors are shown in the following table:

TABLE A7.1　Nuclear Reactor Performance

REACTOR	TYPE	CENTRAL FLUX (neutrons $cm^{-2} sec^{-1}$)	POWER (kW)
BEPO (Harwell)	Uranium–graphite	1×10^{12}	4000
Calder Hall	Uranium–graphite	$1 \cdot 6 \times 10^{13}$	200,000
NRX (Chalk River)	Uranium–heavy water	5×10^{13}	10,000
Brookhaven	Uranium–graphite	5×10^{12}	25,000
DIDO (Harwell)	Enriched uranium–heavy water	2×10^{14}	13,000

* Defined for this purpose as ρv where ρ is the number of neutrons per unit volume and $v = 2200$ m sec^{-1}.

The nuclear reactor is of prime importance in nuclear physics as a source of thermal neutrons. The highest thermal fluxes exist at the centre of the pile, but are accompanied by neutrons of all other energies in the fission spectrum. This may not be a disadvantage if methods of monochromatization are used. If a pure thermal flux, of lower level, is required the 'thermal column', which is essentially a graphite reflector extension passing through the shield wall may be used.

APPENDIX 8

THE COHERENT NEUTRON SCATTERING LENGTH FOR HYDROGEN

A 8.1 Definitions

A neutron and a proton can collide in singlet $(S = 0)$ or triplet $(S = 1)$ spin states, according as the intrinsic spins are opposed or in the same direction. Of the four possible arrangements of the individual spin components $\frac{1}{2}\hbar$ with respect to an axis, three belong to the triplet state and one to the singlet. The total cross-section for the interaction of slow neutrons with protons (by scattering) is therefore, as noted in Sect. 18.2.2,

$$\sigma_{\mathrm{el}}^0 = 4\pi(\tfrac{3}{4}l_{\mathrm{t}}^2 + \tfrac{1}{4}l_{\mathrm{s}}^2) \qquad (\mathrm{A}\ 8.1)$$

where l_{s} and l_{t} are the scattering lengths for the singlet and triplet states. This is the cross-section that would be measured by passing slow neutrons through a randomly oriented assembly of protons. For a single proton–neutron encounter, however, we may define a *coherent* scattering length*

$$l_{\mathrm{coh}} = \tfrac{3}{4}l_{\mathrm{t}} + \tfrac{1}{4}l_{\mathrm{s}} \qquad (\mathrm{A}\ 8.2)$$

which is necessary in the discussion of interference phenomena. This quantity is defined for a free proton, but if the proton is bound in a solid lattice the reduced mass in the neutron–proton collision is doubled and so also is the scattering length. This accounts for the rise in the neutron–proton scattering cross-section at low neutron energies when this is deduced from measurements made on hydrogen contained in heavy molecules; the neutron energy is then insufficient to break the chemical bonds and the cross-section increases (Fig. 18.4). For the same reason the coherent scattering length for the diffraction of slow neutrons from crystals containing hydrogen is

$$l_{\mathrm{H}} = 2l_{\mathrm{coh}} = \tfrac{1}{2}(3l_{\mathrm{t}} + l_{\mathrm{s}}) \qquad (\mathrm{A}\ 8.3)$$

---

* We follow here the nomenclature of chapter 18 in preference to the more conventional use of f or a for this quantity. Strictly the scattering *amplitude* $f_0(\theta)$ as used in chapter 14, is angle and energy dependent and is complex unless δ_0 (18.15) is $0°$ or $180°$. This is a good approximation for slow neutron scattering, and for zero energy neutrons $(k \to 0)$ the scattering amplitude becomes the scattering *length* $l\ (= -f)$, which is a constant, and independent of angle, for a given interaction.

Determination of σ_{el}^0 and l_H will thus permit l_t and l_s to be obtained separately.

A 8.2   Scattering of slow neutrons by ortho- and para-hydrogen

The possibility of using these two forms of hydrogen to establish the spin dependence of nuclear forces (which makes l_t different from l_s) was first discussed by Schwinger and Teller.* If the forces between a neutron and proton depend on the relative spin orientation, then the scattering from ortho- and from para-hydrogen should differ providing that there is some coherence between the waves scattered from the two protons. This will be so if the wavelength of the incident neutrons is long compared with the internuclear separation in hydrogen, i.e. $\lambda \gg 0 \cdot 78 A$. The analysis of the scattering cross-sections in terms of the singlet and triplet amplitudes is complicated by the possibility of inelastic scattering, which can always take place for ortho-hydrogen, with conversion to the para- form (and increase of neutron energy) and can take place for parahydrogen with conversion to the ortho- form for neutrons of energy greater than $0 \cdot 023$ eV. Such neutrons can be obtained by velocity selector or filtration techniques (Ref. A 8.1).

The appearance of the ortho- and para- molecules to an incident neutron of arbitrary spin direction is represented in Fig. A 8.1a. For parahydrogen the two protons appear un-correlated and the coherent scattering length (neglecting the reduced mass effect) is double the length for a single proton, i.e.

$$l_{para} = 2l_{coh} = 2(\tfrac{3}{4}l_t + \tfrac{1}{4}l_s) \qquad (A 8.4)$$

If the neutrons are of such a low energy ($E_n < 0 \cdot 023$ eV, $T < 90°K$, $\lambda > 2A$) that there is no para $\rightarrow$ ortho conversion, the total cross-section for parahydrogen scattering is proportional to $(l_{para})^2$. For orthohydrogen, an interference term depending on $(l_t - l_s)$ appears in addition, and a term also involving this difference occurs to represent the stimulated ortho $\rightarrow$ para transition. Measurement of the orthohydrogen cross-section as well as that for parahydrogen enables both quantities $(3l_t + l_s)$ and $(l_t - l_s)$ to be found. Recent values of the

---

* J. Schwinger and E. Teller, *Phys. Rev.*, **52**, 286, 1937.

scattering lengths, obtained in experiments with gaseous
hydrogen, are given at the end of this section; the observed
cross-sections (Fig. A 8.1 b, c) immediately show that the two
types of molecule scatter differently so that the neutron–proton

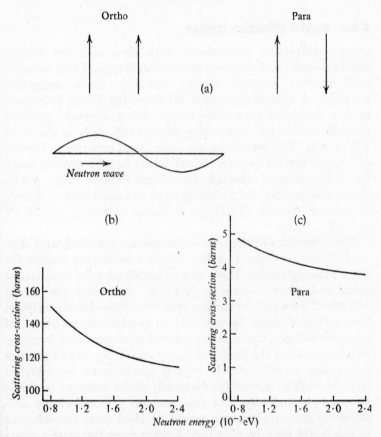

Fig. A 8.1. Scattering of slow neutrons by ortho- and para-hydrogen.
a) Spin orientations.
b), c) Variation of scattering cross-section with neutron energy (Sutton
et al., *Phys. Rev.*, **72**, 1147, 1947).

interaction is spin-dependent. It is also clear that the parahydrogen cross-section is very small, which indicates that the
singlet and triplet scattering lengths are of opposite sign, as
would be expected for a virtual singlet state (l_s negative).

The relative size of σ^0_{para} and σ^0_{ortho} renders accurate determinations by this method difficult, because of the possibility of contamination of the parahydrogen by the ortho- form. Alternative methods of finding l_{coh} have therefore been devised.

A 8.3   Crystal diffraction method

Crystal diffraction experiments with slow neutrons require strong sources and accurate measurements could not be made until nuclear reactors became available for experimental purposes. A typical apparatus for detecting Bragg reflections from a powdered crystalline sample using neutrons rendered monochromatic by a preceding crystal reflection is shown in Fig. A 8.2a. This technique has been found superior to the use of a single crystal because imperfections in such crystals make the calculation of absolute intensities difficult. Fig. A 8.2b shows the powder diffraction pattern obtained with a sample of sodium hydride (NaH) for neutrons of energy 0·0724 eV ($\lambda = 1A$).

The intensities of the diffraction spectra obtained with slow neutron beams depend on the coherent scattering lengths for the scattering nuclei. These add as amplitudes for each lattice point and create beams in just the directions for Bragg reflection; for a polycrystalline scatterer, these directions lie on the surface of cones. In principle an absolute measurement of intensity will give the coherent scattering length, using formulae well known from the theory of X-ray scattering, but in practice it is better to calibrate the crystal spectrometer by using an element such as carbon (in diamond) whose coherent length is known independently. For this purpose a monoisotopic substance of zero nuclear spin would be ideal since the coherent length could then be obtained directly from the elastic cross-section measured in a transmission experiment.

In their analysis of the diffraction peaks from NaH Wollan and Shull (Ref. A 8.4) had first to consider the probable structure of this crystal, and then the relative signs of the bound scattering lengths l_H snd l_{Na} for the two atoms concerned. From the relative intensities of several peaks, including that indicated in Fig. A 8.2b, they concluded that Na and H scatter neutrons in opposite phase, i.e. the intensity of the peak shown in the figure is proportional to $(l_H - l_{Na})^2$. By making use of a previously determined value for l_{Na} the hydrogen scattering length was found; the result is quoted at the end of this section.

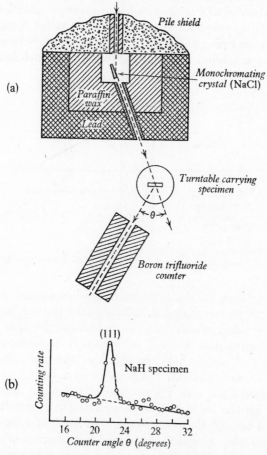

(a)

(b)

Fig. A 8.2. Slow neutron diffraction.
a) Experimental arrangement showing monochromator (Ref. A 8.4).
b) Typical results for diffraction from NaH, with neutrons of energy 0·0724 eV (Shull *et al.*, Ref. A 8.4).

A 8.4 Reflection of slow neutrons from liquid mirrors

The crystal diffraction method of determining the coherent length for hydrogen is open to the objection that correction must be made for the effect of thermal vibrations in destroying coherence. This can be avoided by a method based on another optical property of slow neutrons, that of total reflection from a mirror surface at small glancing angles.

The existence of a critical angle for neutron reflection may be understood in exactly the same way as that for X-rays. For a material containing scattering centres in random positions the coherently scattered wave interferes with the incident wave in

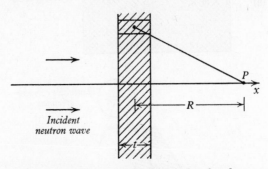

Fig. A 8.3. Calculation of refractive index for slow neutrons.

such a way that the resultant wave appears to have a different wavelength in the material. This endows the medium with a refractive index which may be calculated by the following method, using the Fresnel construction formula of optical diffraction: Consider the amplitude of the wave transmitted through a small thickness t of material at a point P (Fig. A 8.3) and imagine a series of Fresnel half-period zones drawn on the material for the point P. The amplitude for an infinite sheet is known to be half that due to the first zone, of area $\pi R \lambda$, and if the scattering amplitude, assumed independent of angle is f, then the amplitude at P for the total number of centres in the half-period zone is

$$\frac{i}{2}\frac{\pi R \lambda N t f}{R}\times\frac{2}{\pi} = iNt\lambda f \qquad (A\ 8.5)$$

where N is the number of centres per unit volume and we allow for the $1/R$ dependence of amplitude on distance. The $2/\pi$ factor averages the first zone amplitude at the point P and the quantity i $(=\sqrt{-1})$ represents the $\pi/2$ phase displacement. The scattered wave at P adds to the incident wave to create the transmitted wave and the transmitted amplitude is thus

$$A_T = A_0(1 - iNt\lambda f) \approx A_0 e^{i\delta}$$

where A_0 is the incident amplitude. The phase-lag thus introduced is

$$\delta = -Nt\lambda f$$

In terms of the macroscopic refractive index n of the slab, we also have

$$\delta = \frac{2\pi}{\lambda}(n-1)t$$

and by comparing these two expressions we find

$$n = 1 - \frac{N\lambda^2 f}{2\pi}$$

For neutrons f is the bound coherent nuclear scattering length l, taken positive for $180°$ phase shift. For X-rays, f is the amplitude of a wave scattered by an electron multiplied by an atomic form factor for the forward direction. We thus see that if f is positive the refractive index is less than unity and total *external* reflection may be expected. This is the normal case for X-rays and for neutrons scattered by a large number of elements. For hydrogen, however, the coherent amplitude is negative* and total *internal* reflection would be expected. In either case the critical angle θ_c for a neutron wavelength λ is given by

$$\cos \theta_c = n$$

or

$$1 - \theta_c^2/2 = 1 - \frac{\lambda^2 N l_H}{2\pi}$$

whence

$$\theta_c = \lambda \sqrt{\frac{N l_H}{\pi}} \approx 10' \text{ of arc}$$

and a determination of θ_c/λ yields l_H.

The advantage of mirror reflection methods is that the coherent effect is determined by the average properties of the surface,

---

* This fact, established by the ortho/parahydrogen measurements, is also shown conclusively by the mirror experiments.

i.e. it does not depend on the *structure* of the surface and liquids, solids or gases may be used. The effect is uncomplicated by thermal motion since the scattering is predominantly in the forward direction, and in the case of liquid, the scattering from the surface can be shown to be elastic. In the actual application of the mirror method by Hughes, Burgy and Ringo (Ref. A 8.5 and Fig. A 8.4), liquid hydrogen was not used because of low intensity and because of the inconvenience of the total *internal*

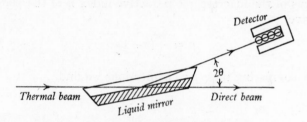

Fig. A 8.4. Scattering of thermal neutrons from a liquid hydrocarbon mirror (Ref. A 8.1).

reflection. Instead, liquid hydrocarbon mirrors were used; the addition of carbon, whose coherent amplitude is well known, converts the total reflection into an *external* phenomenon. By studying the intensity of the reflected beam at angles near critical as a function of the carbon to hydrogen ratio of the liquid hydrocarbon mirror, the coherent scattering length for hydrogen was obtained in terms of that for carbon; the result is given below.

A 8.5   Values of l_H

The most recent values for l_H obtained by the methods just described are:

METHOD	REFERENCE	$l_H(10^{-13}$ cm$)$
Ortho/parahydrogen scattering	Squires and Stewart (Ref. A 8.3)	$-3 \cdot 80 \pm 0 \cdot 05$
Crystal diffraction	Shull *et al.* (Ref. A 8.4)	$-3 \cdot 96 \pm 0 \cdot 2$
Liquid mirrors	Hughes, Burgy and Ringo (Ref. A 8.5)	$-3 \cdot 78 \pm 0 \cdot 02$

References

A 1.1   H. G. Kuhn, *Atomic Spectra*, Longmans, 1961.

A 2.1   F. Mandl, *Quantum Mechanics*, Butterworth, 1957.

A 3.1   E. Segrè and A. C. Helmholz, 'Nuclear Isomerism', *Rev. mod. Phys.*, **21**, 271, 1949.

A 3.2   W. Heitler, *The Quantum Theory of Radiation*, Oxford University Press, 1944.

A 3.3   M. A. Preston, *Physics of the Nucleus*, Addison-Wesley, 1962, Ch. 11.

A 3.4   J. M. Blatt and V. F. Weisskopf, *Theoretical Nuclear Physics*, Wiley, 1952.

A 6.1   W. J. Whitehouse, 'Fission', *Progr. nucl. Phys.*, **2**, 120, 1952.

A 6.2   I. Halpern, 'Nuclear Fission', *Ann. Rev. Nucl. Sci.*, **9**, 245, 1959.

A 6.3   R. D. Evans, *The Atomic Nucleus*, McGraw-Hill, 1955.

A 6.4   D. J. Hughes and R. B. Schwartz, *Neutron Cross Sections*, Brookhaven National Laboratory Report BNL 325, 1958.

A 7.1   H. D. Smyth, 'Atomic Energy for Military Purposes', *Rev. mod. Phys.*, **17**, 351, 1945.

A 7.2   *Peaceful Uses of Atomic Energy* (Geneva International Conference Series, ed. J. G. Beckerly), 1955/6.

A 7.3   D. J. Littler and J. F. Raffle, *An Introduction to Reactor Physics*, Pergamon Press, 1955.

A 8.1   D. J. Hughes, *Neutron Optics*, Interscience, 1954; see also *Ann. Rev. Nucl. Sci.*, **3**, 93, 1953.

A 8.2   G. E. Bacon, *Neutron Diffraction*, Camb. Univ. Press, 1955.

A 8.3   G. L. Squires and A. T. Stewart, *Proc. roy. Soc.*, A **230**, 19, 1955.

A 8.4   E. O. Wollan and C. G. Shull, *Phys. Rev.*, **73**, 830, 1948; C. G. Shull, E. O. Wollan, G. A. Morton and W. L. Davidson, *Phys. Rev.*, **73**, 842, 1948.

A 8.5   D. J. Hughes, M. T. Burgy and G. R. Ringo, *Phys. Rev.*, **84**, 1160, 1951.

FUNDAMENTAL CONSTANTS

The constants and conversion factors are taken from Cohen, DuMond, Layton and Rollett, *Rev. mod. Phys.*, **27**, 363, 1955 and from Ref. 1.7, p. 898. Errors in these quantities have been omitted. See also Cohen, Crowe and DuMond, *Fundamental Constants of Physics*, Interscience, New York, 1957, J. W. M. DuMond, *Annals of Physics*, **7**, 365, 1959, and J. H. Sanders, *The Fundamental Atomic Constants*, Oxford, 1961.

QUANTITY	SYMBOL	VALUE
General		
Velocity of light in vacuum	c	$2 \cdot 99793 \times 10^{10}$ cm sec^{-1}
Avogadro's number	N_0	$6 \cdot 02486 \times 10^{23}$ atoms mole^{-1}
Loschmidt's constant	N_0/V_0	$2 \cdot 68719 \times 10^{19}$ atoms cm^{-3}
Faraday	$N_0 e/c$	$9652 \cdot 19$ e.m.u. mole^{-1}
Electron charge	$-e$	$4 \cdot 80286 \times 10^{-10}$ e.s.u.
Electron rest mass	m	$9 \cdot 1083 \times 10^{-28}$ g
Electron charge to mass ratio	e/mc	$1 \cdot 75890 \times 10^7$ e.m.u. g^{-1}
Classical electron radius	$r_0 = \dfrac{e^2}{mc^2}$	$2 \cdot 81785 \times 10^{-13}$ cm
Thomson cross-section	$\frac{8}{3}\pi r_0^2$	$6 \cdot 65205 \times 10^{-25}$ cm^2
Gas constant	R	$8 \cdot 31696 \times 10^7$ erg mole^{-1} deg.$^{-1}$
Boltzmann constant	$k = R/N_0$	$1 \cdot 38044 \times 10^{-16}$ erg deg.$^{-1}$
Planck constant	h	$6 \cdot 62517 \times 10^{-27}$ erg sec
Dirac constant	$\hbar = \dfrac{h}{2\pi}$	$1 \cdot 05443 \times 10^{-27}$ erg sec
Compton wavelength of electron	$\dfrac{h}{mc}$	$2 \cdot 42626 \times 10^{-10}$ cm
Compton wavelength of proton	$\dfrac{h}{m_p c}$	$1 \cdot 32141 \times 10^{-13}$ cm
Wavelength of photon of energy E (eV)	$\lambda = \dfrac{hc}{E}$	$\dfrac{12{,}397 \cdot 67}{E} \times 10^{-8}$ cm
Atomic and nuclear masses ($^{16}O = 16$)		
Atomic mass of electron	$N_0 m$	$5 \cdot 48763 \times 10^{-4}$ a.m.u.
Atomic mass of proton	$M_p = M_H - N_0 m$	$1 \cdot 007593$ a.m.u.

QUANTITY	SYMBOL	VALUE
Ratio of proton mass to electron mass	$M_p/N_0 m$	$1836 \cdot 12$
Mass of hydrogen atom	M_H	$1 \cdot 008142$ a.m.u.
Rest mass of proton	$m_p = M_p/N_0$	$1 \cdot 67239 \times 10^{-24}$ g
Atomic mass of neutron	M_n	$1 \cdot 008982$ a.m.u.
Rest mass of neutron	$m_n = M_n/N_0$	$1 \cdot 67470 \times 10^{-24}$ g
Neutron–H atom mass difference	$M_n - M_H$	$0 \cdot 782$ MeV

Spectroscopic constants

QUANTITY	SYMBOL	VALUE
Rydberg constant for infinite mass	$R_\infty = \dfrac{2\pi^2 m e^4}{h^3 c}$	$109{,}737 \cdot 309$ cm^{-1}
Radius of first Bohr orbit of hydrogen atom	$a_0 = \dfrac{h^2}{4\pi^2 m e^2}$	$0 \cdot 529172 \times 10^{-8}$ cm
Fine structure constant	$\alpha = \dfrac{2\pi e^2}{hc}$	$1/137 \cdot 0373$
Fine structure doublet separation in hydrogen	ΔE_H	$10{,}968 \cdot 56$ Mc/s

Magnetic quantities

QUANTITY	SYMBOL	VALUE
Bohr magneton	$\mu_0 = \dfrac{eh}{4\pi mc}$	$9 \cdot 2731 \times 10^{-21}$ erg gauss^{-1}
Nuclear magneton	$\mu_N = \dfrac{eh}{4\pi m_p c}$	$5 \cdot 05038 \times 10^{-24}$ erg gauss^{-1}
Magnetic moment of electron	μ_e	$1 \cdot 001145358$ Bohr magnetons (theoretical) $9 \cdot 2837 \times 10^{-21}$ erg gauss^{-1} (experimental)
Electron g-factors	g_l	-1
	g_s	$-2(1 \cdot 0011454)$
Magnetic moment of proton	μ_p	$2 \cdot 79275$ nuclear magnetons $= 1 \cdot 41044 \times 10^{-23}$ erg gauss^{-1}
Magnetic moment of neutron	μ_n	$-1 \cdot 913148$ nuclear magnetons*
Proton g-factors	g_l	1
	g_s	$5 \cdot 585$
Neutron g-factors	g_l	0
	g_s	$-3 \cdot 826$

* V. W. Cohen, N. R. Corngold and N. F. Ramsey, *Phys. Rev.*, **104**, 283, 1956.

QUANTITY	SYMBOL	VALUE
μ^+-meson g-factors	g_l	1
	g_s	$= 2(1 \cdot 001162)$†
Gyromagnetic ratio of proton (corrected for diamagnetism)	γ_p	$2 \cdot 67530 \times 10^4$ radians $\sec^{-1}$ gauss^{-1}

Conversion factors $(^{16}O = 16)$

	1 a.m.u.	$931 \cdot 141$ MeV
	1 MeV	$0 \cdot 001074$ a.m.u.
	1 eV	$1 \cdot 60206 \times 10^{-12}$ erg
		$2 \cdot 41814 \times 10^8$ Mc/s
		$8 \cdot 06604 \times 10^3$ cm^{-1}
	1 cm^{-1}	$1 \cdot 98618 \times 10^{-16}$ erg
		$(= 1 \cdot 44°K)$
	1 electron mass	$0 \cdot 51098$ MeV
	1 proton mass	$938 \cdot 211$ MeV
	1 neutron mass	$939 \cdot 505$ MeV
	1 hydrogen atom mass	$938 \cdot 72$ MeV

† G. Charpak, F. J. M. Farley, R. L. Garwin, T. Muller, J. C. Sens, and A. Zichichi, *Physics Letters*, **1**, 16, 1962.

PROBLEMS

Chapter 1

1.1 A neutron beam is diffracted by a lattice containing planes separated by 3×10^{-8} cm in such a way that the incident and diffracted beams are both inclined at 30° to these planes. Calculate the energy of the neutrons in electron volts. (University of Cambridge, 1946)

1.2 Calculate the de Broglie wavelength of:

a) an electron of energy 1 MeV, [$8 \cdot 8 \times 10^{-11}$ cm]
b) a proton of energy 1000 MeV, [$7 \cdot 3 \times 10^{-14}$ cm]
c) a nitrogen nucleus of energy 140 MeV. [$9 \cdot 2 \times 10^{-14}$ cm]

1.3 Express the gravitational force on an electron in terms of (a) an electric field, (b) a transverse magnetic field, for an electron velocity of 10^4 cm sec^{-1}. [$5 \cdot 5 \times 10^{-13}$ volts cm^{-1}; $5 \cdot 5 \times 10^{-9}$ gauss]

Chapter 2

2.1 If two radioactive nuclei A and B, produced in the process of nuclear fission, are characterized by the disintegration constants λ_1 and λ_2, and if the probability that a time less than T elapses between the subsequent disintegrations of A and B is represented by $W(T)$, show that

$$W(T) = 1 - \frac{1}{\lambda_1 + \lambda_2} (\lambda_1 e^{-\lambda_2 T} + \lambda_2 e^{-\lambda_1 T})$$

(University of Cambridge, 1942)

2.2 A sample of uranium oxide (U_3O_8), freshly prepared from an old uranium mineral, was found to emit 20.5 α-particles per milligram per second. Comment on this result. ($U = 238$, $O = 16$, $\lambda^{238}U = 4 \cdot 8 \times 10^{-18}$ sec^{-1}.) (University of Cambridge, 1944)

2.3 What proportion of ^{235}U was present in a rock formed 3000×10^6 years ago, given that the present proportion of ^{235}U to ^{238}U is $1/140$? (University of Liverpool, 1954)

2.4 An atom of mass 226·10309 a.m.u. is α-active, decaying to one of mass 222·09397 a.m.u. Estimate the velocity of the emitted α-particle given that the mass of the helium atom is 4·00388 a.m.u. and $c = 3 \times 10^{10}$ cm sec^{-1}. (University of Hull, 1957)

2.5 The maximum permissible concentration of ^{24}Na (half-life 15 h) in water is 8 μC l^{-1}. It is necessary to dispose of an effluent containing 200 μC l^{-1} produced continuously at the rate of 30 l h^{-1} by feeding it continuously through a holding tank. Assuming perfect mixing, what would be the minimum capacity of the tank if only a further sixfold dilution of the overflow may be safely assumed? (University of Birmingham, 1959)

2.6 Calculate the relative proportions of the nuclides ^{238}U, ^{226}Ra and Rn in an ore in which equilibrium has been reached. [$4·3 \times 10^{11}$; $1·6 \times 10^{5}$; 1]

2.7 Given that the lifetimes of the uranium isotopes ^{238}U and ^{234}U are $4·5 \times 10^{9}$ years and $2·6 \times 10^{5}$ years calculate the relative abundance of these two nuclides in nature, assuming that one is produced by decay from the other. [0·006%]

2.8 If one gram of natural chlorine was bombarded by 1000 thermal neutrons sec^{-1} cm^{-2} for 10^{6} years, calculate the resultant activity of each of the radioactive isotopes of chlorine from the data given below:

(Atomic weight of chlorine = 35·5; natural chlorine contains 75·4% of the isotope of mass number 35 and 24·6% of the isotope of mass number 37; the cross sections for thermal neutron capture are 44×10^{-24} cm^{2} for ^{35}Cl and $0·56 \times 10^{-24}$ cm^{2} for ^{37}Cl. The half-life of ^{36}Cl is $4·4 \times 10^{5}$ yr; the half-life of ^{35}Cl is 38·5 min. Avogadro's number is $6·0 \times 10^{23}$ per gram molecule.) (University of Keele, 1963)

2.9 Three bodies A, B, C of a radioactive series have decay constants λ_a, λ_b, λ_c and the period of A is very long compared with that of B and of C. Show that in a time t after the separation of B, short compared with the lifetime of B and C, the quantity of C formed from A is given by

$$C = \tfrac{1}{2}\lambda_b \lambda_c C_0 t^2$$

where C_0 is the ultimate equilibrium amount of C.

2.10 Show that if two consecutive radiations from a long-lived parent have decay constants λ_1 and λ_2, the apparent mean life of the second radiation is $(1/\lambda_1)+(1/\lambda_2)$.

2.11 Show that if the delayed coincidence method (p. 44) is applied to a radioactive sequence $A \to B \to C$ where the decay constants of the disintegrations of B and C are each λ, then the delayed signals from C, with respect to the formation of B, are distributed according to the formula $\lambda^2 t e^{-\lambda t}$.

Chapter 3

3.1 What would be the hyperfine structure of the mercury line 2537 assuming this line to arise solely from a $^3P_1 \to {}^1S_0$ transition in an isotope of nuclear spin $\frac{3}{2}$?

3.2 The pure rotation spectrum of HCl gives rise to absorption lines in the infra red which are nearly equally spaced and the wave number difference between successive lines is 20·79 cm^{-1}. Calculate the moment of inertia of HCl. (University of Liverpool, 1951)

3.3 Calculate the energy necessary to remove the remaining electron in a singly ionized helium atom. [54·1 eV]

3.4 A spectral line is known to be due to an electronic state of width $5 \cdot 0 \times 10^{-8}$ eV and the ground state of the atom. What will be the lifetime of the excited state? (University of Birmingham, 1960)

3.5 A diatomic molecule has a moment of inertia of 10^{-38} gm cm^2. Calculate the wavelength of the radiation required to excite a transition between rotational states with $J = 1$ and $J = 2$. (University of Birmingham, 1956)

3.6 Calculate the Zeeman displacement per gauss for the s-state of hydrogen. [$4 \cdot 67 \times 10^{-5}$ cm^{-1} gauss^{-1}]

3.7 Derive an expression for the orbital frequency of an electron in a Bohr orbit with principal quantum number n. Show that the frequency of radiation emitted according to Bohr's postulate in a transition between states n_1 and n_2 approaches the orbital frequency when n_1 and n_2 are both large.

3.8 If the frequencies of the lines in the visible band spectrum of nitrogen are represented by:

$$A + (1 \cdot 5 \times 10^{11})m + (2 \cdot 04 \times 10^9)m^2$$

where A is a constant and m an integer, calculate the diameter of the nitrogen molecule. [10^{-8} cm]

3.9 One of the lines of the hydrogen spectrum of wavelength 4862·7 A is accompanied by a weak line due to deuterium at a wavelength which is shorter by 1·313 A. Show that this observation is consistent with the known mass of the deuterium atom.

Chapter 4

4.1 The frequency of the hyperfine transition ($F = 0 \to F = 1$) in the hydrogen atom is 1426×10^6 c/s. Estimate the average distance between the electron and proton in the atom, assuming only the values of h, the Bohr magneton and the magnetic moment of the proton. [0·38A]

4.2 Estimate the frequency at which nuclear magnetic resonance might take place in atomic hydrogen in free space, given the following information:

Magnetic moment of the proton $= 1 \cdot 41 \times 10^{-23}$ erg gauss^{-1}.
Magnetic moment of the electron $= 9 \cdot 27 \times 10^{-21}$ erg gauss^{-1}.
Radius of the first Bohr orbit in hydrogen atom $= 0 \cdot 53 \times 10^{-8}$ cm. [530 Mc/s]

4.3 Calculate the Stern-Gerlach (angular) deflection in a field of gradient 50,000 gauss cm^{-1} and length 10 cm for:

a) a beam of sodium atoms,
b) a beam of neutrons, each of thermal velocity ($kT = 0 \cdot 025$ eV). [2·2°, 4×10^{-5} radians]

4.4 How many magnetic substates are expected for an orthohydrogen molecule in its ground state, assuming that spin and orbital motion are decoupled? [9]

Calculate the maximum deflection experienced by such a molecule when it passes through an inhomogeneous field of length 5 cm and gradient 5×10^4 gauss cm^{-1} at a velocity of 5×10^4 cm sec^{-1}. [$2 \cdot 48 \times 10^{-3}$ cm]

4.5 Show that if the proton may be represented as a uniform object with angular momentum quantum number $s = \frac{1}{2}$, the absolute magnetic moment is $\frac{1}{2}\sqrt{3}\mu_N$.

4.6 In an application of the ENDOR technique (p. 134) to the nucleus ^{57}Fe Woodbury et al., (*Phys. Rev.*, **117**, 1286, 1960) find radio-frequency transitions at a frequency of $f = 0 \cdot 7096$ Mc/s in a field of 4869 gauss. Use Eq. (4.18) to deduce the g-factor for the ground state of the ^{57}Fe nucleus, and its nuclear moment assuming that $I = \frac{1}{2}$. [0·191, 0·0955 nuclear magnetons]

Chapter 5

5.1 An α-particle ($M_1 = 4$) passes through the gas of an expansion chamber and is scattered through an angle of 56° by collision with a heavier nucleus, which is observed to move off at an angle of 54° with the original direction of the α-particle. Find the probable mass number of the struck nucleus ($M_2 \approx 12$).

5.2 Show that in the collision of an α-particle ($M_1 = 4$) with a proton ($M_2 = 1$) the maximum angle of scattering is 14° 30′.

5.3 Using symbols as in Fig. 5.1 draw a momentum diagram for the laboratory system and show that $v_2 = v_1 \dfrac{M_1}{M_2} \dfrac{\sin \theta_L}{\sin (\theta_L + \phi_L)}$.

5.4 A target of lithium ($M_2 = 7$) is bombarded by protons ($M_1 = 1$) of energy 5 MeV. Calculate:

a) the energy of protons scattered elastically through an angle of 90°. [3·75 MeV]

b) the energy of protons observed at 90° which have excited the 0·48 MeV state of ^{7}Li. [3·33 MeV]

5.5 A particle M_1 of energy E_1 bombards a nucleus M_2 producing particles M_3 and M_4, with an energy release Q. Show that if particles M_3 are observed at angle θ, their energy E_3 is given by the equation:

$$(M_3 + M_4)E_3 - 2\sqrt{M_1 M_3 E_1 E_3} \cos \theta = (M_4 - M_1)E_1 + M_4 Q$$

5.6 Calculate approximately the number of primary pairs of ions per centimetre path produced by a proton of energy 1 MeV in helium at N.T.P. (Assume $I_0 = 24 \cdot 5$ eV) [250]

Suggest how formula (5.44) might be modified to predict the ionization produced by a 1 MeV electron and estimate a value for this, also in helium at N.T.P. [0·55]

5.7 Show that, except for small ranges, the straggling of a beam of ^{3}He particles is greater than that of a beam of ^{4}He particles of equal range. (University of Cambridge, 1940)

5.8 Calculate the closest distance of approach of an α-particle of energy 6 MeV to a gold nucleus ($Z = 79$). [$3 \cdot 8 \times 10^{-12}$ cm]

For what angle of scattering would an α-particle of energy 9 MeV approach the nucleus to the same distance? [60°]

5.9 A finely collimated beam of α-particles of energy 10 MeV bombards a metal foil (thickness 200 μg cm^{-2}) of a material of atomic weight 107·8. A detector of area 1 cm^2 is placed at a distance of 10 cm from the foil so that scattered α-particles strike it normally on the average at an angle of 60° with the direction of incidence. When the incident α-particles represent a current of 1 μA the counting rate in the detector (which is 100% efficient) is 6×10^4 particles sec^{-1}. Calculate the atomic number of the element forming the scattering foil. [46]

5.10 An α-particle is found to have a range of 300 μ in a photographic emulsion. What range would you expect for (a) a ^{3}He nucleus, (b) a ^{3}H nucleus each of the same initial velocity as the α-particle? [225μ; 900μ]

5.11 The α-particles from ThC′ have an initial energy of 8·8 MeV and a range in standard air of 8·6 cm. Find their energy loss per cm in standard air at a point 4 cm distant from a thin source. (University of Liverpool, 1954)

5.12 A triton (^{3}H) of energy 5000 MeV passes through a transparent medium of refractive index $n = 1 \cdot 5$. Calculate the angle of emission of Cherenkov light. [44°] Calculate also the number of photons emitted per cm path between wavelengths 4000 A and 6000 A using, e.g., 5·51a. [195]

5.13 A proton enters a rectangular block of glass of refractive index 1·47 along a line perpendicular to one pair of faces. For what energy will the Cherenkov light be totally reflected at the opposite face? [1600 MeV]

5.14 Discuss the significance of the relation of the mass absorption coefficient for soft X-rays in light elements ($0.2 \, \text{gm}^{-1} \, \text{cm}^2$) to the Thomson scattering cross section $\frac{8\pi}{3} r_0^2$.

5.15 The range of protons in C2 emulsion is given in the following table (range in microns, energy in MeV).

Range	0	50	100	150	200	250	300	350	400	450	500
Energy	0	2.32	3.59	4.61	5.48	6.27	7.01	7.69	8.32	8.91	9.47

Draw graphs of the range-energy relations for deuterons and helium 3 particles. (University of Birmingham, 1961)

5.16 Show that the differential cross-section $\sigma_L(\theta_L)$ for scattering of protons by protons in the laboratory system is related to the corresponding quantity in the centre of mass system by the equation: $\sigma_L(\theta_L) = 4 \cos \theta_L \sigma(\theta)$. (University of Birmingham, 1962)

5.17 Calculate the number of photons produced per m of air ($n = 1.000293$) by the Cherenkov effect from the path of a relativistic electron in the wavelength range $\lambda = 3500$ to 5500 A. [27]

Calculate also the energy below which Cherenkov radiation is not observed. [20.3 MeV]

5.18 A beam of X-rays is attenuated by a factor of 0.64 in passing through a block of graphite ($A = 12$) of thickness 1 cm. Estimate the atomic number of carbon from this information.

5.19 The cross-section for the reaction:

$$^{10}\text{B} + n \rightarrow \, ^7\text{Li} + \, ^4\text{He}$$

is 4×10^3 barn. Calculate the fraction of a ^{10}B layer which disappears in a year in a flux of $10^{12} \, n \, \text{cm}^{-2} \, \text{sec}^1$. [0.12]

5.20 Calculate, for the Compton scattering of X-rays of wavelength 0.1 A:

a) the wavelength of scattered radiation at $45°$. [0.107A]

b) the velocity of the corresponding recoil electron. [5.3×10^9]

24+N.P.

5.21 The cross-section for 2-quantum annihilation of non-relativistic positrons may be written.

$$\sigma = \pi r_0^2 \frac{c}{v}$$

where v is the positron velocity and r_0 is the classical electron radius. Calculate the annihilation rate in carbon ($Z = 6$, $A = 12$, density $= 2 \cdot 22$ gm cm^{-3}) and the mean life in this material. [$R = 4 \cdot 9 \times 10^9$ sec^{-1}, $2 \cdot 04 \times 10^{-10}$ sec]

5.22 Using Eq. (5.37) for a positron of velocity 10^{10} cm sec^{-1}, and the result of problem 5.21, compare the rate of energy loss by ionization in carbon with the rate of loss by annihilation. [Annihilation/ionization $\approx 1/1600$]

5.23 Show that in the annihilation of positrons at rest by negative electrons of momentum p the angle between the two annihilation quanta is $\pi - p_{\perp r}/mc$ where $p_{\perp r}$ is the momentum of the electron at right angles to the line of flight of one of the quanta.

Show further that the energy of the two quanta is $mc^2 \pm \frac{1}{2} p_{\parallel} c$ approximately where $p_{\parallel}$ is the momentum of the electron along the line of flight of one of the quanta. Calculate the angle and the energy difference between the quanta for annihilation in a solid in which the average electron energy is 10 eV. [$\pi - 0 \cdot 36°$, 3200 eV]

5.24 Two radioactive sources are to be compared as accurately as possible by counting, with a single low background counter, for a total time t. Show that the time should be divided in the ratio $\sqrt{\dfrac{c_a}{c_b}}$, where c_a, c_b are the individual true counting rates. Show also that the fractional standard deviation of the ratio is $\dfrac{1}{\sqrt{t}} \left(\dfrac{1}{\sqrt{c_a}} + \dfrac{1}{\sqrt{c_b}} \right)$.

5.25 Show that the threshold quantum energy for the production of an electron-positron pair in the field of a free electron is $4mc^2$. (Calculate the invariant mass $E^2 - p^2 c^2$ for the initial system using relativistic formulae and set it equal to $3mc^2$.)

5.26 In the elastic collision of a particle of mass M_1 with a particle of mass M_2 $(\langle M_1)$, the heavier particle cannot be scattered through an angle greater than θ_L^m. Show that

$$\sin \theta \, {}_L^{\,m} = \frac{M_2}{M_1}$$

and that the corresponding angle in the centre-of-mass system is given by

$$\cos \theta^m = -\frac{M_2}{M_1}$$

Show also that the corresponding laboratory angle of projection of M_2 is given by

$$\sin \phi_L^m = \sqrt{\frac{M_1 - M_2}{2M_1}}$$

5.27 For the conditions of the previous problem, when the particles M_1 are scattered through the greatest possible angle, show that their energy is

$$E_1 \frac{M_1 - M_2}{M_1 + M_2}$$

where E_1 is the energy before scattering.

5.28 Show that the velocity v_p of protons projected forward by α-particles incident with velocity v_α is given by $v_p = 1\cdot6 v_\alpha$.

5.29 In the annihilation of a fast positron of kinetic energy T by a free electron at rest, two quanta are usually produced. Show that when $T \gg mc^2$ the energy of the annihilation radiation observed in the forward direction is

$$E_\gamma = T + \tfrac{3}{2}mc^2$$

5.30 In the slow neutron reaction

$$^{10}\text{B} + \text{n} \rightarrow {}^{7}\text{Li} + {}^{4}\text{He} + Q$$

the energy release Q is $2\cdot79$ MeV. Calculate the initial velocity of the ^{4}He nucleus. $[9\cdot4 \times 10^8 \text{ cm sec}^{-1}]$
Assuming that the reaction takes place in nitrogen at N.T.P., find the initial primary ionization due to the α-particle, taking I_0 (Eq. 5.44) to be 15. $[26{,}500 \text{ ion pairs cm}^{-1}]$

Chapter 6

6.1 A cylindrical ionization chamber, filled with BF_3 gas, captures 100 thermal neutrons per second ($^{10}B + n \rightarrow {}^7Li + {}^4He + 2 \cdot 8$ MeV). Assuming that all the reaction products are stopped in the gas calculate the ionization current produced. If the anode voltage is increased to give a gas amplification of 11, could the neutron be detected by an amplifier of 50 pf input capacitance and 3 mv sensitivity? (University of Birmingham, 1961)

6.2 The γ-rays from a radioactive source are observed using a scintillation spectrometer and the pulse height spectrum shows peaks at 46·3 v, 39·9 v and 33·5 v, together with a continuum. Assuming that the source emits only one γ-ray, calculate the energy of this γ-ray and the upper limit of the continuum. (Rest energy of the electron = 0·511 MeV.) (University of Birmingham, 1957)

6.3 Calculate the electric field at the surface of the wire of a proportional counter with a wire radius $\frac{1}{10}$ mm and a cylinder radius 1 cm when 1500 v is applied between the two. [32,500 v cm^{-1}]

Assuming that ionization by collision begins at a field of 22,500 v cm^{-1} and that the mean free path of an electron in the counter is 5×10^{-4} cm, calculate the multiplication factor. [512]

6.4 A cylindrical Geiger counter with a wire of diameter 0·02 cm and a cylinder of diameter 2 cm is operated with a potential difference of 1500 volts. If the mean free path of an electron in the gas filling is 10^{-3} cm and if the ionization potential is 15·7 volts, express in mean free paths the radial thickness of the region over which ionization by collision is possible. [10·7λ]

6.5 Verify the statement on p. 243 that the drop radius corresponding to the maximum of the curve in Fig. 6.19 is 6×10^{-8} cm. Use $\gamma = 76$ dyne cm^{-1} and assume that the drops carry one electronic charge. Show further that the radius of such a drop from which no evaporation to surroundings in equilibrium with a plane liquid surface takes place is about 4×10^{-8} cm.

Chapter 7

7.1 Neutrons from the $d+d$ reaction, of energy 4·0 MeV, are detected by an instrument based on recoil protons. If the instrument has a threshold corresponding to protons of 100 keV what fraction of recoil events will *not* be recorded? (University of Birmingham, 1962)

7.2 Calculate the flight times for 1 keV and 1 eV neutrons for a flight path of 10 metres. [22·9, 723 μsec]

7.3 Find the value of $H\rho$ (gauss cm) for the following :

a) an α-particle of energy 8 MeV (He^{++}). [$4·05 \times 10^5$]
b) an electron of energy 5 MeV. [$1·8 \times 10^4$]
c) a proton of energy 100 MeV. [$1·5 \times 10^6$]
d) an oxygen ion of energy 160 MeV ($^{16}O^{4+}$). [$1·8 \times 10^6$]

7.4 By using arguments similar to those on pp. 279–280 show generally that in the case of the scattering of a neutron by a nucleus, the energy distribution of the recoil nuclei in the laboratory system has the same functional form as the angular distribution of the scattered neutron in the centre of mass system.

7.5 In the counting of charged particles discrimination between particles of different mass may be obtained if the signals from a thin counter (giving dT/dx) and a stopping counter (giving T) are multiplied. Show that the value of $T\dfrac{dT}{dx}$ is to a first approximation independent of velocity, and find the ratio of this quantity for deuterons and ^{3}He particles. [1/6]

7.6 A time-of-flight spectrometer has a pulse width Δt and a flight path l. Show that the energy spread ΔE at mean energy E, corresponding to this pulse width, is proportional to $E^{3/2} \Delta t$. Evaluate the energy resolution of such a spectrometer for neutrons of energy 100 eV if $\Delta t/l = 0·1$ μsec metre^{-1}. [2·8%]

Chapter 8

8.1 The peak potential difference between the dees of a cyclotron is 25,000 v and the magnetic field is 16,000 gauss. If the maximum radius is 30 cm, find the energy acquired by a proton in electron volts and the number of revolutions in its path to the extreme radius. [9·7 MeV, 194]

8.2 Calculate the velocity of a proton of energy 10 MeV as a fraction of the velocity of light. [0·15] How long would a proton take to move from the ion source to the target in a uniform 10 MeV accelerating tube 3 metres long? [1·4 × 10⁻⁷ sec]

8.3 A pulse of 10^{10} particles of single charge is injected into a cyclic accelerator and is kept circulating in a stable orbit by the application of a radio-frequency field. What is the mean current when the radio-frequency is 7 Mc/s? [11·2 milliamps]

8.4 A magnetic field of 12,000 gauss is being explored by the 'floating wire' method. If the current in the wire is 2 amperes and the tension is set at 500 gm weight, what is the energy of the proton whose trajectory is followed by the wire? [252 MeV]

8.5 Assuming that the output voltage drop in a cascade generator of n stages is given by:

$$\Delta v = \frac{2}{3} n^3 \frac{i}{fC}$$

derive an expression for the n-value for which the terminal voltage is a maximum.
Calculate:

a) the number of stages,
b) the output voltage,
c) the ripple voltage $\frac{1}{2} n(n+1) \frac{i}{fC}$

for a cascade generator with $C = 0.02$ μF, $f = 200$ c/s, transformer peak voltage 110 kV, $i = 4$ mA. [11, 1533 kV, 66 kV]

8.6 A belt system of total width 300 cm charges the electrode of an electrostatic generator at a speed of 2000 cm sec⁻¹. If the breakdown strength of the gas surrounding the belts is 30 kV cm⁻¹ calculate:

a) the maximum charging current, [1·6 mA]
b) the maximum rate of rise of electrode potential, assuming a capacity of 100 cm and no load current. [16·2 MV sec⁻¹]

8.7 A cascade generator operating from a 500 c/s mains supply delivers a current of 1 mA at an output voltage of 1 MV and the peak to peak voltage fluctuation of the output is 1%. What is the % fluctuation when the load is taken from a *RC* circuit consisting effectively of a 5 MΩ resistance and a condenser stack of 0·001 μF capacity? [0·54%]

8.8 Calculate the cyclotron frequency for non-relativistic deuterons in a field of 10,000 gauss. [7·65 Mc/s]

Calculate also the frequency at which nuclear magnetic resonance with $\Delta m = 2$ would be observed for deuterons at rest in the same field. [13 Mc/s]

8.9 Protons of energy 100 MeV with their spins aligned in the direction of motion enter a transverse magnetic field. Calculate the ratio between the angle of deviation of the proton and the angle through which the spin is turned because of the magnetic moment of the particle. [0·3]

8.10 Show that the orbit radius of a singly charged particle of kinetic energy T and rest mass M_0 in a magnetic field H is:

$$R = \frac{T}{eH}\left(1 + \frac{2M_0 c^2}{T}\right)^{1/2}$$

Calculate this radius for a proton of kinetic energy equal to its rest mass and a field of 12,500 gauss. [432 cm]

8.11 Consider a synchrocyclotron which accelerates protons to an energy of 420 MeV in a field of 19,000 gauss. Calculate for the energies of 100 and 420 MeV,

a) the velocity of the protons, [$\beta = 0·43$, 0·72]
b) the radius of the orbit, [78 cm, 171 cm]
c) the mass of the proton, in units of the rest mass. [1·11, 1·45]

8.12 For the synchrocyclotron specified in problem 8.11 calculate:

a) the synchronous frequency for energies 0, 100 and 420 MeV [29, 26·1, 20 Mc/s]
b) the time taken for a particle to reach the final energy for an increment of 0·01 MeV per turn. [1770 μsec]
c) the maximum repetition rate at which the machine can be operated. [565 c/s]

8.13 Deuterons of energy 15 MeV are extracted from a cyclotron at a radius of 20″ by applying an electric field of 60 kV cm⁻¹ over an orbit arc of 90°. Calculate the equivalent reduction of magnetic field and the resulting increase in orbit radius Δr. [1600 gauss, 2·1″]

8.14 In the previous problem verify that if the electric field is applied for an angle θ, the *maximum* orbit separation is

$$2\Delta r \sin \frac{\theta}{2}$$

and that this occurs at an angle $\frac{\pi}{2} + \frac{\theta}{2}$ beyond the entrance to the deflector.

8.15 From the formula

$$\frac{\Delta E}{mc^2} = \frac{4\pi}{3} \frac{r_0}{R} \left(\frac{E}{mc^2}\right)^4$$

where $r_0 = e^2/mc^2$, calculate the energy loss per turn for an electron in a synchrotron in which the electrons are moving with an energy of 5 GeV on a radius of 26 metres. [2·1 MeV]

Calculate also the power rating of the oscillator necessary to supply this loss for a bunch of 10^{12} electrons. [625 kvA]

8.16 Using Eq. (8.30 and 8.33) find the maximum energy gain per turn in a 50 c/s betatron in which the radius of the stable orbit is 100 cm and the maximum field at this orbit is 5000 gauss. [1000 eV]

8.17 In high energy physics, it is customary to measure momenta in the unit MeV/c. Using the relativistic formula

$$E^2 = (T + M_0 c^2)^2 = p^2 c^2 + m_0^2 c^4$$

find the momentum (in MeV/c) of

a) a 1000 MeV proton, [1680]
b) a 1 MeV proton, [43·4]
c) a 10 MeV photon, [10]
d) a 100 MeV electron. [101]

8.18 Calculate the value of β ($= v/c$) for protons of the following energies: 100 MeV, 500 MeV, 1000 MeV. [0·43, 0·76, 0·88]

Chapter 9

9.1 Starting from Schrödinger's equation find the number of bound s-states for a particle of mass 2200 electron masses in a square well potential of depth 70 MeV and radius $1·42 \times 10^{-13}$ cm ($\hbar/mc = 3·85 \times 10^{-11}$ cm, $mc^2 = 0·51$ MeV). (University of Glasgow, 1959)

9.2 Using the relativistic relation between momentum and energy find the minimum kinetic energy of (a) an electron, (b) a proton confined within a dimension of 10^{-12} cm (assume $\Delta p \times \Delta r = \hbar$). [19·8 MeV, 0·2 MeV]

9.3 Show that the kinetic energy of a relativistic electron confined within a box of linear dimension R may be written

$$ T = \frac{\hbar^2}{m_0 R^2 (1+\gamma)} $$

where $\gamma = E/m_0 c^2$ and E is the total energy.

9.4 Show that in a Fermi gas of neutrons, the number of states with energy less than $\hbar^2 k^2/2M$ is $(2/9\pi)(kR)^3$, where R is the linear dimension of the containing volume.

9.5 Write down the expected configuration of the following nuclei, omitting closed shells or subshells:

$^{27}_{13}$Al; $^{29}_{14}$Si; $^{40}_{19}$K; $^{93}_{41}$Nb; $^{157}_{64}$Gd. [$d^5_{5/2}$; $s_{1/2}$; $d_{3/2} + f_{7/2}$; $g_{9/2}$; $h^3_{9/2}$.]

9.6 No decay process linking the nuclei $^{150}_{60}$Nd and $^{150}_{61}$Pm is known. The (atomic) mass difference between the nuclei $^{150}_{60}$Nd and $^{150}_{62}$Sm has, however, recently been measured as 3633 ± 4 μu on the carbon scale (McLatchie *et al.*, *Physics Letters*, **10**, 330, 1964) and the accepted decay energy for the beta process $^{150}_{61}$Pm $\rightarrow$ $^{150}_{62}$Sm is $3·46 \pm 0·03$ MeV. Determine the relative stability of ^{150}Nd and ^{150}Pm and the decay energy. Suggest a possible mode of decay. [^{150}Pm decays to ^{150}Nd with an energy release of 76 ± 30 keV. Probably K-electron capture]

Chapter 10

10.1 In a mass spectrograph comparison of H^+ with He^+ the interval of mass observed corresponded to 73·73, expressed in the usual units, while a comparison of H_2D^+ with He^+ gave

24*

the corresponding interval 269·1, helium being on the lighter side in each instance. Given that the packing fraction of helium is 5·4, calculate the packing fractions of H and D. (University of Cambridge, 1943)

10.2 Given that the mass defect curve falls from $+0·14$ mass units for uranium to $-0·06$ mass units in the middle of the periodic table, estimate in kWh the energy which could theoretically be obtained from 1 kg of ^{235}U. [$2·8 \times 10^7$]

10.3 How much energy is necessary to split up an α-particle ($M_\alpha = 4·00279$ a.m.u.) into its constituent nucleons ($M_p = 1·008982$ a.m.u., $M_n = 1·007593$ a.m.u.) [28·2 MeV]

10.4 Assuming that the binding energy of an even-A nucleus may be written

$$-B(A,Z) = 0·014A^{2/3} + \frac{0·083}{A}\left(\frac{A}{2} - Z\right)^2$$
$$+ 0·000627\frac{Z^2}{A^{1/3}} \pm 0·036A^{-3/4}$$

($+$ for Z odd, $-$ for Z even) determine the number of stable nuclides of mass $A = 36$. Take $A^{1/3} = 3·3$, $A^{1/4} = 2·45$ and confine your attention to the range $13 \leqslant Z \leqslant 20$. (University of Birmingham, 1961)

10.5 In the carbon atom the K edge is at 300 eV and the L_I, L_II edges at 60 eV. The atomic mass (new scale) is 12·0000. Calculate:

a) the mass of the carbon nucleus in a.m.u. neglecting electron binding, [11·99671]

b) the percentage correction introduced when electron binding is allowed for. [10^{-5}]

10.6 From the mass spectrographic doublets

$$CO_2\text{–}CS = b = 17·78 \times 10^{-3} \text{ a.m.u.}$$
$$C_3H_8\text{–}CO_2 = c = 72·97 \times 10^{-3} \text{ a.m.u.}$$
$$C_6H_4\text{–}CS_2 = d = 87·33 \times 10^{-3} \text{ a.m.u.}$$

show that $H = 1 + \frac{1}{32}[4b + 5c - 2d]$ and determine the mass of the hydrogen atom [1·008166]. (Evans, *The Atomic Nucleus*, p. 117)

10.7 Show that 1 a.m.u. $= \dfrac{c^2}{N_0}$ ergs, where c is the velocity of light and N_0 is Avogadro's number on the physical scale (i.e. the number of atoms in 16 g of ^{16}O).
Calculate the equivalent energy in MeV. [931·5]

10.8 On the scale $^{16}O = 16·0000$, the mass of the carbon (12) atom is 12·0038 and the mass of the hydrogen atom is 1·00814. Find:

a) the mass of the oxygen atom and of the hydrogen atom on the scale $^{12}C = 12·0000$, [15·9949, 1·00783]
b) the value of Avogadro's number on the scale $^{12}C = 12·0000$. [6·023 × 10^{23}]

10.9 Oxygen has isotopes of mass number 16, 17, 18 with relative abundance 99·758, 0·0373 and 0·2039. If Avogadro's number on the physical scale ($^{16}O = 16$) is 6·0249 × 10^{23}, calculate its value on the chemical scale (O = 16). Calculate further the value of this constant on the physical scale ($^{12}C = 12$) if the mass of ^{16}O on the ^{12}C scale is 15·9949. [6·0233, 6·0230 × 10^{23}]

10.10 The mass scale $^{12}C = 12$ gives a unit which is 318 parts per million larger than that of the present physical scale ($^{16}O = 16$). By how many parts per million is this unit larger than that of the present chemical scale (O = 16)? [50, using figures given above]

Chapter 11

11.1 If, in the usual notation, $R = 1·45 × 10^{-13} A^{1/3}$ cm, calculate a value for the maximum kinetic energy of the positrons emitted in the decay

$$^{15}_{8}O \rightarrow {}^{15}_{7}N + \beta^+ + \gamma$$

indicating any assumption made. (University of Hull, 1958)

11.2 Estimate the energy of the μK X-ray for a phosphorus nucleus ($Z = 15$). (Ionization potential for hydrogen = 13 eV, $m_\mu = 207 m_e$.) (University of Birmingham, 1962)

11.3 Calculate the radius of the π-mesic atom s-orbit for the nucleus calcium ($Z = 20$). Assuming a nuclear radius parameter $r_0 = 1·2 × 10^{-13}$ cm, show that the orbit lies outside the nucleus.

Calculate the density of nucleons available for interaction and the mean free path corresponding to a cross-section $\pi\left(\dfrac{\hbar}{\mu c}\right)^2$ where $\mu = 273 m_e$. [$1\cdot6 \times 10^{-12}$ cm]

11.4 For the nucleus with $Z = 40$, calculate the n-value of the μ-mesic orbit which is just inside the electronic K-shell. [14]

11.5 Write down the equations which describe the scattering of a high energy electron (energy E) by a nucleus of mass M. Show that if $E \gg mc^2$ the recoil energy of the nucleus (treated non-relativistically) is

$$\frac{E^2(1 - \cos \theta)}{Mc^2 + E(1 - \cos \theta)}$$

when θ is the angle through which the electron is scattered.

11.6 Show that the electrostatic potential $U(r)$ at distance r from the centre of a sphere containing a uniform density of positive charge is

$$U(r) = \frac{q}{R}\left[\frac{3}{2} - \frac{1}{2}\left(\frac{r}{R}\right)^2\right] \text{ for } r \leq R$$

if q is the total charge in a sphere whose radius is R.

Evaluate the electric field strength for all values of r and show that it is continuous at the boundary $r = R$. (Evans, *The Atomic Nucleus*, p. 45.)

11.7 Assuming that the nuclear radius is given by $R = 1\cdot2 \times 10^{-13} A^{1/3}$ and that the μ-meson of a mesic atom moves in an orbit of radius given by equation A 1.6, p. 681, with $m_\mu = 207 m_e$, find the atomic number of an atom for which these two radii are equal. Assume that $A = 2Z$. [$Z = 47$]

Chapter 12

12.1 Suppose that it were conceivable that a photon of energy 100 keV should be emitted from a point on the surface of a nucleus (in fact the photon wavelength makes such a concept unreasonable). Find the Doppler spread of energy in the photon spectrum due to classical rotation of the nucleus with one quantum of angular momentum. Assume a nuclear radius of 7×10^{-13} cm and $A = 125$. [$0\cdot1$ keV]

12.2 The masses of the atoms ^{10}Be, ^{10}B and ^{10}C are 10·0167, 10·0161 and 10·0202 in a.m.u. (^{16}O scale). Calculate in a.m.u. the masses of the bare nuclei of these atoms, as shown relatively in Fig. 12.1a [10·0147, 10·0136, 10·0172]. Adjust the masses of ^{10}Be and ^{10}B with respect to ^{10}B by correcting for the mass difference between the neutron and proton [10·0133, 10·0136, 10·0186], and express the difference between the ground state energies in MeV. [^{10}Be $-$ ^{10}B $= -0·3$ MeV, ^{10}C $-$ ^{10}B $= 4·65$ MeV]

Now use the expression for Coulomb energy change given on p. 414, (with $\dfrac{3}{5}\dfrac{e^2}{r_0} = 0·58$ MeV), to calculate the true excitation of the ground states of ^{10}Be and ^{10}C with respect to ^{10}B. This should correspond to the position of the first $T = 1$ level of ^{10}B as indicated in Fig. 12.1b. [2·1 MeV, 1·7 MeV]

Chapter 13

13.1 A nucleus X emits a beta-particle forming a residual nucleus Y in an excited state of energy 250 keV. What is the minimum energy of the beta transition necessary to permit the gamma radiation from Y to be absorbed resonantly in an external nucleus Y at rest? Neglect thermal motions and natural line widths and assume that the gamma radiation is emitted before the nucleus Y loses any energy by collision. [0·56 MeV]

13.2 In an experiment to determine the lifetime of an excited nucleus by the recoil-distance method, the counting rate was found to decrease by a factor of 2 for a source displacement of 0·07 mm. If the mean lifetime of the decaying state is 7×10^{-11} sec, find the velocity of recoil. [$1·4 \times 10$ cm^8 sec^{-1}]

13.3 In example 4.6 the magnetic moment of the ground state of the nucleus ^{57}Fe is calculated. The 14·4 keV γ-ray transition in ^{57}Fe has been extensively investigated using the Mössbauer effect (see, for example, Hanna *et al.*, *Phys. Rev. Letters*, **4**, 177, 1960) and it is found that the ground state is split with an energy difference corresponding to a source (Doppler shift) velocity of 3·96 mm sec^{-1}. Calculate the internal magnetic field at the ^{57}Fe nucleus. [$3·15 \times 10^5$ gauss]

Chapter 14

14.1 Neutrons are produced by bombarding a heavy hydrogen compound with 0·9 MeV deuterons. Calculate the energy of the neutrons emitted from the target at an angle of 115° to the bombarding beam and show that the energy spectrum at this angle is practically independent of target thickness. (Energy released in the reaction is 2·2 MeV) (University of Cambridge, 1946)

14.2 An aluminium foil was bombarded with the 7·3 MeV α-particle beam from a cyclotron. Observation of protons emitted in the resulting reaction at 90° to the incident beam revealed the presence of groups with energies 9·24, 6·98, 5·55 and approximately 4·4 MeV. No γ-rays were observed in coincidence with the highest energy group. State the reaction equation and from the available data derive the Q-values. (University of Hull, 1960)

14.3 In the photodisintegration of the deuteron, the neutron and proton are in general projected with unequal energies. Deduce an expression showing how the kinetic energy of the proton depends on its angle of projection (with respect to the direction of incidence of the quantum) and calculate the angle for the special case in which proton and neutron have the same energy. Assume equal masses for the heavy particles. (University of Cambridge, 1941)

14.4 A thin hydrogenous target is bombarded with 5 MeV neutrons, and a detector is arranged to collect those protons emitted in the same direction as the neutron beam. The neutron beam is replaced by a beam of γ-rays; calculate the photon energy needed to produce protons of the same energy as with the neutron beam. (University of Birmingham, 1959)

14.5 Calculate the mass of the neutron from the following data: Threshold for the reaction

$$^2\mathrm{H}(\gamma,n)^1\mathrm{H} \ = \ 2\cdot225 \pm 0\cdot002 \ \mathrm{MeV}$$

Mass spectrometer doublet $2\,^1\mathrm{H}_1^+ - {}^2\mathrm{H}^+ = 1\cdot5380 \pm 0\cdot0021 \times 10^{-3}$ a.m.u. $M_H = 1\cdot008145 \pm 0\cdot000003$ a.m.u. $[M_n = 1\cdot008998]$

14.6 The reaction ^{34}S$(p,n)^{34}$Cl has a threshold at a proton energy of 6·45 MeV. Calculate (non-relativistically) the threshold for the production of ^{34}Cl by bombarding a hydrogenous target with ^{34}S ions. [219·3 MeV]

14.7 Neutrons are produced by bombarding a target nucleus of mass number A with protons. The threshold energy for the reaction in the laboratory system is E_T. Show that when the incident energy increases above E_T by a small amount δ, the neutrons are emitted into a forward cone of semi-angle $A\sqrt{\delta/E_T}$. Calculate this angle for $A = 26$, $E_T = 5$ MeV and $\delta = 1$ keV. [21°] Show also that the neutron energy at threshold is $E_T/(A+1)^2$ and evaluate this for the case quoted. [6·9 keV] Show further that neutrons are just observed at 180° when the incident energy reaches $E_T\dfrac{A^2}{A^2-1}$ and evaluate this for the case quoted. [5007·4 keV]

14.8 Calculate the quantum energy which would be necessary, according to the hypothesis of a Compton effect, to produce (a) recoil protons of energy $5·7 \times 10^6$ eV, [55 MeV] (b) recoil nitrogen nuclei of velocity 4×10^8 cm sec^{-1}. [90 MeV]

14.9 Calculate the perpendicular distance of the line of flight of a 10 MeV proton from the centre of a nucleus when it has an orbital angular momentum, with respect to this point, of $3\hbar$. Calculate also the distance for a photon of energy 5 MeV and angular momentum $\hbar$. [$4·3 \times 10^{-13}$ cm, $3·9 \times 10^{-12}$ cm]

14.10 The nuclear disintegration ^{12}C(n,n') 3^4He is observed in a nuclear emulsion, and in one particular event the three α-particles (energies E_1, E_2, E_3) are coplanar. If the energy release in the reaction is Q show that the kinetic energy of the incident neutron is given by

$$\frac{1}{8Mp^2}[2M(E_1+E_2+E_3-Q)+p^2+q^2]^2$$

where p and q are the total momenta of the α-particles parallel and perpendicular to the direction of the incident particle.

Chapter 15

15.1 A photon cannot be absorbed completely by a free electron, since this particle cannot exist in states of excitation,

A complex particle of mass M may, however, absorb the photon. Show that the energy of excitation of M is

$$Mc^2 \left\{ \sqrt{1 + \frac{2h\nu}{Mc^2}} - 1 \right\}$$

where $h\nu$ is the photon energy.

15.2 Show that in the scattering of a particle M_1 by a target nucleus M_2 the linear momentum transfer to the nucleus M_2 is the same in both the laboratory and centre-of-mass systems of coordinates.

Calculate this momentum transfer for the scattering of 65 MeV α-particles by ^{16}O nuclei in the case that the angle at which the recoil nucleus is projected is 60°. Express the result (a) in cgs units and (b) as an inverse length, by dividing by $\hbar$. [2.95×10^{-14} cgs; 2.81×10^{13} cm^{-1}]

15.3 If a target nucleus has mass number 24 and a level at 1.37 MeV excitation, what is the minimum proton energy required to observe scattering from this level? (University of Birmingham, 1957)

15.4 A lithium target is bombarded with homogeneous protons of controllable energy. If a sharp rise in the yield of radiation from the process

$$^7\text{Li} + {}^1\text{H} \rightarrow {}^8\text{Be} + \gamma$$

is observed at a proton energy of 441 keV calculate the excitation energy of the corresponding resonance level in ^{8}Be. (^{7}Li $= 7.0182$, ^{1}H $= 1.0081$, ^{8}Be $= 8.0079$, 1 a.m.u. $= 931$ MeV) (University of Birmingham, 1956)

Chapter 16

16.1 The maximum energy E_{max} of the electrons emitted in the decay of the isotope ^{14}C is 0.156 MeV. If the number of electrons with energy between E and $E + dE$ is assumed to have the approximate (non-relativistic) form:

$$n(E)dE \propto E^{1/2}(E_{max} - E)^2 dE,$$

find the rate of evolution of heat by a source of ^{14}C emitting 3.7×10^7 electrons per sec. (University of Cambridge, 1953)

16.2 Calculate the maximum energy of the positron spectrum associated with the decay of $^{13}_{7}N$ to $^{13}_{6}C$. Assume that the atomic masses of $^{13}_{7}N$ and $^{13}_{7}C$ are 13·00986 and 13·00747 a.m.u. respectively, that the mass of an electron is $5·5 \times 10^{-4}$ a.m.u. and that 1 a.m.u. is equivalent to 931 MeV. (University of Hull, 1958)

16.3 ^{37}A decays by electron capture with a Q value of 0·82 MeV; the recoil energy of ^{37}Cl produced by this decay is $9·7 \pm 0·8$ eV. Show that these data are consistent with a zero rest mass for the neutrino.

16.4 Calculate the maximum electron and proton energies in the decay of the neutron. What is the energy of the proton when the electron has half its maximum energy? ($^{1}H = 1·008123$, $^{1}n = 1·00893$, $e = 5·489 \times 10^{-4}$ a.m.u., 1 a.m.u. $= 931$ MeV) (University of Birmingham, 1956)

16.5 A radioactive isotope of copper has two stable neighbouring isobars. The one is of nickel, with atomic number 28 and atomic mass 63·9485 a.m.u. The other is of zinc with atomic number 30 and the atomic mass 63·9485 a.m.u. The mass of an electron is 0·00055 a.m.u. (0·512 MeV).

The following radiations are observed from a sample of this isotope of copper:

a) negative beta particles of 0·57 MeV.
b) positive beta particles of 0·66 MeV.
c) gamma rays of 1·35 MeV.
d) X-rays that are characteristic of nickel.

Coincidence counting experiments (with a resolving time of 10^{-6} sec) show coincidences only between the X-ray and the gamma rays.

Deduce what you can about the decay scheme. (University of Keele, 1963)

16.6 The reaction $^{34}S(p,n)^{34}Cl$ has a threshold at a laboratory proton energy of 6·45 MeV. Calculate (non-relativistically) the upper limit of the positron spectrum of ^{34}Cl, assuming $mc^2 = 0·51$ MeV, $n-^{1}H = 0·78$ MeV. [4·45 MeV]

16.7 The nucleus ^{11}C disintegrates mainly by the emission of a positron, but electron capture is also possible, with an energy release of 2 MeV. Write down the equation for the electron capture process, and calculate the initial energy of the recoil nucleus, assuming that the energy of the K-edge in ^{11}B is 187 eV. [^{11}C$(e, {}^-\nu)^{11}$B, 381 eV]

16.8 At what distance from the centre of a ^{238}U nucleus is the α-particle of its radioactive decay released with zero kinetic energy? The disintegration energy (Table 2.1) is 4·27 MeV. [$6·1 \times 10^{-12}$ cm]

16.9 A nucleus of mass M captures an electron and the resulting energy release is Q. Show that the nucleus recoils with a kinetic energy of approximately

$$\frac{Q^2 - m_\nu^2 c^4}{2(Mc^2 + Q)}$$

where m_ν is the mass of the neutrino (which has been shown to be ≈ 0 by a measurement of the recoil energy in the case of ^{7}Li).

16.10 On the assumption that the energy distribution in a low-energy allowed β-spectrum may be approximated by the formula given in problem 16.1 show that the mean kinetic energy of the spectrum is $\frac{1}{3}$ of the maximum energy.

Show also that for a high-energy allowed spectrum, if the electron rest mass may be disregarded, the mean energy of the spectrum is $\frac{1}{2}$ of the maximum.

16.11 If two α-emitting nuclei, with the same mass number, one with $Z = 84$ and the other with $Z = 82$, had the same decay constant and if the first emitted α-particles of energy 5·3 MeV, estimate the energy of the α-particles emitted by the second. (University of Birmingham, 1964)

16.12 In the so-called ξ-approximation, sometimes used in beta-particle theory, it is assumed that the Coulomb energy of an electron at the nuclear radius is very much greater than the end-point energy of the beta spectrum. Evaluate the ratio of this Coulomb energy to end-point energy for the cases of RaC [see Table 2, p. 54] and $^8_3$Li (β end-point 12 MeV) assuming that the nuclear radius is given by $1·2 \times 10^{-13}A^{1/3}$. [5·2, 0·15]

16.13 The nucleus of ThC ($^{212}_{83}$Bi) emits an α-particle of 6·06 MeV energy, leaving the residual nucleus in a 40 keV excited state. The resulting electromagnetic transition leads to internal conversion and Auger electrons. Calculate the difference between the Auger electron energy observed at an angle of 0° and 180° with the direction of emission of the α-particle, assuming that the energy of the unshifted line is 7·6 keV [2·5%]

Chapter 17

17.1 Assuming the expression given on p. 635 for the angular correlation between the two photons in the transition $0 \to 1 \to 0$, show that the most probable angle between these two photons is 55°.

17.2 A beam of protons of intensity I and polarization P is to be used in a study of the left–right asymmetry produced by elastic scattering. Show that it is desirable to choose conditions such that $P^2 I$ is a maximum.

Chapter 18

18.1 A particle of mass M and energy E is scattered by a square well potential of depth V_0 and radius a. Show that the s-wave phase shift is given by

$$\tan \delta = \frac{k}{k'} \tan k'a - \tan ka$$

where

$$k^2 = \frac{2ME}{\hbar^2} \qquad k'^2 = \frac{2M}{\hbar^2}(E + V_0)$$

Derive an expression for the cross-section when E is small. (University of Glasgow, 1958)

18.2 Using the tabulated values of the magnetic moment of the neutron and proton, calculate the force between these two particles in a triplet state at a separation of 3×10^{-13} cm and the work required, on account of this force, to bring the neutron from infinity to this distance from the proton. Assume that the spins always point along the line joining the particles. [10^5 dynes, 6250 eV]

18.3 Show that a better approximation than 18·19 for the s-wave phase-shift in the limit $k \to 0$ is:

$$\delta_0 = -\frac{k}{\alpha}(1 + a\alpha)$$

Evaluate the correction factor to be applied to the cross-section (18.21) for $k = 0$ using the values of a and α given on p. 652. [1·95]

Appendices

1 The cross-section of the isotope of uranium of mass number 235 for the capture of thermal neutrons is about 500×10^{-24} cm^2, which is about 500 times greater than the total cross-section of the nucleus. How is the capture cross-section determined, how can the existence of so large a cross-section be understood, and what is the importance of this large cross-section for the design of uranium reactors? (University of Cambridge, 1955)

2 Calculate the binding energy of the ground state of a positronium atom $(e^+ + e^-)$, assuming that the ionization potential of hydrogen is 13.5 eV. [6·8 eV] Calculate also the orbit radius. [$1·06 \times 10^{-8}$ cm]

3 An intimate mixture of uranium 235 and graphite is required for certain experiments. The graphite is known to be contaminated with one part per million by weight of boron 10. What is the maximum fraction by weight of uranium 235 in the mixture if the infinite multiplication constant is not to exceed unity?

$$\sigma_a = 4 \times 10^{-3} \text{ barn for carbon}$$
$$= 3·8 \times 10^3 \text{ barn for boron}$$
$$= 7·0 \times 10^2 \text{ barn for uranium}$$
$$\sigma_f = 5·8 \times 10^2 \text{ barn for uranium}$$

Assume 2·5 neutrons per fission and ignore the effects of fast neutrons. (University of Birmingham, 1961)

4. In the Fermi mass formula the surface and Coulomb energy terms may be written as $a_s A^{2/3}$ and $a_c \dfrac{Z^2}{A^{1/3}}$ respectively where $a_s = 13·0$ MeV and $a_c = \dfrac{3}{5}\dfrac{e^2}{r_0} = 0·58$ MeV. The nuclear radius R may be assumed equal to $r_0 A^{1/3}$. Calculate the value Z^2/A at which the division of a nucleus into 2 equal parts (symmetric spontaneous fission) becomes possible, assuming that this happens when the energy release is equal to the mutual potential

energy of the fragments at the instant of formation. (University of Birmingham, 1962)

5 An aqueous solution of a plutonium salt is to be stored in a tank having a square base and rectangular sides. What is the maximum permissible area of the base if the arrangement must never become critical? (σ_a for Pu = 1030 b, σ_f = 730 b, ν = 2·9, M^2 = 32 cm^2 (migration area).) (University of Birmingham, 1963)

6 For the neutron-induced fission of ^{235}U leading to ^{148}La and ^{88}Br, the masses of the nuclides in a.m.u. are:

$$^{235}\text{U} \quad 235\text{·}112 \qquad ^{148}_{57}\text{La} \quad 147\text{·}989$$
$$n \quad 1\text{·}009 \qquad\qquad ^{88}_{35}\text{Br} \quad 87\text{·}961$$

Calculate the release of energy per fission of this type. [142 MeV]

7 With the following data for ^{137}Cs:

mass of uranium irradiated = 1·00 gm
irradiation time = 1 week
thermal neutron fission cross-section = 4·2 b
fission yield of ^{137}Cs = 6%
counting rate = 100 c/m
chemical yield 50%
counter efficiency = 15%
half life of ^{137}Cs = 33 years,

calculate the effective slow neutron flux. (University of Birmingham, 1958)

8 A source consisting of 1 μgm of ^{242}Pu is spread thinly over one plate of an ionization chamber. Alpha-particle pulses are observed at the rate of 80 per sec and spontaneous fission pulses at the rate of 3 per hour. Calculate the half life of ^{242}Pu and the partial decay constants for the two modes of decay. (University of Birmingham, 1958)

9 A 20 megaton hydrogen bomb produces 100 kg of neutrons. Assuming all of these to be utilized in the reaction $^{14}\text{N}(n,p)^{14}\text{C}$ and the ^{14}C to be converted to carbon dioxide and dispersed throughout the atmosphere, estimate the effect on the background of a 6-litre proportional counter filled to 3 atmospheres pressure with atmospheric carbon dioxide. (Half-life for ^{14}C = 5570 years.) (University of Birmingham, 1958)

10   The binding energy of a nucleus of atomic number Z and mass number A is often written in the form

$$B(Z,A) = a_v A - a_s A^{2/3} - a_c \frac{Z^2}{A^{1/3}} - a_a \frac{(A - 2Z)^2}{A} \pm \delta$$

where a_v, a_s, a_c, a_a and δ are empirically determined constants. Given that $a_s = 13$ MeV and $a_c = 0.6$ MeV calculate the energy release in the fission of the nucleus $^{238}_{92}\text{U}$ into two identical nuclei. (University of Birmingham, 1959)

11   An empirical expression for the fall in γ-ray activity after a very short pulse of fission processes is:

$$\text{Number of photons sec}^{-1}\ \text{fission}^{-1} = 1.9 \times 10^{-6} t^{-1.2}$$

where t is the time in days after the pulse. Calculate the number of curies of γ-activity in a rod of uranium 10 days after being taken out of a reactor where it has been producing a constant power due to fission of 10 kW for 100 days. (University of Birmingham, 1957)

12   Cadmium has a resonance for neutrons of energy 0.178 eV and the peak value of the total cross-section is about 7000 b. Estimate the contribution of scattering to this resonance. (University of Birmingham, 1958)

13   For a thermal reactor a typical neutron lifetime is 1.4×10^{-3} sec. Calculate the change in power level in a thermal reactor in 1 sec for an excess reactivity of 1%, neglecting the effect of delayed neutrons. [$\times 1250$]

14   Calculate the glancing angle for Bragg reflection of neutrons of 101 eV energy from the (111) planes of LiF ($d = 2.32$ A). [$0.35°$]

15   Fast neutrons are slowed down in a moderator of an element with mass number A. Show that the maximum fractional energy loss per collision is

$$\frac{4A}{(A+1)^2}$$

16   Calculate the electrostatic field at a distance of one Bohr radius from a proton. [5150 MV cm^{-1}]

17   Calculate the time in which, according to classical electrodynamics, a hydrogen atom would shrink to zero radius. (Use Eq. 1.1 and A 1.3) [1.5×10^{-11} sec]

INDEX